SPANGLER

Light

SECOND EDITION

Light

by

R. W. DITCHBURN, F.R.S.

Professor of Physics, University of Reading

·

Volume I
Chapters I–XII

INTERSCIENCE PUBLISHERS
A DIVISION OF JOHN WILEY & SONS, INC.

© R. W. DITCHBURN, 1963

First published 1952
Second edition 1963
Reprinted 1964

This book is also issued complete
in one binding with cloth boards

PUBLISHED IN GREAT BRITAIN
BY BLACKIE & SON LIMITED, LONDON AND GLASGOW
AND IN THE UNITED STATES OF AMERICA
BY INTERSCIENCE PUBLISHERS INC.
NEW YORK

Printed in Great Britain by Blackie & Son, Limited, Glasgow

Preface to the First Edition

Sixty years ago, a single theory of light—the electromagnetic theory—seemed capable of describing all the experimental results. The position was very different thirty years ago when wave theory and quantum theory were each successful in its own field but apparently mutually irreconcilable. In this book I have endeavoured to show the student that we have again a single theory of light, a logical whole. I have tried to describe the wave theory in such a way that the quantum theory may appear as a natural development rather than as an alternative theory. For this reason I have, at an early stage, stressed the concept of a wave group.

It is expected that the student has studied physics to intermediate standard before commencing to read this book, and that his knowledge of electricity and magnetism, and of mathematics, will advance in parallel with his study of light. The electromagnetic theory is not introduced until Chapter XIII, and the more difficult mathematics is placed in appendices (or in separated paragraphs in small type) which are intended to be omitted on first reading. The whole of Chapter XVI forms a separate section whose reading need not precede that of Chapters XVII–XIX.

I wish to acknowledge the help of many friends with whom I have discussed sections of this book. I particularly wish to thank Dr. O. S. Heavens who has been associated with me in the final stages of preparing the diagrams, proof reading, etc. I am grateful to Prof. K. G. Emeléus with whom the general plan of the book was discussed, Dr. E. H. Linfoot who made suggestions in connexion with Chapter VIII, Mr. T. L. Tippell who read and commented on the first draft of Chapter IX, and to Dr. P. White in regard to Appendix IVB. The responsibility for the final text is, of course, my own. I wish to thank the following for providing material for plates and figures:

Dr. W. M. Gray and Mr. P. J. Jutsum (Plate II *b, c, d, e, f*),

Mr. M. E. Haine, A.E.I. Research Laboratories (Plate V *f, g*),

Dr. H. G. Kuhn (fig. 8.7 and information in text),

Dr. A. C. Menzies (Plate V *a, b, c, d*),

Prof. R. W. Pearse (Plate II *a*),

Prof. E. T. S. Walton (fig. 3.11).

I also acknowledge with thanks permission to make reproductions of copyright material as follows:

> Messrs. Hilger & Watts for figs. 1–7 (inclusive), 9, 11 and 13 of Chapter IX; the Council of the Royal Irish Academy for fig. 8.5; and the Director, N.P.L., the Council of the Royal Society and the authors for fig. 9.16 from a paper by Sears and Barrell.

R. W. DITCHBURN.

University of Reading,
February, 1952

Preface to the Second Edition

In preparing this edition, I have sought to include an account of important recent developments while leaving unchanged as much as possible of the original text. I have also rearranged some of the material, particularly the section on diffraction, so that a reader may conveniently postpone consideration of some of the more difficult ideas. On the theoretical side, the main developments are concerned with coherence and with the concept of a lens system as a device for transmitting information about spatial frequencies. On the practical side, the increasing use of physical receptors has emphasized continuity between instruments for the ultra-violet, visible and infra-red regions of the spectrum. The theory of the performance and of the ultimate limitations of these receptors is an essential part of the theory of optical instruments and is also an important section of modern physics. As an introduction to this fundamental theory I have included some material on geometrical optics and on photometry and colorimetry.

The chapter on the velocity of light has been rewritten and combined with that on relativistic optics. The theory of stimulated emission was given in the First Edition and I have now added an account of the application of this theory to masers. I have not included technical details of masers because development is at present very rapid.

Many readers will be working under the guidance of lecturers who will select portions of the subject for elementary and advanced courses. For those students who have not this help, I suggest the following as a first course lasting two years:—Chapter I (for general reading); Chapters II and III and §§ 4.1–4.9; 5.1–5.19 (except 5.4, 5.5, 5.8 and 5.11), 5.22 and 5.40; 6.1–6.19 (except 6.9) and 6.50; 7.1–7.23, 7.30–7.35 and 7.39; 8.1–8.8, 8.10 and 8.17–8.23; 9.16, 9.20 and 9.21; 10.1–10.6,

10.11 and 10.12; 11.1–11.11 and 11.15; 12.1–12.15 (except 12.14); 17.1–17.19 (except 17.15 and 17.16).

I wish to thank the following for help in preparing this edition: Dr. D. H. Fender, Dr. H. A. Gebbie, Dr. H. H. Hopkins, Dr. L. A. Sayce, Dr. S. D. Smith, Dr. C. G. Wynne and Prof. W. D. Wright. I also wish to thank, for permission to reproduce figures:—

Prof. M. Born, Prof. E. Wolf and the Pergamon Press for fig. 12.18.

Dr. H. H. Hopkins and Oxford University Press for fig. 8.14.

The Director, N. P. L. and Dr. L. A. Sayce for fig. 6.21.

The Director, N. P. L. and Dr. H. A. Gebbie for fig. 9.14.

Mr. J. A. Ratcliffe and the Institute of Physics and The Physical Society for fig. 5.25.

Prof. R. A. Smith, Dr. F. E. Jones, Mr. R. P. Chasmar and the Oxford University Press for figs. 10.1, 10.3, 10.4, 10.8.

Messrs. Evans Electroselenium for fig. 10.9.

Messrs. Hilger and Watts for fig. 10.12.

The late Dr. J. W. T. Walsh and Messrs. Constable for figs. 10.16, 10.17, 10.18, and 10.19.

Prof. W. D. Wright and Messrs. Hilger and Watts for figs. 10.22 and 10.23.

Messrs. Springer for figs. 11.4, 11.5 and 11.6.

The *Annales d'Astrophysique* for fig. 12.27.

R. W. DITCHBURN.

UNIVERSITY OF READING,
October, 1962

Contents

		PAGE
Chapter I	HISTORICAL INTRODUCTION	1
II	WAVE THEORY—INTRODUCTION	18
III	WAVE THEORY—COMBINATION OF WAVE MOTIONS	42
IV	REPRESENTATION OF LIGHT BY WAVE TRAINS OF FINITE LENGTH	73
V	INTERFERENCE	118
VI	DIFFRACTION	162
VII	OPTICAL INSTRUMENTS: COAXAL SYSTEMS OF LENSES AND MIRRORS	238
VIII	DEFECTS OF OPTICAL IMAGES	276
IX	MEASUREMENTS WITH INTERFEROMETERS	333
X	DETECTION AND MEASUREMENT OF RADIATION	371
XI	VELOCITY OF LIGHT AND RELATIVISTIC OPTICS	409
XII	POLARIZED LIGHT	451
XIII	THE ELECTROMAGNETIC THEORY	503
XIV	THE ELECTROMAGNETIC THEORY OF REFLECTION AND REFRACTION	530
XV	THE ELECTROMAGNETIC THEORY OF ABSORPTION AND DISPERSION	549
XVI	ANISOTROPIC MEDIA	592
XVII	THE INTERACTION OF RADIATION AND MATTER	648
XVIII	QUANTUM THEORY OF RADIATION	691
XIX	INTERACTION PROCESSES IN RELATION TO QUANTUM MECHANICS	730
XX	THE LIMITATIONS OF OPTICAL INSTRUMENTS	779
	LIST OF SYMBOLS	
	INDEX	

CHAPTER I

Introduction

1.1. The Scientific Picture.

New experimental data nearly always cause some alteration in scientific theories, but in certain periods of history the changes are very gradual. The new material is assimilated by extending and modifying the theories while leaving unchanged certain fundamental ideas on which all the theories are based. Progress of this kind went on during most of the nineteenth century, but near the end of the century it became impossible to modify the current theories so as to accept the new experimental results. Certain fundamental difficulties affecting the whole basis of physical science were revealed and, in order to overcome these difficulties, it has been necessary to clarify our views concerning the nature and purpose of scientific inquiry. It would not be appropriate to discuss this matter at length in a book on one branch of science. On the other hand, it would be very difficult to give an adequate account of the modern theory of light without some reference to these general considerations. It therefore appears desirable to state, at the outset, the objective which the author has in mind during the development of the theory of light. Later, the reader may be able to judge for himself whether the objective has been attained. He may also decide whether he feels that the objective is satisfactory both from the practical and from the intellectual point of view.

1.2.—The practical scientific worker makes observations with the senses of sight and hearing, and also with scientific instruments which increase the range, delicacy and number of his observations. The theoretical worker accepts these observations as given data which he has to co-ordinate. In order to be able to reason about them, he first collects them into groups. Each group is then organized in a system which exhibits relations between the members of the group. A system of this kind is called a scientific theory. The whole body of scientific theories and the connections between them constitute a scientific picture of the world. In the process of making scientific theories, words like "electron", "energy", "organism" are introduced.

These words are symbols invented in order to create a language capable of describing the results of observation in a logical and elegant way.

1.3.—The construction of a scientific theory may be compared to the preparation of a weather map at a central meteorological station. A large number of observations of pressure, temperature, etc., are received and recorded, at the appropriate places, on a large chart. When all the data are entered, the meteorologist inserts isobars, etc., and proceeds to make predictions. In discussing the map, he uses terms like "depression" or "cold front". These terms form a convenient way of summarizing certain aspects of the observations. They help him to think quickly and clearly about the meteorological situation. The weather map is, however, primarily a representation of the observations. The isobars are useful only in so far as they represent the observations. In a similar way, in the theory of light, we use terms like "waves" and "particles" for the description and discussion of the results of experiments. We need to remember that the meaning of these words is derived from the experiments which they describe. We must not attempt to deduce the special properties of light waves or light particles from any preconceived ideas about waves or particles in general. All that we can say about light must be deduced from experimental observation.

1.4.—New scientific theories usually begin by relating new observations to familiar concepts, based upon older observations. For a long time the theory of light was discussed in terms of waves or particles, because it is easy to form mental pictures of waves and particles. Recent advances have forced us to accept the fact that a complete theory of light cannot be expressed in terms of simple analogies of this type. We are, however, able to construct a summary of our observations in mathematical terms. This mathematical theory is precisely defined and enables us to make certain kinds of predictions concerning the probable results of future observations. It is logically consistent within itself. We often find it convenient to "translate" part of this theory into words, but the translation is never quite perfect, though it may frequently be very useful. A wave picture of light furnishes an adequate description of a wide range of observations just as a set of isobars expresses the results of certain meteorological observations. The wave theory is unsuited to describe certain other types of observations and these may be discussed in terms of light particles or "photons". In a similar way certain types of meteorological observations cannot be described simply by drawing isobars, but can be included in the weather map in other ways. Any attempt to make a complete theory of light in terms of waves *or* particles must lead to confusion and error. We must admit that the results of our experiments on light are, in some ways, so different from the results of observations on things like waves on water, or moving particles, that analogies break down. They cease to be useful and become a burden. At this point it is necessary to leave the analogies and revert to the mathematical equations. When all this has been said, it still remains true that most people think more readily in terms of words than in terms of equations. We therefore use the analogies as far as possible —like a man who travels as far as possible by train even though he knows that none of the places he wishes to visit lies exactly on the railway line.

1.5.—In the historical development of a subject ideas are gradually introduced in order to include fresh observations within the theoretical description. In the treatment given in a textbook it is often convenient to disregard the historical order and to introduce many of the current ideas as hypotheses to be tested by experiment. The author knows, in advance, that most of the hypotheses which he introduces are going to be " approved " by the experimental results which he subsequently describes. In this way he avoids the necessity of burdening the reader with details of theories which have been found to be unsatisfactory and are now only of historical interest. The formal treatment of the subject, in this book, follows this plan. It begins in Chapter II. In the remainder of the present chapter our object is to consider the theory of light more from the historical point of view and to show how each of the more important types of experimental observation has been incorporated in, and has led to alterations in, the theory of light. A summary of this process is given in fig. 1.6 which will be considered in detail at the end of the chapter. In the course of this review of the progress of the theory of light we also seek to indicate the general relations of the theory of light to other departments of science.

1.6. Light in Relation to Biological Science.

The scientific picture of the world would be seriously incomplete if it did not include an account of the physical and physiological processes by which man makes his observations. The scientific picture must include an account of the link or links between the human brain and the things—atoms, molecules, etc.—whose existence is postulated in order to describe the observations. Historically, it has been recognized from the earliest times that a very important set of our observations involves light and vision. Early theories of light were therefore theories of vision. One school postulated that the eye sends out invisible antennae or sensitive probes and is thus able to feel objects which are too distant to be touched by hands or feet. This theory may be called the " tactile " theory. Another view was that something is emitted by bright objects and that when this thing enters the eye it is able to affect some sensitive part of the eye and so give rise to the sensation of sight. This theory was called the " emission " theory. Both these theories were current among Greek thinkers about 500 B.C.*

1.7.—The tactile theory is inherently simple because it describes the unknown in terms of the known. The more mysterious sense of vision is directly related to the simpler and more obvious sense of touch. The tactile theory has some difficulty in explaining why things can be felt, but not seen, in the dark, and why bodies can be made visible in the dark by heating them. The fact that certain bright bodies are able to make neighbouring bodies visible also receives no obvious explanation.

The tactile theory can include this type of observation by postulating that the visual probes are able to feel only certain kinds of surfaces and then making a series of assumptions that surfaces can be modified under various conditions. When this is done, the simple relation to the sense of touch has been lost. The theory becomes intolerably complicated. These observations are described in a simple and satisfactory way by the emission theory if it be assumed that some bodies emit a radiation to which the eyes are sensitive, and that others are able to reflect or scatter this radiation so that it enters the eye. For these and similar reasons, the emission theory gradually displaced the tactile theory. The process was very slow and it was not until about 1000 A.D. that, under the influence of the Arabian astronomer Alhazen, the tactile theory was finally abandoned.

1.8.—The emission theory being accepted, light may be defined as " visible radiation ", and we may give the following general account of the visual process. Light, being emitted, reflected, or scattered, enters the eye and is focused by the lens of the eye on a surface situated at the back of the eye. This surface is called the *retina*. It

* Many variations and combinations of these theories were also suggested. We need not consider them since they are more complicated than the two theories we have described and have no important compensating advantages.

contains a large number of nerve endings. When light falls on one of them, a chemical and physical action takes place. As a result, a series of electrical impulses is sent along an appropriate nerve fibre to the brain.

A complete theory of vision thus involves many sciences. The description of the emission, reflection and scattering of light and of its transmission to the eye is a part of physical science. The description of the structures of the eye, of the optic nerve and of the associated parts of the brain, belongs to the anatomist. The description of the processes by which the eye lives and transmits its messages to the brain is within the science of physiology. The description of the way in which the mind interprets a pattern of visual sensation and relates it to other visual and non-visual experience falls within the domain of psychology. Most of the theory of vision is clearly outside the scope of a book which is primarily concerned with the physical properties of light, though knowledge of some of the non-physical aspects of vision is necessary in order to understand the subject of photometry and the physical specification and measurement of colour.

1.9. Light in Relation to Physical Science.

Although the theory of light started as the study of vision, this is not, to the physicist, the most important part of the subject. He can detect light through its heating effect on a thermopile or through its electrical effect on a photocell. He can also detect it as an agent capable of causing chemical action or through its effect on a photographic plate. To him, light is a form of energy which travels from one place to another. It can interact with matter and can be transformed into thermal, electrical or chemical energy. The physical equations would be incomplete and the energy conservation law would fail if the transfers and transformations of energy due to the action of light were not taken into account. To the physicist the effect of light on the retina is only one example of photo-chemical action.

1.10. Waves or Corpuscles.

If light is a form of energy which can be transferred from one place to another, it is reasonable to seek to describe it by analogy with other methods of transport of energy. Moving bodies possess kinetic energy. This energy accompanies the body in its movement and thus passes from one place to another. Another mechanical mode of transfer of energy is by means of the propagation of waves. This mode is not, in general, accompanied by any bodily movement of the medium.

Many physicists of the seventeenth and eighteenth centuries sought to describe light either in terms of moving particles or of waves. To them, these forms of moving energy were sharply differentiated, in that particle energy is highly localized. The kinetic energy of a rifle-bullet travels from one well-defined, small region of space to another, and does not spread during transit. If, however, a wave is started by dropping a stone into a pond, the energy quickly spreads over the whole surface, and usually no small region receives a very high proportion of it.

1.11. Rays of Light.

In the seventeenth century it was known that the propagation of light could be represented by means of rays. If the light from a very small source was interrupted by an opaque obstacle, a very sharp

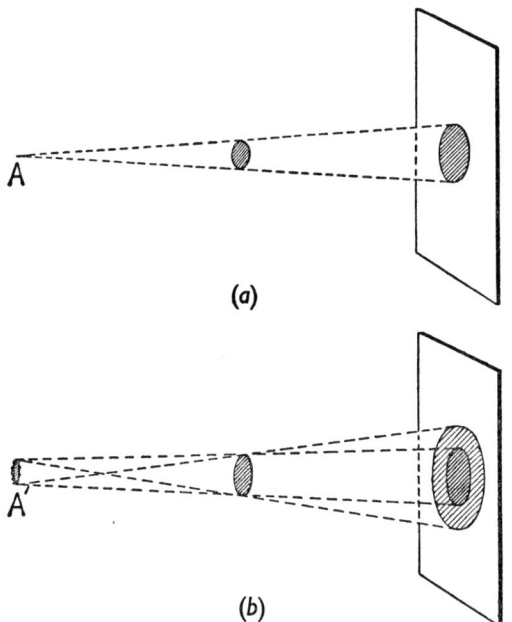

Fig. 1.1.—Formation of shadows by (a) a point source A, and (b) an extended source A', in relation to rectilinear propagation of light

shadow was formed (see fig. 1.1a). If the source was not very small the edge of the shadow was not so sharp. There was a dark shadow known as the *umbra* and a diffuse edge known as the *penumbra* (see fig. 1.1b). These observations are simple examples of a large number which are generally described by the statement that light travels out from the source along rays which are straight lines. On this view, the change of illumination which occurs in the penumbra is due to the fact that a point in this region receives light from only a portion of the source. There is no evidence here that light energy spreads outside the region defined by the rays. A ray may therefore be defined as a path along which light energy travels from a source to a receptor. Transit along this path is prevented if the ray is cut by an opaque obstacle at any point. If all the rays from a given source to a receptor are interrupted by opaque obstacles, no light energy can reach the receptor from the source. Note that two ideas are involved—first, that light is propagated in rays, and, second, that these rays are straight lines. The motion of a small particle inevitably sweeps out a line, but not necessarily a straight line. According to Newton's Laws of Motion, particles travel in straight lines in the absence of any " impressed " force. It therefore appeared to Newton that light should be described as a system of particles following paths described by his Laws of Motion. It is true that, owing to the action of the earth's gravitational field, the trajectories of material particles are not straight lines. The rectilinear propagation of light must therefore be explained, either by assuming that the light-particle has no weight, or that its speed is always so high that the curvature due to the action of gravity is too small to be detected.

1.12. Interference and Diffraction.

Although Newton knew of no evidence for the spreading of light energy, he first studied what were later called *interference* phenomena. These are described in an elegant way by the wave theory of light. He placed a convex lens of large radius of curvature (about 50 feet) in contact with a plane piece of glass and viewed the reflected light (see fig. 1.2). A series of coloured rings—alternately bright and dark—was observed (see Plate I*e*, p. 74). These are known as Newton's Rings.

Newton recognized that these rings indicated the presence of some kind of periodicity and that this suggested a wave theory of light. He believed that the rectilinear propagation of light was an insuperable objection to a simple wave theory. He therefore suggested that light consists of corpuscles which either possess an internal vibration of their own or are in some degree controlled by waves or vibrations of the medium through which they travel. The objection to a simple wave theory was removed when it was discovered that the propagation of light is not strictly linear. Light *does* spread, though to a very small extent, from the edges of beams defined by rays (see Plate III, p. 162). For example, the shadow of a straight edge formed by a small source is not *perfectly* sharp when seen under high magnification. Some light penetrates into the region which ought to be completely dark if light were propagated entirely in straight lines, and there is a

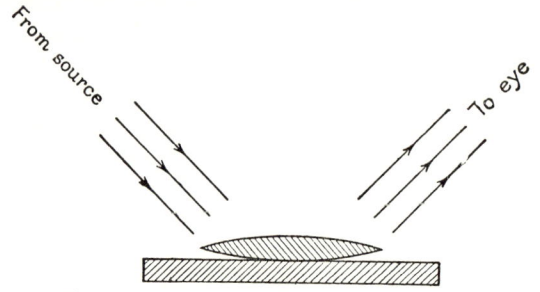

Fig. 1.2.—Apparatus for viewing Newton's rings

series of fine, light and dark bands at the edge of the region outside the shadow. Some observations of this type were made by Grimaldi in Newton's lifetime, but it was not until 150 years later that this phenomenon (which is known as *diffraction*) was clearly understood. The discovery of diffraction showed that the propagation of light is not exactly rectilinear. The concept of the ray of light does not *exactly* correspond to the results of observations. It is only an approximation.

1.13. Development of the Wave Theory.

We shall see later (Chapters VI and VIII) that whilst the wave theory cannot give a satisfactory account of *exactly* linear propagation, it is well suited to describe *approximately* linear propagation, provided that it be assumed that the wavelength is small in relation to the relevant dimensions of the apparatus. The nineteenth century saw very important advances in the technique of experimental physics, and the number and accuracy of experiments on light increased greatly. The observations obtained were well described by the wave theory which became more exactly defined. We may note three important types of observation.

(i) *The Wavelength of Light.*

Many detailed experiments on interference and diffraction were made. These led to a set of determinations of the wavelength of light.

It was shown that, in a spectrum, the wavelength is related to the colour. The wavelength is about 6.5×10^{-5} centimetre for red, 5.6×10^{-5} for green and 4.5×10^{-5} for blue light. Different methods of measurement gave consistent results.

(ii) *The Velocity of Light.*

In 1676, a Danish astronomer, Römer, made the fundamental discovery that the velocity of light was finite, and estimated it from astronomical observations. About 200 years later the velocity was measured by terrestrial experiments and was shown to be very near to 3×10^{10} centimetres per second (or 186,000 miles per second).

(iii) *The Polarization of Light.*

In 1670, Bartholinus discovered that when a beam of ordinary light passes through certain crystals (such as calcite) each ray splits into two. On passing the two rays into a second crystal, the effect depends on the orientation of the crystal with respect to the beam. For certain orientations the two rays proceed unchanged. For other orientations the two rays each split into two (see fig. 1.3). This phenomenon is known as double refraction. It indicates that a beam of

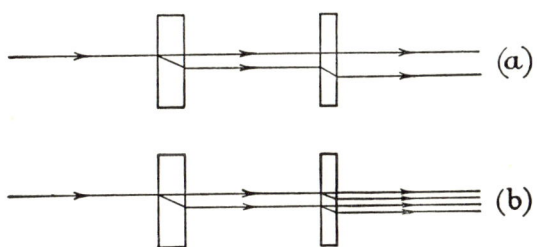

Fig. 1.3.—Double refraction: (*a*) two crystals with similar orientations, (*b*) two crystals with different orientations of crystal axes.

light which has passed through a crystal is differentiated in respect of planes including the direction of propagation. The simplest experiment on this property was made much later (1808) and is due to Malus. He reflected a beam of light at the surfaces of two unsilvered pieces of glass (see fig. 1.4). He showed that when the two reflections are in the same plane (as shown in the figure) a high proportion of the light incident on the second mirror (M_2) is reflected. If the mirror M_2 is turned so that the second reflection is directed out of the plane of the paper, the reflected beam becomes weaker. It is of nearly zero brightness when the two reflections are in planes at right angles. This shows that after the first reflection the beam of light has a special property in relation to the plane of the paper. It can be strongly reflected, at a glass surface, in this plane but not in a plane at right angles. A beam of light which possesses this property is said to be plane-polarized. This type of property finds no place in a theory of longitudinal waves. For this reason it was regarded by Newton, who considered only such waves, as an additional important objection to the wave theory. It

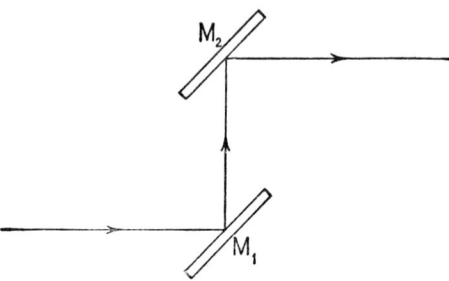

Fig. 1.4.—Malus' experiment. Note that M_1 and M_2 are *unsilvered* mirrors

is, however, adequately represented in a theory of *transverse* waves. This was realized by Huygens (1690) but it was not until the nineteenth century that really detailed experiments on the reflection and refraction of polarized light became available. With a longitudinal wave, the direction of vibration is always the same as that of propagation, so the wave motion can be represented as the variation of a scalar quantity. A transverse wave motion must be represented by a vector whose direction is related to the plane of polarization.

1.14. Electromagnetic Theory.

The wave theory of light was formulated before the development of the fundamental laws of electromagnetism. It was assumed that there existed some kind of medium which had properties like that of an elastic solid. This medium pervaded all space but was modified by the presence of matter. A theory of transverse waves in such a medium formed a qualitative description of the fundamental phenomena of interference, diffraction and polarization. In order to fill in the details of the wave theory, it was necessary to make special assumptions concerning the density and elasticity of this medium, and also concerning the conditions obtaining at the surface separating two media such as glass and air. Discussion of these details revealed certain difficulties and appeared to indicate that there were some inconsistencies in the theory. All these difficulties were resolved by Maxwell's electromagnetic theory of light.

Maxwell formulated the equations of electromagnetism in a general form, and he showed that they suggest the possibility of the propagation of transverse electromagnetic waves. The velocity of propagation can be derived from constants measured in laboratory experiments on electricity and magnetism. The value calculated is in close agreement with the directly measured velocity of light. Maxwell's theory included an account of the propagation of electromagnetic waves in media such as glass. He was able to show that it gave a general account of the phenomena of reflection and refraction, including the formation of a spectrum by the dispersion of light. It is important to realize that all this was achieved without introducing any arbitrary assumptions. The theory of light became, in the hands of Maxwell, a part of the theory of electricity and magnetism.

1.15. The Electromagnetic Spectrum.

The elastic-solid theory of light could not explain why all the observed waves had wavelengths between about 7×10^{-5} and 4×10^{-5} centimetre. The theory of electromagnetic waves suggested the possibility of producing waves of other wavelengths by electrical means. Success was first obtained by Hertz, who in 1887 succeeded in propagating electromagnetic waves of about 10 metres wavelength. A great deal of the progress of experimental physics since that time has consisted in the discovery of methods of producing electromagnetic waves of different wavelengths. Some of the properties of these waves depend upon their wavelength, but they are all propagated with the same velocity (in free space) and they are all described by the equations of Maxwell. Fig. 1.5 shows them arranged in order of wavelength. Modern technical advances have provided methods of producing or of detecting waves of nearly every wavelength from above 3000 metres to below 10^{-11} centimetre.

There are certain regions in the spectrum where it is still very difficult to excite the waves. These regions are not completely explored but they are not really gaps in the spectrum. The limits of the spectrum at the two ends are not perfectly definite. At the long-wavelength end, methods of producing and detecting radiation gradually become less efficient as the wavelength increases. At the short-wavelength end, an enormous concentration of energy is needed to produce the vibrations of extremely high frequency. Also these radiations are difficult to detect since they are very little absorbed by matter. The range of wavelengths to which the eye is sensitive and to which

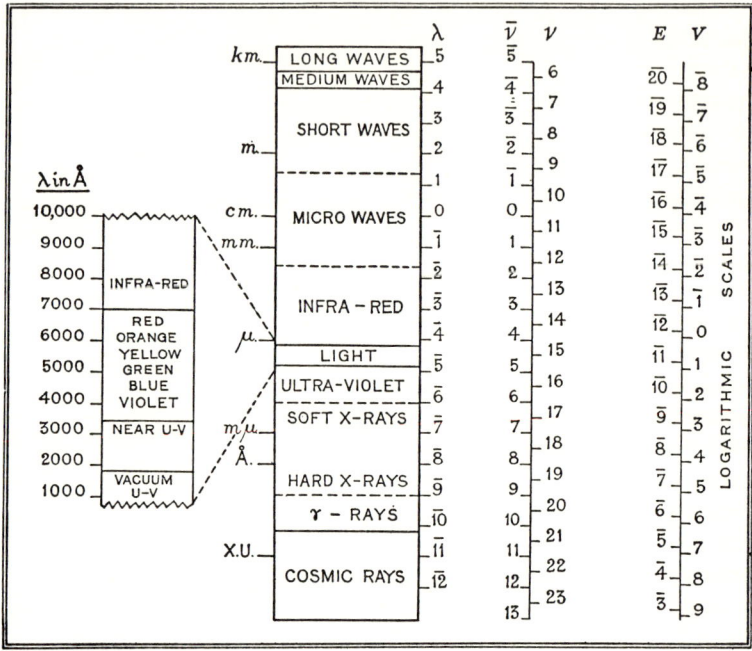

Fig. 1.5.—The Electromagnetic Spectrum

The main diagram shows the names given to electromagnetic waves of different wavelengths. The logarithm (to base 10) of the wavelength in centimetres is shown on the right. The relation between different units of length is shown on the left, e.g. 1 Ångström unit (Å.) = 10^{-8} cm. The data given enable wavelengths to be converted from one unit of length to another, e.g. for red-orange light, $\lambda = 6 \times 10^{-5}$ cm. = 6000 Å. = 0·6 μ.

The inset figure on the left is an enlargement of the region between 10,000 Å. and 1000 Å. The scale for this enlargement shows the wavelength directly. The scales to the right (which are intended for use in connection with later chapters of the book) show

(i) $\log_{10} \bar{\nu}$, where $\bar{\nu}$ is the wave number, i.e. the reciprocal of λ in cm.
(ii) $\log_{10} \nu$, where ν is the frequency in sec.$^{-1}$
(iii) $\log_{10} E$, where $E = h\nu$ is the energy in ergs of a quantum of frequency ν.
(iv) $\log_{10} V$, where V is the energy in electron-volts (see Example 1(iii)).

we give the name "light" is thus seen as part of a very much wider spectrum. The electromagnetic theory brings light into relation with the other types of electromagnetic radiation and also with the fundamental theories of electricity and magnetism.

1.16. Photons.

Let us now return to the fundamental conflict between wave and particle theories of light.

The wave theory, in explaining the approximately rectilinear propagation, seemed to have defeated the particle theory, and all the experimental results of the nineteenth century appeared to be adequately described in terms of wave concepts. Early in the twentieth century, a series of observations on photo-electricity created a really serious difficulty for the wave theory. It was found that light could cause atoms to emit electrons and that, when light released an electron from an atom, the energy possessed by the electron very greatly exceeded that which the atom could, according to the electromagnetic-wave theory, have received. Einstein suggested that, in order to give an adequate description of these observations, it was necessary to assume that the energy of a light beam is not evenly spread over the whole beam, but is concentrated in certain regions. These localized concentrations of energy he called *photons*. They are propagated like particles. It is assumed that there are usually a very large number of them, the energy in any one photon being very small. Thus to most ordinary experiments, the energy of a light beam is evenly distributed, just as a gas exerts a very nearly uniform pressure on the surface of an ordinary vessel, because each molecule is very small and the number of molecules is very large. When very small areas are involved (e.g. when the movement of an ultra-microscopic particle is observed), the irregularities of the Brownian movement show the discontinuous " structure " of the gas. In a similar way, the atom presents to the light beam an area so small that it indicates the presence of " molecules of light " or photons. In order to describe the observation in detail, it is necessary to assume that the photons corresponding to light of one wavelength all have the same energy.

Shortly before Einstein suggested the concept of photons, Planck had found it necessary to use a somewhat similar hypothesis for entirely different reasons. He was concerned with the light emitted by hot bodies. He found that the observations indicated that light energy is emitted by atoms in multiples of a certain energy unit. It is not possible to emit a fraction of a unit. The size of the unit, which is called a *quantum*, depends on the wavelength (λ) of the radiation. Its value is

$$E = hc/\lambda, \qquad \ldots \ldots \quad 1(1)$$

where h is a universal constant, known as *Planck's constant,* and c is the velocity of light. The value of Planck's constant (h) is $6 \cdot 6 \times 10^{-27}$ erg-second. If ν is the frequency of the radiation, we have $c = \nu\lambda$, and hence

$$E = h\nu. \qquad \qquad \qquad 1(2)$$

Planck's hypothesis did not require that the energy should be emitted in *localized* bundles and it might, though with some difficulty, have been reconciled with the electromagnetic-wave theory of radiation. When Einstein showed that it seemed necessary to assume the existence of *concentrations* of energy travelling through free space, a solution of this kind was excluded. The concept of a particle appeared to be necessary.

1.17. Relativity Theory.

Mainly as a result of experiments on the propagation of light in moving media, Einstein investigated the foundations of dynamics. In 1905 he published what is known as the Restricted Theory of Relativity. This theory is a new system of dynamics, modifying and in a certain sense superseding the Newtonian theory. The difference between the relativistic dynamics and the Newtonian dynamics is very important when the particles under consideration are moving with speeds near to that of light. Any satisfactory theory of light must therefore agree with the concepts of the relativistic dynamics. When the theory of light is brought into relation to the theory of relativity, it is possible to give a complete account of observations on light which is emitted by a source moving with respect to the observer, or on light which passes through a medium moving with respect to either source or observer. In 1915, the theory of relativity was extended to include the dynamics of bodies moving in fields of force. The theory made specific predictions concerning the properties of light emitted in, or passing through, strong gravitational fields. The verification of these predictions by astronomical observations gave support to the general theory of relativity and showed that it, too, is relevant to the theory of light.

1.18. Modern Theory.

The modern theoretical physicist is required to invent a unified description of two very different types of experiment. On the one hand stand all the phenomena of interference, diffraction and polarization, which are so well described by the wave theory. On the other hand, modern experiment has greatly increased the number and range of the experiments which are readily described in terms of photons. The electromagnetic picture has no place for the photons, and the particle theory has no place for the waves, yet both are required to give a complete description of the phenomena. In a similar situation, Newton considered the possibility of particles which possessed periodic properties or were guided by waves. Many suggestions of this type were considered during the first quarter of this century but none of these was entirely successful.

1.19.—The solution which is now accepted is more radical. The modern quantum mechanics constitutes one theory including the properties of light and of matter. The description is very closely knit together so that it is not possible to separate one part and call it the " theory of light ". The theory is not easy to understand but it is not unnecessarily complicated in view of the wide range of phenomena covered. As indicated at the beginning of this chapter, it can be stated completely only in mathematical form. It must not be thought that the theory is complete and will never require modification. With this qualification, it may fairly be said that the main difficulties of the particle-wave conflict have been resolved, and that a really unified theory has been produced. In this unified theory the particle and wave ideas appear as complementary rather than as rival conceptions. The theory shows, in a systematic and logical way, that wave and particle concepts are each to be used in appropriate contexts, and it shows the relation between them.

1.20.—This introduction to the theory of light is summarized diagrammatically in fig. 1.6, which indicates how the theory has gradually been extended and modified to include, within one description, the increasing range of experimental material. Starting at the top left-hand side, we see that the rectilinear propagation of light was included in both the tactile and the emission theory. The former, which could not explain many phenomena which indicate that light is a form of energy, was abandoned about 1000 A.D. The emission theory is divided into (a) the corpuscular emission theory, and (b) the wave emission theory. The phenomena of interference and diffraction appeared to give a clear decision in favour of a wave theory. Slightly later it became necessary to use a tranverse-wave theory in order to include the phenomena of double refraction, etc. The transverse (or vector) wave theory was initially stated in terms of an elastic solid theory, but the theory of Maxwell was preferred because it gave an elegant explanation of the relation between the velocity of light and the ratio of the electromagnetic units. Early in this century, experiments on the interaction of radiation and matter led to formulation of the quantum theory which had some features in common with the

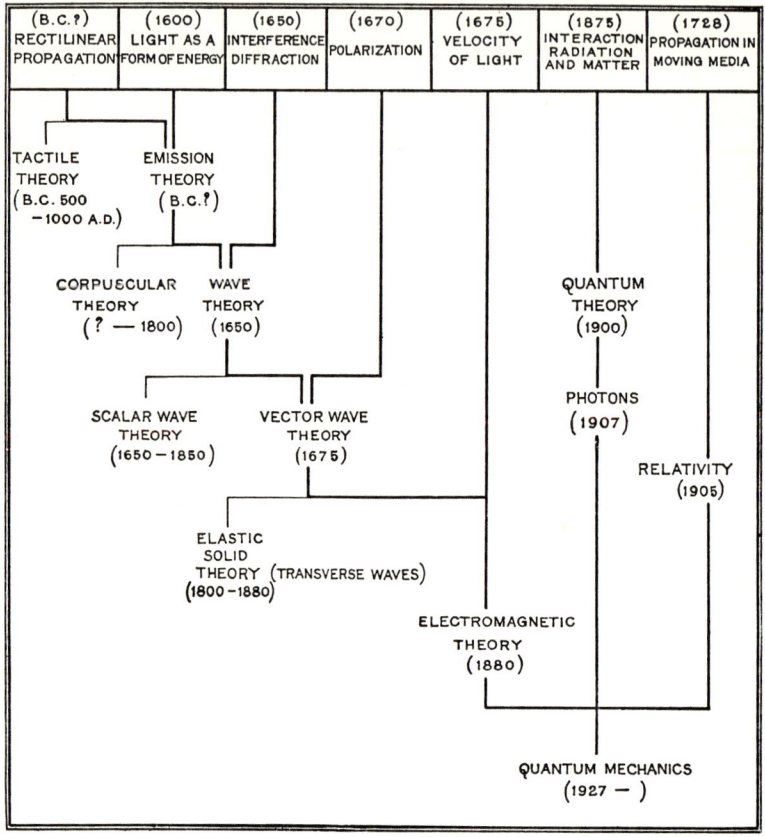

Fig. 1.6.—Development of the theory of light

(The dates given are intended to give a general indication of the times at which the different types of experimental result became available, and the times at which the different theories became current.)

earlier corpuscular theory. The theory of relativity was formulated about the same time. The modern quantum mechanics (developed since 1927) incorporates the appropriate parts of the electromagnetic wave theory, the quantum theory and the relativity theory.

EXAMPLES [1(i)–1(v)]

1(i). What is the energy of a quantum of red light of wavelength $6 \cdot 6 \times 10^{-5}$ cm.? What is the associated frequency?
$$[E = 3 \times 10^{-12} \text{ erg}; \; \nu = 4 \cdot 5 \times 10^{14} \text{ sec.}^{-1}]$$

1(ii). What are (a) the frequency and (b) the wavelength of the radiation for which the quantum of energy is equal to the kinetic energy of an electron which has been accelerated by a potential difference of 1·24 volt? The charge of an electron is $4 \cdot 8 \times 10^{-10}$ e.s.u. $\quad [\nu = 3 \cdot 0 \times 10^{14} \text{ sec.}^{-1}; \; \lambda = 10^{-4} \text{ cm.} = 1\mu.]$

1(iii). One electron-volt is the energy of an electron which has fallen through a potential difference of one volt. How many electron-volts are equivalent to a quantum of X-rays whose frequency is 3×10^{19} sec.$^{-1}$? $\quad$ [123,800.]

1(iv). What are the dimensions of Planck's constant? $\quad [ML^2T^{-1}.]$

1(v). If N atoms each emit a quantum of frequency ν, how much energy (in joules) is available? 1 joule = 10^7 ergs. $\quad [6 \cdot 6 \times 10^{-34} N\nu \text{ joules.}]$

CHAPTER II

Wave Theory—Introduction

2.1. Fundamental Ideas.

The theory of wave motion forms a descriptive system appropriate, with minor modifications, to a wide range of observations in sound and light, as well as to waves propagated along the surface of a liquid. The same system of equations may be used because the different groups of phenomena have many properties in common and it is these common properties which are described by the equations of wave motion. In the general account of wave theory, and in all the applications discussed in Chapters III–IX, it is not necessary to specify the detailed physical properties of the disturbance which represents light. It is even a matter of indifference whether the disturbance considered is a scalar quantity, like the pressure of a gas, or a vector quantity, like the electric or magnetic field vectors.

2.2.—The theory of wave motion involves three distinct concepts:

(*a*) There is some physical property which, at any given instant, has a defined and measurable value at every point.

(*b*) The value of this property at any given point can undergo a periodic fluctuation or disturbance.

(*c*) A disturbance at one point at a given time produces a similar disturbance at a neighbouring point at a slightly later time so that the pattern of the disturbance is continuously transferred from one place to another.

In studying wave motion it is convenient to start with the simple harmonic oscillator. This is the simplest and most fundamental of the many types of vibrating source which may give rise to waves. Moreover, its motion is essentially the same as the motion of any point in a medium through which waves are passing. The picture of a progressive wave is obtained by combining the equations of simple harmonic motion with certain general equations of propagation.

2.3. The Simple Harmonic Oscillator.

The undamped simple harmonic oscillator is a mathematical abstraction, just as a frictionless pulley is a mathematical abstraction

Although no completely undamped oscillator is found in nature, the motion of an undamped oscillator forms a good first approximation to the motion of many physical systems. By its use certain important results are obtained in a simple way, and it is not difficult to insert the effects of damping as a second approximation.

In studying the simple harmonic oscillator, it is convenient to picture a particular physical system, and we therefore start by considering a torsional pendulum (fig. 2.1). The pendulum consists of two equal masses A and A' connected by a weightless rod. The rod is suspended from its mid-point M by a thin wire whose upper end E is fixed. Suppose that the system is initially at rest, that the rod is rotated through a small angle about the vertical line EM and is then

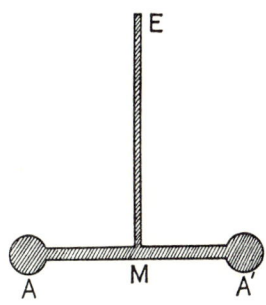

Fig.2.1.—Torsional pendulum

released. The subsequent motion may be studied by considering the variation of the quantity q which is defined to be the linear displacement of A (or A') from its mean position. It is to be understood that q is measured along the circular arc through which the masses move. Then

$$q = f(t), \qquad \ldots \ldots \quad 2(1)$$

where t is the time measured from any convenient original moment.

2.4. *Experimental Observations.*

The following experimental observations might be made on such a system:

(i) The pendulum oscillates to and fro in a horizontal plane and there is a constant interval between the times when A passes through its equilibrium position, i.e. between the times when $q = 0$. The time between successive transits *in the same direction* is called the *period* (T).

(ii) The value of q varies between two limits $\pm a$. The quantity a is called the *amplitude*. In practice the amplitude slowly decreases, but with a suitable choice of material for the wire (EM) the decrease in one period is small. As stated above, it is neglected in the present discussion.

(iii) The variation of q with t is represented by a graph similar to that shown in fig. 2.2a.

This graph can be represented by the equation

$$q = a \sin(\omega t + \delta) = a \sin \phi, \qquad 2(2)$$

where $\omega = 2\pi/T$ and is called the *angular frequency** or *circular frequency*, δ is a constant called the *epoch* or *epoch angle*, ϕ is called the *phase* and is defined to be equal to $(\omega t + \delta)$. The angular frequency

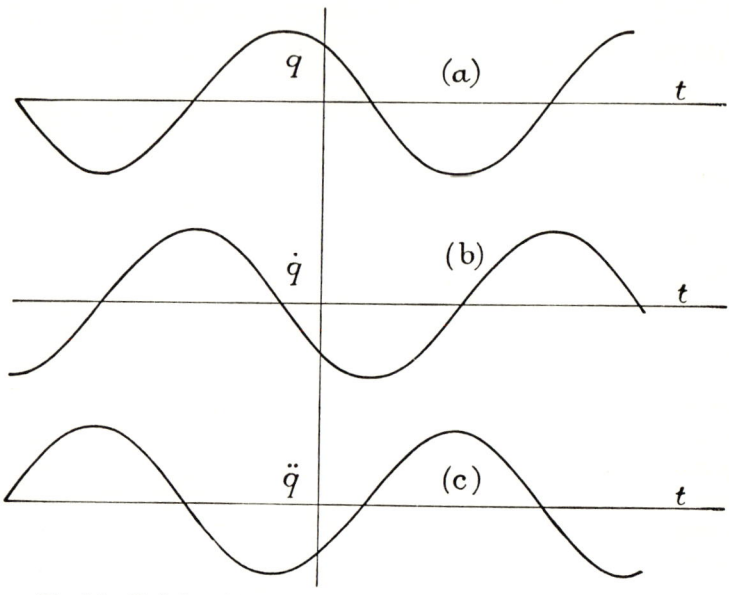

Fig. 2.2.—Variation of displacement, velocity, and acceleration with time, for a simple harmonic oscillator

is closely related to the *frequency* or number of vibrations per second. If ν is the frequency,

$$\nu = \frac{1}{T} = \frac{\omega}{2\pi}. \qquad 2(3)$$

The value of δ is determined by observing the value of q when $t = 0$, i.e. $q_0 = a \sin \delta$. If the origin of time is chosen so that $t = 0$ when $q = 0$, then $\delta = 0$ and 2(2) becomes

$$q = a \sin \omega t. \qquad 2(4)$$

It is usually convenient to choose the origin of t in this way when dealing with a single system but, when two systems are being considered, they do not in general

* This quantity is sometimes called the *pulsance*.

have the same epoch. While one can be reduced to the form 2(4), the more general relation 2(2) must be used for the other. Although only one system is now under consideration the more general form 2(2) is retained in view of later applications.

(iv) The force required to turn the rod AA' so as to maintain a deflection q is found to be proportional to q. Write it equal to kq. The work done in deflecting the pendulum (slowly) through a distance q is

$$V = \tfrac{1}{2}kq^2. \quad \ldots \ldots \quad 2(5)$$

(v) The period of oscillation of the system is found to be

$$T = 2\pi\sqrt{\frac{m}{k}}, \quad \ldots \ldots \quad 2(6)$$

where $\tfrac{1}{2}m$ is the mass of either A or A'.

2.5. *Equations of Motion.*

By differentiating equation 2(2) with respect to time, we obtain

$$\dot{q} = \omega a \cos(\omega t + \delta) = \omega a \cos\phi = \pm\omega(a^2 - q^2)^{\tfrac{1}{2}}. \quad 2(7)$$

and

$$\ddot{q} = -\omega^2 a \sin(\omega t + \delta) = -\omega^2 a \sin\phi = -\omega^2 q. \quad . \quad 2(8)$$

These equations are represented in figs. 2.2*b* and 2.2*c*. Both the positive and the negative sign have to be used in 2(7) because each value of q is associated with two equal and opposite values of $\dot{q}$. The system passes through each point twice in one period. On these two occasions the magnitude of $\dot{q}$ is the same but the sign is different. Equation 2(8) may also be obtained directly from the dynamical laws of motion. The torsion of the wire provides a couple which is equivalent to two forces each equal to $\tfrac{1}{2}kq$ and each acting on a mass $\tfrac{1}{2}m$.

Thus
$$\ddot{q} = -\frac{k}{m}q. \quad \ldots \ldots \quad 2(9)$$

The minus sign is required because the force always acts in a direction opposite to the displacement (q) and so acts as a *restoring force* tending to return the system to its equilibrium position. Equation 2(9) is equivalent to equation 2(8) provided that

$$\omega = \sqrt{\frac{k}{m}}, \quad \ldots \ldots \quad 2(10a)$$

or
$$T = 2\pi\sqrt{\frac{m}{k}}. \quad \ldots \ldots \quad 2(10b)$$

This equation is verified by direct observation (see § 2.4). The period (or angular frequency) is thus determined by the ratio of the restoring force per unit displacement to the mass.

From 2(7) the kinetic energy ($\tfrac{1}{2}m\dot{q}^2$) is seen to be $\tfrac{1}{2}m\omega^2(a^2 - q^2)$, and using 2(5) it may be seen that the total energy (W) is given by

$$W = \tfrac{1}{2}m\omega^2 a^2. \qquad \ldots \ldots \quad 2(11)$$

This energy is the same at all stages of the motion.

EXAMPLES [2(i)–2(vi)]

2(i). Write down the more important steps of the above discussion, using the angle through which the rod AA′ is deflected as the variable. If this angle is θ, show that $\ddot{\theta} = -\omega^2 \theta$ and obtain a solution of this equation.

2(ii). What are the dimensions of the constant k? Show that equations 2(5), 2(6) and 2(9) are dimensionally correct.

[The dimensions on each side of 2(5) are [ML^{2}T^{-2}] and, on each side of 2(9), [LT^{-2}].]

2(iii). What are the dimensions of ω, ν, ϕ and δ? Show that equation 2(10) is dimensionally correct.

[The dimensions of ω and ν are [T^{-1}]; ϕ and δ are angles and hence are pure ratios.]

2(iv). Show that the small oscillations of a simple pendulum are simple harmonic and find the angular frequency. [$\omega = \sqrt{(g/l)}$.]

2(v). Find the period of oscillation of a compound pendulum supported at a distance h from the centre of gravity.

[$T = 2\pi\sqrt{\{(h^2 + k^2)/gh\}}$, where k is the radius of gyration about the centre of gravity.]

2(vi). Make a list of some other physical systems whose motion is approximately simple harmonic.

[Any system in which there is a restoring force proportional to the displacement, e.g. a common balance, a magnet suspended in a magnetic field, the coil of a moving-coil galvanometer, etc.]

2.6. Arbitrary Constants.

Equation 2(8) is the fundamental differential equation of the motion. Its solution contains two *arbitrary constants* and may be written

$$q = a \sin(\omega t + \delta) = a \sin \phi, \qquad \ldots \ldots \quad 2(2)$$
or
$$q = -a \cos(\omega t + \delta') = -a \cos \phi', \qquad \ldots \quad 2(12)$$
or
$$q = A \sin \omega t + B \cos \omega t. \qquad \ldots \ldots \quad 2(13)$$

In 2(2) the arbitrary constants are a and δ; in 2(12) they are a and δ', and in 2(13) they are A and B.

§ 2.6   ARBITRARY CONSTANTS   23

These arbitrary constants are determined by the *initial conditions*. They may be derived if the values of q and $\dot{q}$ at some time t_0 are given. For example, if we are given $q = 0$ and $\dot{q} = u$ when $t = 0$, then $\delta = 0$ and $a = u/\omega$, so that $q = (u/\omega) \sin \omega t$ in this case. If 2(2), 2(12) and 2(13) all refer to the same initial conditions, the following relations must hold:

$$\left.\begin{aligned} \delta' - \delta &= \tfrac{1}{2}\pi, \\ \phi' - \phi &= \tfrac{1}{2}\pi, \\ A = a \cos \delta \quad \text{and} \quad B &= a \sin \delta, \\ \text{so that} \quad a^2 &= A^2 + B^2. \end{aligned}\right\} \quad \ldots \quad 2(14)$$

The initial conditions may be given in various ways, e.g. the values of q and $\ddot{q}$ (or $\dot{q}$ and $\ddot{q}$) might be stated for a certain value of t, or one of these variables might be given for two values of t. In general, two independent pieces of information must be supplied. Note that ω and the two associated quantities ν and T are not arbitrary constants. They depend on the physical properties of the oscillator and not upon the initial conditions.

EXAMPLES [2(vii) and 2(viii)]

2(vii). Determine the arbitrary constants and write down equations corresponding to 2(2), 2(12) and 2(13) when

(a) $q = 0$ and $\dot{q} = u$, when $t = nT$ (n being any integer),

(b) $q = q_0$ when $t = 0$, and $\dot{q} = u_0$ when $t = t_1$,

(c) $q = q_1$ when $t = t_1$, and $q = q_2$ when $t = t_2$.

$$\left[(a) \ q = \frac{u}{\omega} \sin \omega t, \right.$$

(b) $q = \left\{\dfrac{u_0 + q_0 \omega \sin \omega t_1}{\omega \cos \omega t_1}\right\} \sin \omega t + q_0 \cos \omega t.$

$$\left. (c) \ q = \left\{\frac{q_1 \cos \omega t_2 - q_2 \cos \omega t_1}{\sin \omega (t_1 - t_2)}\right\} \sin \omega t + \left\{\frac{q_2 \sin \omega t_1 - q_1 \sin \omega t_2}{\sin \omega (t_1 - t_2)}\right\} \cos \omega t. \right]$$

2(viii). Why do you fail to obtain the arbitrary constants if you are given $q = q_1$, when $t = 0$ and $q = q_1$ when $t = nT$?

[Because the dynamical equations imply that the value of q when $t = nT$ is the same as when $t = 0$. Thus only one piece of information about initial conditions is supplied.]

2.7. General Equations of Motion.

The general equation which applies to all simple harmonic oscillators is 2(5). This leads to the equation

$$H = \tfrac{1}{2}\frac{p^2}{m} + \tfrac{1}{2}kq^2, \qquad \qquad 2(15)$$

where p is the generalized momentum and H is the total energy expressed as a function of p and q. Equation 2(9) may then be obtained from one of Hamilton's equations

$$\frac{\partial H}{\partial q} = -\frac{dp}{dt}.$$

2.8. Vector Representation of Simple Harmonic Motion.

A straight line joining two points has direction and magnitude. Such a line is called a vector. When we are confined to lines in a given plane, two quantities are needed to define a vector. These may be (i) the length of the line, and (ii) the angle which it makes with some fixed axis. A vector may also be specified by giving its components along two fixed axes, and in various other ways. Always two quantities are involved and, for this reason, a vector (in one plane) is suitable for the simultaneous representation of two quantities. If the vector is given, the two associated quantities can be derived and, conversely, if the two quantities are given, we can draw the vector. The vector representation of simple harmonic motion may be carried out in either of two ways:

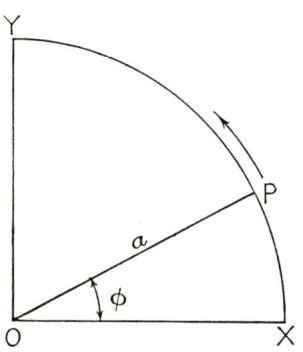

Fig. 2.3.—Representation of simple harmonic motion by a rotating vector.

(i) A *rotating* vector may be used. The line OP (fig. 2.3) is the representative vector. Its length is equal to the amplitude (a) and the angle which it makes with the line OX is equal to ϕ [see equation 2(2)]. The component of the vector in the direction OY is equal to $a \sin \phi$ and is thus equal to q. As ϕ increases with t the vector rotates at a constant rate of ω radians per second. Its rotation represents the progress of the simple harmonic motion. The reader may verify that the components of the velocity and acceleration of the point P, resolved in the direction OY, are equal to $\dot{q}$ and $\ddot{q}$ as given by equations 2(7) and 2(8).

(ii) A *stationary* vector may be used to represent the two arbitrary constants. This vector may be regarded as an instantaneous "snapshot" of the vector OP at the instant for which the initial conditions are given.

Suppose that the length of OQ (fig. 2.4) is equal to a and the angle QOX is equal to δ. Then the vector OQ, together with the axis OX, states the initial conditions. It does not rotate with the motion, but if we are given OQ, and equation 2(2), we can determine the subsequent motion of the system.

It is important to recognize that the vector representation of simple harmonic motion is not related to any possible vector property of the disturbance which is represented. What has been said about vector representation applies equally whether the magnitude which fluctuates is a scalar quantity or a vector quantity.

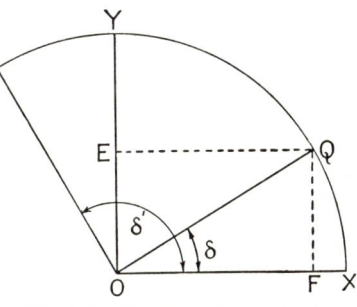

Fig. 2.4.—Representation of simple harmonic motion by a stationary vector

The relation between equations 2(2), 2(12) and 2(13) may be seen from fig. 2.4. In 2(2) the vector OQ is specified by its magnitude (a) and its angle (δ) to the axis OX. In 2(12) the angle δ' is given instead of δ. In 2(13) the components of OQ along the two axes are given, for OE $= a \sin \delta = B$ and OF $= a \cos \delta = A$.

2.9. Equation of Propagation—One Dimension.

We shall now consider the propagation of a disturbance ξ which, at any given time t, has a defined value at any point on a given straight line which is taken as the axis of x. We then have

$$\xi = f(x, t). \qquad \ldots \quad 2(16)$$

If the disturbance considered is a ripple running along a stretched string, then ξ will be the displacement of the string (at the point x and the time t) from its equilibrium position. ξ might equally well represent the kind of disturbance which forms a set of ripples on the surface of a liquid, provided that the ripples form a series of lines parallel to each other, and perpendicular to the axis of x. ξ is then a function of x and not of y. In a similar way, ξ might represent a very wide parallel beam of light travelling in the direction of the axis of x. For each of these disturbances 2(16) is satisfied.

The values of ξ at a particular time t_1 form a function of x only.

The curve connecting ξ and x at a given time is called the *profile* of the disturbance. If the disturbance is propagated unchanged in the direction OX, then in a given interval of time (t') all the values of ξ move a certain distance (x') along the axis of x. Algebraically, an increase in t has the same effect as an alteration in the origin of x. If the disturbance is propagated with speed b, in the positive direction of x, then $x' = bt'$, i.e. an increase of t' in t and a movement in the origin of x in the negative direction by an amount bt' produce equal and opposite alterations in the values of ξ. Therefore

$$f(x, t) = f(x + bt', t + t'), \quad \ldots \quad 2(17)$$

remembering that a movement of the origin in the negative direction is equivalent to an *increase* in all the values of x.

Equation 2(17) will be true for all values of x and t if, and only if,

$$\xi = f(bt - x), \quad \ldots \quad 2(18)$$

since $\quad b(t + t') - (x + bt') = (bt - x).$

Similarly a disturbance propagated in the negative direction of x is represented by

$$\xi = g(bt + x), \quad \ldots \quad 2(19)$$

where f and g represent any two continuous functions. *If the speed of propagation (b) is the same for all values of x and t*, we obtain by differentiation of 2(18),

$$\left. \begin{array}{l} \dfrac{\partial^2 \xi}{\partial x^2} = f'', \\[6pt] \dfrac{\partial^2 \xi}{\partial t^2} = b^2 f'', \end{array} \right\} \quad \ldots \quad 2(20)$$

where dashes represent differentiation with respect to $(bt - x)$.

Equations 2(20) lead to

$$\frac{\partial^2 \xi}{\partial x^2} = \frac{1}{b^2} \frac{\partial^2 \xi}{\partial t^2}. \quad \ldots \quad 2(21)$$

This is the fundamental differential equation for the propagation of a disturbance with constant velocity and without change of profile.

It may easily be verified by differentiation that 2(19) is a solution of this equation and that any linear combination of 2(18) and 2(19), such as

$$\xi = H_1 f(bt - x) + H_2 g(bt + x) \quad \ldots \quad 2(22)$$

(where H_1 and H_2 are constants), is also a solution. Equation 2(22) represents one disturbance propagated in the positive direction, and a second disturbance (not necessarily of the same profile) propagated in the negative direction.

2.10.—Consider a disturbance defined by

$$\xi = a \sin \frac{\omega}{b} (bt + x), \quad \ldots \quad 2(23)$$

where a, b and ω are constants for all values of x and t. This disturbance has the following three properties:

(i) It is of the same form as 2(19) and is therefore propagated unchanged with velocity b in the negative direction of x.

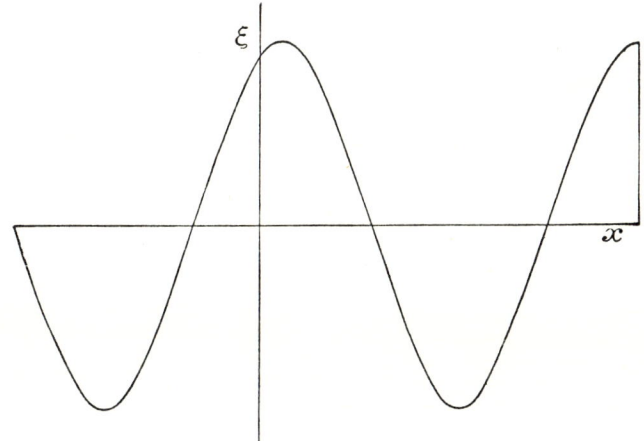

Fig. 2.5.—Profile of a simple sine wave

(ii) At any given point the disturbance is simple harmonic; for, if we put $x = x_0$ in 2(23), and make $\delta = \omega x_0/b$, the resultant expression is the same as 2(2). ω is again the angular frequency of the simple harmonic motion.

(iii) At any given instant the profile forms a simple sine function since, if t is put equal to t_0,

$$\xi = a \sin \frac{\omega}{b} (x + bt_0). \quad \ldots \quad 2(24)$$

This profile is shown in fig. 2.5. It is of the same shape as that shown in fig. 2.2a, but the variables are now ξ and x instead of q and t.

2.11. Wavelength and Spatial Frequency.

The profile shown in fig. 2.5 is space-periodic. It is repeated at distances of $2\pi b/\omega$. This distance is called the *wavelength* and is denoted by λ. An associated constant $\kappa = 2\pi/\lambda$ is called the *wavelength constant* (or *propagation constant*). This quantity may also be called the *spatial frequency in circular measure* because the wave is repeated 2π times in a distance $1/\kappa$. These definitions, together with equation 2(3) give

$$\lambda\nu = b; \quad \lambda = bT; \quad b = \omega/\kappa. \qquad \ldots \quad 2(25)$$

2.12. Phase of the Wave.

The disturbance represented by 2(23) may be written

$$\xi = a \sin(\omega t + \kappa x) = a \sin\phi, \qquad \ldots \quad 2(26)$$

and the phase $\phi = (\omega t + \kappa x)$ is seen to be a function of x and t. The phase increases by 2π whenever t increases by T, and whenever x increases by λ. When ϕ increases by 2π all the trigonometric functions which define ξ and its derivatives return to their original values.

Equation 2(26) represents a wave whose phase is zero when $t = 0$ and $x = 0$. A slightly more general form is

$$\xi = a \sin(\omega t + \kappa x + \delta_1) = a \sin\phi_1. \qquad \ldots \quad 2(27)$$

When a single wave is under consideration it may usually be reduced to the form of 2(26), but when two or more waves are considered together it is usually necessary to use 2(27).

EXAMPLES [2(ix)–2(xi)]

2(ix). Show that the discussion of §§ 2.10–2.12 applies to the following disturbances:

$$\xi = a \cos(\omega t - \kappa x + \delta_2). \qquad \ldots \ldots \quad 2(28)$$

$$\xi = a \sin(\omega t - \kappa x + \delta_3). \qquad \ldots \ldots \quad 2(29)$$

$$\xi = a \cos(\omega t + \kappa x + \delta_4). \qquad \ldots \ldots \quad 2(30)$$

What kinds of waves do these expressions represent? What is the phase difference between a wave represented by 2(29) and one represented by 2(28)?

$$[\delta_3 - \delta_2 - \pi/2.]$$

2(x). Differentiate 2(27) twice with respect to t and twice with respect to x. Hence verify directly that equation 2(21) is satisfied.

2(xi). Show that the sum of a number of expressions similar to 2(27), 2(28), 2(29) and 2(30) is always a solution of the wave equation.

2.13. Propagation of Waves in Three Dimensions.

When a disturbance is propagated in a three-dimensional space, the value of ξ at any given point in the space undergoes a periodic variation. In the simplest type of wave, the variation of ξ with t at any point is simple harmonic. The phase ϕ varies from point to point and is a continuous function of x, y, z, and t. The variation of ϕ is such that, at any given time, the phase has the same value over the whole of certain surfaces. These surfaces are called *wave surfaces*. They are defined by the relation

$$\phi_{t_0} = g(x, y, z) = \chi_0, \quad \ldots \quad 2(31)$$

where χ_0 is the value of the phase for one particular wave surface at time t_0. In general, the wave surfaces form a family of surfaces, χ being the variable parameter which selects a particular member of the family. Wave surfaces may constitute a family of concentric spheres, or a family of parallel planes, or they may take other forms. The waves are called spherical waves, plane waves, etc., according to the shape of the wave surfaces.

2.14. Plane Waves.

When ϕ has the form

$$\phi = \omega t - \kappa(\alpha x + \beta y + \gamma z) + \delta, \quad \ldots \quad 2(32)$$

where α, β, γ are real constants connected by the relation

$$\alpha^2 + \beta^2 + \gamma^2 = 1, \quad \ldots \quad 2(33)$$

then the wave surfaces constitute a family of planes whose direction-cosines are α, β, γ.

Differentiating 2(32) with respect to t we have

$$\dot{\phi} = \omega - \kappa(\alpha \dot{x} + \beta \dot{y} + \gamma \dot{z}). \quad \ldots \quad 2(34)$$

A point which moves with a velocity such that $\dot{\phi} = 0$ will always have the same phase and be in the same wave surface. From 2(34) such a point will have a velocity b whose magnitude is ω/κ and whose components along the co-ordinate axes are αb, βb, and γb. Such a point moves in a direction perpendicular to the wave surfaces. This applies to any point on any of the original wave surfaces and therefore every wave surface advances perpendicular to itself with speed $b = \omega/\kappa$. The plane wave in three dimensions is similar to the wave discussed in §§ 2.10–2.12 and may indeed be reduced to the form of 2(26) by a suitable change of axes. The more general form is required when more than one set of waves (not all travelling in the same direction) have to be considered, as, for example, in the theory of reflection and refraction.

2.15. The Wave Equation.

A wave whose phase is of the form given in 2(32) may be represented by

$$\xi = a \sin \phi = a \sin [\omega t - \kappa(\alpha x + \beta y + \gamma z) + \delta]. \qquad 2(35)$$

Differentiation of 2(35) gives

$$\frac{\partial^2 \xi}{\partial t^2} = -\omega^2 \xi, \qquad \ldots \ldots \quad 2(36)$$

$$\frac{\partial^2 \xi}{\partial x^2} = -\kappa^2 \alpha^2 \xi, \qquad \ldots \ldots \quad 2(37)$$

and two similar equations.

Combining 2(36) and 2(37), using 2(33), we obtain

$$\frac{\partial^2 \xi}{\partial x^2} + \frac{\partial^2 \xi}{\partial y^2} + \frac{\partial^2 \xi}{\partial z^2} = \frac{\kappa^2}{\omega^2} \frac{\partial^2 \xi}{\partial t^2} = \frac{1}{b^2} \frac{\partial^2 \xi}{\partial t^2}. \quad \ldots \quad 2(38)$$

This is a general equation of propagation in three dimensions and 2(35) is the particular solution which represents plane waves of angular frequency ω.

A more general solution * is

$$\xi = f(bt - \alpha x - \beta y - \gamma z), \quad \ldots \ldots \quad 2(39)$$

where α, β, γ are related by 2(33).

This solution represents a plane wave whose profile is, in general, not of the simple sine-wave form.

---

* Further solutions are discussed in Reference 2.1.

EXAMPLES [2(xii)–2(xv)]

2(xii). Verify by differentiation that both 2(39) and
$$\xi = g(bt + \alpha x + \beta y + \gamma z) \quad \ldots \ldots \quad 2(40)$$
are solutions of 2(38).

Show that any linear combination of these solutions such as
$$\xi = Hf(bt - \alpha x - \beta y - \gamma z) + Kg(bt + \alpha x + \beta y + \gamma z) \quad . \quad 2(41)$$
is a solution. What does this solution represent?

[Show that the wave surfaces, as defined in § 2.14, are planes, and deduce their speed and direction of motion.]

2(xiii). What does the solution
$$\xi = H_1 f_1(bt - \alpha_1 x - \beta_1 y - \gamma_1 z) + H_2 f_2(bt - \alpha_2 x - \beta_2 y - \gamma_2 z) \quad 2(42)$$
represent? Make this solution more general.

[2(42) represents two plane waves travelling in directions represented by $\alpha_1, \beta_1, \gamma_1$ and $\alpha_2, \beta_2, \gamma_2$.]

The more general form—representing waves in various directions—is
$$\xi = \Sigma\, H_n f_n(bt - \alpha_n x - \beta_n y - \gamma_n z). \quad \ldots \ldots \quad 2(43)$$

2(xiv). Write down equations similar to 2(32)–2(39) for the propagation of waves in two dimensions. Note that the wave surfaces reduce to lines. Strictly speaking, there are no plane waves in two dimensions, but "straight-line waves" are often called plane waves since they are regarded as sections of three-dimensional plane waves whose wave surfaces are at right angles to the plane in which the line waves are propagated.

2(xv). Show that the expression
$$\xi = f(bt - x\cos\theta - y\sin\theta) \quad \ldots \ldots \quad 2(44)$$
represents a line wave travelling at an angle θ to the x axis. Write down an expression for waves whose lines of constant phase are given by $y = mx + C$ (the variable parameter being C).

[$\xi = f(bt - \alpha mx + \alpha y)$, where $\alpha^2 = (1 + m^2)^{-1}$.]

2.16. The Velocity of Propagation.

In § 2.5 it was shown that ω is determined not by the initial conditions but by the physical properties of the oscillator; e.g. for the torsional pendulum ω is equal to $\sqrt{(k/m)}$ and for the simple pendulum it is equal to $\sqrt{(g/l)}$. In a similar way the velocity of wave propagation is determined by the physical properties of the medium. The calculation of the velocity of light in terms of certain fundamental electromagnetic units will be given in Chapter XIII. For the present we may illustrate the problem and show the way in which a velocity of propagation may be determined by considering longitudinal waves transmitted along a rod of elastic material (see fig. 2.6).

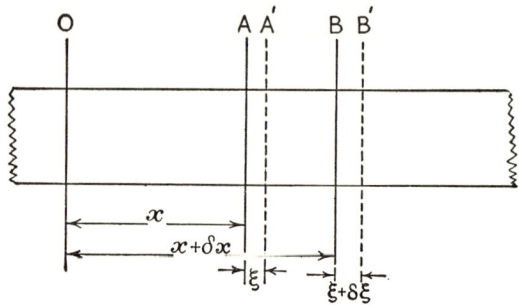

Fig. 2.6.—Transmission of waves along a rod

2.17. *Waves on a Rod.*

Consider a rod whose diameter is much less than the wavelength so that when it is stretched the lateral contraction occurs at the same time as the extension. Suppose that the area of cross-section of the rod is σ, the density of the material is ρ, and the value of Young's modulus is q. Let x be the distance of the plane A from the plane O when the rod is undisturbed, and let $x + \delta x$ be the corresponding distance for the plane B. Suppose that the rod is subject to a disturbance ξ which is a continuous function of x and t so that at a given instant A is displaced by ξ to A', and B by $\xi + \delta\xi$ to B'. Then the extension per unit length and the tension Q are given by

$$\frac{A'B' - AB}{AB} = \frac{\delta\xi}{\delta x},$$

and
$$Q = \sigma q \frac{\delta\xi}{\delta x}, \quad \ldots \ldots \quad 2(45)$$

provided that $\delta\xi/\delta x$ is everywhere so small that Hooke's law is obeyed. The tension Q is also a continuous function of x and t. The net force on the element is the difference between the tension at A' and the tension at B'. This is equal to

$$\frac{\partial Q}{\partial x} \delta x = \sigma q \frac{\partial^2 \xi}{\partial x^2} \delta x, \quad \ldots \ldots \quad 2(46)$$

§ 2.18 TRANSPORT OF ENERGY AND MOMENTUM

and equating force to mass × acceleration we have

$$\sigma q \frac{\partial^2 \xi}{\partial x^2} \delta x = \sigma \rho \frac{\partial^2 \xi}{\partial t^2} \delta x,$$

which reduces to

$$\frac{\partial^2 \xi}{\partial x^2} = \frac{\rho}{q} \frac{\partial^2 \xi}{\partial t^2}. \qquad \ldots \ldots \quad 2(47)$$

This is equivalent to 2(21) if

$$b = \sqrt{\frac{q}{\rho}}. \qquad \ldots \ldots \quad 2(48)$$

Thus the velocity of propagation is determined by the values of density and Young's modulus for the material of which the rod is made.

2.18. Transport of Energy and Momentum.

In § 2.5 it was shown that a vibrating system possesses both kinetic and potential energy. In simple harmonic motion, the energy passes to and fro between the kinetic and potential forms but the total remains constant and is proportional to $\omega^2 a^2$. The elastic waves discussed in the last paragraph possess both kinetic energy, because the medium is moving, and potential energy, because it is in a state of strain. It may be shown that the total energy per unit volume is constant, and is proportional to $\omega^2 a^2$ [see Example 2(xvi), p. 41]. Thus the wave motion of the medium implies the existence of an *energy density D* which is proportional to the square of the amplitude.

It is often more convenient to deal with the square of the amplitude rather than with the actual energy density. We shall refer to the square of the amplitude as the *relative energy*, because it is the ratio of the energy density of the given wave to that of a wave of the same frequency with unit amplitude. The importance of the relative energy is that most physical instruments for measuring light of one frequency are devices for comparing the relative energies at different places.

The energy density is constant during the whole time for which a wave of constant amplitude is present in the medium. This constant energy density is maintained by energy being transported into any particular portion of the rod from the direction of the source and an equal amount being transported out in the direction in which the wave is travelling.

2.19.—If a disturbance is exactly represented by 2(26), everywhere and at all times, the wave train must extend from $-\infty$ to $+\infty$. The wave trains which represent light are never infinitely long, and in Chapter IV it will be necessary to consider in detail how equation 2(26) must be modified to take account of the finite length of the wave train. In a general consideration of the transmission of energy it is not necessary to assume any definite limit to the length of the wave train, but it is necessary to assume that there is a source somewhere (even though at an indefinitely great distance in the negative direction of x), and that either the wave is being absorbed (at some far point in the positive direction of x) or that the front of the wave is advancing into hitherto undisturbed portions of the medium.

In either case it is implied that there is a transport of energy. Under the simple conditions which we have so far considered, the energy crossing unit area of a plane parallel to the wave surface per second is equal to bD, because in one second the energy in a tube of length b crosses a surface placed at right angles to the direction of propagation.

A detailed account of the transference of energy and momentum in a beam of light cannot be given until the properties of the waves which represent light have been specified more exactly. For the present it is reasonable to assume as a working hypothesis, from analogy with elastic waves, that the energy density in the medium, and the rate of transfer of energy, are proportional to the square of the amplitude.

It may be shown * that the propagation of elastic waves involves a transfer of momentum, so that a system of waves exerts a pressure on any body which absorbs or reflects it. We shall show later that light also exerts a pressure in similar circumstances and that, for a parallel beam of light, the pressure is numerically equal to the energy density.

2.20. Spherical Waves—Inverse Square Law.

It is found by experiment that light is propagated from a small source in such a way that the flow of energy per unit area is proportional to the inverse square of the distance from the source. It is natural to attempt to represent this propagation of radiation from a small source by a system of spherical waves. If we assume that the flow of energy per unit area is proportional to the square of the amplitude, then the inverse-square law requires that the amplitude be inversely proportional

---

* Reference 2.2.

to the first power of the distance, i.e. the spherical wave may be represented by

$$\xi = \frac{A}{r} f(bt - r), \qquad \ldots \ldots \quad 2(49)$$

where A is a constant. The first factor gives the variation of amplitude required to conserve the rate of flow of energy, the second implies spherical wave-surfaces with a common centre at the origin.

Hence we derive

$$\frac{\partial \xi}{\partial r} = -\frac{A}{r^2} f - \frac{A}{r} f', \qquad \ldots \ldots \quad 2(50a)$$

$$\frac{\partial^2 \xi}{\partial r^2} = \frac{2A}{r^3} f + \frac{2A}{r^2} f' + \frac{A}{r} f'', \qquad \ldots \quad 2(50b)$$

where dashes denote differentiation with respect to $(bt - r)$,

$$\frac{\partial^2 \xi}{\partial t^2} = \frac{A}{r} b^2 f'', \qquad \ldots \ldots \quad 2(51)$$

so that
$$\frac{\partial^2 \xi}{\partial r^2} + \frac{2}{r} \frac{\partial \xi}{\partial r} = \frac{1}{b^2} \cdot \frac{\partial^2 \xi}{\partial t^2}. \qquad \ldots \ldots \quad 2(52)$$

It may be shown that equation 2(38), transformed into spherical polar co-ordinates yields an equation which, when there is spherical symmetry, reduces to 2(52). An alternative form of this equation is

$$\frac{\partial^2}{\partial r^2}(r\xi) = \frac{1}{b^2} \frac{\partial^2}{\partial t^2}(r\xi). \qquad \ldots \ldots \quad 2(53)$$

A general solution of this equation corresponding to 2(22) is

$$\xi = \frac{A}{r} f(bt - r) + \frac{B}{r} f(bt + r). \qquad \ldots \quad 2(54)$$

The expression $\quad \xi = \frac{A}{r} \sin(\omega t - \kappa r) = \frac{A}{r} \sin \phi \quad \ldots \quad 2(55)$

is a special form of 2(54), and is therefore a solution. It represents a spherical wave since at any given time the phase is the same over the whole of any sphere centred on the origin. The phase existing on any sphere of radius r_0 is transferred to a larger sphere of radius $(r_0 + bt_0)$ after a time t_0, and therefore the expression represents a spherical wave diverging from the origin. The amplitude of this wave is not constant but is inversely proportional to r. The rate of transfer of energy across unit area of a wave surface is thus proportional to $1/r^2$

and the inverse square law of propagation is included in the description. The total energy crossing any sphere concentric with the origin is independent of r, since the area of a sphere of radius r is $4\pi r^2$. Once the wave is established, the total amount of energy entering the space between any two spheres centred on the origin is equal to the amount leaving this space in the same time.

The expression
$$\xi = \frac{B}{r}\sin(\omega t + \kappa r) \quad \ldots \ldots \quad 2(56)$$

represents a wave converging towards the origin and has properties analogous to those of the wave* represented by 2(55). Equations 2(55) and 2(56) represent idealized concepts. In practice, light never diverges from, or converges to, a mathematical point and wave surfaces are not exactly spherical.

2.21. Photometry—Definitions.

The subject of photometry deals with the measurement of amounts of light chiefly in relation to the uses of light (and especially of artificial light) for visual tasks such as reading. The inverse square law for the rate of transfer of radiant energy across unit area of a spherical surface surrounding a point source is a basic assumption in most photometric calculations. Actual sources are treated by dividing them into small elementary parts, each of which is small enough to be regarded as a point source. The technique of photometric measurements is considered in Chapter X, but it is convenient to introduce some of the definitions at this stage. Confining ourselves to light of one wavelength, we state these definitions:

(i) *Flux* (across a given surface)—a quantity proportional to the rate at which light energy crosses the surface. In the absence of absorption and similar effects, the flux across any surface surrounding a source is proportional to the rate of emission of energy. Symbol, F.

(ii) *Illumination* (at a given point on a surface) is proportional to the flux per unit area across a small element of area including the point in question. Symbol, E.

(iii) *Intensity* (of a source in a given direction) is equal to the flux per unit solid angle in the given direction from the source. Symbol, I.

(iv) *Luminance* (of a source in a given direction) is equal to the intensity per unit area of the source in the given direction. Symbol, L.

In the discussion of the interference and diffraction of light, the most important quantity is the illumination. When interference

---

* Other types of spherical wave are of importance in the theory of sound (see References 2.1 and 2.2).

fringes are seen on a screen, we are interested in the variation of illumination over the screen. When they are viewed either directly by eye or through an instrument, we are interested in the variation of illumination over the plane on which the instrument is focused. When a system of fringes is viewed by an eyepiece, we may alternatively regard them as forming a source of light situated in the focal plane. We may then speak of the distribution of brightness in this plane.

It will be seen that, if the above definitions are accepted, it is not correct to speak of the intensity distribution in a system of fringes, or to use the word intensity for the square of the amplitude of a light wave. We have called the latter the "relative energy" (see § 2.18). We may, however, use the term "relative intensity of a spectrum line" to refer to the ratio of the amount of energy emitted by the source in a given spectral region to the total energy emitted by the same source.

In practical photometric measurements, illumination, brightness, etc., for different coloured lights have to be measured in units which take account of the effectiveness of different wavelengths in regard to vision. Since we are here concerned only with physical measurements, we use the above symbols to denote flux, illumination, etc., measured in *energy units*. Our values of these quantities would require to be multiplied by a *visibility factor* (depending on the colour) to convert them to the units used in practical photometry (e.g. candle-power as unit of intensity).

2.22. Doppler-Fizeau Principle.

The sound produced by a source such as a tuning fork may be detected by certain instruments, and its frequency measured. The frequency of the vibrating source may also be measured independently. It is found that, when a source and a receptor have no relative motion, the frequency of the sound received is equal to the frequency of vibration of the source. If, however, the source and receptor are approaching one another, the frequency of the sound received is higher than that of the source. If they are receding from one another, it is lower. The effect is observed as a sudden fall in pitch whenever a rapidly moving source of sound passes an observer. This phenomenon is included in the wave picture in the following way.

Suppose that a source and a receptor are at a distance L apart at time t_0, and that they are approaching one another with velocity v (which is a small fraction of b) so that they pass at time $(t_0 + L/v)$. Then, during the approach, the receptor receives the waves which initially lay between it and the source, as well as those emitted by the source during the interval L/v. The waves initially between the source and receptor were emitted during a time L/b. Therefore the source receives during the interval L/v all the waves emitted during a time $L/v + L/b$. Thus if ν is the frequency of the waves received and ν_0 is the frequency of the waves emitted,

$$\nu = \nu_0\left(1 + \frac{v}{b}\right). \qquad \ldots \ldots \quad 2(57)$$

2.23.—This effect was first discovered by Doppler in relation to sound and was later discovered independently by others including Fizeau, who probably made the first correct application to light. It was known that the light emitted from certain gaseous sources could be closely represented by the types of simple wave trains which have been considered in the preceding paragraphs. The wavelengths could be accurately measured by methods to be described later. Since the velocity of light is unaffected by the movement of the source or the observer (see Chapter XI), 2(57) together with 2(25) implies, when v is small compared with b, that

$$\lambda = \lambda_0\left(1 - \frac{v}{b}\right) \qquad \ldots \ldots \quad 2(58)$$

and a change of wavelength is to be expected when source and observer are approaching one another or receding from one another. The effect predicted by Fizeau could not immediately be observed in the laboratory because of the technical difficulty of producing a source moving with an appreciable fraction of the velocity of light. In more modern times this difficulty has been overcome in two different ways and the observed change of wavelength agrees well with that predicted.

2.24.—One set of experiments was carried out by Bélopolsky and a later set by Galitzin and Wilip. They used rotating mirrors to produce a virtual source moving at 400 metres per second. The change in wavelength was only one part in a million, but using the delicate methods described in Chapter IX, they were able to measure this change. The change observed agreed with that calculated from 2(58) to within about 5 per cent.

The effect was also found in experiments on the "canal rays". The apparatus is shown in fig. 2.7. Positively charged atoms or molecules are accelerated by the electric field in a discharge tube at low pressure. They thus acquire a speed which is related to the potential (V) through which they have fallen by the equation

$$\tfrac{1}{2}mv^2 = Ve, \qquad \qquad 2(59)$$

where m is the mass and e the charge.

For hydrogen atoms $m = 1\cdot 67 \times 10^{-24}$ gramme and $e = 4\cdot 8 \times 10^{-10}$ electrostatic unit. Thus an atom which has fallen through a potential of 30,000 volts (or 100 e.s.u.) has a speed of 2×10^8 centimetres per

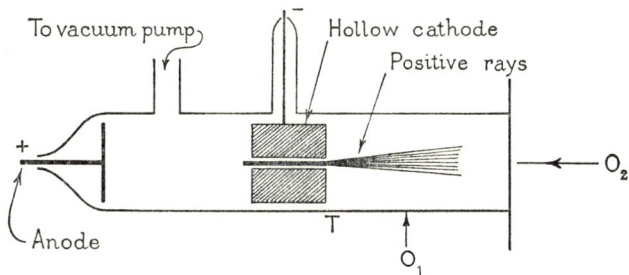

Fig. 2.7.—Apparatus for observing the Doppler effect

second. The fast-moving ions are neutralized during their passage through the tube T without any appreciable loss of speed and emit light in the region to the right of T.

The light is observed first from O_1, and then from O_2. The difference of wavelength (which is now about one part in 150) can be observed with a small spectroscope.

2.25.—The Doppler-Fizeau principle is of interest in two ways:

(i) It is an important experimental result which is satisfactorily included in the wave description of light and has no obvious place in a particle theory.

(ii) Once the principle has been verified by the above experiments it may be used to determine the velocities of sources of light under conditions where any other measurement would be difficult or impossible, e.g. the velocities of stars, or the velocities of atoms in gaseous discharges.

It will be noticed that the above account of the Doppler-Fizeau principle is valid only when the velocity of the source relative to the observer is a small fraction of b. The equation 2(58) is valid only when terms of order v^2/b^2 may be neglected. It will be shown in Chapter XI that when we consider terms of order v^2/b^2, equation 2(58) must be amended.

2.26. Representation of Wave Motion by Complex Quantities.†

The vector representation of the motion of a simple harmonic oscillator shown in fig. 2.3 may be applied to the representation of simple wave motion provided it be understood that ϕ is now a function of both x and t. Another method of representing simple harmonic motion has a special advantage in relation to wave motion because it allows the part of ϕ which varies with x to be separated from the part which varies with t in a convenient way. A solution of the wave equation 2(21) is

$$\xi = a \exp i(\omega t - \kappa x + \delta) = a e^{i\phi}. \qquad . \quad . \quad 2(60) \ddagger$$

The displacement at a given place and time is a *real* and not a complex number. Some convention is therefore required to enable us to apply 2(60) to the representation of the results of observations. In this book, we assume that an expression like 2(60) represents a vector whose two components are the magnitudes of the real and imaginary parts of the complex quantity. This is the vector whose magnitude is equal to the amplitude of the wave, and whose angle, with a chosen fixed line, represents the phase. The real part of the quantity ξ, which by itself is a solution of the wave equation, gives the physical displacement at x and t. The sum of the squares of the magnitudes of the real and imaginary parts of the complex number thus represents the square of the amplitude (i.e. the relative energy). Equation 2(60) may be written

$$\xi = a e^{i\delta} \cdot e^{i\omega t} \cdot e^{-i\kappa x} \qquad . \quad . \quad . \quad . \quad . \quad 2(61)$$

or
$$\xi = P e^{i\omega t} e^{-i\kappa x}, \qquad . \quad . \quad . \quad . \quad . \quad . \quad 2(62)$$

where
$$P = a e^{i\delta}. \qquad . \quad . \quad . \quad . \quad . \quad . \quad . \quad . \quad 2(63)$$

The complex quantity P represents both the constants a and δ. If P^* is the complex quantity conjugate to P, it follows that PP^* is equal to a^2 and is proportional to the illumination. The quantity P is sometimes called the *complex amplitude*.

2.27.—Let two simple harmonic motions be represented by

$$\xi_1 = P_1 \exp i(\omega t - \kappa x) \qquad . \quad . \quad . \quad 2(64)$$

and
$$\xi_2 = P_2 \exp i(\omega t - \kappa x), \qquad . \quad . \quad . \quad 2(65)$$

† An account of the theory of complex quantities is given in Reference 2.3.
‡ The abbreviation " exp " will be used for " exponential " in all but the simplest expressions.

where P_1 and P_2 are complex. Then the *phase difference* δ is given by

$$\tan \delta = \frac{B}{A}, \quad \ldots \ldots \quad 2(66)$$

where
$$\frac{P_1}{P_2} = A + iB = Ce^{i\delta}. \quad \ldots \ldots \quad 2(67)$$

This result is obtained directly if we write $P_1 = C_1 e^{i\delta_1}$ and $P_2 = C_2 e^{i\delta_2}$, C_1 and C_2 being real numbers.

EXAMPLES [2(xvi)–2(xviii)]

2(xvi). Obtain a solution of equation 2(47) and write down the expression for the kinetic energy of the rod. Using equation 2(45), obtain the expression for the potential energy of the rod and hence find the total energy per unit volume.

2(xvii). Show that if $P = A + iB$, then 2(62) may be written

$$\xi = (A + iB)\cos(\omega t - \kappa x) + (iA - B)\sin(\omega t - \kappa x),$$

and that A and B have the values given in 2(14).

2(xviii). Show that if $\xi_1 = P_1 \exp i(\omega t + \kappa x)$ and $\xi_2 = P_2 \exp i(\omega t - \kappa x)$ are solutions of 2(21), then $\xi_s = \xi_1 + \xi_2$ is also a solution, and that ξ_s may also be written as

$$(P_1 + P_2)e^{i\omega t}\cos \kappa x + i(P_1 - P_2)e^{i\omega t}\sin \kappa x.$$

REFERENCES

2.1. COULSON: *Waves* (Oliver and Boyd).

2.2. WOOD: *Acoustics* (Blackie).

2.3. GREEN: *The Theory and Use of the Complex Variable* (Pitman).

CHAPTER III

Wave Theory—Combination of Wave Motions

3.1. Principle of Superposition.

The type of wave motion discussed in Chapter II is produced by the action of a single simple harmonic oscillator. We shall now consider the disturbance produced by the simultaneous action of two or more oscillators. The simplest hypothesis which can be made is that if ξ_1, ξ_2, ξ_3, etc., are the disturbances produced by the individual oscillators at a given place and time, and ξ is the resultant disturbance due to them all, then

$$\xi = \xi_1 + \xi_2 + \xi_3 + \cdots \qquad \cdots \qquad 3(1)$$

If the resultant motion is represented by the wave equation, i.e. by equation 2(38), it is necessary that ξ shall be a solution of this equation. The form of the wave equation is such that solutions are additive [see § 2.9, and Examples 2(xi), 2(xii), 2(xviii)], and therefore 3(1) is a solution of the wave equation. It is important to recognize that this mathematical result does not by itself guarantee that 3(1) correctly represents the effect of the simultaneous action of several wave motions at a given point. The *principle of superposition* is a physical hypothesis which states that for light waves the disturbance (at a given place and time) due to the passage of a number of waves is equal to the algebraic sum of the disturbances produced by the individual waves. Equation 3(1) is a mathematical formulation of this principle. This hypothesis is confirmed in so far as calculations based upon it give a satisfactory description of the relevant observations on light.

3.2.—With sound waves it is found that, for waves of large amplitude, the velocity of propagation is not independent of the amplitude. It is also found that when two loud sources of different frequencies operate simultaneously, sum and difference tones are heard.* In order to describe this type of phenomenon it is necessary to assume

* Reference 2.2.

§ 3.3   ADDITION OF SIMPLE HARMONIC MOTIONS   43

that sound waves of finite amplitude are not exactly represented by the simple waveforms discussed in Chapter II, and that the disturbance ξ due to the simultaneous operation of two sources is given by

$$\xi = \xi_1 + \xi_2 + \alpha_1 \xi_1^2 + \alpha_2 \xi_2^2 + \alpha_{12} \xi_1 \xi_2 + \ldots \quad . \quad 3(2)$$

where α_1, α_2, and α_{12} are constants which are small compared with $1/\xi_1$.

Some hypothesis of this type would be necessary if corresponding phenomena were observed with light, but so far all attempts to observe these phenomena have produced negative results. Schrödinger has considered the effect of introducing certain non-linear terms (of a type suggested by Born) into the equations of propagation of electromagnetic waves. The calculation indicates that, for very high intensities, certain effects should be observed (see Appendix XIXB).

3.3. Addition of Simple Harmonic Motions.

In the theory of light, many calculations have to be made of the resultant produced by the superposition of two or more simple harmonic motions of the same frequency. Three different methods are available for carrying out these calculations. The choice of method to be used in solving a particular problem is a matter of mathematical convenience since each of the three methods must yield the same result if used correctly. In order to show how the three methods are applied, two simple problems will now be solved by each method in turn. These problems are (a) the addition of two simple harmonic motions whose amplitudes and epochs are different, and (b) the addition of several simple harmonic motions whose amplitudes are equal and whose epoch angles are in arithmetical progression.

3.4. Algebraic Method.

Consider two simple harmonic motions represented by

$$\xi_1 = a_1 \sin(\omega t - \kappa x + \delta_1) \quad . \quad . \quad . \quad 3(3)$$

and
$$\xi_2 = a_2 \sin(\omega t - \kappa x + \delta_2). \quad . \quad . \quad . \quad 3(4)$$

Then
$$\xi = \xi_1 + \xi_2$$
$$= a_1 \sin(\omega t - \kappa x + \delta_1) + a_2 \sin(\omega t - \kappa x + \delta_2) \quad . \quad 3(5)$$
$$= (a_1 \cos \delta_1 + a_2 \cos \delta_2) \sin(\omega t - \kappa x)$$
$$+ (a_1 \sin \delta_1 + a_2 \sin \delta_2) \cos(\omega t - \kappa x).$$

This is identical with

$$\xi = a \sin(\omega t - \kappa x + \delta), \quad \ldots \quad 3(6)$$

provided that

$$\left. \begin{array}{l} a^2 = (a_1 \cos \delta_1 + a_2 \cos \delta_2)^2 + (a_1 \sin \delta_1 + a_2 \sin \delta_2)^2 \\ \text{and} \quad \tan \delta = \dfrac{a_1 \sin \delta_1 + a_2 \sin \delta_2}{a_1 \cos \delta_1 + a_2 \cos \delta_2}. \end{array} \right\} \quad 3(7)$$

This calculation might have been simplified a little by choosing the origins of x and t so as to make $\delta_1 = 0$ and by putting $(\omega t - \kappa x) = \chi$. Then instead of 3(5) we have

$$\xi = a_1 \sin \chi + a_2 \sin(\chi + \delta_2), \quad \ldots \quad 3(8)$$

and the resultant is then

$$\xi = a \sin(\chi + \delta), \quad \ldots \quad 3(9)$$

where

$$a^2 = (a_1 + a_2 \cos \delta_2)^2 + a_2^2 \sin^2 \delta_2$$

$$\left. \begin{array}{l} = a_1^2 + a_2^2 + 2a_1 a_2 \cos \delta_2 \\ \text{and} \quad \tan \delta = \dfrac{a_2 \sin \delta_2}{a_1 + a_2 \cos \delta_2}. \end{array} \right\} \quad 3(10)$$

The simpler forms of equations 3(9) and 3(10) would be used in a practical example, but equation 3(7) is given here in order to show the symmetrical character of the result. This form will also be useful for comparison with a calculation based on the vector representation. The form of equations 3(6) and 3(9) implies that the resultant of two simple harmonic motions of the same frequency is itself a simple harmonic motion. Also the frequency of the resultant is the same as that of the component motions. By repeated application of this process it may be shown that *the resultant of any number of simple harmonic motions of the same frequency is itself a simple harmonic motion of this frequency.* The general algebraic formula for the addition of m simple harmonic motions, all of the same frequency, but differing in amplitude and epoch, is

$$\left. \begin{array}{l} \xi = \sum\limits_{r=1}^{m} \xi_r \\ = \sum\limits_{r=1}^{m} a_r \sin(\omega t - \kappa x + \delta_r). \end{array} \right\} \quad 3(11)$$

§3.4 ADDITION OF SIMPLE HARMONIC MOTIONS

Since ξ represents a simple harmonic motion of angular frequency ω, this expression is equivalent to

$$\xi = a \sin(\omega t - \kappa x + \delta),$$

where
$$\left.\begin{array}{l} a^2 = \left(\sum_{r=1}^{m} a_r \cos \delta_r\right)^2 + \left(\sum_{r=1}^{m} a_r \sin \delta_r\right)^2 \\[1em] \text{and} \quad \tan \delta = \dfrac{\sum_{r=1}^{m} a_r \sin \delta_r}{\sum_{r=1}^{m} a_r \cos \delta_r}. \end{array}\right\} \quad 3(12)$$

When the amplitudes are all equal, and the epoch angles are in arithmetic progression, we have

$$a_1 = a_2 = a_3 = \ldots = a_0 \text{ and } \delta_r = r\delta_0,$$

so that
$$\sum_{r=1}^{m} a_r \cos \delta_r = a_0 (\cos \delta_0 + \cos 2\delta_0 + \ldots + \cos m\delta_0).$$

But $\quad 2 \sin \tfrac{1}{2}\delta_0 \cos \delta_r = \sin \tfrac{1}{2}(2r+1)\delta_0 - \sin \tfrac{1}{2}(2r-1)\delta_0,$

and $\quad 2 \sin \tfrac{1}{2}\delta_0 \cos \delta_{r+1} = \sin \tfrac{1}{2}(2r+3)\delta_0 - \sin \tfrac{1}{2}(2r+1)\delta_0,$

so that $\quad 2 \sin \tfrac{1}{2}\delta_0 \sum_{r=1}^{m} \cos \delta_r = \sin \tfrac{1}{2}(2m+1)\delta_0 - \sin \tfrac{1}{2}\delta_0.$

Hence $\sum_{r=1}^{m} a_r \cos \delta_r = a_0\{\sin \tfrac{1}{2}(2m+1)\delta_0 - \sin \tfrac{1}{2}\delta_0\}/2 \sin \tfrac{1}{2}\delta_0$

$$= a_0 \cos \tfrac{1}{2}(m+1)\delta_0 \cdot \frac{\sin \tfrac{1}{2}m\delta_0}{\sin \tfrac{1}{2}\delta_0}. \quad \ldots \quad 3(13)$$

Similarly it may be shown that

$$\sum_{r=1}^{m} a_r \sin \delta_r = a_0 \sin \tfrac{1}{2}(m+1)\delta_0 \cdot \frac{\sin \tfrac{1}{2}m\delta_0}{\sin \tfrac{1}{2}\delta_0}; \quad . \quad 3(14)$$

and, substituting in 3(12), we obtain for the relative energy

$$\left.\begin{array}{l} a^2 = a_0^2 \left(\dfrac{\sin \tfrac{1}{2}m\delta_0}{\sin \tfrac{1}{2}\delta_0}\right)^2 \\[1em] \text{and} \quad \tan \delta = \tan \tfrac{1}{2}(m+1)\delta_0. \end{array}\right\} \quad \ldots \quad 3(15)$$

3.5. *Vector Method.*

Since ξ_1 and ξ_2 may both be represented by vectors, in the way described in § 2.8 the sum $\xi = \xi_1 + \xi_2$ should be represented by the vector sum of these two vectors. Using the second type of vector representation in fig. 3.1, it may be seen from the trigonometry of the figure that the law of vector addition does give the same result as equations 3(7). The algebraic calculation is, indeed, equivalent to resolving each vector parallel to the lines OX and OY, adding the components and recombining the resultant components to give the final resultant. In fig. 3.1, $OP_1 = a_1$, $OA_1 = a_1 \cos \delta_1$, and

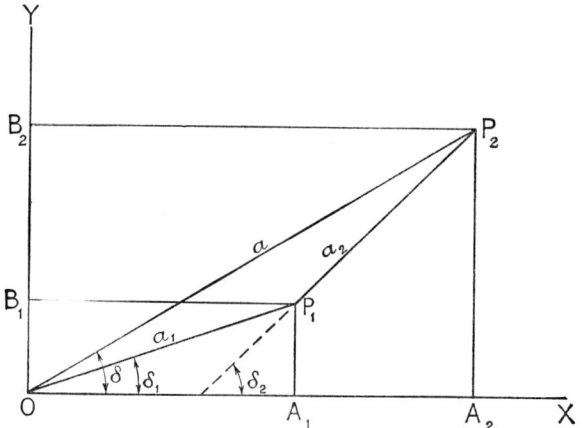

Fig. 3.1.—Vector method of determining the resultant of two simple harmonic motions

$A_1 A_2 = a_2 \cos \delta_2$. Hence $OA_2 = a_1 \cos \delta_1 + a_2 \cos \delta_2$ and similarly $OB_2 = a_1 \sin \delta_1 + a_2 \sin \delta_2$. Since $OP_2{}^2 = OA_2{}^2 + OB_2{}^2$, the resultant amplitude is that given in equation 3(7). The epoch of the resultant is obtained in a similar way.

The use of the vector polygon to add a number of simple harmonic motions is equivalent to equations 3(11) and 3(12). The case of several motions all of the same amplitude and with epoch angles in arithmetic progression is shown in fig. 3.2a. The representative vectors OA_1, A_1A_2, A_2A_3, etc., are so arranged that O, A_1, A_2, etc., all lie on the same circle (with centre C) and the vectors each subtend an angle δ_0 at the centre of the circle. The resultant subtends an angle $m\delta_0$, and hence if R is the radius of the circle $a_0 = 2R \sin \tfrac{1}{2}\delta_0$ and $a = 2R \sin \tfrac{1}{2}m\delta_0$, and this leads at once to equation 3(15) for the relation between a_0 and a.

If the number of sides of a regular polygon increases indefinitely it approximates to a circle (see fig. 3.2b). Thus if $m \to \infty$ while $a_0 \to 0$

and $\delta_0 \to 0$ in such a way that the products ma_0 and $m\delta_0$ tend to the finite limits A and δ, the resultant becomes

$$a = \frac{A \sin \frac{1}{2}\delta}{\frac{1}{2}\delta}, \qquad \ldots \ldots \quad 3(16)$$

where δ is the phase difference between the infinitesimal elements at the two ends of the series.

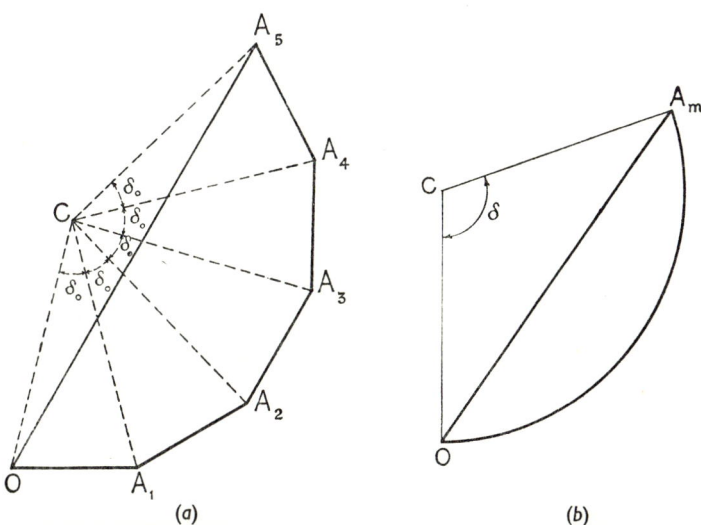

Fig. 3.2.—(a) Vector diagram showing the combination of a finite number of simple harmonic motions whose amplitudes are all equal and whose epoch angles are in arithmetic progression. (b) Limiting case of continuously varying phase.

3.6. *Calculation using Complex Quantities.*

Using the convention stated in § 2.26, a simple harmonic motion of angular frequency ω may be represented by

$$\xi_1 = a_1 \exp i(\omega t - \kappa x + \delta_1)$$
$$= P_1 \exp i(\omega t - \kappa x),$$

where $\qquad P_1 = a_1 e^{i\delta_1}.$

The sum of a number of simple harmonic motions of the same frequency is then given by the relation

$$\xi = \Sigma \, \xi_r = (P_1 + P_2 + P_3 + \ldots + P_r) \exp i(\omega t - \kappa x)$$
$$= P \exp i(\omega t - \kappa x),$$

where $\qquad P = \Sigma \, P_r.$

Thus we have the simple rule that the complex amplitude of the resultant displacement is equal to the sum of the complex amplitudes of the individual motions. The resultant relative energy (i.e. the square of the real amplitude of the resultant) is equal to the square of the modulus of P. When all the simple harmonic motions have the same amplitude a_0 and the epoch angles are δ_0, $2\delta_0$, $3\delta_0$, etc., we have

$$P_1 = a_0 e^{i\delta_0}, \quad P_2 = a_0 e^{2i\delta_0}, \quad P_3 = a_0 e^{3i\delta_0}, \text{ etc.},$$

and $$P = a_0(e^{i\delta_0} + e^{2i\delta_0} + \ldots + e^{mi\delta_0}). \qquad \ldots \quad 3(17)$$

The sum of this geometrical progression is

$$P = a_0 e^{i\delta_0} \cdot \frac{e^{im\delta_0} - 1}{e^{i\delta_0} - 1} \qquad \ldots \ldots \ldots \quad 3(18)$$

$$= \frac{a_0 e^{i\delta_0}}{2(1 - \cos \delta_0)} (e^{im\delta_0} - 1)(e^{-i\delta_0} - 1),$$

using the relation

$$(1 - \cos \theta) = \tfrac{1}{2}(e^{i\theta} - 1)(e^{-i\theta} - 1); \qquad \ldots \quad 3(19)$$

similarly, $$P^* = \frac{a_0 e^{-i\delta_0}}{2(1 - \cos \delta_0)} (e^{-im\delta_0} - 1)(e^{i\delta_0} - 1), \qquad . \quad 3(20)$$

so that

$$a^2 = PP^* = 4\left[\frac{a_0}{2(1 - \cos \delta_0)}\right]^2 (1 - \cos m\delta_0)(1 - \cos \delta_0), \quad 3(21)$$

using 3(19) again.

Hence $$E = a^2 = a_0^2 \left(\frac{\sin \tfrac{1}{2} m\delta_0}{\sin \tfrac{1}{2} \delta_0}\right)^2 \qquad \ldots \ldots \quad 3(22)$$

in agreement with 3(15).

3.7.—From the above, it may be seen that the three methods are equivalent. The vector method is probably the most elegant and gives an especially clear insight into the physical conditions. From the vector diagram it is usually possible to see which members of a set of vectors are opposing the resultant and which ones are in phase with the resultant. It is often convenient to carry out the calculation of the resultant by algebraic methods or using the complex amplitudes. When this is done, it is usually worth while to draw a rough vector diagram in order to obtain a general view of the problem as a whole.

EXAMPLES

EXAMPLES [3(i)–3(vi)]

3(i). Show that the resultant relative energy for an infinite series of simple harmonic motions whose amplitudes are a, $\tfrac{1}{2}a$, $\tfrac{1}{4}a$, etc., and whose epochs are 0, $\pi/2$, π, $3\pi/2$, etc., is $4a^2/5$.

[The calculation is very similar to equations 3(15)–3(22). The vector diagram is shown in fig. 3.3a.]

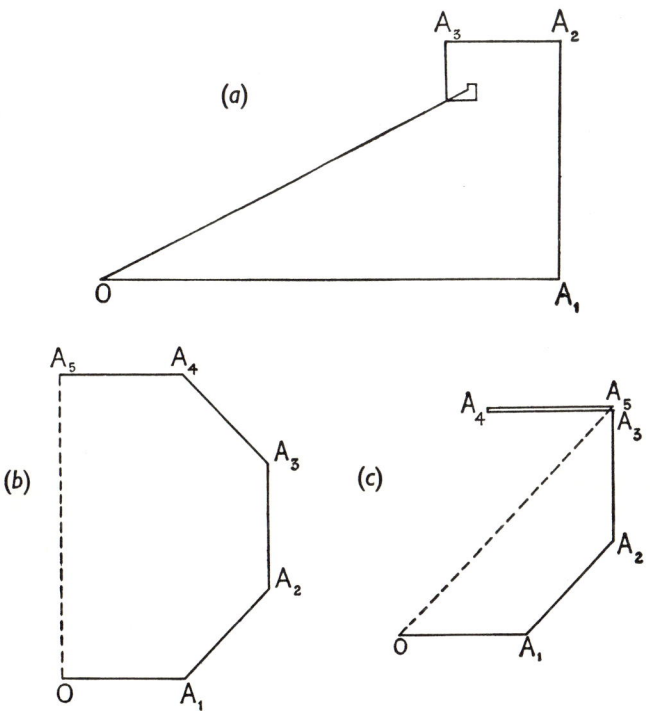

Fig. 3.3.—Vector diagrams showing the resultants of certain combinations of simple harmonic motions [see Examples 3(i) and 3(ii)]

3(ii). Calculate the resultant relative energy for 5 simple harmonic motions of equal amplitude, (a) when the epochs are 0, $\tfrac{1}{4}\pi$, $\tfrac{1}{2}\pi$, $\tfrac{3}{4}\pi$, π, and (b) when the epochs are 0, $\tfrac{1}{4}\pi$, $\tfrac{1}{2}\pi$, π, 2π. Draw the appropriate vector diagrams and compare your diagrams with figs. 3.3b and 3.3c. [(a) $a^2(3+2\sqrt{2})$; (b) the same as (a).]

3(iii). Find the resultant amplitude for n simple harmonic motions of equal amplitudes, (a) when the epochs are π/n, $2\pi/n$, $3\pi/n$, etc., and (b) when the epochs are $2\pi/n$, $4\pi/n$, $6\pi/n$, etc. [(a) $a\,\operatorname{cosec}(\pi/2n)$; (b) zero.]

3(iv). Find the resultant relative energy for $(2n + 1)$ simple harmonic motions of equal amplitudes when the epochs are

$$\pi, \frac{n-1}{n}\pi, \frac{n-2}{n}\pi, \ldots, \frac{\pi}{n}, 0, \frac{\pi}{n}, \frac{2\pi}{n}, \ldots, \frac{n-1}{n}\pi, \pi.$$

3(v). Would the resultant relative energy in Example 3(iv) be increased or decreased by removing (a) the first or (b) the last or (c) the centre member of the series? [(a), (b), decreased, (c) increased.]

3(vi). Calculate the resultant relative energy for Example 3(i) when the second term of the series is removed.

> [The resultant is $0.65a^2$. This calculation should be made by *sub-tracting* the simple harmonic motion due to the second term from the resultant, due regard being paid to the epoch angles, i.e. the complex amplitude for the second member is subtracted from the complex amplitude of the resultant.]

3.8. Huygens' Principle.

In an attempt to form a mental picture of wave propagation, Huygens suggested that each point at the front of a wave might be regarded as a small source of wave motion. The waves produced by

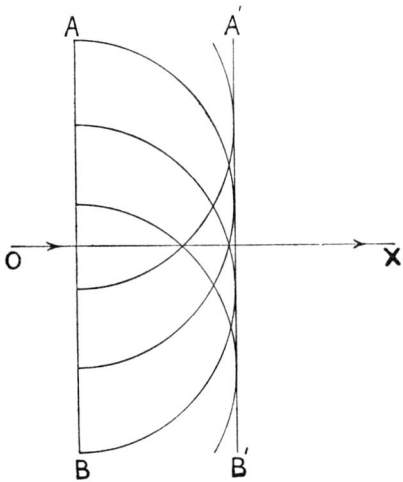

Fig. 3.4.—Huygens' principle applied to a plane wave in uniform medium

these small sources were called *secondary waves*, and it was assumed that the position of the main (or primary) wave at some later time was the envelope of the secondary waves.

We may illustrate this method by applying it to a plane wave (see fig. 3.4). The direction of propagation is OX and the position of a certain wave surface at time t_0 is represented by a plane through AB and perpendicular to the plane of the paper. We draw a series of spheres with a common radius bt_1, and with centres at various points on AB. Clearly the plane through A'B' situated at a distance bt_1 in front of, and parallel to, the plane through AB is part of the envelope of these spheres and the phase on this plane when $t = t_1 + t_0$ will be the same as the phase at AB when $t = t_0$. Hence, in this simple case, the construction based on Huygens' principle does enable us to deduce the position of one wave surface from that of another, and the result is correct. It is not difficult to verify that the same construction gives the correct result when non-planar wave surfaces are involved.

Although, in a certain sense, the principle gives the correct result, it carries with it implications which require further consideration. Huygens postulated that the action of the secondary wavelets was confined to the points at which they touched their envelope, and he considered only those parts of the envelope which lay in the forward direction of propagation. There is no direct physical or mathematical justification for this arbitrary decision to ignore all the unwanted parts of the secondary waves.

3.9.—Fresnel later attempted to provide a physical justification for a modified form of Huygens' principle. He assumed that a wave surface could be divided into a very large number of small elements of area and that each of these elements was a source of secondary waves. He assumed that these secondary waves were effective everywhere, but that the amplitude of the disturbance at any point Q due to the secondary wave from an element dS of the wave surface (situated at P) was a function both of the distance QP and of the angle θ between the line QP and the normal to the element dS (see fig. 3.5). The variation with angle is called the *obliquity function* or the *inclination factor*. Fresnel and later workers attempted to adjust the obliquity function so that the resultant disturbance due to all the secondary waves was zero everywhere except at the points where they touched the envelope. These attempts were never completely successful.

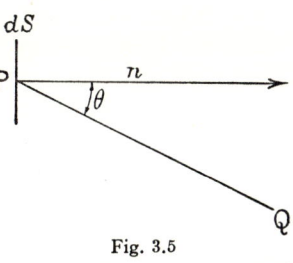

Fig. 3.5

3.10.—The detailed theory of wave propagation, which is given in Chapters V and VI, shows that it is possible to use a knowledge of the disturbance on one wave surface to derive the amplitude and phase of the disturbance at a later time, and at a place situated a suitable distance ahead. The distribution of light energy thus calculated agrees with that observed. This more fundamental method (mainly due to Kirchhoff) determines the obliquity function from the wave equation instead of introducing it as a new *ad hoc* hypothesis. It also requires a special adjustment in the phases of the secondary wavelets. The exact calculation justifies Fresnel's methods rather than Huygens' principle. It shows that the construction of wave envelopes by Huygens' method gives a satisfactory description of the progress of a wave. We shall therefore use this construction in § 3.11 and in other appropriate places.

3.11. Reflection and Refraction at Plane Surfaces.

It is found that when a parallel beam of light is incident upon a surface separating two transparent media, such as air and glass, part of the light is reflected back into the medium in which it originated, and another part is transmitted into the second medium. The direction of propagation of this second part is not in the same line as the original direction of propagation and the light is said to be refracted. Observations on the angular relations between the directions of propagation of the incident, the reflected and the refracted beams are summarized in the following laws:

(i) The direction of incidence, the direction of reflection and the normal to the surface are coplanar. The angle between the direction of reflection and the normal (called the *angle of reflection*) is equal to the angle between the direction of incidence and the normal (called the *angle of incidence*). The direction of reflection is on the side of the normal opposite to the direction of incidence.

(ii) The direction of incidence, the direction of refraction and the normal are coplanar. The sine of the angle between the direction of refraction and the normal (called the *angle of refraction*) bears a constant ratio to the sine of the angle of incidence.

Thus, if θ_1 = angle of incidence (see fig. 3.6),

θ_1' = angle of reflection,

θ_2 = angle of refraction,

then
$$\theta_1 = \theta_1' \qquad \ldots \ldots \ldots \quad 3(23)$$

and
$$\frac{\sin \theta_1}{\sin \theta_2} = \mu_{12}. \qquad \ldots \ldots \ldots \quad 3(24)$$

The constant μ_{12} is characteristic of the two media. It is found that the constants for different pairs of media are subject to the relation

$$\mu_{13} = \mu_{12} \cdot \mu_{23}. \quad \ldots \ldots \quad 3(25)$$

The constant μ_{12} is called the *index of refraction of the two media*, it being understood that the light travels from the medium 1 into the medium 2. The value of the constant obtained when light travels from a vacuum into a medium is called the *index of refraction of that medium*

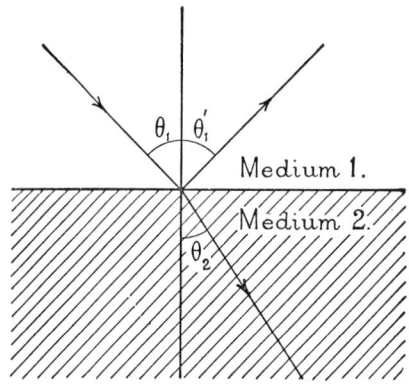

Fig. 3.6.—Reflection and refraction of light

and is denoted in this book by the symbol n (with a suffix when necessary). The index of refraction from air to a medium is denoted by μ (with a single suffix to specify the medium when necessary). Since the refractive index of air is nearly unity, the values of μ_g and n_g for glasses are nearly equal, and it is only in a few applications that it is necessary to distinguish them.

3(25) implies that 3(24) may be written in the symmetrical form

$$n_1 \sin \theta_1 = n_2 \sin \theta_2, \quad \ldots \ldots \quad 3(26)$$

and that

$$\frac{n_2}{n_1} = \mu_{12}. \quad \ldots \ldots \quad 3(27)$$

Indices of refraction for common gases (at standard temperature and pressure) range from 1·000035 for helium to 1·00030 for nitrogen. Indices for liquids and solids include 1·33 for water, 1·48 for soda glass and 1·7 for heavy flint glass. A few substances have appreciably

54 COMBINATION OF WAVE MOTIONS

higher indices. A medium of high refractive index is said to be of greater *optical density* than a medium of low refractive index.

3.12.—The law of reflection was certainly known to the Greek philosophers and was probably discovered independently by many different observers. Ptolemy and others drew up tables connecting the angles of incidence and of refraction. Many attempts were made to enunciate a law of refraction but they all failed, partly because the necessary mathematics was not sufficiently developed. The law given above was first discovered by Snell (1621) though it was not published until after his death. This law of refraction applies only when the media are *isotropic*. (A material is said to be isotropic when the physical properties of a thin slice cut from a mass of the material are independent of the original orientation of the slice before it was cut out.) When the medium on one side of the surface is *anisotropic* more complicated laws of refraction apply.* This type of medium is discussed in Chapters XII and XVI, but here we deal only with isotropic media. In this chapter we also neglect diffraction effects.

3.13. *Wave Theory of Reflection and Refraction.*

Huygens' construction enabled the wave theory to give the following account of reflection and refraction. It is assumed that the wave velocity in the second medium is different from the wave velocity in the first medium, and that this is the essential difference between the two media. Let the magnitude of the velocity of light in the first medium be b_1, and in the second medium be b_2. The plane wave AB which represents the parallel beam of incident light falls on the plane surface OP (see fig. 3.7). The line NON' is normal to this surface. When the wave reaches a point O on the surface it becomes a source of secondary waves which spread both in the first medium and in the second medium. Suppose that the wave surface AB reached the line OO' at time $t = 0$ and that it would reach the line PP' at time t if there were no reflection and refraction. Then

$$O'P = b_1 t = OP \sin \theta_1 = OP'. \quad \ldots \quad 3(28)$$

At time t, the secondary waves from O form a hemisphere of radius $b_1 t$ ($= OP \sin \theta_1 = OP_1$) in medium 1 and a hemisphere of radius $b_2 t$ [$= (b_2/b_1) OP \sin \theta_1 = OP_2$] in medium 2. The secondary waves are then just starting from P and it may easily be seen that tangent planes PP_1 and PP_2 from P to the above hemispheres also touch the hemispheres corresponding to the secondary waves from points such as Q and R, intermediate between O and P. The new wavefronts A'B' and A"B" are parallel to the planes PP_1 and PP_2. The new

---

* Such media are sometimes called *aeolotropic*.

§ 3.13   REFLECTION AND REFRACTION   55

directions of propagation of the waves make angles θ_1' and θ_2 with the normal to the surface of OP, where

$$\sin \theta_1' = \frac{\mathrm{OP}_1}{\mathrm{OP}} = \frac{b_1 t}{\mathrm{OP}} = \sin \theta_1. \qquad 3(29)$$

and

$$\sin \theta_2 = \frac{\mathrm{OP}_2}{\mathrm{OP}} = \frac{b_2 t}{\mathrm{OP}} = \frac{b_2}{b_1} \sin \theta_1. \qquad 3(30)$$

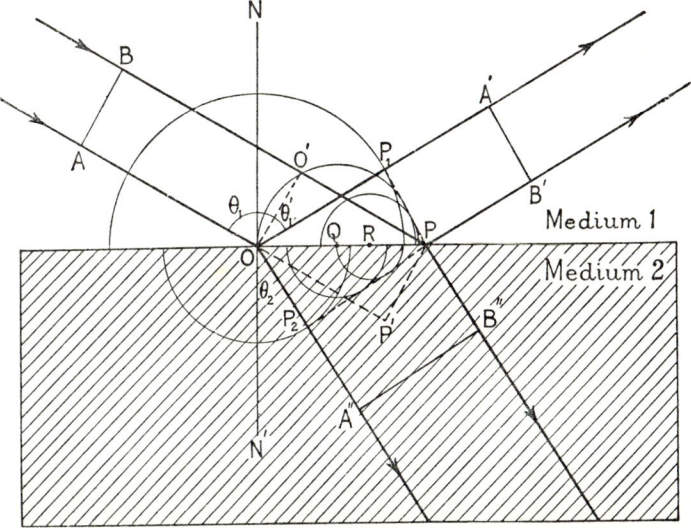

Fig. 3.7.—Huygens' principle applied to the reflection and refraction of light at a plane surface

Thus 3(29) agrees with 3(23), and 3(30) agrees with 3(24) and 3(27) provided that

$$\mu_{12} = \frac{b_1}{b_2} = \frac{n_2}{n_1}. \qquad 3(31)$$

Equation 3(31) is in agreement with direct measurements of the velocity of light in different media (see Chapter XI).

The wave-theory picture of reflection and refraction gives a simple description of the observations on the relation between the values of μ for different pairs of media; for

$$\mu_{13} = \frac{b_1}{b_3} = \frac{b_1}{b_2} \cdot \frac{b_2}{b_3} = \mu_{12} \cdot \mu_{23},$$

which agrees with 3(25).

3.14. Reflection and Refraction at Spherical Surfaces: Mirrors and Lenses.

When a beam of light diverging from a point O on the axis of a spherical mirror is reflected, it forms a real or virtual image of O at some point I also on the axis, i.e. after reflection the beam converges

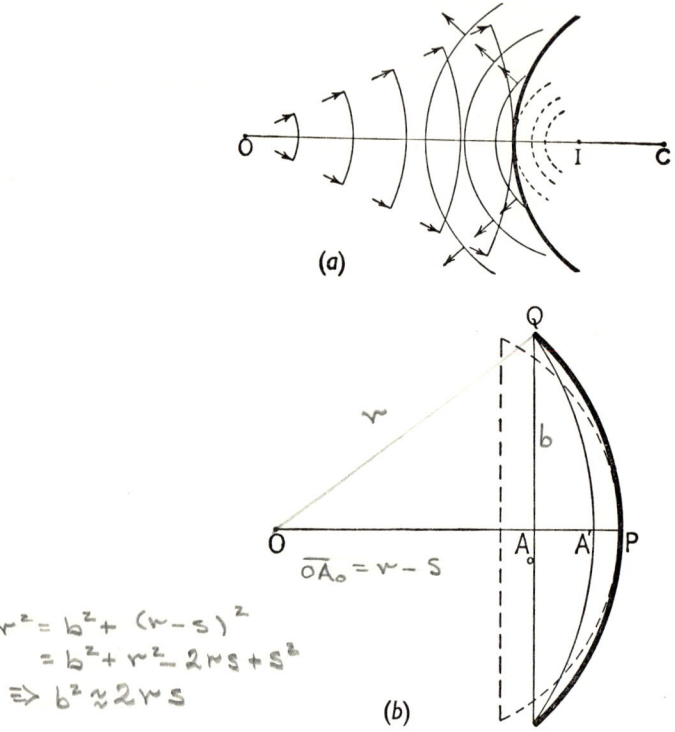

(a)

(b)

Fig. 3.8.—Huygens' principle applied to the reflection of light at spherical surfaces

towards I or appears to diverge from I (see fig. 3.8a). If the distances of O and I from the mirror are u and v respectively, and if r is the radius of curvature of the mirror, then it is found that

$$\frac{1}{v} + \frac{1}{u} = \frac{2}{r} = \frac{1}{f} = F. \qquad \qquad 3(32)$$

The constant f is called the *focal length* and the constant F is called the *power* of the mirror.

§ 3.15   REFLECTION AND REFRACTION   57

Distances are always measured from the mirror and the direction of the incident light is taken to be positive.

Similarly, for a lens with spherical surfaces of radii r_1 and r_2, it is found that

$$\frac{1}{v} - \frac{1}{u} = (\mu - 1)\left(\frac{1}{r_1} - \frac{1}{r_2}\right) = \frac{1}{f} = F, \quad . \quad . \quad 3(33)$$

where μ is the index for refraction from the surrounding material (usually air) to the material from which the lens is made (usually glass). These empirical formulæ are approximations which apply when the aperture (i.e. the ratio of the diameter to the radius of curvature) of the lens or mirror is small.

3.15.—The wave theory gives the following account of these observations. The beam of light approaching the mirror is represented by a spherical wave diverging from the point O (fig. 3.8a). As each part of the wave reaches the mirror, it gives rise to a system of secondary waves and Huygens' construction may be applied to find the position of the wavefront after reflection. When this is done it is found that, to a first approximation, the reflected wave is spherical and is centred upon the point I, the relation of the distances of O and I from the mirror being given by 3(32).

To show that application of Huygens' construction leads to equation 3(32), we use the well-known geometrical relation between the sagittal distance and the curvature of a *small* circular arc. If in fig. 3.8b we put $A_0P = s_r$ and $A_0Q = b$, we have, as a sufficient approximation when $b \ll r$,

$$2rs_r = b^2,$$

or
$$s_r = \tfrac{1}{2}b^2 R, \quad . \quad . \quad . \quad . \quad . \quad 3(34)$$

where $R (= 1/r)$ is the curvature. The sagittal distance (s_r) is proportional to b^2 and to the curvature. A wavefront advancing on the mirror from O (see fig. 3.8b) has a curvature $U (= 1/u)$. One part of the wavefront reaches Q when another part is at A′, where

$$A'P = \tfrac{1}{2}b^2(R - U).$$

Thus when the central part of the wavefront reaches the mirror and gives rise to a wavelet from P, the corresponding wavelet from Q has travelled out a distance A′P from Q. The secondary waves from P and

Q thus both touch a curve whose sagittal distance s_v exceeds s_r by A'P, i.e. we have for this curve

$$s_v = s_r + \text{A'P} = \tfrac{1}{2}b^2(2R - U).$$

Since the sagittal distance is proportional to b^2, the curve is a circle whose curvature is given by

$$V = 2R - U,$$

i.e.
$$\frac{1}{v} + \frac{1}{u} = \frac{2}{r},$$

which agrees with 3(32). It is important to remember that this result is valid only when b is small compared with r, v and u.

EXAMPLES [3(vii) and 3(viii)]

3(vii). Show, by a discussion similar to that of § 3.15, that, when a plane wave normal to the axis is incident upon a paraboloidal mirror, the reflected wavefront is *exactly* spherical, and has its centre at the focus.
[Use the polar equation of the parabola.]

3(viii). Show that the wavefront obtained in the preceding Example is the envelope of the wavelets emitted from the paraboloidal mirror.

> [Obtain the equation of the family of surfaces constituting the reflected wavelets in terms of the constant of the parabola as parameter. Differentiating this equation partially with respect to the parameter, and eliminating the parameter between the resultant equation and that of the family of surfaces, yields the envelope of the reflected wavelets.]

3.16.—By similar applications of Huygens' construction the wave theory is able to describe the behaviour of lenses and mirrors generally. On this view the effect of refraction at a spherical surface is to change the curvature of the incident wave surfaces. For a given lens the change in curvature is a constant and is equal to the reciprocal of the focal length of the lens. This constant change in curvature is called the *power* of the lens. The effect of reflection is both to change the curvature of the wave surfaces and to reverse the direction of propagation. This second effect is responsible for the difference of sign between equations 3(32) and 3(33). It corresponds to the fact that a lens of zero power (e.g. a very thin sheet of glass) has no effect on a beam of light, while a mirror of zero power (i.e. a plane mirror) alters the direction of propagation without altering the magnitude of the curva-

§ 3.17 DISPERSION 59

ture of the wave surfaces. Thus for a lens of zero power 3(33) gives $v = u$ and the image and object coincide. For a mirror of zero power 3(32) gives $v = -u$, and the image and object are on opposite sides of the mirror.

3.17. Dispersion.

Newton showed that, when an approximately parallel beam of white light falls upon a glass prism, the emergent light is spread out into a coloured strip which he called a *spectrum*. This phenomenon is called *dispersion*. It implies that the refractive index from air to glass is not the same for all colours of the spectrum, and hence that the ratio of the speed of light in air to that in glass depends on the colour of the light. This is confirmed by direct measurements of the velocity of light in different media. It is found that in a vacuum the speed of light is the same for all colours but that in a medium such as water blue light travels more slowly than red (see § 11.15). Experiments on interference and diffraction make it necessary to assume that the different colours in the spectrum must be represented by waves which have different values of λ and therefore of κ, ω and ν. The frequency is highest at the blue and lowest at the red end of the spectrum. The dispersion of light then implies that:

$$b = f(\lambda) \qquad \ldots \ldots \ldots \quad 3(35)$$
and
$$n = F(\lambda). \qquad \ldots \ldots \ldots \quad 3(36)$$

In the various differentiations, etc., by which the wave equation was derived it was not assumed that b was independent of ω or κ. Therefore the existence of dispersion does not invalidate the proof that the pure sine wave (represented by 2(2)) is propagated without change of profile. It does, however, imply that a composite wave, made up of two or more sine waves of different frequency, changes profile as it advances, because each component is propagated with its own speed, and the phase differences between the different components alter as the wave advances. These effects will be considered in Chapter IV.

The *speed of light in vacuo* is one of the fundamental physical constants. It is usually represented by the symbol c. This velocity has been found to be very close to $3 \cdot 00 \times 10^{10}$ centimetres per second (see § 11.13). Since the velocity in air (at standard temperature and pressure) is only about one part in 1000 less than that *in vacuo*, it is often sufficient to use the value c for the velocity of propagation in air, though it must be understood that it is used as an approximation.

A medium in which b varies with λ is called a *dispersive medium*. The only truly non-dispersive medium for light waves is a vacuum.

3.18.—The form of the function in equations 3(35) or 3(36) is of considerable practical importance. Cauchy proposed the following empirical formula:

$$n - 1 = A(1 + \frac{B}{\lambda^2} + \frac{C}{\lambda^4} + \ldots) \qquad \ldots \quad 3(37)$$

where A, B, C, etc., are constants whose magnitudes are such that each term of the series in the bracket is much less than the preceding one. The quantity $(n-1)$ is called the *refractivity*. In *normal* dispersion the refractive index increases regularly along the spectrum from red to blue, i.e. A and B are both positive. For a few substances the dispersion differs very greatly from the form given by 3(37) and it may happen that over a short part of the spectrum the refractive index increases when the wavelength increases. This phenomenon is called *anomalous* dispersion. For most gases the variation of the refractive index with wavelength is fairly well represented by a formula including the first two terms of 3(37). Formulæ of this type also form a moderately good representation of the properties of optical glasses. The following alternative formula for the refractive indices of glasses is due to Hartmann:

$$n = n_0 + \frac{\alpha}{(\lambda - \lambda_0)^{1 \cdot 2}}. \qquad \ldots \quad 3(38)$$

This formula gives a better agreement than a three-constant formula of the type proposed by Cauchy.

3.19.—The effect of dispersion on lenses may be seen from equation 3(33). The focal length of a lens is smaller, and its power greater, for blue light than for red. This means that the image formed by blue light is not quite the same in size or in position as the image formed by red light. Thus the images formed with white light appear coloured at the edges and are not so clear as images formed with monochromatic light. This effect is known as *chromatic aberration*.

3.20. **Stationary Waves.**

When a parallel beam of light represented by

$$\xi_1 = a \sin(\omega t - \kappa x) \qquad \ldots \quad 3(39)$$

is reflected at a perfect reflector, the reflected wave is represented by

$$\xi_2 = a \sin(\omega t + \kappa x + \delta), \qquad \ldots \quad 3(40)$$

where the constant δ depends on the position of the reflector. There is also a possibility that the process of reflection itself may be accompanied by a change of phase. Let this change, if any, be included in δ.

If the origins of x and t are moved to the right by $\delta/2\kappa$ and $\delta/2\omega$ respectively, equation 3(39) is unchanged and 3(40) becomes

$$\xi_2 = a \sin(\omega t + \kappa x). \quad \ldots \ldots \quad 3(41)$$

In this way the origin is moved so that $x = 0$, $t = 0$ corresponds to the same phase for both waves.

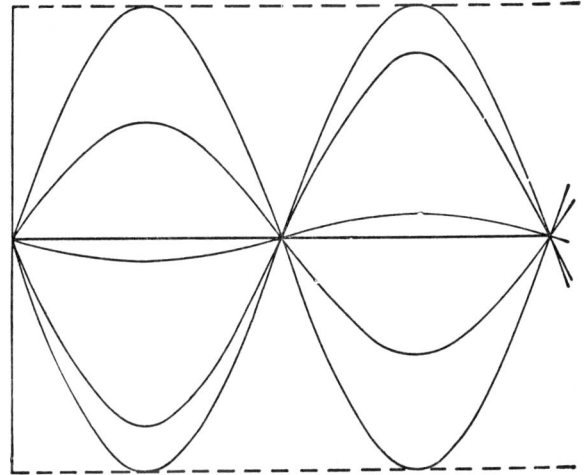

Fig. 3.9.—Profile of a stationary wave at different times

Applying the principle of superposition we have

$$\xi = \xi_1 + \xi_2 = a \sin(\omega t - \kappa x) + a \sin(\omega t + \kappa x), \quad 3(42)$$

and this may be written

$$\xi = 2a \cos \kappa x \sin \omega t. \quad \ldots \ldots \quad 3(43)$$

This type of wave is represented in fig. 3.9. At every point the motion is simple harmonic but the amplitude of the motion varies from point to point. The profile of the wave expands and shrinks as shown in the figure, but does not move forwards or backwards. Waves of this type are known as *stationary waves*.

3.21.—In a stationary wave there is no net transference of energy in either direction, though there is an energy density in the medium with a mean value proportional to a^2. This energy density is not uniformly distributed. It is a maximum at points for which $\cos^2 \kappa x = 1$, i.e. at $x = 0$, $x = \pi/\kappa$, $x = 2\pi/\kappa$, etc., and a minimum at points where $\cos^2 \kappa x = 0$, i.e. at $x = \pi/2\kappa$, $3\pi/2\kappa$, $5\pi/2\kappa$, etc. The points where the energy is a maximum are called *antinodes* or *loops*. Those where it is a minimum are called *nodes*. If a detector is moved along the x axis it gives a maximum reading at the antinodes and zero at the nodes (see fig. 3.10). The distance from a node to the nearest antinode is $\pi/2\kappa = \lambda/4$ and the distance between successive nodes is $\lambda/2$.

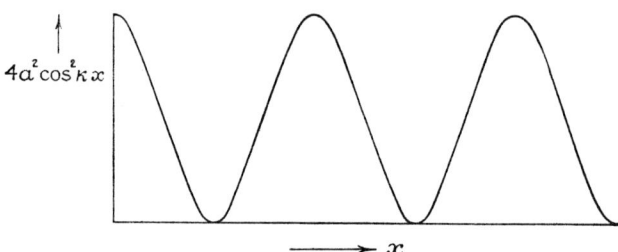

Fig. 3.10.—Distribution of energy in a medium in which there is a simple stationary wave

Now consider the case when the reflection is not perfect. The *coefficient of reflection* (ρ) is defined to be the ratio of the energy of the reflected beam to the energy of the incident beam. This implies that the ratio of the amplitudes is $\rho^{\frac{1}{2}}$.

Equation 3(41) must now be replaced by

$$\xi_2 = a\rho^{\frac{1}{2}} \sin(\omega t + \kappa x), \qquad \ldots \quad 3(44)$$

and 3(43) is replaced by

$$\xi = 2a\rho^{\frac{1}{2}} \cos \kappa x \sin \omega t + a(1 - \rho^{\frac{1}{2}}) \sin(\omega t - \kappa x). \quad 3(45)$$

The wave is now partly stationary and partly progressive. A detector moved along the x axis will still record maxima and minima. The readings at minima will not be zero since at points where the first term of 3(45) is zero the detector gives a reading proportional to the square of the amplitude of the second term. Waves which are mainly stationary, though containing a progressive component, occur commonly in acoustics in connection with the theory of organ pipes, etc. A series of observations made by Walton on stationary electromagnetic waves is shown in fig. 3.11. These waves are produced by allowing radiation emitted by a small high-frequency oscillator to fall upon a large sheet of metal placed at $x = 0$. The waves are measured by means of a small crystal detector connected to an amplifier. The metal has a high coefficient of reflection for these waves and the waves are mainly

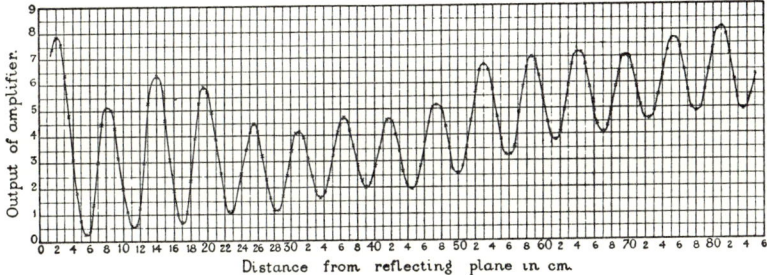

Fig. 3.11.—Experimental observations on stationary electromagnetic waves

stationary waves with a small progressive component. From the distance between the nodes the wavelength is found to be 11.6 centimetres.

3.22. Wiener's Experiment.

The detection of stationary light waves is difficult because the nodes and antinodes are very close together, the distance from node to antinode being only of order 10^{-5} centimetre. The experimental difficulties were first overcome by Wiener (1890). Before discussing

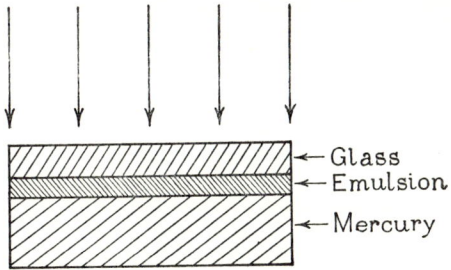

Fig. 3.12.—Ives' experiment

his work we shall describe the experiments of Ives which though more difficult to carry out are theoretically simpler. Ives prepared special photographic plates with a thin fine-grained emulsion. The emulsion side of the plate was placed in contact with a film of mercury and a parallel beam of monochromatic light was directed normally upon the glass side of the plate (see fig. 3.12). The light passed through the glass and the film and was reflected at the mercury surface, standing waves being formed in the film. The nodes form a series of laminæ distant $\frac{1}{2}\lambda$ apart with the antinodes half-way between them. In Ives' experiments the waves are detected by cutting a section of the film in a plane normal to the surface of the glass and examining it under a high-power microscope. The nodes and antinodes can be clearly seen; 250 successive laminæ were counted in one experiment.

3.23.—Wiener used an extremely thin transparent photographic film, about 2×10^{-6} centimetre thick, for the detection of the waves. He arranged that this film should lie at a very small angle to the system of waves formed by reflection at a front-silvered mirror, so that it cut the successive antinodal laminæ as shown in fig. 3.13. The photographic emulsion is blackened along a series of lines where the plane

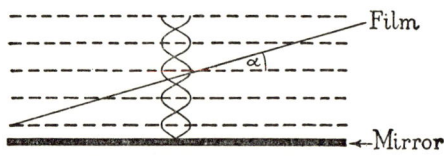

Fig. 3.13.—Wiener's experiment

of the film cuts the antinodal laminæ. The angle α (see fig. 3.13) was made about 10^{-3} radian and the distance between successive fringes was then 1000 times greater than the distance between the laminæ. From these experiments the wavelength of green light could be estimated to be $5 \cdot 5 \times 10^{-5}$ centimetre, and it could be shown that the wavelength of red light is nearly double that of blue light.

Wiener's technique was criticized on the grounds that light reflected from the photographic film, as well as that reflected from the mirror, should be taken into account, so that the fringes were formed in the manner described in § 5.12. Wiener proved that this was not so by putting a film of benzol between the mirror and the film. Since benzol has nearly the same refractive index as the gelatine, it almost eliminates the reflection from the lower surface of the photographic film. Wiener still obtained the fringes under these conditions.

3.24.—An interesting addition to Wiener's experiment is due to Drude and Nernst. They first repeated the main experiment using a fluorescent film as the detector instead of a photographic plate. They then took a glass plate, silvered half of the plate and coated the whole with a very thin film of fluorescent material. A parallel beam of radiation was allowed to fall normally upon the whole plate, and it was found that there was strong fluorescence in the unsilvered region and none in the silvered region. This indicates that the surface of the reflector forms a node of the stationary waves, and implies that reflection of light at a silvered surface produces a change of phase of approximately π. Thus if the *origin of x be taken at the reflector* and if the incident wave is represented by 3(39), the reflected wave must be represented by

$$\xi_2 = -a \sin(\omega t + \kappa x), \quad \ldots \quad 3(46)$$

and the system of stationary waves by

$$\xi = -2a \sin \kappa x \cos \omega t, \quad \ldots \quad 3(47)$$

so that the displacement is always zero at $x = 0$.

3.25.—Wiener's experiment was later again repeated by Ives, using a photo-electric method for detecting the nodes and antinodes. Although Wiener's experiment does not form an accurate method of measuring the wavelength of light, it is of considerable theoretical interest. The formation of stationary light waves is probably the simplest application of the principle of superposition and forms a very direct, though not a very exact, test of the principle. Stationary light waves are the foundation of a method of colour photography. They have also important applications in connection with photo-electric cells and in the theory of polarized light.

Stationary waves in three-dimensional enclosures are discussed in connection with the theory of temperature-radiation.

3.26. Coefficient of Reflection—Normal Incidence.

The coefficient of reflection at the boundary separating two transparent media can be calculated if the *boundary conditions* are known. Consider a parallel beam of light travelling in the OX direction and a boundary formed by a plane normal to the direction of propagation. For all ordinary kinds of waves the value of ξ is the same at any two points which are an infinitesimal distance apart, but on opposite sides of the boundary, at all times. This forms one boundary condition.

The second boundary condition depends upon the type of wave involved and on the difference between the two media. Fresnel, using an elastic-solid theory of light, deduced the condition that $\partial \xi / \partial x$ should have the same value on the two sides of the boundary. Hence he calculated the coefficient of reflection for normal incidence and obtained the value given in 3(56). In the next paragraph, this boundary condition will be used. From our point of view, it is justified, for the present, by its success in giving a formula for the coefficient of reflection which is in agreement with experimental observations. It will require to be re-examined when we come to consider the reflection of electromagnetic waves.

3.27.—Suppose that a parallel beam of light represented by

$$\xi_1 = a_1 \sin(\omega t - \kappa_1 x) \quad \ldots \quad 3(48)$$

is incident normally on a plane surface separating two media. Suppose that the light is passing from medium 1 to medium 2 and that the index of refraction is μ_{12}. Then if ξ_1' represents the reflected and ξ_2 the refracted wave, the boundary conditions are

$$\xi_1 + \xi_1' = \xi_2, \text{ for all } t, \quad \ldots \quad 3(49)$$

$$\frac{\partial \xi_1}{\partial x} + \frac{\partial \xi_1'}{\partial x} = \frac{\partial \xi_2}{\partial x}, \text{ for all } t. \quad \ldots \quad 3(50)$$

Equations 3(49) and 3(50) hold at the boundary which we take to be the plane $x = 0$.

Equation 3(49) requires that reflected and refracted waves shall have the same frequency as the incident wave. Since the velocities are different in the two media, the values of λ and κ for the refracted wave must be different from the corresponding values for the incident wave, in order to comply with equations 2(25). We therefore write

$$\xi_1' = a_1' \sin(\omega t + \kappa_1 x) \quad \ldots \quad 3(51)$$

and
$$\xi_2 = a_2 \sin(\omega t - \kappa_2 x), \quad \ldots \quad 3(52)$$

where
$$\kappa_2 = \mu_{12} \kappa_1. \quad \ldots \quad 3(53)$$

In writing 3(51) and 3(52) we assume that the phase differences between the reflected and refracted waves and the incident wave are zero or π.

The boundary conditions now give

$$a_1 + a_1' = a_2 \quad \ldots \quad 3(54a)$$

and
$$\kappa_1 a_1 - \kappa_1 a_1' = \kappa_2 a_2, \quad \ldots \quad 3(54b)$$

and from 3(53) we obtain

$$a_1 - a_1' = \frac{\kappa_2}{\kappa_1} a_2 = \mu_{12} a_2,$$

and hence
$$a_1' = -a_1 \frac{\mu_{12} - 1}{\mu_{12} + 1}, \quad \ldots \ldots \quad 3(55)$$

$$\rho = \left(\frac{\mu_{12} - 1}{\mu_{12} + 1}\right)^2. \quad \ldots \ldots \quad 3(56)$$

When reflection takes place at an air-glass surface, equation 3(56) gives a reflection coefficient of 4 per cent for a glass of index 1·5.

3.28.—Equation 3(55) indicates that there is a reversal of phase (i.e. a change by π) when light is reflected, if the reflection takes place in the medium of lower optical density, but no change if it takes place in the medium of higher optical density. This change of phase is verified by direct experiment (see § 5.10). Equation 3(56) predicts that the coefficient of reflection is the same on whichever side the beam strikes the surface since the value of ρ is unchanged when μ_{21} is substituted for μ_{12}. If these coefficients were not equal, it would be possible to construct a thermodynamic cycle which would infringe the Second Law.

3.29.—In the derivation of 3(56) it was assumed that the boundary between the two media was mathematically sharp. Most real surfaces are not perfectly clean. Glass surfaces commonly contain traces of polishing material and also occluded air. In practice, it appears that ordinary clean surfaces are sufficiently sharp to give results substantially in accord with 3(56). The sizes of irregularities are probably a little greater than the diameters of atoms and molecules (i.e. only 1/100 of a wavelength of light). The presence of thin films of grease, etc., or of any slight roughness in the surface seriously affects the reflection.

3.30. Optical Path Difference.

In many optical problems it is necessary to calculate the phase difference between two beams of light which have started from the same source and reached the same point by different paths, having been reflected or refracted by systems of mirrors or prisms (see fig. 4.1). The phase difference between such beams is made up of two parts. The first part, which has just been considered, consists of changes of phase on reflection; the second is due to a possible difference in length of the two paths. A sine wave undergoes a phase change of 2π when the wave advances through a distance equal to a wavelength. Thus the phase change $\delta\phi$ when the wave advances a distance δs in a medium of refractive index n_1 is given by

$$\delta\phi = \frac{2\pi}{\lambda_1} \delta s, \quad \ldots \ldots \quad 3(57)$$

where λ_1 is the wavelength in the medium.

If λ and κ are the wavelength and wavelength constant for a wave of the same frequency in a vacuum we have

$$\delta\phi = \frac{2\pi}{\lambda} n_1 \, \delta s = \kappa n_1 \, \delta s. \qquad \ldots \quad 3(58)$$

The phase difference is thus proportional to $n_1 \, \delta s$ and the *optical distance* between two points is defined to be the integral of this function along the path traversed.

The *optical path difference* is the difference between the values of this integral taken along the two alternative paths. The phase difference is κ times the optical path difference. If one beam of light passes through a plate of glass of thickness e and another follows a parallel path in air, the optical path difference is $(n_1 - 1)e$, although there is no difference in the lengths of the geometrical paths.

3.31. Wave Guides.

Consider two beams of light whose directions of propagation are both in the YOZ plane and which make angles $\pm \theta$ with the OZ axis,

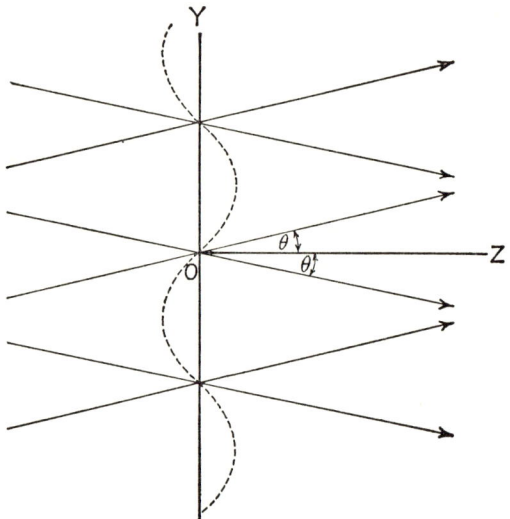

Fig. 3.14.—Sinusoidal distribution of displacement.

as shown in fig. 3.14. Suppose that there is a phase difference 2δ at the origin. Then

$$\xi_+ = a \sin(\omega t - \kappa_y y - \kappa_z z - \delta), \quad \ldots \quad 3(59a)$$

$$\xi_- = a \sin(\omega t + \kappa_y y - \kappa_z z + \delta), \quad \ldots \quad 3(59b)$$

where $\kappa_y = \kappa \sin \theta; \quad \kappa_z = \kappa \cos \theta$ and $\kappa = 2\pi/\lambda$. 3(60)

The resultant is represented by

$$\xi = 2a \cos (\kappa_y y + \delta) \sin (\omega t - \kappa_z z)$$
$$= a' \sin \omega \left(t - \frac{z}{b'}\right), \quad \ldots \ldots \quad 3(61)$$

where $a' = 2a \cos (\kappa_y y + \delta)$ and $b' = b \sec \theta$. . . 3(62)

The displacement $\xi(0)$ on the plane $z = 0$ is

$$\xi(0) = 2a \cos (\kappa_y y + \delta) \sin \omega t. \quad \ldots \quad 3(63)$$

This is similar to the displacement given by 3(43) and illustrated in fig. 3.9. The spatial frequency is κ_y instead of κ. The value of δ determines the positions of the nodes. If $\delta = \pi/2$ there is a node at the origin and we then have

$$\xi(0) = 2a \sin (\kappa_y y) \sin \omega t. \quad \ldots \ldots \quad 3(64)$$

The displacement represented by 3(61) and 3(64) is called a *sinusoidal distribution of displacement with spatial frequency* κ_y. Although the variation in the y direction is similar to that of a standing wave, that in the z direction corresponds to a wave of spatial frequency κ_z propagated with phase velocity $b \sec \theta$.

3.32.—From fig. 3.14 it may be seen that there is no resultant disturbance on the planes $y = \pi n/\kappa_y$, where n is an integer. If, therefore, these planes were perfect reflectors the system of waves described in § 3.24 would be propagated unchanged. It thus appears that a pair of infinite planes separated by a distance d can act as guides for a system of waves. The waves can be propagated in the way described provided that the spatial frequency for the waves in free space is not less than π/d, i.e. that the wavelength is not greater than $2d$. The pair of infinite parallel planes is the simplest type of *wave guide*. Tubular conductors of circular or rectangular cross-section are commonly used as wave guides for electromagnetic waves of wavelengths from a few centimetres to a few millimetres.

3.33. Corpuscular Theory of Reflection and Refraction.

In the corpuscular theory of light, the law of reflection, equation 3(23), is easily pictured as a form of elastic reflection. The corpuscles impinge on a perfectly smooth and perfectly elastic surface; the component of their velocity perpendicular to the surface is reversed, while that parallel to the surface is unchanged.

In order to be able to explain refraction, the corpuscular theory has to assume that some, but not all, of the corpuscles are able to penetrate the surface. This constitutes a fundamental difficulty, because the natural assumption is that the corpuscles representing one kind of light are all the same. If this is so, it would be possible to explain why some particles penetrate the surface and others do not, by assuming that the surface has some form of structure—due perhaps to the atomic structure of matter. On this view a corpuscle would be reflected if it struck one of the surface atoms directly (see fig. 3.15), and would be refracted if it fell on one of the spaces, just as some particles penetrate a thin sheet of metal while others do not.

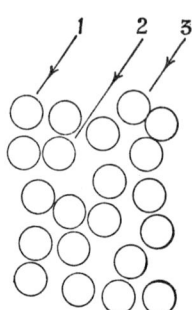

Fig. 3.15.—Corpuscular theory of reflection and transmission of light.

This type of theory involves many difficulties. If it were correct the corpuscles would almost certainly be scattered at the surface and there would be diffuse instead of regular reflection and refraction. Also it would be very difficult to explain rectilinear propagation in a medium whose atoms exerted such powerful forces on the corpuscles. It is therefore necessary to consider the possibility that the corpuscles may not be identical.

3.34.—If a beam of monochromatic light falls normally on a sheet of transparent glass, a certain fraction is transmitted. If the transmitted light falls upon a second sheet of glass similar to the first, the same fraction is transmitted. Thus it appears that, in this case, the light transmitted does not differ essentially from the incident light—both contain the same proportion of corpuscles capable of being transmitted. This implies that there are not some corpuscles permanently capable of transmission and others which must be reflected. On the contrary, all the corpuscles must be capable both of transmission and of reflection. As Newton suggested they must have " fits of reflection " and " fits of transmission ", and must pass periodically from one to the other. There is also no way of predicting when any one corpuscle will be in a " fit of reflection ". Thus the corpuscular theory would appear to involve a certain element of *indeterminacy*—to admit that the behaviour of the corpuscles cannot be followed in detail and described in terms of cause and effect: it also seems to involve a kind of periodicity —a characteristic feature of the wave theory.

3.35.—Even if the corpuscular theory should succeed in giving an account of the fact that some light is reflected and some refracted, it would still have to provide means for calculating (i) the proportion of light transmitted, and (ii) the relation between the angle of incidence and the angle of refraction (Snell's law). It has never been able to attack these problems with any degree of success. It is well known that an attempt was made to explain Snell's law by the special assumption that the speed of the corpuscles increased in a certain ratio in passing from a light to a dense medium, the component of velocity parallel to the surface remaining unchanged. This is a very artificial assumption since normally energy would be needed to increase the speed of the corpuscles. It is directly opposed to the results of measurements of the velocity of light.

§ 3.36   CORPUSCULAR THEORY   71

3.36.—It thus appears that while the wave theory can give an elegant account of the basic phenomena of reflection and refraction, the corpuscular theory can give only a fragmentary and unsatisfactory description of these phenomena. In order to do even this, it has to import special assumptions which lead towards a wave theory. In considering the great superiority of the wave description, it is desirable to remember that later we shall have to discuss a group of phenomena where a corpuscular theory is entirely successful, and the wave theory has correspondingly great difficulties.

EXAMPLES [3(ix)–3(xiv)]

3(ix). Show that if the refractive index were *exactly* represented by the first two terms of 3(37) it would be possible to construct a lens free from chromatic aberration by combining a positive and negative lens made of different glasses.

[Let the refractive indices be given by

$$n' - 1 = A' + A'B'/\lambda^2$$

and

$$n'' - 1 = A'' + A''B''/\lambda^2.$$

Let the powers of the two lenses be F' and F''' respectively and let $\rho' = (1/r_1 + 1/r_2)$ for the first lens and ρ'' the corresponding function for the second.

Then
$$F = F' + F'' = (n' - 1)\rho' + (n'' - 1)\rho''$$
$$= A'\rho' + A''\rho'' + (A'B'\rho' + A''B''\rho'')/\lambda^2,$$

and if $A'B'\rho' + A''B''\rho'' = 0$, then F is independent of λ.]

3(x). Show that the process suggested in the last example fails if $A'/B' = A''/B''$.

3(xi). The refractive indices of a flint glass and a crown glass are as follows:

	Red light	Blue light
Flint	1·644	1·664
Crown	1·514	1·524

Find the focal lengths of two lenses, one made of flint and the other of crown glass, such that, when combined, the resultant focal length is 10 metres for each kind of light.   [−5·784 m. and 3·664 m. for blue light.]

3(xii). Calculate the ratio of the amount of light transmitted normally through a piece of glass whose refractive index is 1·5, to that transmitted through a piece of fused quartz whose index is 1·55.

[1·019. Allow for reflections at two surfaces.]

3(xiii). Insert epoch angles δ_1' and δ_2 in 3(51) and 3(52) and apply the conditions 3(49) and 3(50). Hence show that δ_1' and δ_2 are either zero or integral multiples of π.

3(xiv). In an experiment similar to Wiener's, the film was one centimetre long. One end was in contact with the reflecting surface and the other was separated from it by a piece of mica 10^{-3} centimetre thick. The distance between successive dark lines on the plate was 0·025 centimetre. Find the wavelength of the light used. [5000 Å.]

CHAPTER IV

Representation of Light by Wave Trains of Finite Length

4.1. Sources of Light. Types of Spectra.

The classification of sources of light is an important preliminary to the application of wave theory. From this point of view, the most significant classification is made by means of *spectra*. Modern instruments, developed from the simple apparatus by which Newton first discovered the dispersion of light, enable the spectra produced by different sources to be examined in detail. These instruments are called *spectroscopes* when they are designed for visual examination of the spectrum, and *spectrographs* when they are arranged so that it may be photographed. Using these instruments, three main types of spectra have been discovered. These are called *line spectra*, *band spectra*, and *continuous spectra*. Each type may be observed either as an emission spectrum or as an absorption spectrum. Plate I (p. 74) and Plate II (p. 130) include some typical spectra.

4.2. Line Spectra and Continuous Spectra.

An emission-line spectrum consists of a number of fairly narrow lines with dark regions between them (see Plate I*a, b, c*). There may be only a few, or there may be several thousand lines. Narrow (or " sharp ") lines are produced when atoms are able to radiate light without being greatly affected by collisions with other atoms. Sharp lines are usually produced by an electrical discharge in gases at low pressure. Each line is characteristic of the kind of atom by which it is emitted. Sodium emits two lines fairly close together in the yellow region of the spectrum (Plate I*a*); cadmium emits a strong red and a strong green line, as well as many weaker lines (Plate I*b*); mercury emits several strong lines (Plate I*c*). When an electrical discharge is produced in a gas at a pressure of a few atmospheres, the lines become less sharp (Plate I*d*), and when the pressure is made higher still the lines run together to form a continuum. The spectra of light from hot solids are also continuous. This type of spectrum is usually produced under conditions such that each atom is strongly influenced by its neighbours.

4.3. Band Spectra.

A band spectrum consists of a very large number of lines which crowd together in certain regions of the spectrum to form characteristic "heads" (Plate IIa). Spectra of this type are due to molecules and a given system of bands is characteristic of the molecule which emits them. The theoretical description of these spectra is more complicated than the corresponding description of line spectra, but does not involve any essentially different principles.

4.4. Infra-red and Ultra-violet Radiation.

Using suitable photographic plates, it is possible to photograph lines, bands, etc., which lie outside the limits of the visible spectrum. This indicates that there are certain types of radiation to which the plate is sensitive but the eye is not. This is confirmed by taking a very sensitive thermopile and moving it through the spectrum. The thermopile gives a reading in the visible region and its reading increases greatly when it passes through a region where a bright line can be seen. The reading does not, however, fall to zero at the ends of the visible spectrum. Beyond the red end it usually increases; beyond the violet end the reading is usually small but still sufficient to indicate the presence of radiant energy. The radiation beyond the red end of the visible spectrum is called *infra-red radiation*; that beyond the violet end is called *ultra-violet radiation** (Plate IIb, p. 130. See also fig. 1.5).

4.5. Absorption Spectra.

When light from a source which normally gives a continuous spectrum is passed through certain vapours or gases, it is found that a number of dark lines appear in the spectrum (Plate IIc, d). Continuous absorption may also be produced by vapours, or by gases, or by liquids. Absorption lines or bands are characteristic of the absorbing gas or vapour, and it is found that their positions in the spectrum coincide with the positions of some of the lines or bands which are emitted by the same gas or vapour under the influence of an electrical discharge (Plate IIc, d, e). These absorption lines or bands enable us to detect the

---

* This radiation is sometimes called *ultra-violet light*. The word "light" should be reserved for "visible radiation".

(a) Emission spectrum (sodium).

(b) Emission spectrum (cadmium).

(c) Emission spectrum (mercury, low-pressure).

(d) Emission spectrum (mercury, higher-pressure).

(e) Newton's rings. (f) Fabry-Pérot fringes (mercury, blue only).

(g) Fabry-Pérot fringes (mercury, blue and green).

PLATE 1

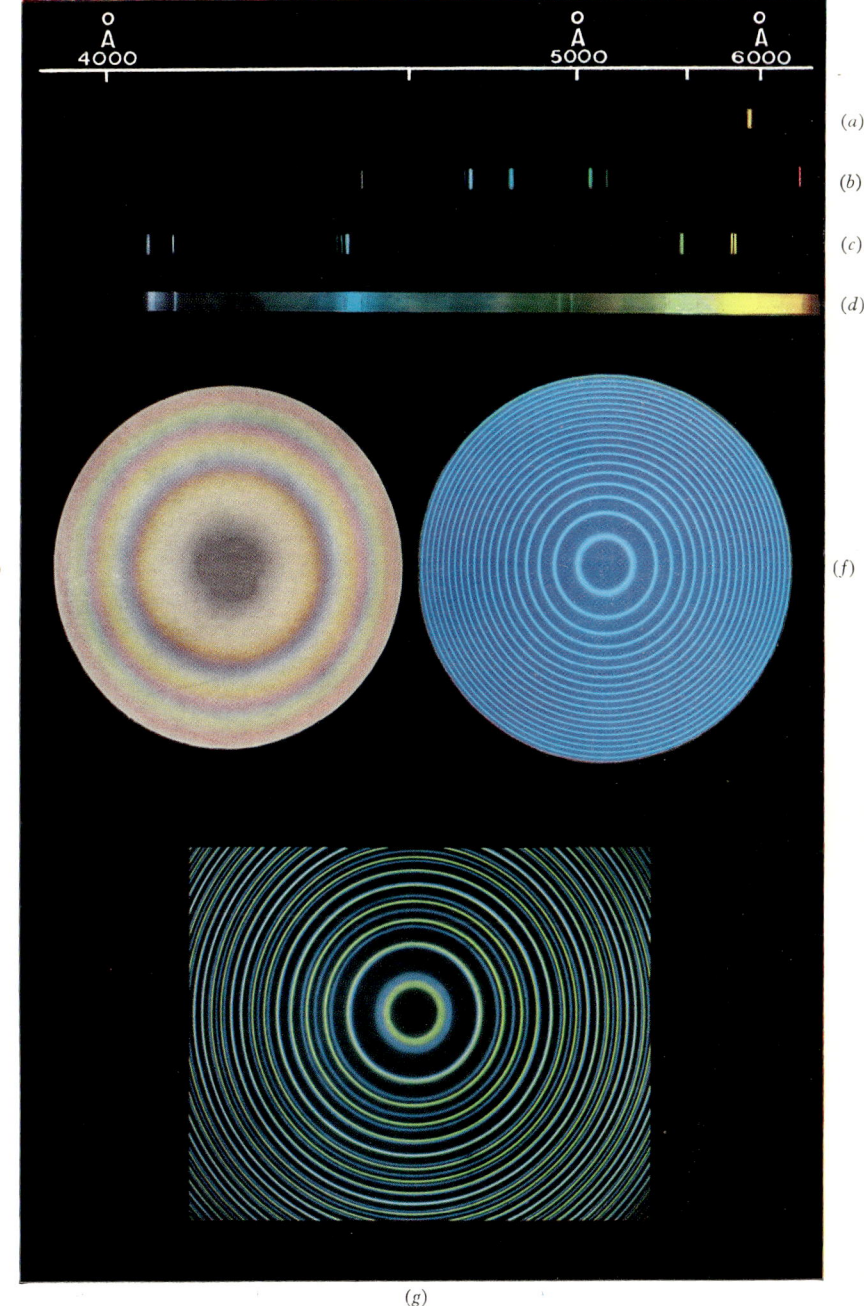

PLATE I Facing p. 74

§ 4.6 TYPES OF SPECTRA 75

presence of the corresponding atom or molecule in the gas or vapour. This type of spectrum was first discovered by J. von Fraunhofer (1787–1826), who showed that the spectrum of light from the sun is crossed with a number of dark lines. The position of these lines in the spectrum coincide with the positions of some of the emission lines obtained in laboratory spectra (Plate IIc, e). These lines originate in the following way. The centre of the sun is a dense mass of very hot gas which emits a continuous spectrum. This light passes through the cooler and less dense outer layers of the sun, where part of the light is absorbed, producing the dark lines. These lines show the presence of certain of the terrestrial elements in the outer layers of the sun. The central region is called the *photosphere*, the main absorbing region is called the *chromosphere*. The *corona* is a much less dense region of the sun which extends far beyond the chromosphere. It is normally seen only at eclipses when the main light of the sun is excluded by the moon. In this region a number of weak but very sharp lines are emitted.

4.6. *Atomic Oscillators.*

Let us now assume, on the basis of certain experiments which will be described later, that each line in a spectrum corresponds to a definite wavelength. It also corresponds to a definite frequency, the relation between wavelength and frequency being given by equation 2(25). The wavelengths and frequencies for different regions of the spectrum are given in fig. 1.5. The emission and absorption of spectra which consist of sharp lines suggest that the atom may be regarded as a system of simple harmonic oscillators. Each oscillator emits light of the wavelength corresponding to its natural frequency and thus produces a line in the spectrum. When white light passes through a gas or vapour, the oscillators in the various atoms resonate and absorb light of the wavelengths which correspond to their own natural frequencies of oscillation. Thus the absorption lines coincide with the emission lines. When an atom is subject to strong interaction with its neighbours (as in a gas at high pressure, or in a solid or liquid) the oscillators are continually being disturbed. They emit irregular pulses instead of simple harmonic waves, and these pulses (which have no well-defined frequency) make up a continuous spectrum. Some of the natural periods of atoms or molecules correspond to wavelengths greater or less than those to which the eye is sensitive, and they give lines in the infra-red and ultra-violet respectively.

4.7.—This general description of the emission and absorption of radiation by atoms and molecules includes many of the observations, but there are certain difficulties. It is not easy to understand why some atoms should emit so many lines if each line corresponds to a distinct mode of oscillation which has its own natural frequency. This difficulty is greater when we consider that even the hydrogen molecule, which consists of only four particles, emits an extremely complicated spectrum containing tens of thousands of lines. It is also found that normally only *some* of the emission lines appear in the absorption spectrum.

In the emission spectra of atoms some lines appear only in the spark spectrum and not in the arc spectrum. Others appear only in the gaseous discharge. These observations indicate that under a given set of conditions some of the oscillators are not available, and the theory does not suggest any simple reason why this should be so. Although there are many difficulties, the simple picture of the atom as a set of harmonic oscillators is still very useful. At a later stage it will be incorporated in a more detailed theory of the emission and absorption of light. At present it may be regarded as a working hypothesis to be amended when more detailed experimental data are available. It suggests that it is desirable to see whether all the properties of the light belonging to one of the sharp lines in the spectrum are characteristic of the long trains of sine waves which would be emitted by a simple harmonic oscillator. For this purpose it is necessary to isolate one of the lines of the spectrum. This may be done by placing a mask over the spectrum with a slit placed so as to allow only a narrow region, containing one line, to pass. Such an arrangement is called a *monochromator*. Sometimes the same result can be more easily achieved by the use of colour filters which transmit only a part of the spectrum. By passing the light through a suitable combination of filters, it is possible to arrange that only one line is transmitted, provided that the source does not have too complicated a spectrum. When the light corresponding to one line of the spectrum has been isolated, its properties may be studied in detail by means of the instrument which will be described in the next paragraph.

4.8. The Michelson Interferometer.

The apparatus shown in fig. 4.1 was invented by A. A. Michelson (1852–1931). S_e is an extended source of light such as a gaseous discharge-tube or a sodium flame. Light from S_e passes through the filter F and is made roughly parallel by the lens L. It then falls upon the mirror M_1. This mirror is a plate of glass half-silvered on the side remote from S_e. M_2 and M_3 are fully silvered on the front surfaces. Some of the light from S_e passes through M_1 and is reflected, first by M_3 and then by M_1, so as to enter the telescope T. Another portion of the light is first reflected by M_1, then by M_2, from which it passes through M_1 to the telescope. The light entering the telescope is viewed through the eyepiece E. The compensator C is a plate of unsilvered glass equal in thickness to M_1. Light reflected from M_3 passes twice

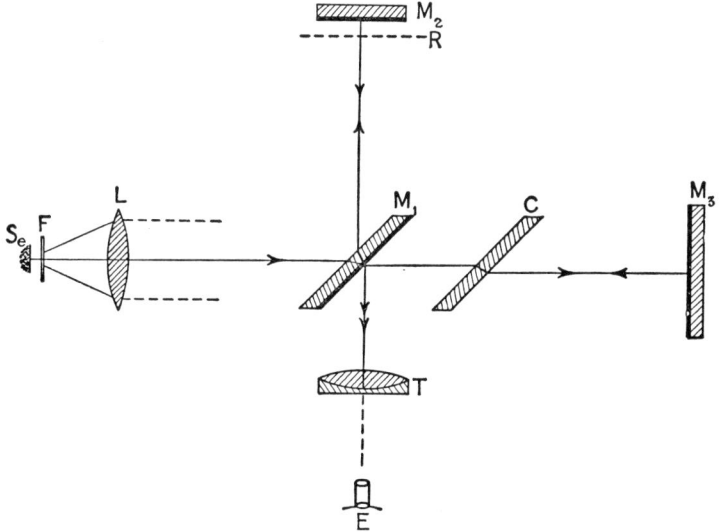

Fig. 4.1.—The Michelson interferometer

through C and thus passes through the same thickness of glass as the beam from M_2, which passes through M_1 three times. The mirror M_2 is mounted on a carriage which can be moved by a screw in a direction parallel to the axis of the telescope. It moves along accurately constructed guides, so that no rotation occurs during its movement. Let R be a plane coincident with the image of the mirror M_3, reflected in the mirror M_1. This plane is called the reference plane. Then the difference in phase between the beam reflected from M_2 and that reflected from M_3 is the same as if the latter beam had been reflected from R.* In the usual adjustment of the instrument M_2 is set parallel

* For studying the interaction between *two* beams of light, the Michelson interferometer is superior to a simple thin film arrangement (such as would be produced by placing a half-silvered mirror at the plane R), because (a) there are no beams due to multiple reflections (such as reflection from M_2 to R, thence to M_2 again and from M_2 to the telescope); (b) M_2 can be made to coincide with R; and (c) it is fairly easy to make the two beams of equal amplitude.

to and about a millimetre from R. Circular fringes are seen in the telescope when it is suitably adjusted.*

4.9.—We account for these fringes in the following way. Since the light from S_e is not accurately parallel some beams reach T having been reflected normally from M_2, others after reflection at a small angle. If e is the distance from M_2 to the reference plane R, the path difference † for beams reflected at an angle θ to the normal is $2e \cos \theta$, and the phase difference is

$$\delta = \frac{2\pi}{\lambda}(2e \cos \theta) = \frac{4\pi e \cos \theta}{\lambda}.$$

If the two beams are of equal amplitude, the relative energy is proportional to

$$2a_1^2 + 2a_1^2 \cos \delta = 4a_1^2 \cos^2 \tfrac{1}{2}\delta. \quad \text{(See § 3.4)}. \quad . \quad . \quad 4(1)$$

The relative energy is a maximum when δ/π is an even integer, i.e. when the path difference $2e \cos \theta$ is an integral multiple of λ. It is zero when δ/π is an odd integer, i.e. when $2e \cos \theta$ is an odd number of half wavelengths. A parallel beam of light falling on a telescope is focused at a point in the focal plane of the objective. The hollow cone of light consisting of all these rays which make a given angle θ with the axis of the telescope is seen as a circular ring. The phase difference for all points on the ring is the same and the ring constitutes a bright fringe if this phase difference is an integral multiple of 2π.

The *order of interference* between two beams for which the phase difference is $2\pi p$ (corresponding to a path difference of $p\lambda$) is p. In this definition of order of interference p is not necessarily integral. The maximum which corresponds to an integral value (p_1) of p is called the *maximum of order* p_1 or the bright fringe of order p_1. In a similar way we may speak of the minimum of order $(p_1 + \tfrac{1}{2})$ or the dark fringe of order $(p_1 + \tfrac{1}{2})$.

Let p_0 (not necessarily integral) be the order of interference at the centre, and let θ_{p_1} be the angular *radius* of the bright fringe of order p_1 (where p_1 is an integer). Then

$$2e = p_0 \lambda \quad . \quad . \quad . \quad . \quad . \quad 4(2a)$$

and
$$2e \cos \theta_{p_1} = p_1 \lambda. \quad . \quad . \quad . \quad . \quad . \quad 4(2b)$$

* Instructions for adjusting the Michelson interferometer are given in Appendix IV A.

† See § 5.13.

§ 4.10   THE MICHELSON INTERFEROMETER   79

Note that the order at the centre (p_0) is always *greater* than the order of any of the rings (p_1). When e is constant the loci of maximum relative energy depend only on θ, and are therefore circular rings.* If M_2 is moved away from R, fresh rings appear at the centre. Each ring moves outwards but the central rings move more rapidly so that, in any given part of the field, the angular separation of the fringes becomes smaller.

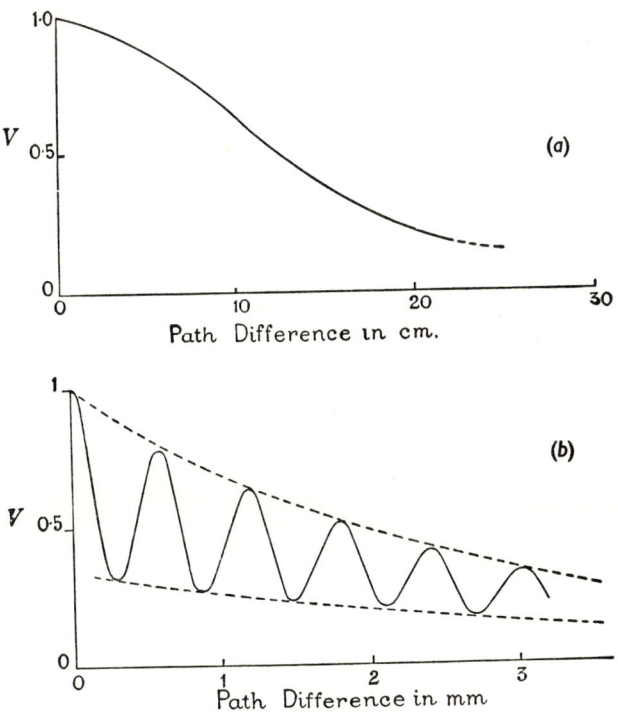

Fig. 4.2.—Variation of visibility with path difference for (*a*) cadmium red line (6438 Å.) and (*b*) sodium yellow lines (5890 Å. and 5896 Å.)

4.10. *Visibility of the Fringes.*

The reduction of the separation of the fringes when the path difference is large makes them more difficult to see if they are viewed with the same telescope, i.e. under constant magnification. Michelson found that apart altogether from this effect the clearness of the fringes

* It is shown in Chapter V that this is still true for sources of finite size.

varies in a way characteristic of the source used. He defined the *visibility* of a fringe to be

$$V = \frac{E_{(\max)} - E_{(\min)}}{E_{(\max)} + E_{(\min)}}, \qquad \ldots \ldots \quad 4(3)$$

where $E_{(\max)}$ is the relative energy for a bright fringe and $E_{(\min)}$ is the relative energy for the neighbouring dark fringes. The visibility so defined is independent of the angular diameters of the rings. Michelson devised an ingenious method * of measuring the variation of V with e. Results of measurements of the value of V for fringes near the centre of the field, obtained with cadmium red light, are shown in fig. 4.2a. Corresponding results for sodium yellow light are shown in fig. 4.2b (p. 79).

4.11.—If the radiation from the source S_e is exactly represented by a pure sine wave, the value of V may be calculated from 4(1). This equation gives $E_{\min} = 0$, so that $V = 1$, no matter how large the path difference. This calculation does not agree with either of the experimental results and therefore the light from the sources cannot be exactly represented by pure sine waves. The next most simple assumption is that the light is represented by a mixture of two sine waves of slightly different wavelengths λ and λ'. The fringes produced by wavelength λ' are then similar to those produced by λ, but if θ'_{p_1} is the angular diameter for order p_1 of λ', we have

$$\frac{\cos \theta'_{p_1}}{\cos \theta_{p_1}} = \frac{\lambda'}{\lambda}. \qquad \ldots \ldots \quad 4(4)$$

In some parts of the field the two sets of rings coincide and reinforce one another. Owing to difference of separation, they go " out of step " in other regions. Certain values of θ correspond to maxima for one wavelength and to minima for the other so that the rings become confused. There are thus series of alternations of rings " in step " and " out of step " leading to a variation of visibility. Just as the ratio of the periods of two pendulums may be determined by observing the frequency of coincidences, so the ratio of the wavelengths may be determined by observing the fluctuations of the visibility of the fringes.

4.12.—Observation of the variation of the visibility may also be used to determine the ratio of the amplitudes of the two waves and hence the relative energies. Two sine waves of equal amplitude give zero visibility when the waves are exactly out of step. If the ampli-

* See Reference 4.1.

tudes are not equal the visibility is never zero since the weaker fringes do not completely obliterate the stronger ones. If the amplitudes of the sine waves are a_1 and a_2, the maximum visibility is unity and the minimum visibility is

$$V_{\min} = \frac{a_1^2 - a_2^2}{a_1^2 + a_2^2}.$$

Thus by measuring (a) the separation of the maxima, and (b) the ratio of the maxima to the minima in the visibility curve, it is possible to determine both the ratio of the wavelengths and the ratio of the amplitudes. Let us now apply this method of analysis to fig. 4.2b, temporarily ignoring the gradual decrease of visibility with increasing values of e, and considering only the alternations. We find that yellow sodium light contains two components whose wavelengths differ by about 1 part in 1000. One contributes about twice as much as the other to the total intensity of the source.

Michelson's method is very powerful in the detection of small amounts of inhomogeneity of the source. He was able to show that the H_α line of hydrogen has two components with a separation of 0·14 Å. Modern methods have shown the presence of weaker components and have yielded a value of 0·136 Å. for the separation of the two strong components. As a method of analysis of spectral lines, Michelson's method was replaced by the Fabry-Pérot etalon (§ 5.28 and §§ 9.27 ff) which gives directly what must be inferred from Michelson's observations by elaborate calculations. Recently, however, a development of Michelson's method has been used for the analysis of complicated infra-red spectra (see § 9.48). This development has been made possible by the use of modern electronic computers to carry out the lengthy calculations which are required.

4.13.—The visibility curve for cadmium red light does not show an alternation of intensity but a gradual decrease of approximately exponential form (fig. 4.2a). The visibility curves for sodium light also show a gradual decrease superimposed upon the alternations. Two explanations of this gradual decrease will now be considered. In the first place let us suppose that cadmium red light is represented by a very large number of sine waves, differing slightly in wavelength but with energies falling off sharply on either side of a certain wavelength for which the energy is a maximum (fig. 4.3). Zero path difference gives a maximum relative energy for all wavelengths. Since most of the light is nearly of the same wavelength, the fringes are clear for small path differences. They become less clear when the path difference is increased, because the positions of the maxima due to wavelengths on the edge of the line (i.e. to wavelengths which have a comparatively large difference from the central wavelength) deviate from those due to the mean wavelength. As the path difference is further increased, more and more of the light goes to form fringes which are not " in register " either with the fringes due to the central wavelength or with each other. Thus the fringes gradually become less and less clear and there are no alternations.

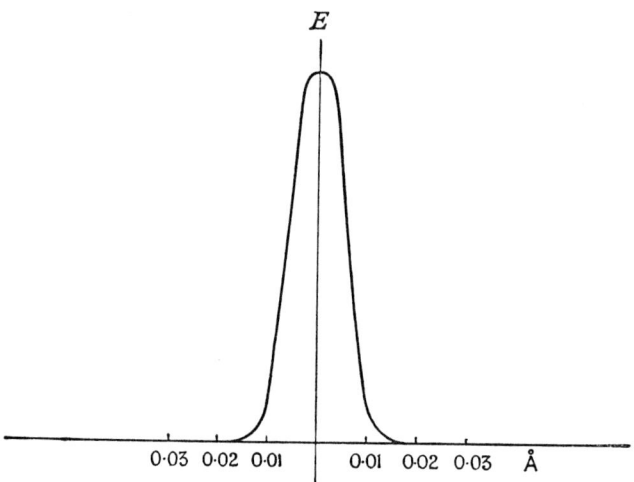

Fig. 4.3.—Distribution of energy with wavelength for the cadmium red spectrum line (low-pressure lamp)

The situation may be illustrated by a simple analogy. If a number of men, with slightly different lengths of stride, start off walking in step, they will gradually fall out of step. They will all be in step again at a distance which is the least common multiple of all the pace lengths, and at 2, 3 . . . times this distance. If the number of men becomes indefinitely large and the differences of pace length become infinitesimal, there are no alternations; the group falls gradually out of step and never comes together again as a whole.

Michelson showed that his results for the cadmium red line were explained if the light was represented by a distribution (see fig. 4.3) in which the *energy* falls to half its maximum value for wavelengths differing from the mean by ± 0.0065 Å. This distance is called the

§ 4.15   WAVES OF IRREGULAR PROFILE   83

half-width of the line.* He showed that, in a similar way, sodium light could be represented by two components, neither of which is strictly monochromatic.

4.14.—As an alternative explanation of the decrease in visibility, we now suppose that cadmium red light is represented, not by a single continuous train of waves but by a series of wave trains of finite length. Each train of waves is divided into two trains of equal length by the mirror M_1 (see fig. 4.1). These return from M_2 and M_3 to the telescope. When the path difference is small, the telescope receives the returning trains of waves nearly simultaneously, and they can interact. When M_2 is at a sufficient distance behind R, the train from M_2 enters the telescope after that from M_3 has passed. It is as though light from two independent sources was being received in the telescope. There is no interaction and no fringe system. For intermediate value of the path difference, the wave trains partially overlap and fringes of reduced visibility are formed. Thus Michelson's results may be explained, at least qualitatively, either by postulating a group of waves of slightly varying frequency or by postulating a wave train of finite length.

In order to discuss this matter further, it is necessary to examine the properties of groups of waves and to employ a mathematical method for the analysis of such groups. The complete theory involves rather lengthy mathematical calculations. In the following paragraphs, the results of these calculations are given without proof. The proofs are given in outline in Appendix IV B.

4.15. Waves of Irregular Profile.

The starting point for our discussion is a mathematical theorem due to J. B. J. Fourier (1768–1830), who showed that a wave of irregular profile may always be regarded as the sum of a series of simple harmonic waves. This analysis is very helpful in solving particular problems when the irregular profile has some special form that gives a simple series. It is also useful because we can prove certain general propositions for a single simple harmonic wave and then, using the principle of superposition, show that they apply to the sum of a set of simple harmonic motions. Fourier's method then shows that they apply generally to waves of irregular profile.

In connection with the Fourier analysis it is important to remember that when we write a mathematical equation without qualification,

* Some writers define a *half-value width* which equals twice the *half-width* defined above.

we imply that it is true for all values of the variables. The displacement for a simple harmonic wave is given by 3(3) and this expression is valid for all space and time. The wave whose profile is shown in fig. 4.4 is not a pure simple harmonic wave. Over a considerable region the profile is that of a simple harmonic wave, but to the left and to the right of this region the displacement is zero. Therefore the profile as a whole is not that of a simple harmonic wave. When the

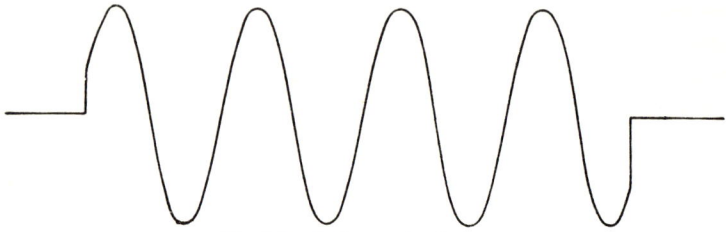

Fig. 4.4.—A short train of waves

profile of a wave follows a simple sine curve (with constant or slowly varying amplitude) over an appreciable region, and the displacement is zero elsewhere, we call it a *wave train*. When the region over which it simulates a simple harmonic wave is large compared with the wavelength we speak of a *long wave train*, even though in our ordinary measure the length may be rather short. A train of light waves one millimetre long would contain 2000 waves and would be a fairly long wave train.

4.16.—In Chapter III we described methods of calculating the resultant of a number of simple harmonic waves of the same frequency. The Fourier mathematical method enables us to calculate the resultant of a large number of simple harmonic waves, not necessarily of the same frequency, provided that the amplitudes and epoch angles are given. One important case to which the Fourier method has been applied is that of the *wave group*. So long as we are confined to one-dimensional problems, we may define a wave group as the resultant of a set of simple harmonic waves closely grouped round a certain mean frequency. If any members of the group have frequencies which differ from the mean frequency by more than a small fraction of this frequency, then their amplitudes are a small fraction of the amplitudes of waves whose frequencies are near the mean frequency. Thus nearly all the energy is concentrated in frequencies near to the central frequency.

We have defined the term " wave train " by reference to the profile, and the term " wave group " by reference to the distribution of energy among different frequencies. We shall show that a long train of waves with constant or slowly varying amplitude is associated with a narrow range of frequency. *A long wave train is a wave group.* When the wave train is *very* long, the frequency range of the corresponding wave group is correspondingly narrow. The reverse relation is also true; the synthesis of a group of waves whose frequencies cover a narrow range is a long wave train. We may deduce this result in a qualitative form from very elementary arguments. In a very short wave train no one frequency is dominant. We should expect any analysis in terms of simple harmonic waves to yield a wide distribution of frequencies. It is well known that irregular sounds give such a distribution. If a wave train covers a large number of wavelengths, one frequency becomes well established. When the train becomes very long it approaches very nearly to a simple harmonic wave, and we should expect the analysis to represent this by a gradual narrowing of the frequency range. In the limit, the frequency range tends to zero as the length of the wave train tends to infinity. Whether we consider the frequency distribution or the profile, the limit is a simple harmonic wave of exactly constant amplitude extending over all space.* If we consider the other extreme, we may imagine a wave train which is so short or so irregular that no one frequency predominates markedly. This is called a *pulse*.

4.17. Fourier's Series.

Fourier's method enables any suitable mathematical function of one variable to be expressed either (*a*) as the sum of a series of cosine functions whose wavelengths are all submultiples of a certain chosen wavelength or (*b*) as an integral involving a set of cosine functions whose wavelengths vary continuously from 0 to ∞. The series expansion is valid over only a finite range of the variable but the integral is valid over the whole range. Generally, the theorem applies to any function which can be shown by a graph and not merely to functions which are given by a single algebraic expression. Thus both continuous functions and functions which have discontinuities of slope or magnitude may be expressed in terms of Fourier's series, provided that the number of discontinuities in the relevant range is finite. Fourier's series is especially convenient for the representation of functions which cannot be expressed by one simple algebraic function

---

* In this chapter we apply the Fourier method to a one-dimensional problem. Later we shall have to generalize the concept of a wave group to deal with problems in two and three dimensions.

but consist of parts each of which can be so expressed. Examples of such functions are shown in figs. 4.5 and 4.6.

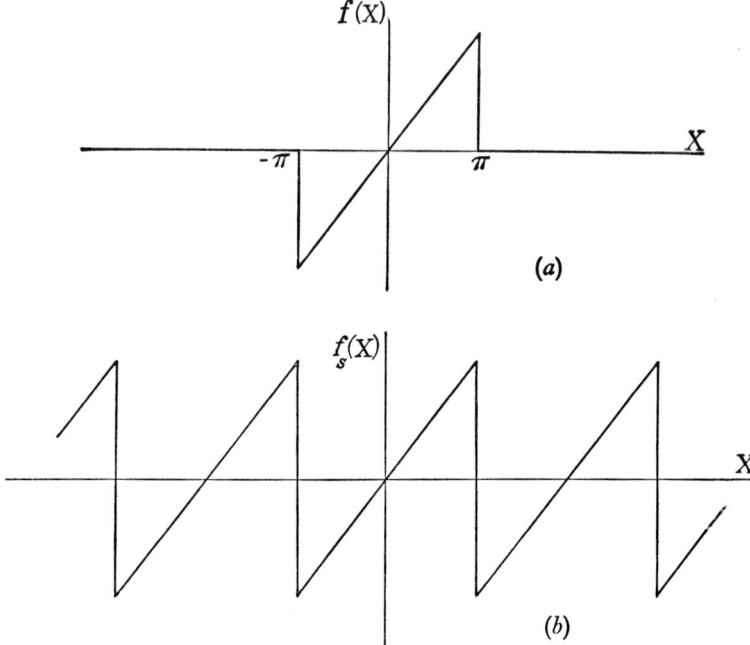

Fig. 4.5.—The relation between (a) a non-periodic function and (b) the sum of a related Fourier series.

Suppose that it is desired to replace $\xi = f(x)$ by a series of sine functions and that *the expansion is to apply to a range from* $-x_0$ *to* $+x_0$. Then if $X = \pi x/x_0$, Fourier's series is defined by the relation

$$f(X) = a_0 + a_1 \cos X + a_2 \cos 2X + \ldots$$
$$+ b_1 \sin X + b_2 \sin 2X + \ldots \quad . \quad . \quad 4(5)$$

It may be shown that *

$$\left. \begin{array}{l} a_0 = \dfrac{1}{2\pi} \displaystyle\int_{-\pi}^{\pi} f(X)\, dX, \\[6pt] a_m = \dfrac{1}{\pi} \displaystyle\int_{-\pi}^{\pi} f(X) \cos mX\, dX, \\[6pt] b_m = \dfrac{1}{\pi} \displaystyle\int_{-\pi}^{\pi} f(X) \sin mX\, dX. \end{array} \right\} \quad . \quad . \quad . \quad 4(6)$$

* See Appendix IV B and Reference 4.2.

By introducing new constants A_0, A_1, etc., and δ_1, δ_2, etc., defined by

$$A_0 = a_0, \quad A_1 \sin \delta_1 = a_1, \quad \text{and} \quad A_1 \cos \delta_1 = b_1, \qquad . \ 4(7)$$

we may write 4(5) in the form

$$f(X) = A_0 + A_1 \sin (X + \delta_1) + A_2 \sin (2X + \delta_2) + \ldots \quad . \ 4(8)$$

Each term in 4(8), except the first, represents a pure sine wave. In a similar way 4(5) may be expressed as the sum of a series of complex exponentials (see § 2.26 and Appendix IV B).

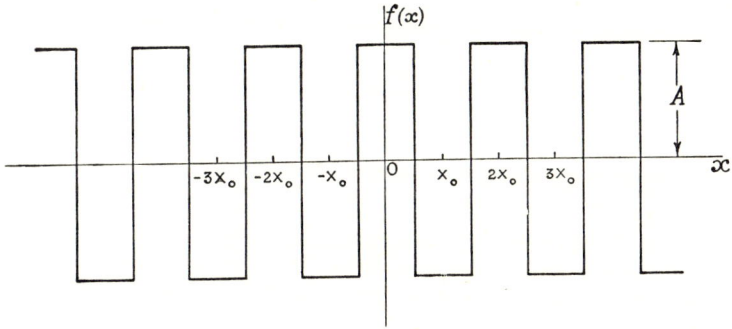

Fig. 4.6.—The " top-hat " curve

4.18.—The values of functions such as $\sin mX$ and $\cos mX$ for $X = X_0 + 2\pi$ are the same as the values of the corresponding functions for $X = X_0$. Let $f_s(X)$ be the sum of the series 4(5) for any value of X. Then, since $f_s(X)$ is the sum of a series of terms such as $\sin mX$ and $\cos mX$, we shall have

$$f_s(X_0 + 2\pi) = f_s(X_0),$$

i.e. the sum of the series must lead to a function which repeats its values when X_0 changes by 2π. The sum of the series $f_s(X)$ always agrees with the original function $f(X)$ in the range $-\pi$ to $+\pi$, but does not agree with it outside this range unless $f(X)$ happens to be a periodic function for which $f(X + 2\pi) = f(X)$.

Fig. 4.5a shows a function which is proportional to X in the range $-\pi$ to π, and zero elsewhere. The Fourier series

$$f_s(X) = 2 \sum_{m=1}^{\infty} (-1)^{m+1} \frac{\sin mX}{m},$$

shown in fig. 4.5b, agrees with the corresponding function in the range

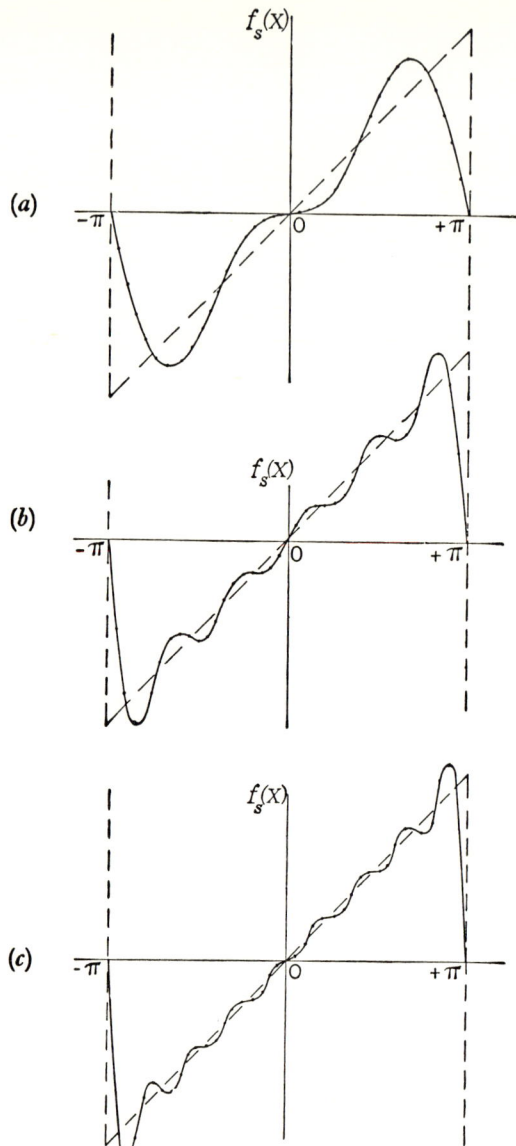

Fig. 4.7.—Representation of a function by a Fourier series: (a) sum of 3 terms of the series, (b) sum of 6 terms of the series, (c) sum of 9 terms of the series.

In (a), (b), (c) the dotted line shows the original function $f(X) = X$.

$-\pi$ to $+\pi$ but not outside this range. On the other hand, the "top-hat curve" shown in fig. 4.6 can be represented by an appropriate Fourier series [see answer to Example 4(iii), p. 103] for all values of x_0 because the curve to be represented is periodic. The relation between a limited number of terms of a Fourier series and the corresponding function is shown in fig. 4.7. [See also Example 4(ii) and fig. 4.13.]

4.19. Fourier's Integral

In the preceding paragraphs we have discussed the analysis of a wave whose profile is given, into a number of simple harmonic waves. This process is the inverse of the combination of a number of simple harmonic waves, each of known frequency and amplitude, which we discussed in Chapter III. Using the principle of superposition, we may calculate the resultant of a large number of simple harmonic waves whose amplitudes are $a_1, a_2, \ldots a_n$, and whose circular frequencies are $\omega_1, \omega_2, \ldots \omega_n$. Fourier's integral theorem, which we shall now state, enables us to extend this calculation to the limit in which the number of simple harmonic waves to be combined is indefinitely large, and in which the differences of frequency and of amplitude between successive members of the set are infinitesimal. It also shows the relation between the processes of analysis and of synthesis in an elegant and symmetrical form.

Let us first consider the combination of n simple harmonic motions, of which one is represented by

$$\xi_r = a_r \exp i(\omega_r t - \kappa_r x) + a_{-r} \exp -i(\omega_r t - \kappa_r x).$$

Then, from the principle of superposition, the resultant is *

$$\xi = \sum_{r=-n}^{n} a_r \exp i(\omega_r t - \kappa_r x), \qquad \ldots \quad 4(9)$$

where $\omega_{-r} = -\omega_r$. Let us define a function $a(\kappa)$ by the relation

$$a_r = a(\kappa)(\kappa_{r+1} - \kappa_r),$$

where κ has some value between κ_r and κ_{r+1}.

We now imagine the number of waves to increase without limit and the intervals to become infinitesimal. Then we put $\kappa_{r+1} - \kappa_r = d\kappa$ and write

$$\xi \equiv f(x, t) = \int_{-\infty}^{\infty} a(\kappa) \exp i(\omega t - \kappa x) \, d\kappa, \quad . \quad . \quad 4(10)$$

---

* The interpretation of the "negative harmonics" is discussed on p. 107.

i.e. we make the usual transition from the sum of a large, but finite, number of elements to the definite integral.* In general $a(\kappa)$ will be a complex quantity of the form

$$a(\kappa) = a'(\kappa) \exp i\delta_\kappa,$$

where δ_κ represents an epoch angle (§§ 2.4 and 2.26). The profile at $t = 0$ is represented by

$$\xi = f_0(x) = \int_{-\infty}^{\infty} a(\kappa) e^{-i\kappa x} d\kappa \quad \ldots \quad 4(11)$$

according to the convention stated in § 2.26. This equation gives the profile when $a(\kappa)$ is known; this is equivalent to knowing the distribution of energy among the different frequencies.

The complementary problem, to find the energy distribution when the profile is given, can be solved by an integral theorem which Fourier derived as an extension of the method of analysis described in §§ 4.17 and 4.18. In the form relevant to the present problem, this theorem states that

$$a(\kappa) = \frac{1}{2\pi} \int_{-\infty}^{+\infty} f_0(x) e^{+i\kappa x} dx. \quad \ldots \quad 4(12)$$

This equation is valid for all values of x and κ. Note that 4(11) and 4(12) differ, not only in the factor $1/2\pi$ (which is unimportant), but also in that 4(12) contains a positive exponential and 4(11) contains a negative exponential.†

4.20.—Fourier's series enables us to analyse a wave of irregular profile into a discrete set of harmonic waves whose wavelengths are all submultiples of a certain fundamental wavelength. This analysis is valid over a range $-x_0$ to $+x_0$ equal to the fundamental wavelength. If we choose a different range, say $-x_1$ to $+x_1$, the composite wave appears to be made up of a different set of harmonic waves [see Example 4(iv), p. 103]. If we extend the range from $-\infty$ to $+\infty$, the analysis is in terms of a continuous distribution. It is important to realize that there is no inconsistency in the fact that different methods of analysis give different results when applied to the same wave-profile. If x_1 is

---

* The discussion of the conditions under which this transition can be made is given in standard works on the integral calculus. The physical interpretation of the " negative values of κ " in 4(10) is discussed in Appendix IV B.

† The function $g(\kappa)$ used in the Appendix is equal to $a(\kappa)\sqrt{(2\pi)}$. Using this function the factor outside the integrals is the same [see equations 4(60) and 4(61)]. It is also shown that equation 4(11) may be replaced by one containing $e^{+i\kappa x}$, and that the negative exponential then appears in the equation corresponding to 4(12).

greater than x_0, the analysis in terms of a set of waves based on the fundamental wavelength x_1 applies in the range $-x_0$ to $+x_0$. *Within this range*, the two sets of harmonic waves are equivalent. They give different resultants in the ranges $-x_1$ to $-x_0$ and x_0 to x_1, but here the analysis based on x_0 does not apply. The equivalence of the two results of analysis exactly represents the results of experiment.

4.21. The Gaussian Wave Group.*

We shall now use the method of Fourier to discuss the properties of the particular kind of wave group for which

$$a(\kappa) = A' \exp\{-\alpha(\kappa - \kappa_0)^2\}, \qquad \ldots \quad 4(13)$$

where A', α, and κ_0 are constants. This type of distribution results when an oscillator is subject to irregular disturbances which cause a large number of small random variations in its period. This is called a Gaussian wave group because many physical problems of random variation were investigated by Gauss. The shape of the wave profile when $t = 0$ [obtained by using equation 4(11)] is represented by

$$f_0(x) = \int_{-\infty}^{+\infty} A' \exp\{-\alpha(\kappa - \kappa_0)^2 - i\kappa x\} d\kappa. \quad . \quad 4(14)$$

In Appendix IV B this is shown † to give

$$f_0(x) = A' \sqrt{\frac{\pi}{\alpha}} \cdot e^{-x^2/4\alpha} \cdot e^{-i\kappa_0 x}. \qquad \ldots \quad 4(15)$$

This profile is shown in fig. 4.8a for the case where $\alpha\kappa_0^2 = 2000$; in fig. 4.8b for the case where $\alpha\kappa_0^2 = 200$; and in fig. 4.8c for $\alpha\kappa_0^2 = 20$. Note that the amplitude of the wave is proportional to $e^{-x^2/4\alpha}$. This curve is shown by the dotted line in fig. 4.8b.

When $\alpha\kappa_0^2$ is very large compared with unity, the expression 4(15) represents a close approximation to a pure sine wave whose wavelength is $2\pi/\kappa_0$. The amplitude remains nearly constant over a region which covers many wavelengths and only begins to decrease at distances from the origin such that x becomes comparable with $\sqrt{\alpha}$. Even there the decrease in a region of one wavelength is small. Thus, when $\sqrt{\alpha}/\lambda$ is large compared with unity, i.e. when $\alpha\kappa_0^2$ is large, 4(15) represents a wave group with a well-defined frequency. As $\alpha\kappa_0^2$

---
* See Appendix IV B, p. 114, and Reference 4.3.
† Use equations 4(99) and 4(103). The constant $A = 2A'$.

becomes smaller the train becomes shorter and shorter until when $\alpha\kappa_0^2$ is of the order of unity, the profile is that of a pulse.

4.22.—Figs. 4.9a, b, c show the function $a(\kappa)$ for different values of $\alpha\kappa_0^2$ corresponding to figs. 4.8a, b, c. From this figure, or by comparison of equations 4(15) and 4(13), it may be seen that when the

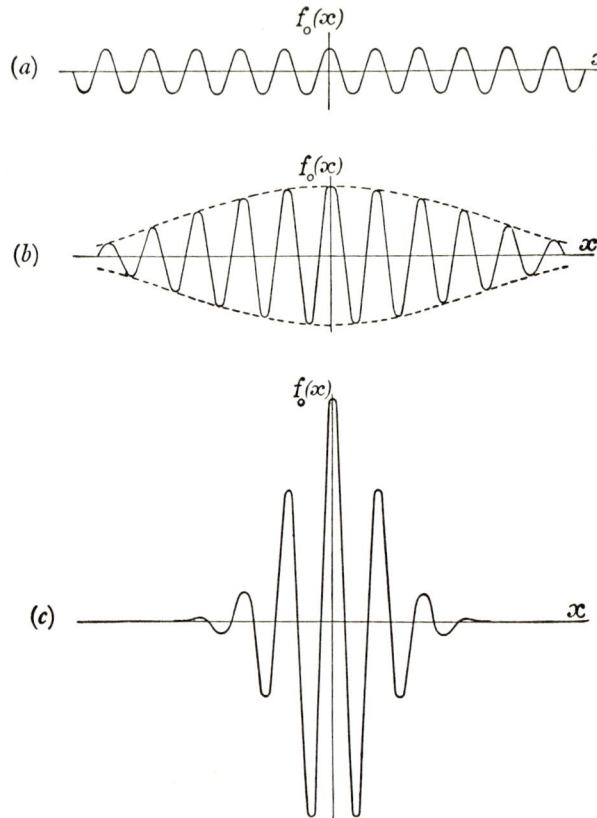

Fig. 4.8.—Gaussian wave groups, (a) $\alpha\kappa_0^2 = 2000$; (b) $\alpha\kappa_0^2 = 200$; (c) $\alpha\kappa_0^2 = 20$. The maxima are adjusted for equal total energy. The real part of $f_0(x)$, which is the physical variable, is shown.

train of waves is short, the energy is spread over a wide range of frequency, but that as the wave train becomes longer the energy becomes concentrated within a narrower and narrower range of frequencies. In the limiting condition the energy all passes into an indefinitely narrow range of frequency as the train of waves becomes

§ 4.22   THE GAUSSIAN WAVE GROUP   93

indefinitely long. Then, and only then, we have a pure sine wave. If we had considered a wave group of any other suitable mathematical form, defined by some function $a(\kappa)$, the details of the calculation would have been different but, qualitatively, the final result would have been the same. When the parameters of $a(\kappa)$ were adjusted

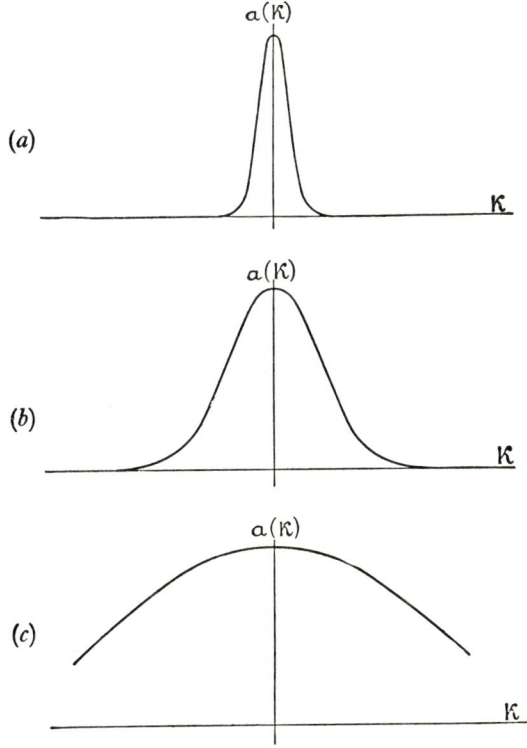

Fig. 4.9.—Gaussian wave groups. Distribution of energy with κ for (a) $\alpha\kappa_0^2 = 2000$, (b) $\alpha\kappa_0^2 = 200$, and (c) $\alpha\kappa_0^2 = 20$. The scales of $a(\kappa)$ have been adjusted to give equal values at the maximum. The actual maxima for (a), (b), (c) are in the ratio 10 : 3 : 1. The scale of κ is arbitrary but is the same for each curve.

so that the frequency distribution became more and more restricted, the length of the group would increase and the amplitude would become more nearly constant. The pure sine wave would appear as the limiting case. Some forms of the function $a(\kappa)$ are discussed in Appendix IV B.

4.23.—In § 4.14 we considered two possible theories of the gradual decrease of visibility with increasing path. One possibility was to represent the light emitted from the cadmium atom by wave trains of finite length, the other was to represent it by a series of infinitely long wave trains having slightly different frequencies. The foregoing discussion has shown that these are not two alternative theories such that if one is right the other must be wrong; on the contrary, they are two ways of stating the same theory, so that if either is right the other must also be right. If we represent the light by a beam of finite length, a sufficiently accurate measurement of wavelength will show the presence of a distribution of energy over a finite interval of wavelength. On the other hand, if we choose to represent the beam by a series of infinitely long wave trains of slightly different frequencies, we shall find that the resultant disturbance is zero except in a finite region of space. In other words, the resultant is a wave train of finite length.

4.24.—Michelson analysed his observations on the visibility of fringes obtained with cadmium red light and he found that this light could be adequately represented by a Gaussian distribution with a value of α such that the half-width is 0·0065 Å. He obtained values of the same order for the half-width of the lines emitted by sodium and other sources at low pressure. The corresponding length of the wave train is about half a metre—or about a million times the wavelength. Although the light is not perfectly homogeneous, it does possess a remarkably high degree of homogeneity.

4.25. Width of Spectral Lines.

Experiments such as those of Michelson can, at best, determine only the distribution of energy with wavelength and cannot lead directly to any theory of the way in which atoms emit spectral lines of finite width. General atomic theory, however, suggests three main causes, operating together, for the broadening of spectral lines. These are (a) natural damping, (b) Doppler effect, (c) pressure broadening.

(a) Natural damping.

Dirac's theory (see Chapter XIX) of the emission of radiation shows that the atom is to be regarded as a damped oscillator. The emission of energy causes the amplitude of oscillation to fall and therefore the amplitude of the emitted wave is falling while it is being emitted. In the simplest case, the wave train emitted is represented by

$$\xi = \exp\left[-\frac{1}{2c\tau}(x + ct) + i(\omega t + \kappa x)\right], \quad \ldots \quad 4(16)$$

where τ is a constant. The energy is proportional to $\xi\xi^*$ and its damping constant is $\gamma = 1/\tau$. Equation 4(16) represents the wave due to an oscillator situated at

$x = x_0$ which began to oscillate with unit amplitude at $t = -x_0/c$. The profile (for $t = 0$) is given by

$$f_0(x) = e^{-x/2c\tau} e^{+i\kappa_0 x}. \qquad \ldots \ldots \quad 4(17)$$

This profile is shown in fig. 4.10. The wave is travelling to the left. It corresponds to a damped wave. Fourier's method * shows that the energy distribution is proportional to $[a(\kappa)]^2$, where

$$[a(\kappa)]^2 = \frac{A'}{\gamma^2 + 4c^2(\kappa - \kappa_0)^2} \qquad \ldots \ldots \quad 4(18)$$

and A' is a constant.

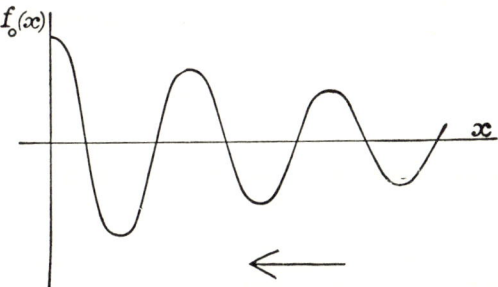

Fig. 4.10.—Profile of a damped wave (travelling to the left.)

The half-width of the line (see § 4.13) is given by

$$\Delta \kappa = \frac{\gamma}{2c} = \frac{1}{2c\tau}. \qquad \ldots \ldots \quad 4(19)$$

It is inversely proportional to τ. The value of τ may be calculated from Dirac's theory. The values obtained differ a great deal according to the emitting state. For the type of line we have considered τ is of order 10^{-8} second. It is seldom much less than this, though it is sometimes much greater. Since about 10^{15} waves are emitted per second the damping is very small. The wave trains are at least 10^7 waves long. The half-widths of the lines may be calculated when γ is known and are found to be of order 0·0005 Å. or less. Natural damping can therefore account for only a small part of the observed widths.

(b) *Doppler effect.*

Owing to thermal motion, the emitting atoms are moving in different directions relative to the measuring apparatus. Even if the light emitted by stationary atoms were perfectly homogeneous, the light observed would not be homogeneous. The observed frequency (ν) for light received from an atom which is approaching the observer with velocity v is given by

$$\nu - \nu_0 = \frac{v}{c} \nu_0. \qquad \ldots \ldots \quad 4(20)$$

* See Appendix IV B, p. 113.

where ν_0 is the frequency for a stationary atom [see equation 2(57)], or

$$\kappa - \kappa_0 = \frac{v}{c}\kappa_0. \qquad \ldots \ldots \quad 4(21)$$

It may be shown that the number of atoms whose component of velocity in a given direction lies between v and $(v + dv)$ is proportional to

$$\exp\left(-\frac{mv^2}{2kT}\right)dv, \qquad \ldots \ldots \quad 4(22)$$

where m is the mass of the atom, T is the temperature, and k is Boltzmann's constant.* Hence the energy distribution due to this cause is a Gaussian distribution whose parameter is

$$2\alpha = \frac{mc^2}{2kT\kappa_0{}^2}. \qquad \ldots \ldots \quad 4(23)$$

The value calculated from the thermal constants gives a half-width of 0·0038 Å. for cadmium red light at room temperature. Note that 2α is the parameter for the energy.

(c) Pressure broadening.

It is not difficult to see that collisions with other atoms may disturb the vibrations of an emitting atom so as to cause it to emit a wave of irregular profile (i.e. an imperfect simple harmonic wave). The complete theory is very complicated, especially when the two atoms are similar, so that a certain type of resonance between them occurs during the interaction. Detailed calculation shows that the distribution of energy is given by an expression somewhat similar to 4(18), but with a value of γ proportional to the pressure. The value varies a good deal from one gas to another. Ten atmospheres' pressure of argon increases the half-width of the mercury line (2537 Å.) by 0·12 Å. Collisions also cause a certain asymmetry in the energy distribution and the centre is moved usually in the direction of shorter wavelengths.†

4.26.—From the above it may be seen that, at low pressures, the most important cause of inhomogeneity is the Doppler effect. Michelson's results give a half-width only a little larger than that calculated from the Doppler effect. Also the variation of visibility is consistent with a Gaussian distribution which would be given by the Doppler effect, but too much importance should not be attached to this last point since the measurement of visibility is not sufficiently accurate to detect small departures from a Gaussian distribution. The width due to natural damping can be detected only when special methods have been used to eliminate the Doppler broadening.‡

---

* See Chapter III, § 11 of Reference 4.4. † See Reference 4.5.
‡ Reference 4.7.

4.27.—It is interesting to compare the distribution given by 4(18) with the Gaussian distribution given by 4(13). When κ is nearly equal to κ_0 they both reduce to the form

$$a(\kappa) = A - B(\kappa - \kappa_0)^2, \qquad \ldots \ldots 4(24)$$

where A and B are constants; i.e. for any given value of α, it is possible to choose a value of γ which gives the same distribution of energy for wavelengths near to the wavelength of maximum energy. Thus measurements on the distribution of energy near the centre of the line cannot directly distinguish between a curve represented by 4(18) and one represented by 4(13). In regions remote from the centre of the line the energy given by 4(13) is very much less than that given by 4(18). Thus, if a line has a half-width of 0·005 Å., the energy at a distance of 0·02 Å. from the centre of the line should be $1·5 \times 10^{-5}$ of the maximum energy according to 4(13), and 6×10^{-2} of the maximum energy according to 4(18) (see fig. 4.11). Moderately accurate measurements on the edges of a line, combined with measurements near the centre, distinguish between a distribution due to Doppler effect and one due to natural damping or collision broadening. Certain observations on the shape of absorption lines in the solar spectrum show that the shape of the line near the centre is mainly due to Doppler effect, but that in the " wings " of the line the distribution of energy is determined by natural damping.*

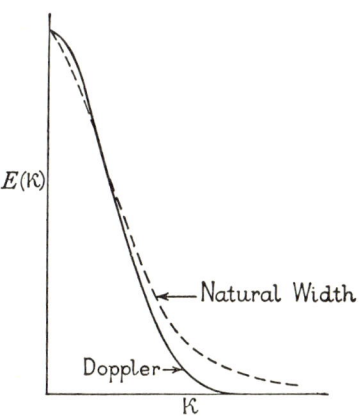

Fig. 4.11.—Energy distribution for a spectrum line

4.28. Propagation of a Wave Group in a Dispersive Medium.

In a dispersive medium, the components of a wave group move with different speeds, and the phase relations between the components are altered. We shall now show that, provided the group includes only a fairly narrow range of frequencies, the alteration of the profile owing to dispersion is fairly slow. Over considerable regions the group is propagated as a whole so that the positions of well-marked features of the profile, such as the point of maximum amplitude, remain well defined. Under these conditions the group has a definite velocity which is called the *group velocity*. This is not, in general, equal to the wave velocity.

* Reference 4.7.

WAVE TRAINS OF FINITE LENGTH

Let us first consider the Gaussian wave group. The displacement at time t is obtained by inserting into 4(10) the expression for $a(\kappa)$ which is given in 4(13). The result is

$$\xi = \int_{-\infty}^{\infty} A' \exp\{-\alpha(\kappa - \kappa_0)^2 + i(\omega t - \kappa x)\}d\kappa. \quad \ldots \quad 4(25)$$

In integrating this equation, we need to remember that ω is in general a function of κ, and not usually a very simple function. We assume that over the range of wavelengths included in the group, the relation between ω and κ is given by taking the first three terms in a Taylor series, i.e. we put

$$\omega = \omega_0 + U(\kappa - \kappa_0) + W(\kappa - \kappa_0)^2, \quad \ldots \quad 4(26)$$

where ω_0 is the value of ω when $\kappa = \kappa_0$, and U and W are the corresponding values of $d\omega/d\kappa$ and $\frac{1}{2}d^2\omega/d\kappa^2$. It is shown in Appendix IV B that, when this expression for ω is substituted in 4(25) and the integration carried out, ξ is given [see 4(104) and 4(105)] by

$$\xi = A'' \exp\left\{-\frac{(x - Ut)^2}{4\alpha'} + i\phi'\right\}. \quad \ldots \quad 4(27)$$

In this equation ϕ' is a rather complicated function of x and t which represents the fact that the phase is now varying in a complicated way with x and t. The value of α' is

$$(\alpha^2 + W^2 t^2)/\alpha. \quad \ldots \quad 4(28)$$

Thus the boundary curves of the profile (shown by the dotted line in fig. 4.8b) is still a Gaussian curve, but the width has been increased in the ratio given by 4(28). When the group is confined to a narrow range of frequencies, α is large and if Wt is small compared with α the group spreads only very slowly. Yet it does spread and, given sufficient time, α' increases without limit. From 4(27) it may be seen that the group as a whole travels forward with velocity $U = d\omega/d\kappa$.

4.29. Group Velocity.

The way in which a group spreads as it advances depends on the form of the group. The velocity with which the group moves, so long as it retains its form, will now be shown to be independent of the distribution of energy between the different components, provided that the group is confined to a fairly narrow range of frequencies. Consider first two components whose wavelength constants are $\kappa - \frac{1}{2}d\kappa$ and $\kappa + \frac{1}{2}d\kappa$ and whose amplitudes are equal. Then

$$\xi = a_1 \sin[(\omega - \tfrac{1}{2}d\omega)t - (\kappa - \tfrac{1}{2}d\kappa)x]$$
$$+ a_1 \sin[(\omega + \tfrac{1}{2}d\omega)t - (\kappa + \tfrac{1}{2}d\kappa)x]$$
$$= 2a_1 \cos\tfrac{1}{2}(t\,d\omega - x\,d\kappa) \sin(\omega t - \kappa x). \quad \ldots \quad 4(29)$$

This is represented in fig. 4.12. The vibration is enclosed between the "beat wave" curves shown as dotted lines. This beat wave is represented by the cosine factor in 4(29) and travels with a speed

$$U = \frac{d\omega}{d\kappa}. \qquad \ldots \ldots \quad 4(30)$$

This is the same as the speed obtained for the movement of the outer curve which encloses the profile of the Gaussian group.

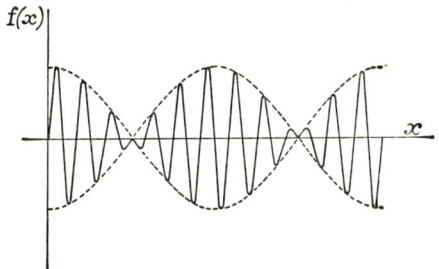

Fig. 4.12.—Simple beat wave

4.30.—Generally the phase of any component of a complex group is given by

$$\phi = \omega t - \kappa x + \delta, \qquad \ldots \ldots \quad 4(31)$$

where δ is a constant.

ϕ varies with x and t, as well as with ω and κ. If we consider a variation of ϕ with x and t (κ and ω constant), we obtain

$$d\phi_1 = \omega\, dt - \kappa\, dx; \qquad \ldots \ldots \quad 4(32)$$

whereas, if we consider ϕ to vary with ω and κ (x and t constant), we have

$$d\phi_2 = t\, d\omega - x\, d\kappa. \qquad \ldots \ldots \quad 4(33)$$

The points for which $d\phi_1 = 0$ move with velocity ω/κ. This is the velocity of a component of one frequency, i.e. it is the phase velocity (b). The points for which $d\phi_2 = 0$ move with velocity U. This is the velocity of the points where the phases of different members of the group are in the same phase relation. In particular, it is the velocity of the point of maximum agreement of phase.

4.31.—The expression 4(30) for U may be put in various forms, most of which will be required in later applications. Since $\omega = 2\pi\nu$ and $\kappa = 2\pi/\lambda$, we have

$$U = -\lambda^2 \frac{d\nu}{d\lambda}; \quad \ldots \ldots \quad 4(34)$$

and since $\omega = b\kappa$, we may write

$$U = \frac{d(b\kappa)}{d\kappa} \quad \ldots \ldots \quad 4(35)$$

$$= b + \kappa \frac{db}{d\kappa} \quad \ldots \ldots \quad 4(36)$$

$$= b - \lambda \frac{db}{d\lambda}. \quad \ldots \ldots \quad 4(37)$$

Since $n = c/b$, we have

$$U = \frac{c}{n}\left(1 + \frac{\lambda}{n}\frac{dn}{d\lambda}\right). \quad \ldots \ldots \quad 4(38)$$

It is sometimes convenient to have an expression for $1/U$, and we put

$$\frac{1}{U} = \frac{1}{c}\frac{d(n\omega)}{d\omega} \quad \ldots \ldots \quad 4(39)$$

$$= \frac{n}{c} + \frac{\omega}{c}\frac{dn}{d\omega},$$

i.e.

$$\frac{1}{U} = \frac{1}{b} + \frac{\omega}{c}\frac{dn}{d\omega}. \quad \ldots \ldots \quad 4(40)$$

From 4(37) it may be seen that in a non-dispersive medium $U = b$. In a dispersive medium U may be greater or less than b. Note that in equations 4(29)–4(40) the symbols λ and κ represent the wavelength and the wavelength constant in the medium of index n [see Example 4(ix), p. 104].

4.32. Representation of Light by Wave Groups.

In experiments on light, we never deal with infinitely long wave trains or with light of one wavelength. It is possible to give a general account of the results of many experiments by means of a picture in which sharp spectral lines are represented by simple harmonic waves of one wavelength and white light is represented by a combination of such waves. The concept of a simple harmonic wave is valuable because it enables us to express many of our data in a convenient way, but it is usually necessary to represent "monochromatic" light by a wave group in order to give a satisfactory account of the details of any experiment. For example, in Michelson's experiments, the concept of pure sine waves is sufficient to account for the presence of the fringes and to explain the relation between the diameters of the different rings. It does not, however, give any account of the variation of the visibility when the path difference is altered.

4.33. White Light.

Towards the end of the last century there was a considerable controversy concerning the nature of white light. One side held that white light "really consisted" of superimposed trains of pure sine waves and the other that it "really consisted" of irregular pulses from which it was possible to create trains of waves by suitable experimental arrangements. Thus the one side held that Newton's famous experiment showed that white light "was composed of" various colours; on the other view, the colours were produced by the prism. Various attempts were made to discover a crucial experiment which would show which view was correct. These all failed since, whenever an experiment was "explained" on one view, the protagonists of the other view were always able to produce an equally good "explanation". Sometimes one explanation was more complicated than the other, but the more complicated one was equally logical.

4.34.—Rayleigh and Schuster showed that the two ways of representing light are equivalent. By means of Fourier's theorem, a pulse may be analysed (mathematically) into a series of simple harmonic waves. Therefore, if white light is adequately represented by pulses, it is equally well represented by a series of sine waves. Thus there are not two theories but only two different ways of stating the same theory. The difference is one of mathematical form. Consequently, there is no possibility of a crucial experiment in which one side would be proved to be right and the other wrong.

In considering the representation of white light by a series of simple harmonic waves, it is necessary to remember that our experimental arrangements are *never* able to produce infinitely long wave trains of one frequency. In practice, when we seek to analyse light, we always analyse it into wave groups—not into infinitely long wave trains. With suitable experimental arrangements we can produce wave trains which are over a million waves in length, but they are not *infinitely* long, i.e. the light is never of *exactly* one frequency.

As an example of the sort of difficulty that arose through neglecting the group concept we may take the paradox suggested by Carvallo. He said that if white light " consisted of " a combination of infinitely long wave trains, these wave trains would be separated by a spectroscope, so that it would be possible to see the spectrum both before the source was lighted and after it had gone out. His mistake lay in the assumption that the spectroscope selected light of exactly one wavelength. If we put a fine slit in a spectrum we select a group of waves covering a small but finite range of frequency. Such a group may be regarded as made up of an infinite series of pure harmonic waves. These interact in such a way that the total amount of energy passing through the slit before the source is lighted, and shortly after it has gone out, is zero. Thus the " analytic " view is quite correct provided that we remember that practical analysis produces wave groups, not pure sine waves.

We shall not give a detailed account of the various arguments put forward during this controversy, though in §§ 8.13–8.14 it is shown how the dispersion of white light (a) by a prism, and (b) by a grating, can be calculated on the two views. It will be understood that these two calculations are, from our point of view, simply different mathematical devices. Although the controversy concerning the " nature of white light " is now chiefly of historical interest, it was important in that it called attention to the necessity for representing actual beams of light by wave groups rather than by infinite wave trains. We shall see later that this concept of wave groups plays an important part in the modern quantum theory of radiation.

EXAMPLES [4(i)–4(ix)]

4(i). Show that when e is large compared with λ, the angular diameters of the rings near the centre (see § 4.9) are given by

$$2\theta_{p_1} = \left[\frac{4(p_0 - p_1)\lambda}{e}\right]^{\frac{1}{2}}.$$

[Put $\cos \theta_{p_1} = 1 - \tfrac{1}{2}\theta_{p_1}^2$.]

4(ii). Show that $f(x) = x^2$ may be represented in the range $-x_0$ to $+x_0$ by a series in which

$$a_0 = \tfrac{1}{3}x_0^2; \quad a_m = \frac{(-1)^m 4x_0^2}{\pi^2 m^2}; \quad b_m = 0.$$

Fig. 4.13 shows the sum of 2, 4, and 8 terms of the series compared with the function.

4(iii). Show that the "top-hat curve" (fig. 4.6) is represented by

$$f(x) = \frac{4A}{\pi} \sum_{m=1}^{\infty} (-1)^{m-1} \frac{\cos(2m-1)\pi x/x_0}{2m-1}$$

for all values of x.

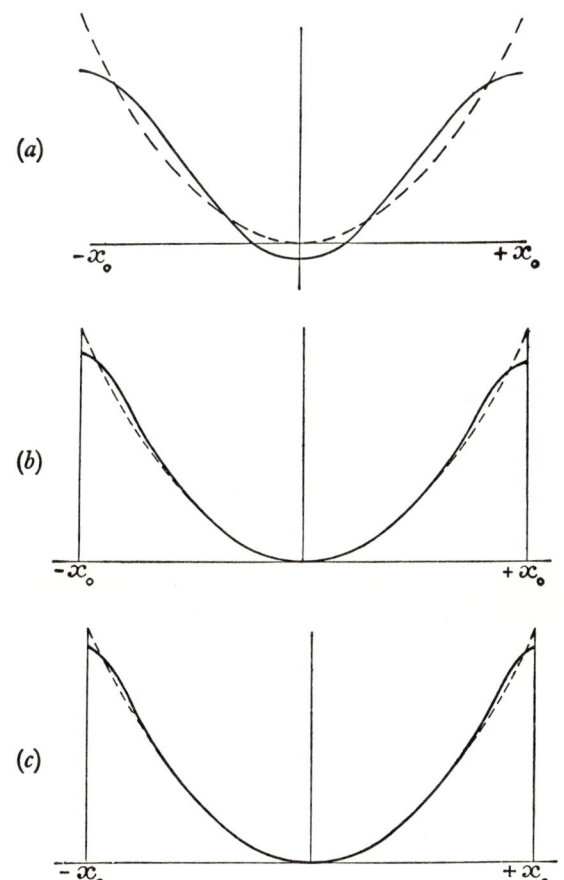

Fig. 4.13.—Representation of a function by a Fourier series: (a) sum of 2 terms of the series, (b) sum of 4 terms, (c) sum of 8 terms. In (a), (b), and (c) the dotted line shows the original function $f(x) = x^2$.

4(iv). Show that if $f(x) = x$ from $-x_1$ (fig. 4.14) to $+x_1$ and $f(x) = 0$ when $x^2 > x_1^2$, the function may be represented *in the range $-x_0$ to x_0* (where $x_0 < x_1$) if

$$f_{0s}(x) = 2\frac{x_0}{\pi} \sum_{m=1}^{\infty} (-1)^{m+1} \frac{\sin(m\pi x/x_0)}{m}$$

Show that the series defined by

$$b_m = -\frac{2}{\pi^2} \sum_{m=1}^{\infty} \left\{ \frac{\pi x_1}{m} \cos \frac{m\pi x_1}{x_2} - \frac{x_2}{m^2} \sin \frac{m\pi x_1}{x_2} \right\}$$

would represent the function from $-x_2$ to $+x_2$ if $2x_1 > x_2 > x_1$.

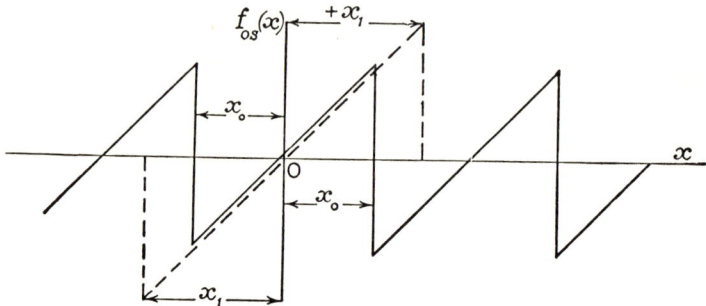

Fig. 4.14.—Representation of a function by a Fourier series: (a) dotted line shows the function to be represented, (b) full line shows the sum of the series $f_{0s}(x)$. (See Example 4(iv).)

4(v). For waves on the surface of a liquid* of depth h

$$b^2 = \frac{g}{\kappa} \frac{e^{\kappa h} - e^{-\kappa h}}{e^{\kappa h} + e^{-\kappa h}}.$$

Show that when h is small the group velocity is nearly equal to the wave velocity, and that when h is large the group velocity is approximately half the wave velocity corresponding to the central frequency of the group.

4(vi). Show that if the relation between n and κ is given by $n^2 = A' + B'\kappa^2 + C'\kappa^4$, then

$$U = \frac{A' - C'\kappa^4}{A' + B'\kappa^2 + C'\kappa^4} b.$$

4(vii). Find the group velocity when (a) $db/d\lambda = b/\lambda$, and (b) when $b = A + B\lambda$ (with A and B constant).   [(a) $U = 0$ and (b) $U = A$.]

4(viii). Show that in a medium which has normal dispersion (§ 3.18) U is less than b.

4(ix). Show that, if $\lambda_v = 2\pi c/\omega$ is the wavelength in vacuum, then

$$\frac{1}{U} = \frac{1}{b} - \frac{\lambda_v}{c} \frac{dn}{d\lambda_v}. \qquad \ldots \ldots \ldots \quad 4(41)$$

* See Chapter V, equation (32) of Reference 4.3.

REFERENCES

4.1. MICHELSON: *Light Waves and their Uses* (University of Chicago Press).
4.2. CARSLAW: *Introduction to the Theory of Fourier Series and Fourier Integrals* (Macmillan).
4.3. COULSON: *Waves* (Oliver and Boyd).
4.4. ROBERTS: *Heat and Thermodynamics* (Blackie).
4.5. *Reviews of Modern Physics*: Vol. 8, pp. 22 and 398.
4.6. TOLANSKY: *High Resolution Spectroscopy* (Oxford University Press).
4.7. HEITLER: *Quantum Theory of Radiation* (Oxford University Press).
4.8. CAMPBELL and FOSTER: *Fourier Integrals for Practical Application* (Bell System Technical Publication Monograph B-584, 1931).

APPENDIX IV A

ADJUSTMENT OF THE MICHELSON INTERFEROMETER

(1) Set the movable mirror M_2 (fig. 4.1) so that its distance from the half-silvered side of M_1 is about equal to that of M_3. This brings M_2 near to the reference plane R. At this stage, M_2 and R will not necessarily be parallel and the centre of M_2 may be up to two millimetres from the centre of R.

(ii) Taking the interferometer alone (i.e. without S_e, F, L and the telescope shown in fig. 4.1), place a small bright source, such as a pea-lamp, in the position indicated for S_e. Look into the instrument in a direction roughly normal to M_2 with the eye in the position indicated by E. Several images of the bright source may be seen. If the silvering of M_1 is in good condition, two images will be much brighter than the others. These are formed by rays which have followed the paths shown in fig. 4.1, the others being due to internal reflections in M_1. The two strong images should be brought into coincidence by adjusting the screws at the back of M_3 (and if necessary M_2). M_3 and R are now parallel within about a minute of arc.

(iii) Replace the pea-lamp by the source S_e and F (conveniently a low-pressure mercury source with a green filter). The lens L must be placed so as to allow an approximately parallel beam to fall on M_1 in a direction approximately normal to M_3. With the eye placed at E, fringes should be seen crossing the field of view. The screws at the back of M_3 are adjusted so as to broaden the fringes. At a certain stage the fringes are seen to be circular but with the centre of the system outside the field of view. For the final adjustment of the Hilger instrument two special screws, which alter the angular setting of M_3, are provided. The centre of the fringes is now brought into the field of view. M_2 is now traversed a little until the diameter of the fringes does not change when the eye is moved from side to side. In the final adjustment, it may be necessary to traverse M_2 a little, and make small alterations in the tilt of M_3, successively.

106 WAVE TRAINS OF FINITE LENGTH

(iv) If white-light fringes are desired, a lamp is placed at the position S_e leaving L in position. M_2 is then traversed slowly until it moves into coincidence with the reference plane R. A movement of not more than about one tenth of a millimetre should be sufficient.

Note.—If a sodium lamp is used instead of a mercury source, the fringes have good visibility when the path difference is 0, 1000λ, 2000λ, etc., and very poor visibility at half-way between these positions (see fig. 4.2*b*). If fringes are not seen in the early stages of (iii) above, the mirror M_2 should be traversed a little.

APPENDIX IV B

Fourier's Series and Fourier's Integral Theorem

1.—The complete mathematical investigation of the validity of the methods by which certain limits are derived is difficult and very lengthy. These limit processes are essential to any formal logical proof of the Fourier integral theorem, and their investigation is needed for a complete understanding of the Fourier series. A reader who is interested in the mathematical side should consult one of the standard mathematical texts.* Other readers may be willing to accept the general result of this investigation, namely that the Fourier expansions, in the forms in which we shall derive them, are applicable to a wide range of mathematical functions, including all the functions in which we are interested. The derivation given below shows that the theorem is at least plausible, and should help the reader to understand and to apply the Fourier methods. It does not claim to be a complete proof.

2.—Let us assume that, in the range $-\pi$ to π, a mathematical function $f(X)$ may be represented by a series of sines and cosines so that

$$f(X) = a_0 + \sum_{n=1}^{\infty} a_n \cos nX + \sum_{n=1}^{\infty} b_n \sin nX. \quad \ldots \quad 4(42)$$

On integrating each side, we find that

$$a_0 = \frac{1}{2\pi} \int_{-\pi}^{\pi} f(X)\, dX. \quad \ldots \ldots \quad 4(43)$$

Multiplying each side by $\cos nX$ and integrating, we obtain

$$a_n = \frac{1}{\pi} \int_{-\pi}^{\pi} f(X) \cos nX\, dX, \quad \ldots \ldots \quad 4(44)$$

since $\int_{-\pi}^{\pi} \cos nX \cos mX\, dX = 0$ when $m \neq n$, and $= \pi$ when $m = n$;

and $\int_{-\pi}^{\pi} \cos nX \sin nX\, dX = 0$ for all values of m and n.

* See References 4.2 and 4.8.

FOURIER SERIES

Similarly
$$b_n = \frac{1}{\pi} \int_{-\pi}^{\pi} f(X) \sin nX \, dX. \quad \ldots \ldots \quad 4(45)$$

The expansion may also be written

$$f(X) = A_0 + \sum_{n=1}^{\infty} A_n \sin(nX + \delta_n), \quad \ldots \ldots \quad 4(46)$$

where
$$A_0 = a_0; \; A_n \sin \delta_n = a_n; \; A_n \cos \delta_n = b_n. \quad \ldots \quad 4(47)$$

In a similar way, the function may be represented by a series consisting of a constant term plus a series of cosines. Essentially the analysis is in terms of a constant plus a number of simple harmonic waves, each of which is represented by two terms in 4(42) and by one term in 4(46). Two constants, a_n and b_n in 4(42), and A_n and δ_n in 4(46), are associated with each harmonic wave. The relative energy associated with the nth harmonic is $a_n^2 + b_n^2$ if we use the representation of 4(42), and A_n^2 if we use that of 4(46).

3.—If we make the substitutions

$$2 \cos nX = (e^{inX} + e^{-inX}) \quad \ldots \ldots \quad 4(48a)$$

and
$$2 \sin nX = i(e^{-inX} - e^{inX}), \quad \ldots \ldots \quad 4(48b)$$

we may express the series in the form

$$f(X) = \sum_{n=-\infty}^{\infty} c_n e^{inX}, \quad \ldots \ldots \quad 4(49a)$$

where
$$\left. \begin{array}{l} 2c_n = a_n - ib_n, \\ 2c_{-n} = a_n + ib_n, \end{array} \right\} \quad \ldots \ldots \quad 4(49b)$$

except that
$$c_0 = a_0.$$

These relations imply that

$$c_n = c_{-n}^* \quad \ldots \ldots \ldots \ldots \quad 4(50)$$

and
$$c_n = \frac{1}{2\pi} \int_{-\pi}^{\pi} f(X) e^{-inX} \, dX. \quad \ldots \ldots \quad 4(51)$$

Equation 4(51) is valid when n is zero or negative, as well as when it is positive.

4.—So far we have considered $f(X)$ simply as a mathematical function. If we now assume that it is a wave profile, we know that it is always a real function and, while we can attach a meaning to the nth harmonic when n is positive, we give no physical meaning to a negative harmonic. In § 2.26 we stated a convention, according to which a wave motion is represented by a complex quantity, with the understanding that the real part of the complex gives the actual physical displacement. When we apply this convention to the interpretation of 4(49), we see that every negative term in the expansion must be taken with the corresponding positive term. By virtue of 4(50) the two together give a real number which represents one pair of terms in 4(42) or one term in 4(46). This term (or pair of terms) refers to "the nth harmonic"—with n always positive. The relative energy associated with the nth harmonic is

$$A_n{}^2 = a_n{}^2 + b_n{}^2 = 4c_n c_n{}^* = 4c_{-n} c_{-n}{}^*. \quad \ldots \quad 4(52)$$

5.—We may extend the range over which a given type of function is represented by a Fourier series in the following way. Let $x = lX/\pi$,

then
$$f(x) = \sum_{n=-\infty}^{n=\infty} c_n \exp\left(\frac{in\pi x}{l}\right), \quad \ldots \quad 4(53)$$

where
$$c_n = \frac{1}{2l}\int_{-l}^{+l} f(x') \exp\left(-\frac{in\pi x'}{l}\right) dx'. \quad \ldots \quad 4(54)$$

Hence
$$f(x) = \sum_{n=-\infty}^{\infty} \frac{1}{2l}\int_{-l}^{+l} f(x') \exp\frac{in\pi}{l}(x-x')\, dx'. \quad \ldots \quad 4(55)$$

We write x' instead of x in 4(54) in order to distinguish the variable to be integrated in 4(55). The expression on the right-hand side of 4(55) represents the function on the left-hand side between the limits $-l$ and $+l$. Since l may be made as large as we please, the representation is available for any finite limits. Subject to the necessary investigation of limit processes we may extend the limits to $\pm\infty$. Consider the nth harmonic of the series, for which the wavelength $\lambda_n = 2l/n$. The corresponding wavelength constant $\kappa_n = 2\pi/\lambda_n = n\pi/l$. Similarly for the $(n+1)$th harmonic, we have

$$\kappa_{n+1} = \frac{(n+1)\pi}{l}.$$

Hence
$$\kappa_{n+1} - \kappa_n = \pi/l = \Delta\kappa. \quad \ldots \quad 4(56)$$

Equation 4(55) may therefore be written

$$f(x) = \frac{1}{2\pi}\sum_{n=-\infty}^{\infty} \Delta\kappa \int_{-l}^{+l} f(x') \exp i\{n\,\Delta\kappa(x-x')\}\, dx'. \quad . \quad 4(57)$$

It is usual to approach the concept of a definite integral by considering the sum of the areas of narrow strips. The integral is the limiting value of the area when the strips are made indefinitely narrow. Thus we have

$$\int_{-\kappa_1}^{\kappa_1} G(\kappa)\, d\kappa = \lim_{\Delta\kappa \to 0} \sum_{n=-N}^{N} G(n\,\Delta\kappa)\,\Delta\kappa, \quad \ldots \quad 4(58)$$

where
$$\lim_{\Delta\kappa \to 0} (n\,\Delta\kappa) = \kappa,$$

as the definition of the integral. Thus we have

$$f(x) = \frac{1}{2\pi}\int_{-\infty}^{+\infty} d\kappa \int_{-\infty}^{+\infty} f(x')\exp i\kappa(x-x')\, dx'. \quad \ldots \quad 4(59)$$

If
$$g_0(\kappa) = \frac{1}{\sqrt{2\pi}}\int_{-\infty}^{+\infty} f(x)e^{-i\kappa x}\, dx, \quad \ldots \quad 4(60)$$

then
$$f(x) = \frac{1}{\sqrt{2\pi}}\int_{-\infty}^{+\infty} g_0(\kappa)e^{+i\kappa x}\, d\kappa. \quad \ldots \quad 4(61)$$

FOURIER SERIES

The accent on x is omitted in 4(60) since it is no longer needed to distinguish one part of the expression. By returning to 4(53) and replacing c_n by c_{-n} and $\exp(in\pi x/l)$ by $\exp(-in\pi x/l)$, we could derive the relations

$$g_1(\kappa) = \frac{1}{\sqrt{2\pi}} \int_{-\infty}^{+\infty} f(x) e^{+i\kappa x} dx, \quad \ldots \ldots \quad 4(62)$$

and

$$f(x) = \frac{1}{\sqrt{2\pi}} \int_{-\infty}^{+\infty} g_1(\kappa) e^{-i\kappa x} d\kappa. \quad \ldots \ldots \quad 4(63)$$

When a pair of functions is connected either by 4(60) and 4(61) or by 4(62) and 4(63), each is said to be the "Fourier transform" of the other. Note that in one relation of the pair there is always a *positive* exponent and in the other a *negative* exponent.

6.—Equation 4(63) may be written

$$f(x) = \frac{1}{\sqrt{2\pi}} \int_0^\infty g_1(\kappa) e^{-i\kappa x} d\kappa + \frac{1}{\sqrt{2\pi}} \int_0^\infty g_1(-\kappa) e^{+i\kappa x} d\kappa \quad \ldots \ldots \quad 4(64)$$

$$= \frac{1}{\sqrt{2\pi}} \int_0^\infty \{g_1(\kappa) + g_1(-\kappa)\} \cos \kappa x \, d\kappa - \frac{i}{\sqrt{2\pi}} \int_0^\infty \{g_1(\kappa) - g_1(-\kappa)\} \sin \kappa x \, d\kappa, \quad 4(65)$$

and similarly we obtain

$$g_1(\kappa) = \frac{1}{\sqrt{2\pi}} \int_0^\infty \{f(x) + f(-x)\} \cos \kappa x \, dx + \frac{i}{\sqrt{2\pi}} \int_0^\infty \{f(x) - f(-x)\} \sin \kappa x \, dx, \quad 4(66)$$

and

$$g_1(-\kappa) = \frac{1}{\sqrt{2\pi}} \int_0^\infty \{f(x) + f(-x)\} \cos \kappa x \, dx - \frac{i}{\sqrt{2\pi}} \int_0^\infty \{f(x) - f(-x)\} \sin \kappa x \, dx. \quad 4(67)$$

Hence

(i) If $f(x)$ is real for all values of x,

$$g_1(\kappa) = g_1^*(-\kappa). \quad \ldots \ldots \quad 4(68)$$

(ii) If $f(x)$ is real everywhere and is an even function [i.e. $f(x) = +f(-x)$], we have also

$$g_1(\kappa) = g_1(-\kappa) \quad \ldots \ldots \quad 4(69)$$

and $g_1(\kappa)$ is real.

Then 4(65) and 4(66) become

$$f(x) = \sqrt{\frac{2}{\pi}} \int_0^\infty g_1(\kappa) \cos \kappa x \, d\kappa \quad \ldots \ldots \quad 4(70)$$

and

$$g_1(\kappa) = \sqrt{\frac{2}{\pi}} \int_0^\infty f(x) \cos \kappa x \, dx. \quad \ldots \ldots \quad 4(71)$$

(iii) If $f(x)$ is real everywhere and is odd [$f(x) = -f(-x)$],

$$g_1(\kappa) = -g_1(-\kappa) \quad \ldots \ldots \quad 4(72)$$

and $g_1(\kappa)$ is a pure imaginary.

Equations 4(65) and 4(66) then become

$$f(x) = -i\sqrt{\frac{2}{\pi}} \int_0^\infty g_1(\kappa) \sin \kappa x \, d\kappa \qquad \ldots \ldots 4(73)$$

and

$$g_1(\kappa) = i\sqrt{\frac{2}{\pi}} \int_0^\infty f(x) \sin \kappa x \, dx. \qquad \ldots \ldots 4(74)$$

7.—In one kind of optical measurement we place a receptor in a system of interference fringes and record its reading at various points. From these readings we deduce a wave profile, i.e. we calculate a wave profile which would lead to the observed distribution of energy in the fringe system. A typical experiment of this kind is the measurement of the visibility of fringes obtained with the Michelson interferometer. In a second kind of experiment, we place a receptor in the focal plane of a spectrograph and observe the variation of reading as it is moved along the spectrum. We usually interpret the result in terms of a distribution of energy with wavelength (or wavelength constant). The purpose of many of the applications of Fourier analysis to optics is to correlate the results of these two kinds of experiment. We may be given a profile, i.e. a space function $f(x)$, and we wish to calculate a relative-energy function $E(\kappa)$ such that the relative energy corresponding to the range $(\kappa - \tfrac{1}{2}d\kappa)$ to $(\kappa + \tfrac{1}{2}d\kappa)$ is $E(\kappa) \, d\kappa$. Alternatively, we may be given $E(\kappa)$ and wish to calculate $f(x)$. Directly, the analysis deals not with $E(\kappa)$ but with $g(\kappa)$, and we must now consider the relation between $g(\kappa)$ and $E(\kappa)$. Let us first consider cases when $f(x)$ is real. When equation 4(62) is used we shall obtain a function $g(\kappa)$ which satisfies 4(68), but is not necessarily real, and which has values corresponding to negative values of κ. Physically we must regard $g(\kappa)$ and $g(-\kappa)$ as both belonging to the frequency range $(\kappa - \tfrac{1}{2}d\kappa)$ to $(\kappa + \tfrac{1}{2}d\kappa)$ just as, in 4(52), c_n and c_{-n} both belong to the nth harmonic. By analogy with 4(52) [since $g(\kappa)$ is analogous to $\sqrt{2\pi} \cdot c_n$] we expect $E(\kappa)$ to be given by

$$E(\kappa) \, d\kappa = \frac{2}{\pi} g_1(\kappa) \, g_1^*(\kappa) \, d\kappa. \qquad \ldots \ldots 4(75)$$

4(75) gives the energy associated with the frequency range $d\kappa$ and, in it, κ is an essentially positive quantity. Detailed examination of the process by which an expression for the energy based on 4(52) passes into the integral form justifies 4(75).

8.—Consider a wave profile represented by

$$f(x) = h(x) \cos \kappa_0 x, \qquad \ldots \ldots 4(76)$$

where $h(x)$ is a real function of x.

We may put

$$f(x) = \tfrac{1}{2} h(x) e^{i\kappa_0 x} + \tfrac{1}{2} h(x) e^{-i\kappa_0 x}. \qquad \ldots \ldots 4(77)$$

Then $\sqrt{2\pi} g_1(\kappa) = \tfrac{1}{2} \int_{-\infty}^\infty h(x) \exp i(\kappa + \kappa_0)x \, dx + \tfrac{1}{2} \int_{-\infty}^\infty h(x) \exp i(\kappa - \kappa_0)x \, dx$

$$g_1(\kappa) = \tfrac{1}{2} g_1'(\kappa + \kappa_0) + \tfrac{1}{2} g_1'(\kappa - \kappa_0), \qquad \ldots \ldots 4(78)$$

where

$$g_1'(\kappa) = \frac{1}{\sqrt{2\pi}} \int_{-\infty}^\infty h(x) e^{i\kappa x} \, dx, \qquad \ldots \ldots 4(79)$$

FOURIER SERIES 111

i.e. $g_1'(\kappa)$ is the Fourier transform of the function $h(x)$ itself. Many physical problems involve functions of the type on the right-hand side of 4(77). It is often convenient to proceed by first finding $g_1'(\kappa)$, using 4(79), and then $g_1(\kappa)$ from 4(78). When this function is inserted in 4(75) we obtain the relative energy. It often happens that the first term on the right-hand side of 4(78) is numerically small compared with the second term and may be ignored in the final calculation.

*9.—The following procedure is sometimes used but is not correct in principle, though it does lead to the correct result in some cases of practical importance. According to the convention discussed in § 2.26, the right-hand side of 4(76) is replaced by $h(x)e^{-i\kappa_0 x}$, with the understanding that the real part of the complex function represents the physical displacement. Equation 4(62) is then used to obtain

$$g_1''(\kappa) = \frac{1}{\sqrt{2\pi}} \int_{-\infty}^{\infty} h(x) \exp i(\kappa - \kappa_0)x \, dx$$
$$= g_1'(\kappa - \kappa_0), \qquad \ldots \ldots \ldots \quad 4(80)$$

i.e. we obtain twice the second term of 4(78). When, as explained in the preceding paragraph, this is the predominant term, the function $g_1''(\kappa)$ differs from $g_1(\kappa)$ only by the constant factor 2. If this function is inserted in 4(75) we obtain a sufficiently good approximation to the *relative* energy. It will, however, be understood that, if we had taken $f(x)$ to be the real part of $h(x)e^{+i\kappa_0 x}$, we should have obtained the *first* term on the right-hand side of 4(78), i.e. the term which is usually negligibly small. The procedure described in this paragraph involves multiplying the complex function $h(x)e^{-i\kappa_0 x}$ by a complex function $e^{i\kappa x}$, integrating, and then extracting a real function at the end. This procedure does not give the Fourier transform of the real part of $h(x)e^{i\kappa_0 x}$, and, although it can sometimes be manipulated to give correct results in an apparently simple way, the procedure of § 8 should always be used.

10.—Analysis of a sharply limited Wave Train.

We may first consider a particular case which is so simple that it can be solved first by elementary methods and then by the procedure described in § 8. Suppose that the profile, at $t = 0$, of a wave is represented by

$$f(x) = A \cos \kappa_0 x \quad \text{from } -x_1 \text{ to } +x_1, \qquad \ldots \quad 4(81)$$

and $f(x) = 0$ outside the above range (see fig. 4.4). Since $f(x)$ is real and even, we use 4(71) to obtain

$$g_1(\kappa) = \sqrt{\frac{2}{\pi}} A \int_0^{x_1} \cos \kappa_0 x \cos \kappa x \, dx \qquad \ldots \ldots \quad 4(82)$$

$$= \frac{A}{\sqrt{2\pi}} \int_0^{x_1} \{\cos(\kappa_0 + \kappa)x + \cos(\kappa_0 - \kappa)x\} \, dx,$$

i.e.
$$g_1(\kappa) = \frac{A}{\sqrt{2\pi}} \left\{ \frac{\sin(\kappa_0 + \kappa)x_1}{\kappa_0 + \kappa} + \frac{\sin(\kappa_0 - \kappa)x_1}{\kappa_0 - \kappa} \right\}, \quad \ldots \quad 4(83)$$

* This paragraph may be omitted on first reading.

and the energy distribution is given by substituting from 4(83) into 4(75). Only positive values of κ need be considered. Using the procedure described in § 8, we note that 4(81) is of the same form as 4(76), with $h(x) = A$ from $-x_1$ to x_1, and zero elsewhere. We have

$$g_1'(\kappa) = \frac{A}{\sqrt{2\pi}} \int_{-x_1}^{x_1} e^{i\kappa x}\,dx$$

$$= \sqrt{\frac{2}{\pi}} A \frac{\sin \kappa x_1}{\kappa}. \quad \ldots \ldots \quad 4(84)$$

Hence using 4(78) we obtain $g_1(\kappa)$, and the result is identical with 4(83). It is easy to verify that, if we had used the incorrect procedure described in § 9, we should have obtained one or other term in 4(83), but not both. Also there would have been an incorrect factor of 2.

11.—We are usually interested in cases where there is a fairly large number of waves in the train, i.e. $\kappa_0 x_1$ is large compared with 2π. We note that the second term in the bracket of 4(83) is equal to x_1 when $\kappa = \kappa_0$. Since κ may take only positive values, the first term never reaches a comparable value and may be neglected. We may put

$$g(\kappa) = \frac{A}{2}\sqrt{\frac{2}{\pi}} \frac{\sin (\kappa_0 - \kappa)x_1}{\kappa_0 - \kappa} = \frac{A}{2}\sqrt{\frac{2}{\pi}} \frac{\sin 2\Delta x_1}{2\Delta}, \quad \ldots \quad 4(85)$$

where $\qquad 2\Delta = \kappa_0 - \kappa.$

The energy distribution is shown in fig. 6.16a (p. 180). A high proportion of the energy is included in the range $\kappa = \kappa_0 - \pi/x_1$ to $\kappa = \kappa_0 + \pi/x_1$, i.e. between the two minima on either side of the central maximum. The width of this range is inversely proportional to x_1 and we see that, for this wave form, a long wave-train implies that the energy is concentrated in a narrow range of κ.

12.—Profile for sharply limited Wave Band.

Let κ_0 and κ_1 be two fixed values of κ with $\kappa_1 > \kappa_0$.

Suppose $g(\kappa) = 1$ when $\kappa_0 < \kappa < \kappa_1$, and $g(\kappa) = 0$ outside this range. Then, using 4(61), we have

$$f(x) = \frac{1}{\sqrt{2\pi}} \int_{\kappa_0}^{\kappa_1} e^{i\kappa x}\,d\kappa$$

$$= \frac{1}{\sqrt{2\pi}} \cdot \frac{1}{ix}(e^{i\kappa_1 x} - e^{i\kappa_0 x}), \quad \ldots \ldots \quad 4(86)$$

and the real part is

$$f_r(x) = \frac{1}{\sqrt{2\pi}} \frac{\sin \kappa_1 x - \sin \kappa_0 x}{x}$$

$$= \sqrt{\frac{2}{\pi}} \frac{\sin \tfrac{1}{2}(\kappa_1 - \kappa_0)x \cos \tfrac{1}{2}(\kappa_1 + \kappa_0)x}{x} \quad \ldots \quad 4(87)$$

$$= \sqrt{\frac{2}{\pi}} \frac{\sin \Delta x \cos \kappa_m x}{x}, \quad \ldots \ldots \ldots \quad 4(88)$$

FOURIER SERIES 113

where $2\Delta = \kappa_1 - \kappa_0$ and $2\kappa_m = \kappa_1 + \kappa_0$. When Δ is small compared with κ_m, the first factor in the numerator of 4(88) varies only slowly, and we have a train of waves whose profile is bounded by the curve $\sqrt{\dfrac{2}{\pi}}\dfrac{\sin \Delta x}{x}$. The effective length of the wave train increases as Δ decreases, i.e. as the effective range of κ decreases.

13. Distribution of Energy for a Damped Harmonic Wave.

It is sometimes convenient to consider the disturbance as a function of t and the energy distribution as a function of ω. Mathematically the relation between $f(t)$ and $g(\omega)$ is similar to that between $f(x)$ and $g(\kappa)$. As an example we may consider the wave whose disturbance at $x = 0$ is given by

$$f(t) = 0 \text{ from } t = -\infty \text{ to } t = 0,$$

$$f(t) = Ae^{-\gamma t/2} \cos \omega_0 t \text{ from } t = 0 \text{ to } t = +\infty. \quad \ldots \quad 4(89)$$

Such a wave would be emitted by an oscillator which commenced to radiate at time $t = 0$ and was subject to logarithmic damping with constant γ. This is the same form as 4(76) with $h(t) = Ae^{-\gamma t/2}$ from 0 to ∞ and zero from $-\infty$ to 0. We have

$$g_1'(\omega) = \dfrac{A}{\sqrt{2\pi}} \int_0^\infty \exp\{-\gamma/2 + i\omega\}t \, dt \quad \ldots \quad 4(90)$$

$$= -\dfrac{A}{\sqrt{2\pi}} \dfrac{2}{(2i\omega - \gamma)}. \quad \ldots \quad 4(91)$$

Using 4(78) we obtain an expression with two terms, one containing $(\omega + \omega_0)$ in the denominator and the other containing $(\omega - \omega_0)$. Under most practical conditions the former is negligible and we write

$$g_1(\omega) = -\dfrac{A}{\sqrt{2\pi}} \dfrac{1}{2i(\omega - \omega_0) - \gamma}.$$

The relative energy is equal to

$$\dfrac{2}{\pi} g_1(\omega) g_1^*(\omega) = \dfrac{A^2}{\pi^2} \dfrac{1}{4(\omega - \omega_0)^2 + \gamma^2}. \quad \ldots \quad 4(92)$$

When the damping is small, the energy is concentrated in a narrow range of frequency round ω_0. Thus, again, a long wave train is associated with a narrow range of frequency. In this example the problem has been worked out in terms of t and ω; it could equally well have been worked in terms of x and κ. For some purposes it is desirable to introduce a constant A_0^2 equal to the total energy for all frequencies. We have, in this case,

$$A_0^2 = \dfrac{2}{\pi} \int_0^\infty g_1(\omega) g_1^*(\omega) \, d\omega = \int_0^\infty \dfrac{A^2}{\pi^2} \dfrac{d\omega}{4(\omega - \omega_0)^2 + \gamma^2}$$

$$= \dfrac{A^2}{2\pi^2 \gamma} \left(\dfrac{\pi}{2} + \tan^{-1} \dfrac{2\omega_0}{\gamma}\right). \quad \ldots \quad 4(93)$$

If γ is small compared with ω_0, then $\tan^{-1}(2\omega_0/\gamma) = \tfrac{1}{2}\pi$ and $2\pi\gamma A_0^2 = A^2$. We then have

$$g_1(\omega)g_1(\omega)^* = \frac{\gamma A_0^2}{\gamma^2 + 4(\omega - \omega_0)^2}. \qquad \ldots \quad 4(94)$$

14. The Gaussian Wave Group.

Consider the wave whose profile at time $t = 0$ is given by

$$f_0(x) = A\sqrt{\frac{\pi}{\alpha}}\, e^{-x^2/4\alpha} \cos \kappa_0 x. \qquad \ldots \quad 4(95)$$

This again is of the form of 4(76) with

$$h(x) = A\sqrt{\frac{\pi}{\alpha}}\, e^{-x^2/4\alpha}.$$

Then
$$g_1'(\kappa) = \frac{A}{\sqrt{2\alpha}} \int_{-\infty}^{\infty} \exp\left[-\left(\frac{x^2}{4\alpha} - i\kappa x\right)\right] dx. \qquad \ldots \quad 4(96)$$

Now
$$\int_{-\infty}^{\infty} \exp(au - bu^2)\, du = e^{a^2/4b} \int_{-\infty}^{\infty} \exp\left[-b\left(u - \frac{a}{2b}\right)^2\right] du$$

$$= e^{a^2/4b} \int_{-\infty}^{\infty} e^{-bv^2} dv = \sqrt{\frac{\pi}{b}}\, e^{a^2/4b}. \qquad . \quad 4(97)$$

Putting $a = i\kappa$ and $b = 1/4\alpha$, we have

$$g_1'(\kappa) = A\sqrt{(2\pi)}\, e^{-\alpha\kappa^2}. \qquad \ldots \ldots \quad 4(98a)$$

We neglect the part of $g_1(\kappa)$ which contains $\exp[-\alpha(\kappa_0 + \kappa)^2]$ and obtain

$$g_1(\kappa) = A\sqrt{(\tfrac{1}{2}\pi)}\, \exp[-\alpha(\kappa_0 - \kappa)^2]. \qquad \ldots \quad 4(98b)$$

The relative energy for a range $d\kappa$ is proportional to $[g_1(\kappa)]^2 d\kappa$. Figs. 4.8 and 4.9 show the relation between the length of the wave train and the distribution of energy.

15.—Progress of the Wave Group in a Dispersive Medium.

Consider the system of waves for which the displacement is given by the real part of

$$\xi = \frac{1}{\sqrt{2\pi}} \int_{-\infty}^{\infty} g_1(\kappa) \exp i(\omega t - \kappa x)\, d\kappa, \qquad \ldots \quad 4(99)$$

where $g_1(\kappa)$ is given by 4(98b). (The physical problem includes only the part of $g(\kappa)$ from 0 to ∞, but since the part from $-\infty$ to 0 is negligibly small, we may take the whole range—and we do so for convenience of manipulation.)

FOURIER SERIES

In a dispersive medium ω is a function of κ and, for a small range of κ near to κ_0, we have

$$\omega = \omega_0 + U(\kappa - \kappa_0) + W(\kappa - \kappa_0)^2$$
$$= \omega_0 + 2U\Delta + 4W\Delta^2, \quad \ldots \ldots \quad 4(100)$$

where $\quad 2\Delta = \kappa - \kappa_0; \quad U = d\omega/d\kappa \text{ and } W = \tfrac{1}{2}d^2\omega/d\kappa^2, \quad . \quad 4(101)$

the values of U and W being taken at κ_0.

Then 4(99) becomes

$$\xi = A \exp i(\omega_0 t - \kappa_0 x) \int_{-\infty}^{\infty} \exp\{2i(Ut - x)\Delta - (4\alpha - 4iWt)\Delta^2\}\, d\Delta. \quad 4(102)$$

As a first approximation we take only the first two terms of 4(100), i.e. we assume $W = 0$. In 4(97) we put $a = 2i(Ut - x)$ and $b = 4\alpha$. We obtain

$$\xi = \frac{A}{2}\sqrt{\frac{\pi}{\alpha}} \exp\left[-\frac{(x - Ut)^2}{4\alpha}\right] \exp i(\omega_0 t - \kappa_0 x), \quad . \quad 4(103)$$

i.e. to this approximation the form of the wave is unchanged, but the curve which bounds the profile moves forward with velocity $U = d\omega/d\kappa$. In the second approximation we integrate, putting $a = 2i(Ut - x)$ and $b = 4(\alpha - iWt)$ in 4(97). The difference is that α in 4(103) is replaced by $(\alpha - iWt)$, and we write

$$\xi = \frac{A}{2}\sqrt{\left[\frac{\pi}{(\alpha - iWt)}\right]} \exp\left[\frac{-(x - Ut)^2(\alpha + iWt)}{4(\alpha^2 + W^2 t^2)}\right] \exp i(\omega_0 t - \kappa_0 x). \quad 4(104)$$

The imaginary parts can be separated to form a complicated phase term which varies slowly with the time. The important effect in which we are interested is that the curve which bounds the profile is still a Gaussian curve, but the parameter α is replaced by

$$\frac{\alpha^2 + W^2 t^2}{\alpha}, \quad \ldots \ldots \quad 4(105)$$

i.e. the half-width is increasing with time, and the group is spreading slowly as it advances.

16. The Power Spectrum.

Let $f(x)$ and $l(x)$ be any two functions of x, real or complex, and let $g(\kappa)$ and $m(\kappa)$ be their Fourier transforms, so that

$$f(x) = \frac{1}{\sqrt{(2\pi)}} \int_{-\infty}^{\infty} g(\kappa)\, e^{-i\kappa x}\, d\kappa, \quad \ldots \ldots \quad 4(106a)$$

$$l(x) = \frac{1}{\sqrt{(2\pi)}} \int_{-\infty}^{\infty} m(\kappa)\, e^{-i\kappa x}\, d\kappa, \quad \ldots \ldots \quad 4(106b)$$

and $\quad l^*(x) = \dfrac{1}{\sqrt{(2\pi)}} \displaystyle\int_{-\infty}^{\infty} m^*(\kappa)\, e^{+i\kappa x}\, d\kappa. \quad \ldots \ldots \quad 4(106c)$

Then $\quad \displaystyle\int_{-\infty}^{\infty} f(x)\, l^*(x)\, dx = \dfrac{1}{\sqrt{(2\pi)}} \displaystyle\int_{-\infty}^{\infty} \int_{-\infty}^{\infty} f(x)\, m^*(\kappa)\, e^{i\kappa x}\, d\kappa\, dx \quad 4(107)$

and, using 4(62),

$$\int_{-\infty}^{\infty} f(x)\, l^*(x)\, dx = \int_{-\infty}^{\infty} g(\kappa)\, m^*(\kappa)\, d\kappa. \quad \ldots \quad 4(108)$$

This is Parseval's Theorem. If we put $l(x) = f(x)$ we obtain

$$\int_{-\infty}^{\infty} f(x) f^*(x)\, dx = \int_{-\infty}^{\infty} g(\kappa)\, g^*(\kappa)\, d\kappa, \quad \ldots \quad 4(109a)$$

or

$$\int_{-\infty}^{\infty} |f(x)|^2\, dx = \int_{-\infty}^{\infty} |g(\kappa)|^2\, d\kappa. \quad \ldots \quad 4(109b)$$

We have seen in §7 above that the right-hand side is proportional to the total energy, and we now see that the total energy may be simply calculated when the profile is given.

If we put $l(x) = f(x + \alpha)$, equation 4(106c) is replaced by

$$f^*(x + \alpha) = \frac{1}{\sqrt{2\pi}} \int_{-\infty}^{\infty} g^*(\kappa)\, e^{i\kappa(x+\alpha)}\, d\kappa, \quad \ldots \quad 4(110)$$

and this leads to $\displaystyle\int_{-\infty}^{\infty} f(x) f^*(x + \alpha)\, dx = \int_{-\infty}^{\infty} |g(\kappa)|^2\, e^{i\kappa\alpha}\, d\kappa, \quad \ldots \quad 4(111)$

instead of 4(109b).

17. The Auto-correlation Function.

The auto-correlation function is defined by the equation

$$\rho'(\alpha) = \int_{-\infty}^{\infty} f(x) f^*(x + \alpha)\, dx, \quad \ldots \quad 4(112a)$$

and the *normalized* auto-correlation function by the equation

$$\rho(\alpha) = \frac{\displaystyle\int_{-\infty}^{\infty} f(x) f^*(x + \alpha)\, dx}{\displaystyle\int_{-\infty}^{\infty} f(x) f^*(x)\, dx}. \quad \ldots \quad 4(112b)$$

Substituting from 4(109b) and 4(111), we obtain

$$\rho(\alpha) = \frac{\displaystyle\int_{-\infty}^{\infty} |g(\kappa)|^2\, e^{i\kappa\alpha}\, d\kappa}{\displaystyle\int_{-\infty}^{\infty} |g(\kappa)|^2\, d\kappa} \quad \ldots \quad 4(113)$$

$$= \frac{1}{E} \int_{-\infty}^{\infty} E(\kappa) e^{i\kappa\alpha}\, d\kappa, \quad \ldots \quad 4(114)$$

where $E(\kappa)$, defined by equation 4(75) is called the power spectrum and $E = \displaystyle\int_{-\infty}^{\infty} E(\kappa)\, d\kappa$ is the total energy. Equations 4(112) and 4(113) imply that the power spectrum is proportional to the Fourier transform of the auto-correlation function $\rho(\alpha)$. It is not possible to derive the profile of a wave if only the power spectrum is known, because calculation of the profile requires the relative phases

FOURIER SERIES 117

(at time $t = 0$) of the different Fourier components as well as the amplitudes, and the power spectrum gives only the latter. Thus the same auto-correlation function applies to all the different profiles which can be produced by combining a set of simple harmonic waves whose amplitudes are fixed but whose phases can be varied in an arbitrary way.

18. The Cross-correlation Function.

The cross-correlation function (σ_{fl}) of two functions f and l is defined by

$$\sigma_{fl}(\alpha) = \int_{-\infty}^{\infty} f(x)\, l^*(x + \alpha)\, dx, \quad \ldots \quad 4(115a)$$

and equation 4(108) shows that

$$\sigma_{fl}(\alpha) = \int_{-\infty}^{\infty} g(\kappa)\, m^*(\kappa)\, e^{i\kappa\alpha}\, d\kappa. \quad \ldots \quad 4(115b)$$

The *normalized cross-correlation* is $\sigma_{fl}/(E_f E_l)^{\frac{1}{2}}$,

where $\quad E_f = \int_{-\infty}^{\infty} f(x) f^*(x)\, dx \quad$ and $\quad E_l = \int_{-\infty}^{\infty} l(x)\, l^*(x)\, dx$.

The correlation function is the integral of the product of two functions after one of them has been displaced by a distance α along the x axis. It is zero if the two functions, when displaced, do not overlap. Similarly the auto-correlation function measures the product of a function with itself (after displacement through a distance α). The auto-correlation function of a periodic function is itself periodic (see fig. 4.15).

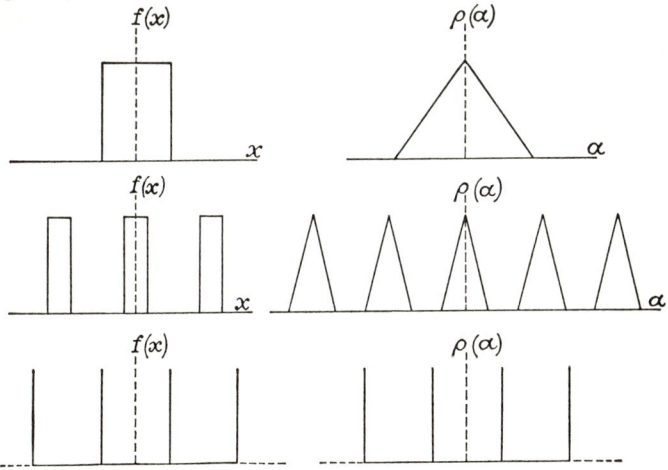

Fig. 4.15.—Some examples of auto-correlation functions. The original function is shown on the left and the auto-correlation function on the right.

CHAPTER V

Interference

5.1. Law of Photometric Summation.

The Michelson interferometer, which we have described in the preceding chapter, is one of a large number of experimental arrangements which produce interference fringes. In the most general sense, interference fringes are variations of resultant amplitude (and hence of the relative energy and the illumination) from point to point in the field of view. The variations are due to varying path differences between the interfering beams of light. These produce varying phase differences, so that the waves reinforce one another at some points and oppose each other elsewhere. The variations of relative energy may be calculated by applying the principle of superposition. We shall later have to make many calculations on fringe systems, but first we consider an important related problem.

It is a matter of common observation that we do *not* obtain interference fringes due to interaction between light from two different sources (such as a ceiling light and a reading lamp). Photometric measurements show that, for such sources, the resultant relative energy at any point is the sum of the relative energies produced by the individual sources, each acting alone. This empirical law, which we shall call the *law of photometric summation*, applies also to energy received from different parts of a large extended source of light. Any satisfactory wave theory must include an account of this law, which is obviously of great practical importance. The theory must be able to show what conditions must be fulfilled in order to obtain fringes, and must be able to describe what happens under the more common conditions of everyday experience, when we do not observe fringes.

5.2. Interaction of Independent Sources of Light.

Suppose that light is being received at a point Q (fig. 5.1) from an extended source of light S_e. Some light will come from an atom at A_1, some from another at A_2, and so on. At any one moment the disturbance at Q is the sum of the disturbances which would be produced

§5.2 INDEPENDENT SOURCES OF LIGHT

by each atom acting independently. If each atom were emitting an infinitely long train of pure sine waves, the resultant relative energy would be given directly by equation 3(12), which is based upon the principle of superposition. The experiments described in Chapter IV show that the light from a given atom must be represented by trains of waves which are seldom more than 10^6 waves long, and which take about 10^{-8} second to pass a given point. The shortest practical period

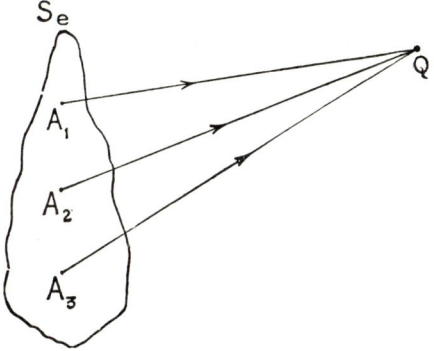

Fig. 5.1

of observation is of the order of a few microseconds. During this time the train of waves from a given atom is interrupted frequently, and each interruption constitutes an arbitrary variation of the relation between the phase of the wave from the given atom and the phases of the waves from other atoms. The illumination at Q due to a number of sources may be calculated if it can be assumed that the phase differences vary in a purely random way.

From 3(12) we have

$$E_R = \left(\sum_{r=1}^{m} a_r \cos \epsilon_r\right)^2 + \left(\sum_{r=1}^{m} a_r \sin \epsilon_r\right)^2$$

$$= \sum_{r=1}^{m} a_r^2 + \sum_{\substack{r=1 \\ (s \neq r)}}^{m} \sum_{s=1}^{m} a_r a_s (\cos \epsilon_r \cos \epsilon_s + \sin \epsilon_r \sin \epsilon_s)$$

$$= \sum_{r=1}^{m} a_r^2 + \sum_{\substack{r=1 \\ (s \neq r)}}^{m} \sum_{s=1}^{m} a_r a_s \cos (\epsilon_r - \epsilon_s). \quad \ldots \quad 5(1)$$

If the phase differences are varying in a purely random way, the average value of the second summation is zero, since to every possible positive value of any term there corresponds an equally probable negative value. Therefore the mean value is

$$E_R = \sum_{r=1}^{m} a_r^2 = \sum_{r=1}^{m} E_r. \quad \ldots \quad 5(2a)$$

The resultant illumination at Q is the sum of the illuminations due to the individual sources.

Equation 5(2a) applies only to an average taken over a time sufficiently long to include many random variations of phase. If a series of extremely short-period observations of the illumination at Q could be made, fluctuations would be obtained (see § 7 of Appendix V A).

5.3. Coherent and Non-coherent Beams of Light.

Two beams of light are said to be *mutually coherent* when the phase difference between the waves by which they are represented is constant during the period normally covered by observations. Two beams are said to be *non-coherent* when the phase difference changes many times and in an irregular way during the shortest period of observation. Coherent beams of equal amplitude give fringes of visibility equal to unity. Non-coherent beams may be said to give fringes of visibility zero. The visibilities of fringes actually observed (even with beams of equal amplitude) are always less than unity, so that it becomes necessary to introduce the concept of *partial coherence*. This concept will be further discussed in § 5.8 and in Appendix V A.

5.4.—We have shown (§ 5.2) that the resultant relative energy at a given point, due to a number of non-coherent sources, is equal to the sum of the relative energies which would be produced at this point by the individual sources acting separately. A similar rule applies to the illumination because this quantity is proportional to the relative energy. With n equal, non-coherent sources each capable of producing a relative energy E_r, the resultant relative energy is nE_r.

When a certain area is irradiated simultaneously by a number of coherent sources, the relative energy usually varies from point to point, giving rise to fringes. In Chapter III it was shown that the relative energy due to a number of coherent sources is $(\Sigma a_n)^2$ when all the waves have the same phase. It was also shown that, when the representative vectors form a closed polygon, the resultant relative energy is zero (§ 3.5). Thus n coherent sources each capable of producing a relative energy $E_r = a^2$ acting jointly will produce a resultant relative energy of

$$(na)^2 = n^2 E_r \quad \ldots \quad \ldots \quad 5(2b)$$

at any point where their waves are all in phase. At another point their resultant may be zero. The interference of waves from coherent sources alters the distribution of energy but not the total amount. Whether the sources are coherent or not, the resultant relative energy integrated over the whole region covered by the waves is equal to the sum of the integrals of the relative energies due to the individual sources.

5.5. Formation of Interference Fringes.

Both interference and photometric summation are involved in the theoretical description of fringes such as those obtained with the Michelson interferometer. Suppose that the instrument is adjusted so that circular fringes are seen through the telescope T (fig 4.1).

Consider the light entering the telescope within a small solid angle. It will consist of a pair of wave trains from an atom A_1 in the extended source S_e, a pair from an atom A_2 and so on (compare figs. 4.1 and 5.1). One member of each pair will have been reflected from M_2 and the other from M_3. The members of a pair are mutually coherent. Also the phase difference between the pair of wave trains from A_1 is the same as that between the pair from A_2. The relative energy corresponding to one pair is given by equation 4(1).

Let θ be the angle between a given direction for light entering the telescope and the axis of the instrument. Then if light from A_1 is a maximum in a direction defined by θ, that from A_2 is also a maximum in that direction. Similarly, if the relative energy due to light from A_1 is zero in a direction defined by θ', that from A_2 is also zero. The resultant of the two wave trains from A_1 has a phase which depends on that of the light emitted from A_1. Similarly the phase of the resultant of the two trains from A_2 depends on that of the light emitted from A_2. Since emissions of light from A_1 and A_2 occur independently, the resultant of a pair of trains from A_1 has no permanent phase relation with the resultant of a pair from A_2, i.e. the resultants are non-coherent. The relative energy propagated in a given direction is, therefore, obtained by first calculating the resultant for a pair of wave trains from one atom, using 4(1), and then summing the relative energies for all the resultants, using 5(2a). Fringes are seen only because all the resultants have their maxima in the same directions (such as θ) and their minima in another set of congruent directions (such as θ'). When the path difference is increased so that it is greater than the average length of the wave trains, the pairs of wave trains no longer enter the telescope simultaneously; *all* the light entering the telescope at any given moment is then non-coherent and no fringes are seen.

5.6. Interference between Two Sources Side by Side.

One of the first attempts to observe interference was made by Grimaldi, who allowed the light from a source S_e to pass through a pair of slits (a_1 and a_2) in the screen B (fig. 5.2a). He observed fringes

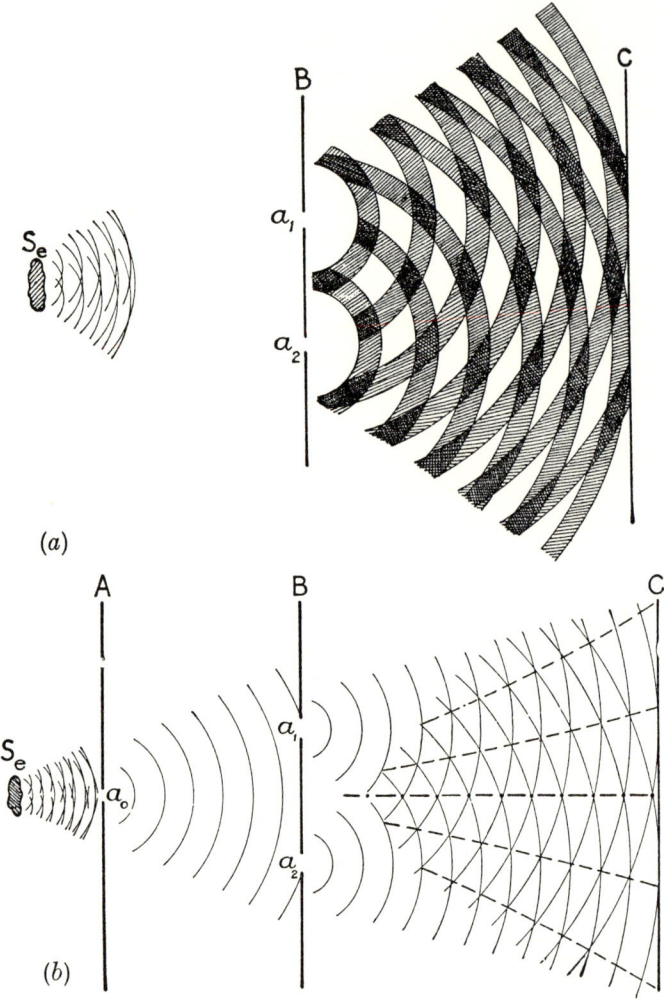

Fig. 5.2.—(a) Grimaldi's experiment, and (b) Young's experiment. In the lower diagram is shown Young's experiment with fringes due to interference of nearly spherical waves from a_1 and a_2. In the upper diagram the wavefronts are blurred because an irregular system of waves from S_e falls on screen B. In practice the blurring would be greater than that shown and the fringes would be obliterated.

§ 5.7 TWO SOURCES SIDE BY SIDE

on the screen C. It was later shown by Young that interference fringes should be seen only if the source S_e is fairly small. He used an extra screen A with a single slit a_0 to reduce the effective size of the source, and observed interference fringes on the screen C (fig. 5.2b). This is generally regarded as the first true observation of interference fringes. The fringes observed by Grimaldi were probably due to diffraction (see Chapter VI). Essentially similar fringes could have been obtained with one slit. In any modern repetitions of Young's or Grimaldi's experiments, a medium-power eyepiece would be used to view the fringes.

5.7.—The maximum size of the slit which will allow fringes to be observed may be calculated in the following way.

Consider the interference of light received at the point Q on the screen C from the point P on the source (fig. 5.3.) Let X'OX be a line perpendicular to the screens and halfway between the slits, which are each placed at a distance h

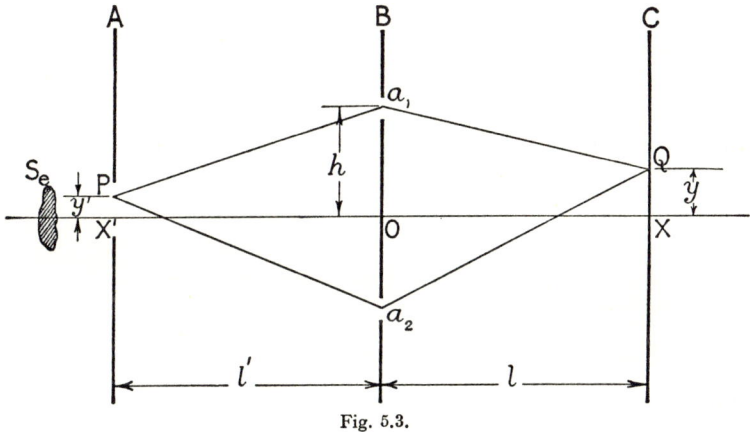

Fig. 5.3.

from it. Let P be distant y' and Q be distant y from this line. Let $X'O = l'$, $XO = l$, and let λ be the wavelength of the light used. Then the path difference of the two beams from P to Q is equal to

$$\Delta s = (Pa_1 + a_1Q) - (Pa_2 + a_2Q). \qquad \ldots \ldots \quad 5(3)$$

Also $(Pa_1)^2 = l'^2 + (h - y')^2$
and $(Pa_2)^2 = l'^2 + (h + y')^2.$
Hence $(Pa_1)^2 - (Pa_2)^2 = 4hy'$
or $(Pa_1 - Pa_2) = \dfrac{4hy'}{2l'} = \dfrac{2hy'}{l'}$ approximately.

The value of $(a_1Q - a_2Q)$ is found in a similar way, so that 5(3) becomes

$$\Delta s = \frac{2hy'}{l'} + \frac{2hy}{l}. \qquad \ldots \ldots \quad 5(4)$$

The positions of the maxima are obtained by putting $\Delta s = n\lambda$. From 5(4), it may be seen that the fringes due to light from P are equidistant, the separation being $l\lambda/2h$. If y' varies, the fringes move as a whole without altering their separation. The change δy in y due to a small variation $\delta y'$ in y' is given by

$$\frac{\delta y'}{l'} = -\frac{\delta y}{l}. \qquad \ldots \ldots \ldots 5(5)$$

To obtain fairly clear fringes, we require the extreme displacement of the maxima from the mean position to be less than one-quarter of the width of a fringe, i.e. $\delta y < l\lambda/8h$. This requires

$$\frac{\delta y'}{l'} \not> \frac{\lambda}{8h}.$$

Thus if the slits a_1 and a_2 are one millimetre apart (so that $h = 0.5$ millimetre) and the wavelength of the light used is 6×10^{-4} millimetre, the angle which the source subtends at the point O should not exceed 1.5×10^{-4} radian. If the screen A is two metres from the screen B, the hole in A should not be more than about three-tenths of a millimetre wide.

5.8. Partial Coherence.

Fringes of high visibility are produced by the interference of two beams of light if:

(1) The path differences involved are short compared with the length of the wave trains (§§ 4.10–14 and 5.34–38).

(2) The location of the maxima in the fringes produced by light from different parts of the source is nearly the same.

(3) The amplitudes of the two beams are nearly equal in the region where they interfere.

The second of these conditions may be considered in the following way. A primary source S (fig. 5.21) illuminates two pin-holes P_1 and P_2 and light from P_1 and P_2 interferes at Q. Light from a small area dS_1 at A_1 arrives at P_1 and P_2 with a phase difference $\Delta\phi_1 = 2\pi(A_1P_1 - A_1P_2)/\lambda$. Similarly there is a phase difference $\Delta\phi_2$ for light arriving at these points from A_2. If the source is small (in relation to A_1P_1, etc.), $\Delta\phi_1$, $\Delta\phi_2$, etc., are nearly equal, and their mean may be called the phase difference between P_1 and P_2 which are now regarded as secondary sources. This statement remains valid even if there are arbitrary variations in the phase of light from different parts, since these variations affect light at P_1 and P_2 equally. P_1 and P_2 are mutually coherent sources since they have a well-defined phase difference.

If S is so large that $\Delta\phi_1$, etc., range over an angle much larger than 2π, there is still a phase difference at any one moment between P_1 and P_2, but variations of phase in different parts of S affect P_1 and P_2 at different times. There is then no permanent phase relation between light from P₁ and P₂, and no interference fringes are observed at Q. P₁ and P₂ are non-coherent sources.

In the intermediate stage between coherence and non-coherence, the sources P₁ and P₂ are said to be *partially coherent*. This condition is obtained when S is fairly small (see § 5.7). The *degree of coherence* (V_{12}) is defined by Zernike to be equal to the visibility of the fringes obtained under the most favourable conditions (i.e. when the path difference is small and the amplitudes are equal). It is usual to speak of two secondary sources as " highly coherent " when V_{12} exceeds 0·85.

A beam of light is coherent when light from two pinholes placed at any two points in a cross-section is mutually coherent.* For a convergent beam this implies that light passing through a focus in different directions is coherent. The statement that an area is coherently illuminated implies a high value of V_{12} for any pair of points within the area. The statement that an area is non-coherently illuminated is usually intended to mean that V_{12} is low for pairs of points of interest in the problem under consideration. Light from points which are extremely close is never truly non-coherent (see Appendix V A).

5.9.—Other arrangements for observing interference with two sources side by side are:

(a) *Fresnel's Mirrors.*

Two images (S′ and S″) of a slit source S are formed by two plane mirrors M′ and M″ set at a small angle (fig. 5.4a, p. 126).

(b) *Fresnel's Biprism.*

Two images (S′ and S″) of a slit source S are formed by refraction in two prisms (P′ and P″) of small angle (fig. 5.4b, and Plate IIIb, p. 162).

(c) *Lloyd's Mirror.*

One image (S′) is formed by reflection in a plane mirror M, and light from this interferes with light coming directly from S (fig. 5.4c).

(d) *The Billet Split Lens.*

The two images are formed by the parts of a lens which has been bisected and the parts separated a little (fig. 5.4d). This is equivalent to the use of one lens and two small prisms. In each case the fringes are usually observed with a low-power eyepiece.

With the arrangement used in fig. 5.2b, no light reaches the centre of screen C (where the interference fringes are seen) by uninterrupted rectilinear paths. The methods illustrated in fig. 5.4 do bring light by rectilinear paths (of the type

* Some writers have recently used the term *coherent* merely to imply that long wave-trains are involved; such light is nearly monochromatic but not necessarily coherent.

to which geometrical optics applies) to the region of interference. It has been suggested, therefore, that Young's fringes are due to a mixture of diffraction and interference, while the Fresnel and Lloyd experiments depend on interference alone. The difference is not very important. The central fringes in Young's experiment disappear if a_1 or a_2 is covered and are clearly due to interference, but the distribution of light in any of the fringe systems cannot be accurately calculated without applying the theory of diffraction. In the arrangements of Fresnel, Lloyd, etc., some diffraction occurs at the edges of the prisms or mirrors.

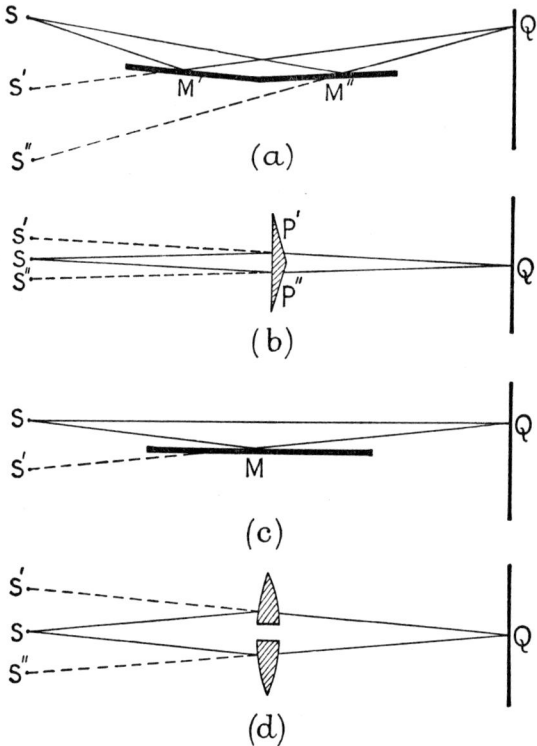

Fig. 5.4.—(a) Fresnel's mirrors. (b) Fresnel's biprism. (c) Lloyd's mirror.
(d) Billet's split lens.

5.10.—The most interesting of these arrangements is that due to H. Lloyd (1800–81). With the arrangement shown in fig. 5.4c, only half the system of fringes is seen. By interposing a thin transparent plate in the path of the direct beam the bands can be shifted so that the central part of the system can be seen. With roughly monochromatic light, such as that produced by a sodium flame, the fringe of zero path difference is not distinguishable from any other fringe. Using white light, the central fringe is seen clearly, a few fringes on either side of the centre are coloured, and farther out the fringes overlap to such an extent that they cannot be distinguished. The fringe corresponding to zero path difference is clear because, with zero path difference, the phase difference has the same value (π) for all wavelengths. The distance between successive bright fringes is, in general, a function of the wavelength. For example, in the simple arrangement of Young, it is proportional to the wavelength. As we go away from the centre, the fringes of different colours become more and more displaced relative to one another.

For path differences which are small, but not zero, the fringes appear coloured, but for larger path differences they become completely confused. If there is no change of phase on reflection, the centre of the system should be bright, since zero path difference would then mean zero phase difference for all wavelengths. Lloyd found that the centre is dark, thus indicating a change of phase of π due to a reflection in a less dense medium. This result (which is confirmed by experiments of Fresnel and others) is in agreement with the theory given in § 3.27, and justifies the choice of the boundary condition.

5.11.—The distribution of light in the above fringe system cannot be calculated without making allowance for the diffraction of light by the slit (Chapter VI). One effect of the slit width may be noted here. In the experiments of Fresnel and Billet the virtual sources are images of the same source and are formed in such a way that the upper part of one source (fig. 5.4a, b, and d) corresponds to the upper part of the other. Thus, with a source S of finite width the distance between different corresponding points on S′ and S″ is constant. The fringe width is the same for all parts of the source, but the fringe systems due to different parts of the source are displaced relative to one another. In Lloyd's experiment, the centres of the fringe systems due to different parts of the source coincide, but the outer bands are confused, because the width of the bands is not the same for different parts of the source. Lloyd's arrangement is thus more suitable for studying the central achromatic fringe. The other arrangement gives clearer fringes in the outer parts of the field with monochromatic light.

5.12. Interference produced by Thin Films.

Coloured fringes are often seen when a thin film of transparent material is viewed by reflected light. The film may be a layer of oil on water or on the surface of a road. Similar colours are seen in the wall of a soap bubble or of a very thin glass bulb. The films may be of lower refractive index than the surrounding medium, e.g. a film of air or liquid between two glass plates. Fringes are often seen between the components of an old cemented lens when the cement has failed locally, leaving a small inclusion of air. These colours are due to interference between beams which, having been reflected at least once in the film, reach the observer by paths of different lengths (fig. 5.5). When the surfaces of the film have a low coefficient of reflection, the fringes are best seen by observing the light which emerges on the

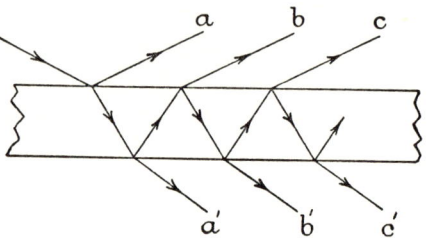

Fig. 5.5.—Beams of light emerging from a thin film. (Each beam is represented by a single ray.)

side of incidence. Such fringes (due to beams a, b, c in fig. 5.5) are said to be seen by reflected light. The fringes due to interference between beams which emerge on the opposite side of the film (beams a', b', c' in fig. 5.5) are said to be viewed by transmitted light. They are very weak and not easy to observe when the coefficients of reflection are small, but they become very sharp and clear when the film has a high reflection coefficient.

Fringes may be obtained by taking two pieces of good plate glass, cleaning them carefully, and then sliding two surfaces into contact. A film of air of varying thickness is formed between the two plates. If the glass is moderately good, the film will be nowhere more than a few wavelengths thick. If the plates are placed on a dark cloth and viewed by reflected light from a window, brilliant coloured fringes are obtained. It is inadvisable for an inexperienced person to carry out this procedure with good optical glass owing to the risk of scratching the surfaces if the plates are not perfectly clean. Also if the plates are of very high quality, the air film may be too thin to show good fringes.

5.13.—The path difference, for a film of constant thickness, may be calculated as follows. Let e be the thickness of the film and μ the index of refraction from air to the material of which the film is composed. Then, in fig. 5.6, the difference in optical path is $\mu(AB + BC) - AD$, and if θ_1 is the angle of incidence and θ the angle of refraction, $AE = AB \sin \theta$ and

$$AD = 2AB \sin \theta \sin \theta_1 = 2\mu AB \sin^2 \theta.$$

The path difference (*l*) is then $2\mu AB(1 - \sin^2\theta)$ and this gives

$$l = 2\mu e \cos\theta. \qquad \qquad 5(6)$$

It may easily be shown that the path differences between *b* and *c*, between *a'* and *b'* and between *b'* and *c'* (fig. 5.5) are all equal to *l*. It may also be shown that when the film is a wedge of small angle α, the path difference is approximately $2\mu e(\cos\theta - \sin\theta \tan\alpha)$, where *e* is the thickness at a point midway between rays *a* and *b*. This may be taken to be equal to $2\mu e \cos\theta$ except when the light is near grazing incidence.

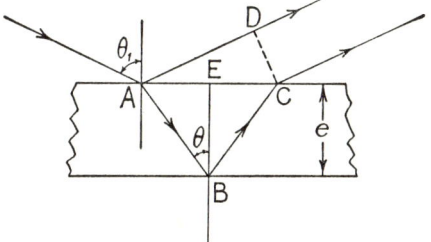

Fig. 5.6.—Path difference between successive beams

There is a change of phase of π at the upper surface if the film is optically denser than the surrounding medium, and at the lower surface if it is optically less dense. Thus the phase difference between the first two beams is

$$\delta = \frac{2\pi}{\lambda}(2\mu e \cos\theta) \pm \pi = \frac{2\pi}{\lambda} l \pm \pi. \qquad \ldots \qquad 5(7)$$

Since a phase difference of 2π is immaterial, it does not matter which sign is used in 5(7), and we shall therefore use always the plus sign. The second term in 5(7) is usually omitted in calculations of the separation of the fringes. If, however, this term is not included when calculating the amount of light reflected from an infinitesimally thin film, we should conclude that such a film would give strong reflection. When the phase change at one, and only one, surface is included, the calculated reflected energy tends to zero when the thickness of the film tends to zero.

5.14. Visibility of the Fringes.

When the two surfaces are unsilvered, the reflection coefficient is low except for very large angles of incidence. We may assume a reflection coefficient of 0·05 at each surface and calculate the fraction of the incident energy in each of the beams shown in fig. 5.5. We find that for the beams a, b, c, which emerge on the upper side of the film, the relative energies are 0·05, 0·045, 0·0001 respectively. The amplitudes of the waves which represent beams a and b are nearly equal and are very much greater than the amplitudes of all the other beams which emerge from the upper surface. Thus we need only consider these two beams in an approximate calculation of the distribution of energy in the fringes seen by reflected light. Moreover, we

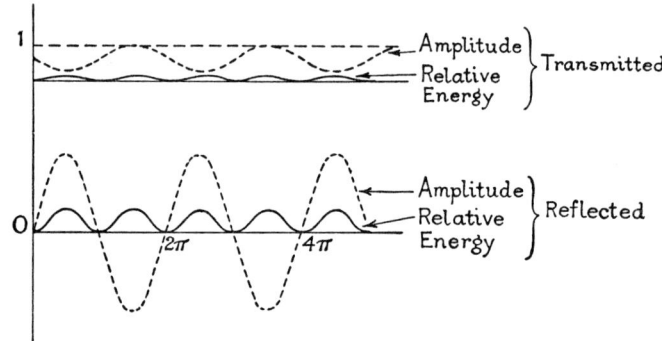

Fig. 5.7.—Variation of amplitude and of relative energy for transmitted and reflected light. (Unsilvered plates, $r^2 = 0·05$.) The negative amplitude corresponds to a resultant whose phase is opposite to that of the incident beam.

shall expect these two nearly equal beams to give fringes of high visibility, provided the path difference is small. The approximate relative energies of beams a', b', and c' are 0·90, 0·002 and 0·000 006 respectively. Again, we need take account of only two beams, but since these beams are represented by waves of very unequal amplitude, the fringes will have a very low visibility. Fig. 5.7 shows the variation of the *amplitude* and the *relative energy* of the resultant with phase difference for the fringes seen by reflected light and the corresponding functions for the fringes seen by transmitted light. (See also Plate IIg and IIh, oppsite.)

5.15.—Interference fringes are observed only if at least two of the beams enter the eye. For moderate angles of incidence the displacement of beam b relative to beam a is of the same order of magnitude as the thickness of the film. When this thickness is a good deal smaller than the diameter of the pupil (i.e. when it is 0·5 millimetre or less) it is easy to place the eye so as to receive both these beams. For films of greater thickness it is necessary to use an optical instrument to

(*a*) and (*b*) are negatives, (*c*), (*d*), (*e*), and (*f*) are positives.

(*a*) Nitrogen emission bands in the region 4000–3000 Å.

(*b*) Hydrogen emission lines with sodium absorption lines in the ultra-violet (3000-2000 Å).

(*c*) Solar spectrum showing Fraunhofer absorption lines.

(*d*) Sodium absorption spectrum (visible region).

(*e*) Sodium emission spectrum (visible region).

(*f*) Channelled spectrum.

The wavelength scale applies only to (*c*), (*d*), and (*e*).

(*g*) Contour fringes (wedge-shaped air film between unsilvered plates viewed by reflection).

(*h*) As (*g*) but wedge of smaller angle viewed by transmitted light.

(*i*) Contour fringes (wedge-shaped air film between silvered plates viewed by reflection).

(*j*) As (*i*) but viewed by transmission.

(*k*) Contour fringes (air film between a piece of mica and an optical flat viewed by reflection).

(*l*) As (*k*) but viewed by transmission.

PLATE II

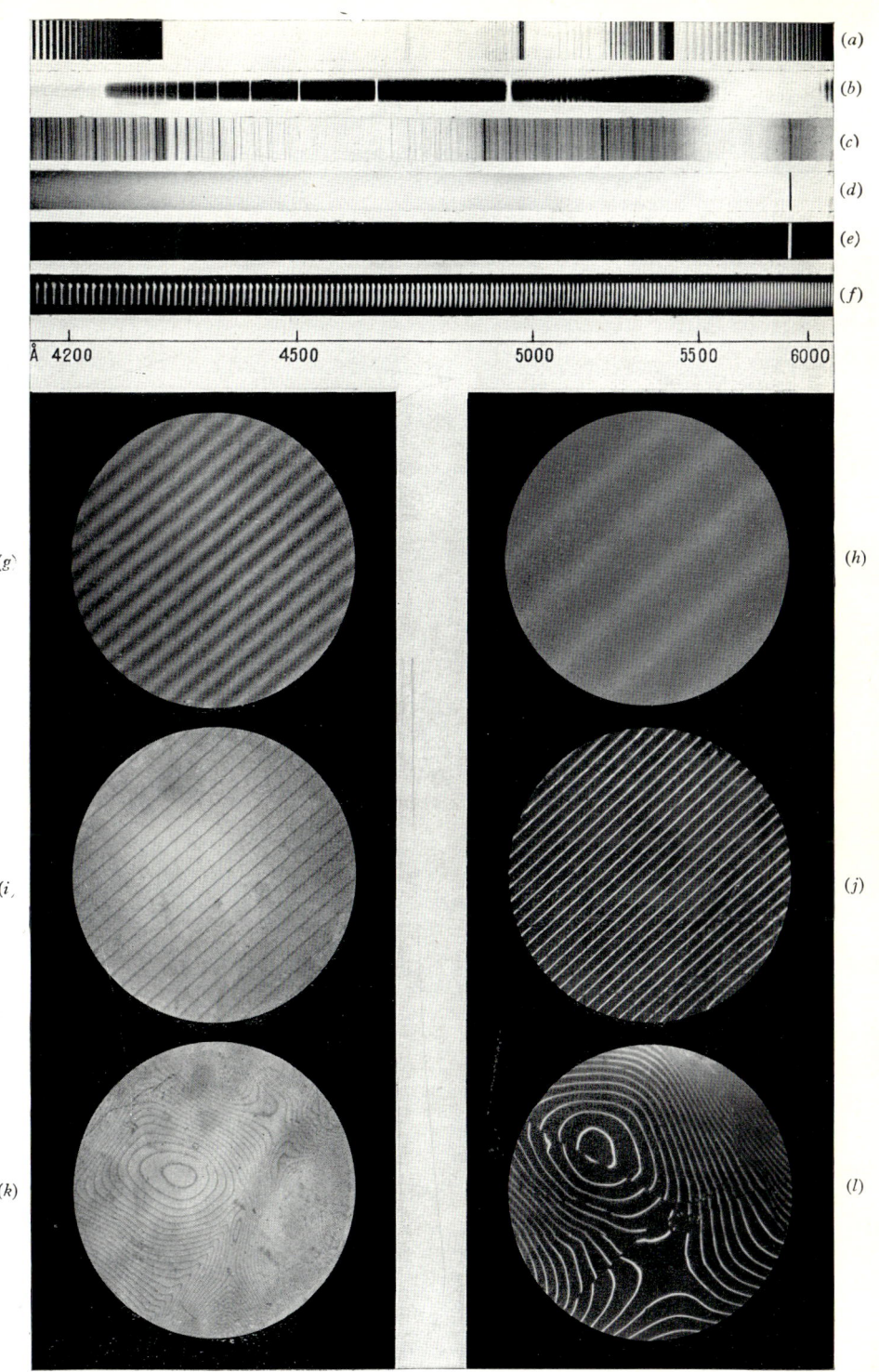

PLATE II

collect the beams or else to arrange to view the film by rays which are nearly normal to the surface of the film (fig. 5.8). The above condition for observing the fringes is necessary, but it is not the only condition which must be fulfilled. When white light is used, coloured fringes are obtained with films which are only a few wavelengths

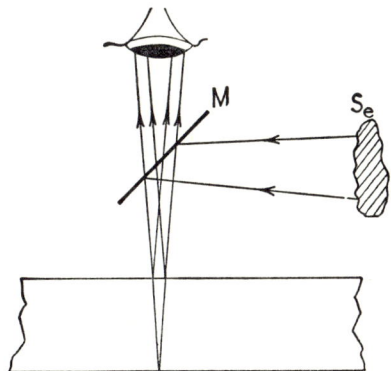

Fig. 5.8.—Thick plate viewed by nearly normal rays. The mirror **M** may be an unsilvered piece of glass

thick, but no fringes are seen under ordinary conditions of observation with thicker films.* With monochromatic light, fringes may be obtained with plates of thickness up to a few centimetres, provided that the eye, or the optical instrument, is focused on the correct plane (§ 5.20).

5.16. Fringes as Loci of Constant Path Difference.

A fringe is a locus of points, in the plane on which the eye is focused, for which the phase difference $\kappa \mu e \cos \theta$ has some constant value, say ϕ_1 for one fringe, ϕ_2 for the next, and so on. The phase difference may vary owing to a change † in any one of the three quantities μ, e, and θ. Consider the arrangement shown in fig. 5.9, where a thin film is viewed with the naked eye, using an extended source of light such as the sky or a sodium flame. The film may be of constant optical thickness, or there may be a slow variation of μe from point to point, due to variation of either μ or e. If the film is a few wavelengths thick, fringes will be seen when the eye is focused on the film. Fringes are

---

* We shall later discuss special methods of producing achromatic fringes (see § 5.34).

† We shall see later that it is also possible for variations in one of the quantities to compensate variations in one of the others (§ 5.20).

seen under these conditions because the eye subtends only a very small angle at a given point on the film.

For example, suppose that the film is being viewed at 30° from the normal with a pupil of 3 millimetres diameter situated 50 centimetres from the film. The angle of incidence for light from S_e entering one side of the pupil is 30·17° and for light entering the other side is 29·83°.

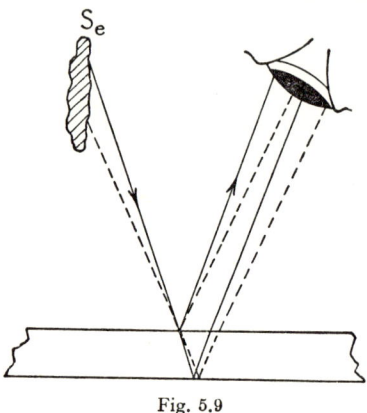

Fig. 5.9

The difference between the cosines is only 0·003. Thus $\cos \theta$ is effectively constant. With sodium light, fringes may be seen when the thickness is more than a few wavelengths, provided that the thickness does not vary too rapidly. If it does vary by more than about 5λ per millimetre, measured along the surface of the film, then the fringes become too close to be observed with the naked eye.

5.17. Fringes of Constant Inclination.

It is not possible to make precise deductions from observations obtained with the above arrangement, because the variation from one fringe to another is partly due to variation of θ, and partly to variation of optical thickness. In laboratory experiments, we usually keep *either* the optical thickness *or* the angle θ constant. The fringes observed with a film of constant optical thickness are loci of constant θ and are known as *fringes of constant inclination*. Such fringes are obtained with the Michelson interferometer when M_2 is set accurately parallel to the reference plane. They may also be seen with a plate of glass several millimetres thick, which is of moderately good quality, using the arrangement shown in fig. 5.8 to obtain nearly normal incidence. With thicker plates or larger angles of incidence, a telescope must be used to collect the beams of light.

The fringes of constant inclination obtained with thick plates are called Haidinger's fringes, though they were first systematically studied by Mascart and by Lummer. Since the light in a given fringe refers to a constant value of θ, the telescope should be focused for infinity and, when the axis of the telescope is normal to the surface, the fringes are circular rings in the focal plane of the objective. When fringes of constant inclination are viewed with the naked eye, it is desirable to focus the eye for infinity but, owing to the small range of angles included by the eye pupil, there is great depth of focus and the fringes may still be seen when the eye is focused near the film, provided it is very thin.

5.18. Fringes of Constant Optical Thickness.

When the sides of a thin film are not quite parallel, we may use an arrangement which makes the angle θ constant over the whole field of view, and may then observe fringes which are essentially contours of constant μe. These are known as *fringes of constant optical thickness*.

For example, consider a wedge of angle 1 in 1000 viewed at nearly normal incidence by an arrangement such as that shown in fig. 5.8. Dark fringes will then occur when $2e = n\lambda$ and the distance between successive dark fringes will be $1000\lambda/2$ or about a quarter of a millimetre. If the eye is placed even a few centimetres from such a film, the variation of θ from one fringe to the next (or even over ten fringes) is very small. The fringes are conveniently viewed with a magnifying glass or a low-power microscope, unless the wedge angle is very small. Fringes of this type may be produced with the Michelson interferometer by setting the mirror M_2 (fig. 4.1) at a small angle to the reference plane. When the wedge is more than a few wavelengths thick, approximately monochromatic light must be used. Using sodium light and a long wedge of angle about 1 in 100, variations in visibility may be observed. The fringes are clear when e is small, disappear when $2e$ is about 500λ, and are very clear again when $2e$ is about 1000λ. The explanation of these variations, in terms of the superposition of the fringe systems due to the two sodium yellow lines, is similar to that given in Chapter IV for the corresponding effects observed with the Michelson interferometer.

5.19. Newton's Rings.

Fringes of constant optical thickness are formed when two spherical surfaces of unequal curvature are placed in contact (see Plate I*e*, p. 74). The loci of equal thickness are then circles. Such fringes were first observed by Hooke (1635–1703) but were first studied by Newton and are known as Newton's rings. They may be observed by placing a

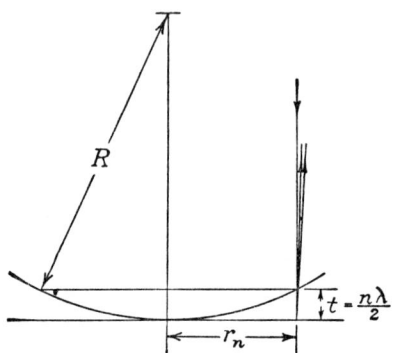

Fig. 5.10.—Newton's rings

convex lens on a flat plate and using the reflex arrangement shown in fig. 5.8. The rings are of convenient size for viewing with a low-power microscope when the radius of curvature of the lower surface of the lens is about one metre. From the geometry of fig. 5.10 it may be seen that, if d_n is the diameter of the nth dark ring and R is the radius of curvature of the lens,

$$d_n{}^2 = 2n\lambda(2R - n\lambda/2)$$

and approximately $\quad d_n = 2\sqrt{(Rn\lambda)}. \quad \ldots \ldots \ldots \quad 5(8)$

Owing to the change of phase of π at the lower surface, the centre is dark. The radii of the rings are thus proportional to the square roots of the natural numbers and the distances between successive rings decrease as n increases. With white light, a few fringes near the point of contact may be seen.

EXAMPLES [5(i)–5(ix)]

5(i). Let r be the ratio of the amplitude of the reflected beam to the amplitude of the incident beam which is taken to be unity. Write down the amplitudes of the beams shown in fig. 5.5; also of the nth beam which emerges on the upper side and the nth beam which emerges on the lower side, assuming that the film is perfectly transparent. Note that the reflection coefficient $= r^2$.

> [Amplitude for beam a is r, for beam b is $r(1 - r^2)$, for beam c is $r^3(1 - r^2)$, and for the nth beam on the upper side $r^{2n-3}(1 - r^2)$. The amplitude for beam a' is $(1 - r^2)$, for beam b' is $r^2(1 - r^2)$, for beam c' is $r^4(1 - r^2)$, and for the nth beam on the lower side $r^{2n-2}(1 - r^2)$. The first formula does not apply when $n = 1$. Note that the relative energy of the beam transmitted through one surface is $1 - r^2$, and its amplitude is $(1 - r^2)^{1/2}$.]

5(ii). Find an expression for the resultant amplitude due to all beams $b, c, \ldots$ etc. up to the nth beam when the phase difference is a multiple of 2π. To what limit does this expression tend when n becomes indefinitely large? What will be the phase relation between this last resultant and the wave which represents beam a?

> [The resultant amplitude is $r\{1 - r^{(2n-1)}\}$ (except when $n = 1$) which tends to r as $n \to \infty$, since $r < 1$. Resultant will differ in phase from beam a by π.]

5(iii). If for a given thickness and angle of incidence the film absorbs a fraction f of the energy which passes through it once, write down expressions corresponding to those required in Example 5(i). Assuming that only two beams need be considered, calculate the visibility for fringes seen by reflected light when $r^2 = 0.05$, (a) when $f = 0$, and (b) when $f = 0.8$.

> [The amplitude for beam a is r, for beam b is $r(1 - r^2)(1 - f)$, for beam c is $r^3(1 - r^2)(1 - f)^2$, and for the nth beam from the upper side $r^{2n-3}(1 - r^2)(1 - f)^{n-1}$. The amplitude for beam a' is $(1 - r^2)(1 - f)^{1/2}$, for beam b' is $r^2(1 - r^2)(1 - f)^{3/2}$, for beam c' is $r^4(1 - r^2)(1 - f)^{5/2}$, and for the nth beam on the lower side $r^{2n-2}(1 - r^2)(1 - f)^{(2n-1)/2}$. When there is no absorption, the visibility of the fringes (as defined in § 4.10) is practically unity. When $f = 0.8$, it is approximately 0.36.]

5(iv). Show that the diameters of Newton's rings, when two surfaces of radii r_1 and r_2 are placed in contact, are related by the equation

$$\frac{1}{r_1} \pm \frac{1}{r_2} = \frac{4n\lambda}{d_n^2}.$$

Consider in what circumstances the sign on the left-hand side is positive.

5(v). Three surfaces A, B, C are placed in contact in pairs successively, and, using light of wavelength 5000 Å., the diameter of the 25th bright ring is found to be:
> 20 mm. when A and B are in contact,
> 26 mm. when B and C are in contact,
> 16 mm. when C and A are in contact.

Find the three radii of curvature. Give the answer to two significant figures.
[8·3 m., 560 m., 14 m.]

5(vi). A film of oil of refractive index 1·7 is placed between an equiconvex lens and a flat plate. The refractive index of the glass is 1·5 and the focal length of the lens is one metre. Find the radius of the 10th dark ring when light of wavelength 6000 Å. is used. (An equiconvex lens is one in which both surfaces are convex and the radii of curvature are numerically equal.)

[Radius of 10th ring = 1·88 mm. Refer to equation 3(32).]

5(vii). Why would the rings be more difficult to see with the arrangement of Example 5(vi) than with an air film?
> [The fringes would be less bright in the ratio 10 : 1 because the index of refraction oil/glass is much smaller than the index glass/air. Some light reflected from the top surface of the lens " dilutes " the fringes and this is the same in both cases.]

5(viii). Show that elliptical rings are obtained when a convex cylindrical surface of radius r_c is placed in contact with a convex spherical lens of radius r_s.
[If the axis of the cylinder is the x axis, the thickness of the air film at point (x, y) is $\dfrac{y^2}{2r_c} + \dfrac{x^2 + y^2}{2r_s}$.]

5(ix). Show that the loci of points at which the path difference of beams from two point sources is constant, are hyperboloids of revolution about the line passing through the sources.

5.20. Localization of Interference Fringes.

Fringes due to the interference of light from two small sources (as in Young's experiment) may be received upon a screen placed at any convenient distance from the sources. If the screen is too close to the sources the fringes are inconveniently small, and if it is too far away the illumination is too weak. Over a considerable range, however, the fringes may be obtained either by photography or by viewing the light through an eyepiece. There are, in fact, a set of surfaces of constant phase difference. It may be shown that when point sources are used these surfaces are hyperboloids. The fringes observed form the intersection of these hyperboloids with the plane of observation. The beams of light from the sources to any point on the plane of observation subtend very small angles and no focusing process is

§5.21 INTERFERENCE FRINGES

involved in the formation of the fringes. The interference of light from extended sources must involve a certain type of focusing. Clear fringes will be observed only when the phase differences of pairs of beams received at a given point from different parts of the source are the same or nearly the same. This condition will, in general, be satisfied only when the point of observation lies on a certain surface, i.e. they will be seen only if the observer's eye (or his instrument of observation) is focused upon this surface. Such fringes are said to be *localized*.

It is found that fringes of equal inclination are best seen with an instrument focused for infinity. Fringes of equal thickness are found to be localized near the film and, for nearly normal incidence, they are most clearly seen by means of a microscope focused on the film. When fringes are formed by narrow pencils of light there may be considerable depth of focus.

5.21.—In a system of fringes of equal inclination a given phase difference corresponds to a definite direction of observation no matter from what part of the source the light originates. The light at a given point in the focal plane of a telescope objective will thus corre-

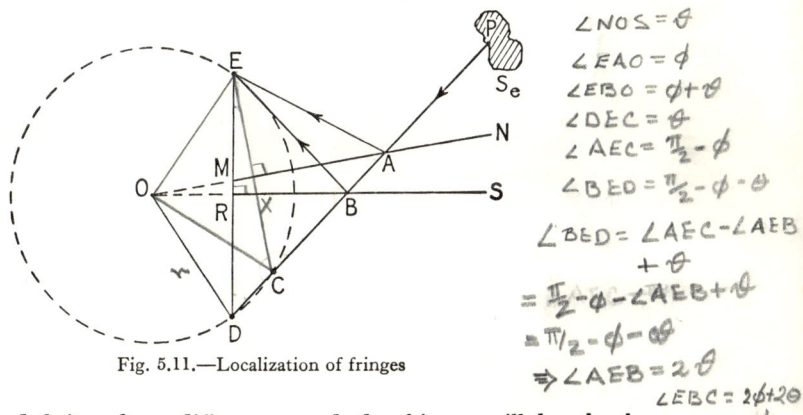

Fig. 5.11.—Localization of fringes

spond to a definite phase difference, and the fringes will be clearly seen through an eyepiece focused upon this plane. The localization of fringes of equal thickness formed by reflections at the surfaces of an air-film between two glass plates may be investigated by the following method which is due to G. F. C. Searle.*

Suppose that the two surfaces of reflection are planes normal to the plane of the diagram (fig. 5.11) which they cut in the lines MN and

* Reference 5.1.

RS, and let these lines meet at the point O. Consider a ray from a particular point P on the extended source (S_e) which is reflected by the upper surface at the point A, and by the lower surface at the point B. Suppose that these two rays meet at the point E. Then E is the image (formed by reflection in the surface MN) of some point C and also the image (formed by reflection in the surface RS) of some point D, both C and D lying on the original direction of the ray PAB. Since MN is the perpendicular bisector of CE and RS of DE, it follows that E, C and D lie on a circle whose centre is O. The path difference of the two beams of light received at E is equal to AB + BE − AE and this is equal to AD − AC, i.e. to CD. If θ is the angle between the plates and r is the radius of the circle, CD is equal to $2r \sin \theta$. Thus the phase difference is the same for all pairs of paths leading from any points on the source to a point on the circle. (The circle is the locus of points of constant phase difference)

Suppose that a microscope is focused on E with its axis directed along the tangent to the circle. The light focused at the centre of the field of view comes from E and, owing to the finite depth of focus, from points on the circle near to E. All this light has the same phase difference and, if $2r \sin \theta = n\lambda$, a maximum is seen at E. The system of fringes is traversed by moving the microscope perpendicular to its axis (i.e. parallel to the radius OE).

One advantage of Searle's treatment is that, since the fundamental relation is derived from the image-forming property of a reflecting surface, it applies even when the ray considered is not in the plane of the diagram. It is also of interest that the separation of the fringes is equal to $\lambda/(2r \sin \theta)$ and is independent of the inclination of the incident light. This result may easily be verified experimentally. The location of the fringes may be studied by viewing the system with the naked eye and moving a pin until coincidence is obtained, using the method of parallax. In this way the circle appropriate to a given fringe may be plotted. For a further discussion of the localization of fringes of constant thickness, see References 5.1, 5.2, and 5.3.

5.22. Non-reflecting Films.

The reflection of light at glass/air surfaces is very undesirable in camera lenses and in many other optical components. In a compound lens with four glass/air surfaces, about 20 per cent of the light is lost by reflection. This reduces the light-gathering power of the lens. Also some of the light reaches the image plane after multiple reflections. This reduces the contrast in the picture. The reflection of light may be reduced by coating the lens surfaces with a film of crystalline material whose refractive index is less than that of the glass (fig. 5.12). The light reflected from the air/crystal surface interferes with the light reflected from the glass/crystal surface. If the index of refraction and the thickness of the film are correctly chosen, the two reflected waves exactly annul one another for one particular wavelength and one angle of incidence.

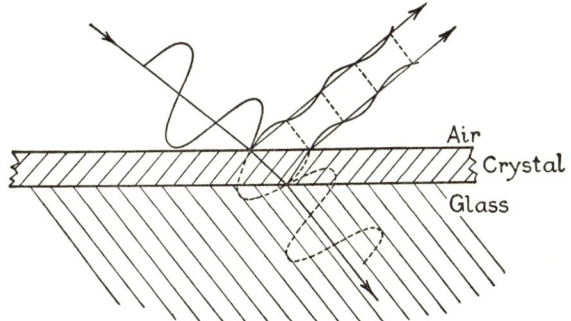

Fig. 5.12.—Non-reflecting film

In order that the two beams shall annul one another two conditions must be fulfilled: (*a*) the amplitudes must be equal, and (*b*) the phase difference must be π. Consider light at normal incidence. If μ_g is the refractive index for air/glass, and μ_c the index for air/crystal, then $\mu_{cg} = \mu_g/\mu_c$, and from 3(55) the condition that the amplitudes shall be equal in magnitude is

$$\frac{\mu_c - 1}{\mu_c + 1} = \frac{\mu_{cg} - 1}{\mu_{cg} + 1}.$$

This is satisfied if
$$\mu_c = \sqrt{\mu_g}. \qquad \qquad \qquad 5(9)$$

Both reflections take place in the less dense medium so the change of phase on reflection is the same for both. Thus in order to produce a phase difference of π it is necessary that

$$2\mu_c e = (2n+1)\tfrac{1}{2}\lambda. \qquad \qquad 5(10)$$

In addition to satisfying 5(9), the ideal crystalline material should be very hard, should not be affected by moisture, etc., and should adhere well to the glass surface. No crystalline material meets all these requirements. Magnesium fluoride or cryolite (sodium aluminium fluoride) is generally used. The refractive indices are 1·38 and 1·36 respectively. When used with heavy flint glasses ($\mu = 1\cdot7$) they satisfy 5(9) approximately, but when used with crown glasses ($\mu = 1\cdot51$) their refractive indices are too high to give the best effect.

It is usual to make the optical thickness equal to a quarter wavelength of green light ($\lambda = 5500$ Å.). The reflection for green light is then very low, while the reflection at the ends of the spectrum is larger. Thus, if white light is incident on the composite surface, the reflected light is mainly red and blue. It has a purple colour rather like the "bloom" on some kinds of ripe plum. For this reason the process of applying the film is known as "blooming". By this process, it is now possible to reduce the reflection of visible light from about 5 per cent to less than 1 per cent.

5.23.—The films are now usually applied by evaporating the crystals *in vacuo* on to the glass surfaces. It is necessary to have a fairly good vacuum and to clean the glass surfaces by special methods in order to secure good adhesion. The thickness of the film is usually adjusted by observing the reflected light and watching for the characteristic purple colour. If the amplitudes are equal the relative energy is given by putting

$$\delta_1 = \frac{2\pi}{\lambda}(2\mu_c\, e \cos\theta)$$

in 4(1). This gives

$$E = 4a_1^2 \cos^2\left(\frac{2\pi}{\lambda}\mu_c\, e \cos\theta\right). \quad \ldots \ldots \quad 5(11)$$

By differentiating 5(11) it may be seen that when 5(10) is satisfied, $\partial E/\partial\theta$, $\partial E/\partial\lambda$, and $\partial E/\partial e$ are all zero at $\theta = 0$. For normal incidence and one wavelength the effectiveness of the film is not greatly reduced if the thickness is not exactly right. Also if the thickness is right for normal incidence and one wavelength, it is nearly right for a considerable range of angle about normal incidence and for a considerable range of wavelength.

5.24. High-efficiency Reflecting Films.

In optical instruments it is sometimes desirable to divide a beam of light into two beams of nearly equal energy. If partly reflecting mirrors are made by coating glass with a thin film of aluminium, a considerable part of the light is absorbed by the metal (a typical film gives 35 per cent transmission, 35 per cent reflection and 30 per cent absorption).* Composite reflecting films of high efficiency may be produced by coating a glass surface with a thin film of low refractive index and then laying down a thin film of high refractive index. If the thicknesses are correctly chosen, the waves from the three reflecting surfaces are all in phase. An overall reflection coefficient of nearly 50 per cent can be obtained and nearly all the light which is not reflected is transmitted. Higher reflection coefficients may be obtained using many layers. With many layers, however, the films become strongly coloured because the condition for strong reflection is exactly satisfied for only one wavelength.

* For a given reflecting power, silver films show much lower absorption when new. They are liable to tarnish rapidly unless protected.

5.25.—Attempts have been made to produce non-reflecting films by treating glass surfaces with chemical reagents which dissolve part of the material. This leaves a surface layer whose refractive index is lower than that of the bulk material. The process is very difficult to control. Films are often seen on old glass or metal surfaces. Sometimes these give low reflection and sometimes high reflection. They are due to the chance production of thin surface layers of abnormal refractive index either during manufacture or by the subsequent action of the air or of cleaning materials on the surfaces.

EXAMPLES [5(x)–5(xii)]

5(x). Calculate the thickness which gives (a) maximum and (b) minimum reflection for light of wavelength 5000 Å. when a crystal of index 2·0 is deposited upon a glass whose index is 1·50. Consider normal incidence.

[(a) $6·25 \times 10^{-6}$ cm., (b) $12·5 \times 10^{-6}$ cm. Note that reflection at the glass/crystal surface takes place in the denser medium].

5(xi). A film of index 1·4 is deposited on a glass of index 1·6, and the thickness is adjusted to give minimum reflection for $\lambda = 5000$ Å. and for normal incidence. Calculate the effective reflection coefficient for (a) 5000 Å., $\theta = 0°$; (b) 6000 Å., $\theta = 0°$; (c) 5000 Å., $\theta = 30°$; (d) 6000 Å., $\theta = 30°$; (e) 4000 Å., $\theta = 30°$. Give two significant figures in the answers. Assume that, to the accuracy required, the reflection coefficient for one surface at 30° is the same as that at normal incidence.

[(a) 1·0%, (b) 1·3%, (c) 1·2%, (d) 1·8%, (e) 1·1%.]

5(xii). Show that the reflecting power for white light of a glass surface coated with a film many wavelengths thick is approximately half that of an uncoated surface.

[Passing from one end of the spectrum to the other, the cosine in 5(11) goes through many periods. The mean value of the square is 0·5.]

5.26. Interference with Multiple Beams.

If the surfaces bounding a film have a fairly high reflection coefficient, fringes of transmission with very sharp bright maxima on a dark ground may be produced (Plate I*f*, p. 74). These fringes are produced by the mutual interference of several beams which have suffered different numbers of reflections. Let us first consider an <u>air-film</u> bounded by two plane, parallel, half-silvered surfaces. Several parallel beams of light are produced by an initial beam incident at an angle θ (fig. 5.13). The transmitted beams are collected by the lens L and brought to a focus at a point Q in its focal plane. The lens brings all the beams together at Q with the phase differences which they had when they crossed the plane AB which is normal to OQ. Suppose that the two films are similar, and that a fraction σ of the light is transmitted and a fraction ρ reflected at each incidence. Let the change of phase on reflection be ϵ. With metallic films, owing to absorption, $\rho + \sigma$ is not equal to unity. Also ϵ is not exactly 0 or π. The ratios of the amplitudes of the transmitted and reflected waves to the amplitude of the incident wave are $\sigma^{1/2}$ and $\rho^{1/2}$ respectively.

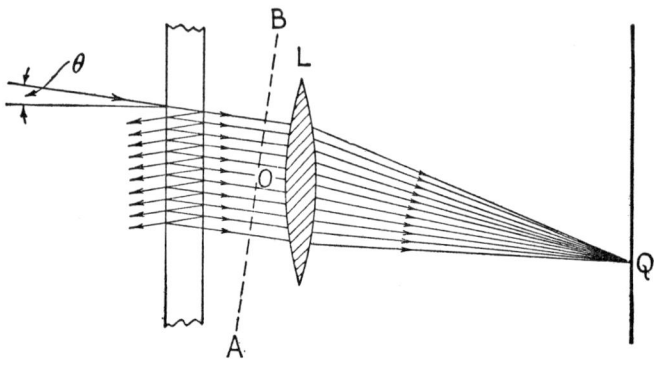

Fig. 5.13.—Multiple-beam interference

The phase difference between two successive beams is

$$\delta = \frac{2\pi}{\lambda} 2e \cos\theta + 2\epsilon. \qquad \qquad 5(12)$$

If the incident beam is represented by

$$a_1 \exp i(\omega t - \kappa x) = a_1 e^{i\varphi},$$

the resultant transmitted wave is represented by

$$\sigma a_1 e^{i\varphi} + \rho \sigma a_1 e^{i(\varphi - \delta)} + \rho^2 \sigma a_1 e^{i(\varphi - 2\delta)} + \ldots$$

If P is the complex amplitude of the resultant (§ 2.26), we have

$$P = a_1 \{\sigma + \rho \sigma e^{-i\delta} + \rho^2 \sigma e^{-2i\delta} + \ldots\}$$

$$= \frac{a_1 \sigma}{1 - \rho e^{-i\delta}}. \qquad \qquad 5(13)$$

The complex conjugate P^* is given by

$$P^* = \frac{a_1 \sigma}{1 - \rho e^{i\delta}},$$

§ 5.26 INTERFERENCE WITH MULTIPLE BEAMS 143

and by a calculation similar to that given in § 3.6 we have

$$E = PP^* = \frac{a_1^2 \sigma^2}{1 + \rho^2 - 2\rho \cos \delta},$$

which may be written

$$E = \frac{a_1^2 \sigma^2}{(1-\rho)^2} \cdot \frac{1}{1 + \dfrac{4\rho}{(1-\rho)^2} \sin^2 \tfrac{1}{2}\delta}. \quad \ldots \quad 5(14)$$

Maxima occur when $\cos \delta = 1$ (i.e. when $\delta = 2n\pi$) and the minima are half-way between the maxima. The positions of the maxima and minima are thus independent of the values of ρ and σ. The maximum relative energy ($E_{\max}$) is $a_1^2\sigma^2/(1-\rho)^2$ and the minimum ($E_{\min}$) is $a_1^2\sigma^2/(1+\rho)^2$. Using equation 5(12), it may be seen that the maxima occur when

$$2e \cos \theta = \lambda\left(n - \frac{\epsilon}{\pi}\right). \quad \ldots \quad 5(15a)$$

This reduces to

$$2e \cos \theta = n\lambda, \quad \ldots \quad 5(15b)$$

if the change of phase on reflection may be neglected.

Circular fringes are obtained with the arrangement shown in fig. 5.14. The order of interference decreases from the centre outwards, because the path difference is smaller when the rays impinge at an

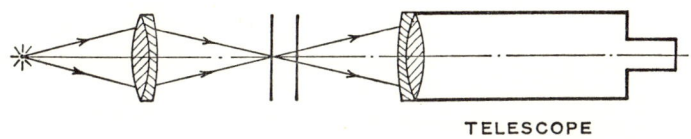

TELESCOPE
Focused for Infinity

Fig. 5.14.—Plate of constant thickness viewed by convergent light

angle than when they are normal to the plates. The fringes are localized at infinity and are usually viewed with a telescope. The light reaching a given point in the focal plane of the objective corresponds to a certain direction of incidence. It comes from all parts of the film.

5.27.—From equation 5(14), it may be seen that a high reflection coefficient produces sharp maxima. If δ differs a little from $n\pi$, so that $\sin^2 \tfrac{1}{2}\delta$ has some value η, then

$$E_\eta = \frac{E_{\max}}{1 + L\eta}, \quad \ldots \ldots \quad 5(16a)$$

where
$$L = \frac{4\rho}{(1-\rho)^2}. \quad \ldots \ldots \quad 5(16b)$$

When ρ is of the order of 0·05 corresponding to unsilvered plates $L = 0·2$, but when ρ is 0·8, corresponding to fairly heavily silvered plates, $L = 80$. Thus with strongly silvered plates the illumination in directions which differ only a little from the directions of the maxima is very low and the fringes appear as sharp bright lines on a dark ground. The value of ρ chosen is determined by the necessity of compromising between the increase of sharpness due to high ρ and the reduction of overall brightness due to the consequent reduction of σ.

5.28. Fabry-Pérot Interferometer.

Several different methods of using the fringes formed by multiple reflections in plates of constant thickness have been designed. The Fabry-Pérot *interferometer* consists of two glass plates, one fixed and the other mounted on a carriage similar to that used in the Michelson interferometer. This plate can be slowly moved in a direction perpendicular to itself. The guides are so accurately constructed that the moving plate remains parallel to the fixed plate to within less than a second of arc. The plates are coated with a film of silver.

In the Fabry-Pérot *etalon* the two plates are at a fixed distance apart. This distance is determined by separators accurately made so as to secure very good parallelism. The applications of the Fabry-Pérot apparatus will be described in Chapter IX. Examples of fringes obtained with a Fabry-Pérot etalon are shown in Plate I*f* and I*g* (p. 74).

5.29. Channelled Spectrum.

When a parallel beam of white light is allowed to fall upon a Fabry-Pérot etalon and the transmitted light is viewed in a spectroscope (fig. 5.15), the spectrum is crossed by a number of dark bands (Plate II*f*, p. 130). It is therefore called a *channelled* or *banded* spectrum though such spectra have, of course, no connection with *band* spectra due to molecules (§ 4.3). From equation 5(14), it is clear that maximum brightness occurs at wavelengths for which $\sin \tfrac{1}{2}\delta = 0$, i.e. when δ is an integral multiple of 2π. If the phase change on reflection [equation

5(12)] may be neglected, maxima occur at wavelengths λ_0, λ_1, λ_2, etc., which satisfy the relation

$$2e \cos \theta = p\lambda_0 = (p+1)\lambda_1 = (p+2)\lambda_2, \quad . \quad 5(17)$$

where p is an integer.

5.30.—By a simple extension of the discussion given in § 5.27, it may be shown that the maxima are sharp when the reflection coefficient is high, but a very high reflection coefficient implies a low transmission and makes the bands difficult to observe. In practice very sharp bands are obtained only if the beam of light is well collimated and if the plates of the etalon are accurately plane and parallel.

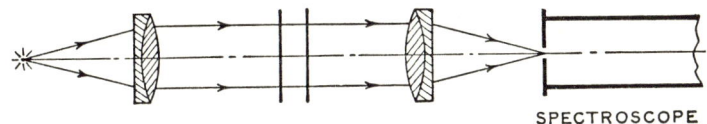

Fig. 5.15.—Edser-Butler method

Channelled spectra may also be observed by spectroscopic examination of light in the outer parts of a fringe system produced by any of the arrangements described in §§ 5.9–5.10. The bands so obtained are not so sharp because only two interfering beams are involved.

5.31. Edser-Butler Method of calibrating the Spectrometer.

If the thickness of the etalon has been measured (by any of the methods described in Chapter IX), the bands may be used to determine a curve, or formula, giving the relation between wavelength and position in the spectrum. The method is a convenient one because the bands provide a series of calibration marks suitably spaced throughout the spectrum. By choosing the right thickness of etalon, the spacing may be made as close as is desirable for the particular spectrograph or spectroscope which is being calibrated. Fringes of this type were first discovered by Fizeau and Foucault (1850) and were first used in the above way by Esselbach (1856). The method of calibration did not come into common use until it was rediscovered in 1896 by Edser and Butler and it is generally known in England by their name.

The banded spectrum may be used, in conjunction with two known wavelengths, to determine the thickness of the etalon. The light from the etalon is allowed to form a banded spectrum and, by means of a small mirror, the line spectrum including the known lines λ_1 and λ_2 is made to appear above or below the channelled spectrum. The number of maxima between the two lines is counted. If this number is m we have approximately

$$2e = p_1\lambda_1 = (p_1 + m)\lambda_2, \quad \ldots \ldots \quad 5(18)$$

and hence
$$2e = m\left(\frac{\lambda_1\lambda_2}{\lambda_1 - \lambda_2}\right). \quad \ldots \ldots \quad 5(19)$$

Equation 5(19) is exactly correct only if two bright bands happen to coincide with the lines. When this is not so, the positions of the maxima on either side of λ_1 and λ_2 may be measured. Using these readings and interpolating by proportional parts, two fractional parts to be added to m may be determined, and 5(19) may then be applied. This method of determining the thickness of the etalon forms an instructive class experiment, but is generally less accurate and less convenient than the method described in § 9.29.

EXAMPLES [5(xiii)–5(xvi)]

5(xiii). Compare and contrast the fringes formed by the Fabry-Pérot etalon using convergent monochromatic light with Newton's rings.

5(xiv). Show that the Edser-Butler method provides a set of marks spaced at equal intervals of wavelength constant (κ).

5(xv). Show that for a given direction of incidence the phase change on reflection is equivalent to a small correction to the separation of the plates of a Fabry-Pérot etalon.

5(xvi). The circular fringes formed by a Fabry-Pérot etalon are numbered 1, 2, 3, ... p from the centre outwards. Show that if the separation of the plates is a large integral multiple of the wavelength, the angular diameter of the pth ring is approximately proportional to $\sqrt{(p-1)}$, when p is fairly small.

5.32. Fringes of Superposition.

Consider a beam of light incident successively upon two etalons (fig. 5.16). There will be a considerable number of emergent beams corresponding to different internal reflections. Under suitable conditions certain sets of emergent beams may have small path differences and give rise to interference fringes with white light. Consider, for example, two etalons of thicknesses e_1 and e_2, inclined at a small angle α to one another. Suppose that the emergent light is observed in a telescope and consider light which makes an angle θ with the normal to the first etalon. The path difference between (a) light which has made two reflections in the first etalon and four in the second, and

§ 5.32 FRINGES OF SUPERPOSITION

(b) light which has made six reflections in the first etalon and two in the second is

$$6e_1 \cos \theta + 2e_2 \cos(\theta + \alpha) - 2e_1 \cos \theta - 4e_2 \cos(\theta + \alpha)$$
$$= 4e_1 \cos \theta - 2e_2 \cos(\theta + \alpha)$$
$$= (4e_1 - 2e_2 \cos \alpha) \cos \theta + 2e_2 \sin \theta \sin \alpha. \quad . \quad 5(20)$$

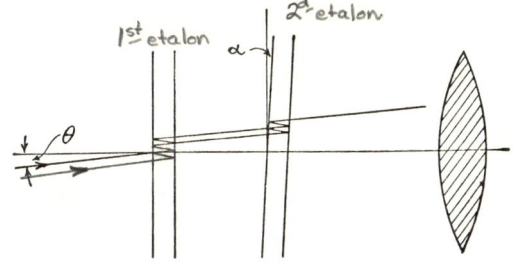

Fig. 5.16.—Fringes of superposition

If the second etalon is slightly more than twice as thick as the first, this path difference will be zero for some fairly small value of θ. Suppose that the inclination (α) has been adjusted so that the path difference is zero for $\theta = 0$. We then have

$$2e_1 = e_2 \cos \alpha \quad . \quad . \quad . \quad . \quad 5(21)$$

or, approximately,
$$e_2 - 2e_1 = \tfrac{1}{2} e_2 \alpha^2 \quad . \quad . \quad . \quad . \quad 5(22)$$

$\left(\cos \alpha = 1 - \frac{\alpha^2}{2!} + \frac{\alpha^4}{4!} - \cdots \right)$

and bright fringes will be obtained when

$$n\lambda = 2e_2 \sin \theta \sin \alpha. \quad . \quad . \quad . \quad . \quad 5(23)$$

Since the maxima correspond to a definite value of θ, the fringes are localized at infinity and may be seen in the telescope. If the telescope is normal to the first etalon, the central achromatic fringe will be in the centre of its field and the angular separation θ' of the fringes will be given approximately by

$$\theta' = \frac{\lambda}{2e_2 \alpha}. \quad . \quad . \quad . \quad . \quad . \quad 5(24)$$

A measurement of the angular separation of the fringes determines α and equation 5(22) gives $(e_2 - 2e_1)$, provided an approximate value of e_2 is available. Fringes of this type are called fringes of superposition. They were first observed by Brewster in 1815. He used two glass plates of nearly equal thickness. The above method of using the fringes to compare the thicknesses of two etalons was suggested by Fabry and Buisson and was used by Sears and Barrell (§ 9.41).

5.33.—An alternative method of using the fringes to compare the thicknesses of two etalons is to set the two etalons so that $\alpha = 0$, and to allow the light to pass also through a thin wedge. In these circumstances fringes localized in the wedge are obtained. The centre of the fringe system is located at the point where the path in the wedge exactly compensates for the difference in path due to the etalons. This method of comparing two etalons was used by Benoît, Fabry and Pérot (§ 9.38).

Either of the methods described may be used to compare etalons the ratio of whose thicknesses is approximately $p:q$, where p and q are two small whole numbers. Fabry and Buisson state that etalons of ratio 10 : 1 may be compared. If the numbers p and q are not small, large numbers of internal reflections are involved with a corresponding loss of light. The fringes then become indistinct because they are seen against a brighter background due to beams which have not made the correct series of reflections to give interference fringes. Although, in the above treatment, we have considered only two beams, fringes of super-position are formed by multiple-beam interference when silvered plates are used. The reflection coefficient affects their sharpness just as it does with the circular fringes.

5.34. Achromatic Fringes.

If the geometrical path difference between two routes from a source of light to a point of observation is the same for all wavelengths, the phase difference will depend on the wavelength. Fringes are then obtained with white light only when the path difference is small. If,

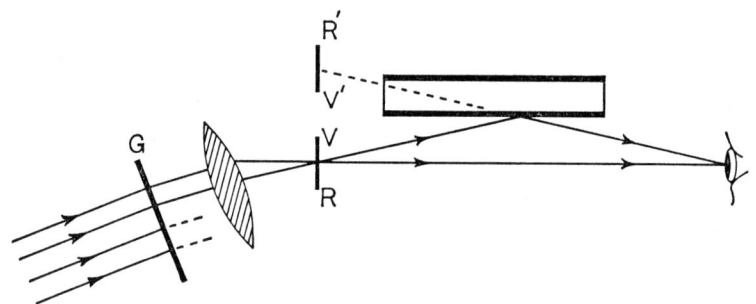

Fig. 5.17.—Lloyd's arrangement for achromatic fringes

however, the geometrical path is different for different wavelengths, then there is a possibility that the geometrical path difference may be made proportional to the wavelength, so that the phase difference is the same for all wavelengths. If this condition is fulfilled, achromatic fringes may be obtained with white light even when the path difference

§ 5.34　　　　　ACHROMATIC FRINGES　　　　　149

is fairly large. A simple arrangement for producing fringes of this type is shown in fig. 5.17. The slit source used with Lloyd's mirror is replaced by a short spectrum RV formed by the slits and a prism or grating placed at G. The grating is to be preferred since it produces a spectrum in which distances are directly proportional to wavelength✓ (§ 6.13). The separation of the " sources " in Lloyd's mirror is then proportional to the wavelength and the separation of the fringes is the same for all wavelengths [equation 5(4)].

5.35.—The example we have just considered shows the possibility of the formation of a system of achromatic fringes, but is too restricted to show the general conditions required for their observation. In discussing the wider problem let us start by considering two extreme cases. With the Michelson interferometer, using cadmium red light, fringes corresponding to orders of interference up to about a million have been obtained. There is a very gradual decrease in visibility at high orders due to the imperfect homogeneity of the light, but apart from this effect all fringes are identical. This, as

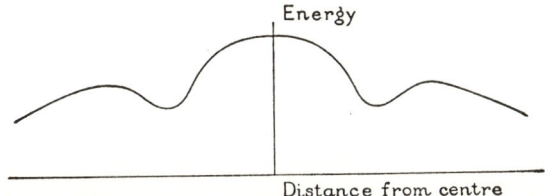

Fig. 5.18.—Energy distribution as measured by bolometer

we shall see later, sometimes occasions a practical difficulty when it is desired to identify the fringe of a particular order (see § 9.24). The other extreme case may be represented by the fringes formed in Young's experiment with white light. The centre of the system corresponds to zero phase difference for all wavelengths, but there is no place where the phase difference is π for all wavelengths. Thus there is not even one fringe which is strictly white on black. By eye, about half a dozen fringes can be seen.

If a bolometer is used to measure the energy arriving at different places on the screen, a curve of the type shown in fig. 5.18 is obtained. The bolometer is a non-selective detector of radiation; it measures the energy and is equally sensitive to all wavelengths. The two minima on either side of the maximum are present because ordinary white light contains more energy of some wavelengths than of others (Chapter

XVII). A source of light for which (in the notation of § 4.19) $a(\kappa)$ is independent of κ shows no trace of interference. If, however, a filter transmitting a small region of the spectrum is placed in front of the bolometer, fringes are recorded just as they would be if the same filter were placed in front of the source. If the light from a certain narrow region is analysed in a spectroscope, bands are seen in the spectrum (§ 5.29). Thus interference is observed when either

(a) the source emits radiation in which some wavelengths predominate, or

(b) the receptor is able to analyse the energy it receives into a spectrum.

To observe high orders of interference, it is necessary either to have a source of very homogeneous light or to use a receptor which can make a very fine analysis. A selective receptor (such as the bolometer covered with a filter) from this point of view makes a very simple analysis of the light, distinguishing between (a) light to which it is sensitive and (b) light to which it is not sensitive. The eye makes an analysis of light in terms of three primary colours and is therefore able to see a few fringes where the non-selective bolometer could detect none.

5.36. Achromatic Systems of Fringes.

In Young's experiment, there is one place in the field of view where the phase difference is the same for all wavelengths. There is thus one achromatic fringe. In the experiment described in § 5.34, in which Lloyd's mirror is combined with a grating, the phase difference is independent of the wavelength at all parts of the field. We then have a *system of achromatic fringes*. It is important to distinguish these two cases. In the one we have a single place where the fringes of all wavelengths coincide, but the separation of the fringes is a function of the wavelength, and therefore the system is achromatized for only one fringe. In the second case the separation is independent of the wavelength so that, if the fringes are made to coincide at one point, they do so everywhere.

5.37.—Analytically, we may suppose the order of interference (p) to be a function of λ and of a co-ordinate x which locates the position of the fringe in the field of view. p is not necessarily integral (§ 4.9). Then for an achromatic fringe we require

$$\frac{\partial p}{\partial \lambda} = 0 \qquad \qquad \qquad 5(25)$$

at some point in the field.

For an achromatic system we require 5(25) and also

$$\frac{\partial}{\partial x}\left(\frac{\partial p}{\partial \lambda}\right) = \frac{\partial^2 p}{\partial x\,\partial \lambda} = 0. \qquad \ldots \ldots \quad 5(26)$$

For *perfect achromatism*, 5(25) should be true for all values of λ, and 5(26) for all values of λ and x. In practice we usually call a lens "achromatic" when the variation of focal length with wavelength has a maximum or minimum for some wavelength near the middle of the visible spectrum (fig. 5.19). In a similar way, we call a *fringe* achromatic if 5(25) is satisfied for some value

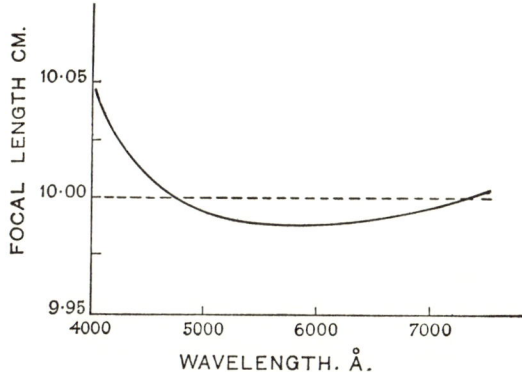

Fig. 5.19.—Variation of focal length with wavelength for an achromatic lens combination

of λ near the middle of a range in which we are interested, and a *system* achromatic if 5(25) and 5(26) are satisfied for one wavelength and at one point. The central fringe in Young's experiment is *perfectly achromatic*, to the extent to which we can neglect secondary effects due to finite slit width, etc. Subject to a similar limitation, the system described in § 5.34 is *perfectly achromatic* when a grating is used. It is achromatic, in the less restricted sense, when a prism is used.

5.38.—It is possible to shift the centre of a system of fringes, such as those obtained by Young, Fresnel or Lloyd, by inserting a plate of optically dense material in front of one of the real or virtual sources of light, e.g. to the right of slit a_1 in fig. 5.2b. If this material is non-dispersive, the central fringe will move to the position where the difference of optical path is zero, i.e. where the paths from the two sources to the point are equal when measured in wavelengths. In general the material has some dispersion. One of the optical paths is a function of the wavelength and the other is not. Therefore, the path difference is a function of the wavelength, and there is no point for which this difference is zero for all wavelengths. In these circumstances the central fringe is located at the point where 5(25) is satisfied, i.e. at the point of maximum agreement of phase difference. This does not, in general, coincide with the place where the path difference is zero for the central, or indeed for any one, wavelength.

5.39.—It was shown in § 4.29 that when a non-homogeneous beam of light travels through a dispersive medium, the point at which the phases of the disturbance, of different wavelengths, are in best agreement, travels with the group velocity. Thus, in the type of experiment which we are considering, the maximum agreement of *difference* of phase will occur at a point P such that the time taken for the light to travel from S to P by the non-dispersive path is equal to the time taken for a wave group to travel from S to P by the dispersive path. We shall now show that when this condition is satisfied, 5(25) is also satisfied.

Suppose that the non-dispersive path from S to P is of length l and that the other path from S to P consists of a distance $L - t_g$ in the non-dispersive medium, which for simplicity we take to be a vacuum, and t_g in the dispersive medium. Then the phase difference between light arriving at P from S by the two routes is

$$p = \frac{2\pi}{\lambda}\{L - l + (n-1)t_g\}, \quad \ldots \ldots \quad 5(27)$$

where λ is the wavelength *in vacuum*.

Differentiating with respect to λ, condition 5(25) gives

$$(L - l) + \left(n - \lambda\frac{dn}{d\lambda} - 1\right)t_g = 0. \quad \ldots \ldots \quad 5(28)$$

This equation determines the position of the new achromatic fringe.

The condition that the wave groups shall arrive together is

$$\frac{l}{c} = \frac{L - t_g}{c} + \frac{t_g}{U}, \quad \ldots \ldots \quad 5(29)$$

where U is the group velocity. Inserting the value of U from 4(41) we have

$$\frac{1}{U} = \frac{1}{b} - \frac{\lambda}{c}\frac{dn}{d\lambda} \qquad (L - l) + \left(n - \lambda\frac{dn}{d\lambda} - 1\right)t_g = 0, \quad \ldots \ldots \quad 5(30)$$

in agreement with 5(28).

It was at one time thought that the achromatic fringe was located at the point where the path difference is zero (presumably for the mean wavelength). The condition so calculated differs from 5(28) in that it does not include the term $\lambda\, dn/d\lambda$. The essentials of the present theory were originally put forward by Sir G. B. Airy (1801–92) in reply to certain critics who, basing their argument on the incorrect formula, thought that the wave theory did not give the right value for the shift of the fringes. The modern development of the theory is due to Rayleigh (Reference 5.4).

5.40. Interference Filters.

Coloured glasses or dyed gelatine filters may be used to isolate a region of the spectrum covering a range of 500 Å. but, for many experi-

§ 5.40 INTERFERENCE FILTERS

ments in photo-chemistry and for other purposes, it is desirable to isolate a band 50 Å. wide centred on a chosen wavelength; and occasionally much narrower bands are desired. *Interference filters* may conveniently be used for these purposes. We have seen in § 5.30 that the spectrum of a parallel beam of light which has passed through a Fabry-Pérot etalon consists of a series of sharp bands separated by wider dark regions (Plate IIf, p. 130). If the distance between the reflecting surfaces is reduced, then the wavelength difference between the transmission maxima is increased. Equation 5(17) shows that for an optical thickness of $\lambda_0/2$, and for normal incidence, the transmission maxima are λ_0, $\lambda_0/2$, $\lambda_0/3$, etc. If λ_0 is placed in the visible spectrum then all transmission bands, except the first, lie in the ultra-violet and are absorbed by a suitable glass. If the silver surfaces have a reflection coefficient of 94 per cent and $\lambda_0 = 5000$ Å., the transmission band-width (measured between wavelengths for which the transmission is half the maximum transmission) is 50 Å. (fig. 5.20a).

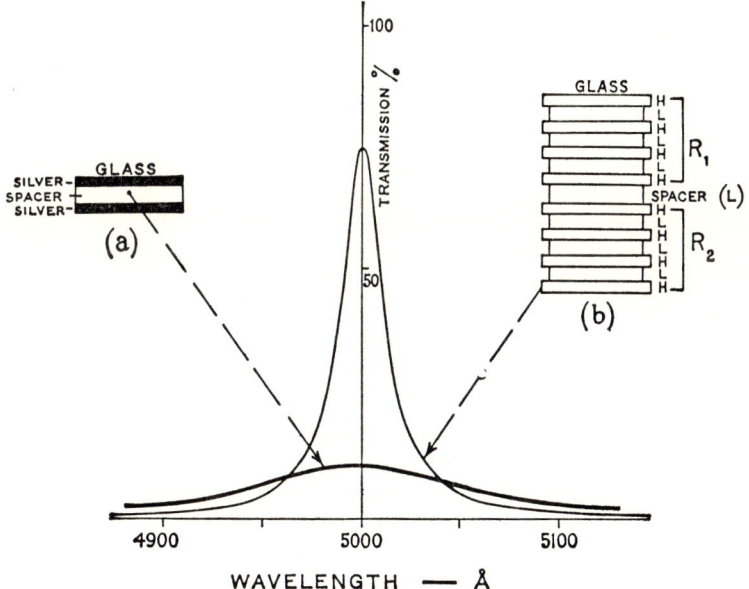

Fig. 5.20.—Interference Filters. Typical transmission curve for (a) filter consisting of two layers of silver (94% reflectivity) separated by a dielectric "spacer" whose optical thickness is 2500 Å, and (b) a filter consisting of two reflectors R_1 and R_2 separated by a similar spacer. The reflectors consist of layers of high (H) and low (L) index material and the optical thickness of each layer is 1250 Å.

When silver films are used the high reflectivity is obtained only by increasing the thickness of the film and so reducing the maximum transmission (§ 5.27). This limitation may be overcome by using, in place of the silver layers, high-efficiency reflectors constructed in the way described in § 5.24. These high-reflecting " stacks " consist of layers of dielectric materials. The layers are of equal optical thickness and alternate layers are of high and of low refractive index. Since the highest reflectivity is needed only in a narrow range of wavelength, it is possible to use stacks of many layers, and reflectivities of 98 per cent may be obtained. The loss of light by absorption is very small. The layers are deposited by vacuum evaporation and there is a small loss of light by scattering since perfectly homogeneous films are not obtained by this process. It is possible to obtain a band-width of 25 Å. with a maximum transmission of 75 per cent (fig. 5.20b). In addition to band-pass filters for desired regions of the visible spectrum, many other devices for giving selective transmission or reflection may be made by suitable combinations of high and low index layers. For further details the reader should consult References 5.5 and 5.6. A different kind of interference filter is described in § 12.53.

EXAMPLES [5(xvii)–5(xix)]

5(xvii). Two etalons have separations of 19·9990 mm and 40·000 mm. Find the angular separation of fringes formed in the way described in § 5.32 when light of wavelength 5000 Å. is used. [6·25 × 10^{-4} radian.]

5(xviii). Discuss the achromatization of Lloyd's mirror fringes by means of a prism of material which obeys Cauchy's law (§ 3.18).

5(xix). What effects are observed when the fringes formed in a thin film enclosed between two plane surfaces are viewed through a prism?

[The fringes are shifted but not made achromatic. The position of the new central fringe is obtained by applying the discussion of § 5.39.]

REFERENCES

5.1. SEARLE: *Phil. Mag.*, 1946, Vol. XXXVII, p. 361.
5.2. ARNOT: *Proc. Camb. Phil. Soc.*, 1938, Vol. XXIV, p. 150.
5.3. GUILD: *Proc. Phys. Soc.*, Vol. XXXIII, p. 40.
5.4. RAYLEIGH: *Scientific Papers*, Vol. III, p. 288.
5.5. HEAVENS: *Optical Properties of Thin Solid Films* (Butterworth).
5.6. HEAVENS: *Reports on Progress in Physics*, Vol. XXIII, p. 1 (Phys. Soc., London).
5.7. HOPKINS: *Proc. Roy. Soc.* A, 1951, Vol. 208, p. 263.
5.8. BORN and WOLF: *Principles of Optics* (Pergamon Press, London).
5.9. HANBURY BROWN and TWISS: *Proc. Roy. Soc.* A, 1957, Vol. 242, p. 300.

COHERENCE

APPENDIX V A

COHERENCE

1.—In this Appendix we develop some formulæ related to the discussion of coherence in §§ 5.1–3 and 5.8. We first wish to calculate the visibility, as a function of the size of the primary source (S) of the fringes produced in the neighbourhood of Q by the interference of light from P_1 and P_2 (fig. 5.21), when the path difference is small compared with the length of the wave train. This problem was investigated by Van Cittert (1934). Further advances are due to Zernike (1938) and to Hopkins (1951) whose treatment is followed in §§ 1–5 below.†

Suppose that P_1 and P_2 receive light from S, that the relative energies at these points are E_1 and E_2, and that interference occurs at Q. The light may reach Q

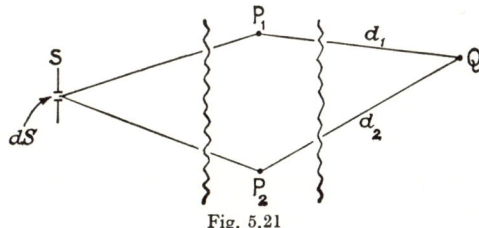

Fig. 5.21

directly, as in Young's experiment, or there may be optical components between S and P_1 or P_2, or between P_1 and P_2 and Q. The optical properties of these systems may be different for the paths P_1 to Q, and P_2 to Q. Let us suppose that they are such that a disturbance at P_1 of unit amplitude and zero phase gives rise to a disturbance at Q of complex amplitude $f_1 = g_1 \exp(i\kappa d_1)$, and let the corresponding quantity for the path P_2 to Q be $f_2 = g_2 \exp(i\kappa d_2)$, where κ is the wavelength constant. d_1 and d_2 are the optical paths and g_1 and g_2 are the transmission factors (for amplitude) from P_1 and P_2 to Q. Suppose that an amplitude a_1 at P_1 is associated with an element dS of the source, and an amplitude a_2 at P_2 is associated with the same element, so that the relative energies at P_1 and P_2 are

$$E_1 = \int a_1 a_1^* \, dS \quad \text{and} \quad E_2 = \int a_2 a_2^* \, dS, \quad \ldots \quad 5(31)$$

the integrals being taken over the whole area of the source.

The amplitude at Q associated with the element dS is $(f_1 a_1 + f_2 a_2)$, and the corresponding energy is

$$dE_Q = (f_1 a_1 + f_2 a_2)(f_1^* a_1^* + f_2^* a_2^*); \quad \ldots \quad 5(32)$$

and, using the relation $Z_1 Z_2^* + Z_1^* Z_2 = 2\mathscr{R}(Z_1 Z_2^*)$, we have

$$dE_Q = f_1 f_1^* \, a_1 a_1^* + f_2 f_2^* \, a_2 a_2^* + 2\mathscr{R}(f_1 f_2^* \, a_1 a_2^*), \quad \ldots \quad 5(33)$$

where $\mathscr{R}$ stands for " real part of ".

† See Reference 5.7.

The whole effect at Q obtained by integrating 5(33) is

$$E_Q = g_1^2 E_1 + g_2^2 E_2 + 2(E_1 E_2)^{\frac{1}{2}} \mathscr{R}(\gamma_{12} f_1 f_2^*), \quad \ldots \quad 5(34)$$

where
$$\gamma_{12} = \frac{1}{(E_1 E_2)^{\frac{1}{2}}} \int a_1 a_2^* \, dS. \quad \ldots \ldots \quad 5(35)$$

γ_{12} is called the *phase coherence factor* for light from P_1 and P_2.

2.—We may write $\gamma_{12} = V_{12} \exp(i\beta_{12})$, i.e. $|\gamma_{12}| = V_{12}$, . . . 5(36)
and
$$g_1^2 E_1 = E_1'; \quad g_2^2 E_2 = E_2'. \quad \ldots \ldots \quad 5(37)$$

We then have

$$E_Q = E_1' + E_2' + 2(E_1' E_2')^{\frac{1}{2}} V_{12} \cos\{\beta_{12} + \kappa(d_1 - d_2)\}, \quad 5(38a)$$

remembering that $f_1 f_2^* = g_1 g_2 \exp\{\kappa(d_1 - d_2)\}$.

To relate the visibility of the fringes to V_{12}, we note that 5(38a) predicts a variation of energy from

$$E_{\max} = E_1' + E_2' + 2V_{12}(E_1' E_2')^{\frac{1}{2}}$$

to
$$E_{\min} = E_1' + E_2' - 2V_{12}(E_1' E_2')^{\frac{1}{2}}. \quad \ldots \ldots \quad 5(39)$$

The visibility as defined by equation 4(3) is given by

$$V = \frac{2(E_1' E_2')^{\frac{1}{2}}}{E_1' + E_2'} V_{12}. \quad \ldots \ldots \quad 5(40)$$

When
$$E_1' = E_2', \quad V = V_{12}, \quad \ldots \ldots \quad 5(41)$$

so that the modulus of the phase coherence factor is equal to the visibility " obtained in the most favourable circumstances ", i.e. to the degree of coherence defined by Zernike.

Equation 5(38a) may be written

$$E_Q = (1 - V_{12})(E_1' + E_2') + V_{12}[E_1' + E_2' +$$
$$2(E_1' E_2')^{\frac{1}{2}} \cos\{\beta_{12} + \kappa(d_1 - d_2)\}], \quad \ldots \ldots \quad 5(38b)$$

i.e. the intensity at Q and the visibility of the fringes are the same as they would be if a fraction V_{12} of the light at P_1 and P_2 were perfectly coherent and a fraction $(1 - V_{12})$ were perfectly non-coherent.

3.—The order of interference (p) is given by

$$\beta_{12} + \kappa(d_1 - d_2) = 2\pi p, \quad \ldots \ldots \quad 5(42)$$

i.e. there is an effective phase difference β_{12} (additional to that due to the path difference $d_1 - d_2$) between the light from P_1 and that from P_2. If $\gamma_{12} = 1$, then the sources are coherent and in phase. If $\gamma_{12} = -1$, the sources are coherent but in antiphase.

4. Calculation of γ_{12}.

Suppose that the element dS is situated at A whose co-ordinates are x, y (fig. 5.22) and that the energy associated with this element is $E_s \, dS$. Then, if $AP_1 = r_1$, we have

$$a_1 = \frac{(E_s)^{\frac{1}{2}}}{r_1} \exp(i\kappa r_1). \quad \ldots \ldots \quad 5(43)$$

Substituting for a_1 and a_2 in 5(35) we obtain

$$\gamma_{12} = \frac{1}{(E_1 E_2)^{\frac{1}{2}}} \int \frac{E_s}{r_1 r_2} \exp\{i\kappa(r_1 - r_2)\} \, dS. \quad \ldots \ldots \quad 5(44)$$

This expression is mathematically similar to the diffraction equation 6(1) except that $E_s/r_1 r_2$ replaces A/r, i.e. energy replaces amplitude.* For our present pur-

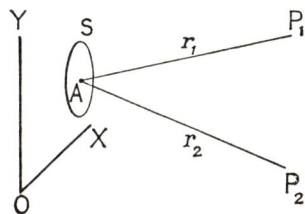

Fig. 5.22

poses, it is convenient to evaluate the expression directly for two special cases. We assume that E_s is the same for all parts of S and that r_1 and r_2 vary so little that we may regard them as constant in the denominator, though not in the exponential. Then 5(44) reduces to

$$\gamma_{12} = C \int \exp i\kappa(r_1 - r_2) \, dS, \quad \ldots \ldots \quad 5(45)$$

where C is a constant which we can determine by the condition that γ_{12} approaches 1 when the source is very small.

For the arrangement shown in fig. 5.3 we may put $r_1 - r_2 = 2hy'/l'$ for the rays in the plane of the diagram. We then have

$$\gamma_{12} = C' \int_{-d}^{d} \exp i\left(\frac{2\kappa h y'}{l'}\right) dy', \quad \ldots \ldots \quad 5(46)$$

if $2d$ is the width of the slit.

We then have, on integration,

$$\gamma_{12} = \frac{\sin(2\kappa h d/l')}{2\kappa h d/l'}, \quad \ldots \ldots \quad 5(47)$$

where we have adjusted the constant so that $\gamma_{12} = 1$ when $d = 0$. The function γ_{12}^2 is shown in fig. 6.16a. When $2\kappa h d/l' = \pi/2$, i.e. when $d = l'\lambda/8h$, the value of $\gamma_{12} = 2/\pi = 0.6$, and the fringes are still fairly clear. When d is twice this

* See p. 267 of Reference 5.7.

width, $\gamma_{12} = 0$ and there are no fringes. When d is greater than $l'\lambda/4h$, the fringes reappear and, since P_1 and P_2 are in antiphase, the maxima are now in the positions previously occupied by the minima.

5. The Michelson Stellar Interferometer.

Suppose that the source S is circular and uniformly bright and at a distance from P_1 and P_2 which is very great compared with its size (and with $2h = P_1P_2$), and that the angle subtended by the source at P_1P_2 is α. The mathematics is very similar to that given in § 6.41, and we obtain

$$|\gamma_{12}| = \frac{J_1(2\kappa\alpha h)}{\kappa\alpha h}, \qquad \ldots \ldots \ldots 5(48)$$

where J_1 is the Bessel function of order 1. If we regard h as variable, $|\gamma_{12}|$ now has a series of zeros corresponding to the zeros of the Bessel function, which may be obtained from tables. The first occurs when

$$h = 0.61\,\lambda/\alpha. \qquad \ldots \ldots \ldots 5(49)$$

Michelson used this result to measure the angular diameter of stars. A slit-and-mirror system was mounted on the objective of a telescope as shown in fig. 5.23. The object glass was 250 cm. and the separation $2h$ could be varied

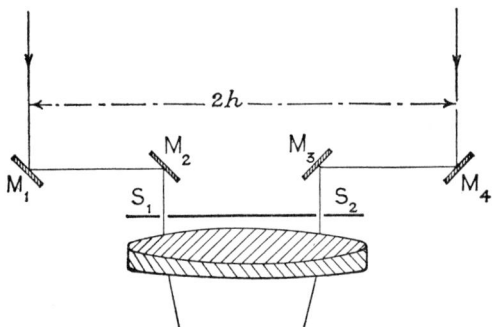

Fig. 5.23.—Michelson stellar interferometer (S_1 and S_2 are slits running into the plane of the paper).

up to 600 cm. With the star Betelgeuse the first minimum in visibility was found when $2h = 308$ cm. and the corresponding angular diameter calculated from 5(49) is 2.4×10^{-7} radian or 0·05 second of arc. Betelgeuse has an exceptionally large angular diameter, and even this method is not sufficient to measure the angular diameters of most stars. A similar method may be useful for radio stars.

When[*] the source is not uniformly bright, the coherence is a function both of the distribution of intensity across the source and of the separation of the mirrors. The distribution of intensity can be determined (provided it is symmetrical) by measuring the variation of visibility with h.

[*] See p. 270 of Reference 5.7.

CORRELATION INTERFEROMETER

6.—The joint effect of finite length of wave train and of the geometrical factors considered above has been calculated by Wolf.* He introduces a mutual coherence function $\Gamma_{12}(\tau)$ equal to the mean value (over a long time) of the quantity

$$\xi_1(t + \tau)\, \xi_2(t),$$

where ξ_2 is the disturbance at P_2 from the source S at time t, and ξ_1 is the disturbance at P_1 and time $t_1 + \tau$, and τ is the difference between the times required for light to travel from P_1 to Q and from P_2 to Q. This function has to be evaluated by integrating over the whole area of the source, and also over the range of frequencies included in the radiation. If $c\tau$ is too large in relation to the length of the wave train, i.e. if the range of frequencies is large, the integral vanishes because positive contributions from some frequencies balance negative contributions from others. It also vanishes when γ_{12} vanishes, because in that case positive contributions from one part of the source are balanced by negative contributions from another.

7. The Intensity Correlation Interferometer.

Suppose that a source S (fig. 5.24) emits light in a range of frequencies $(\omega + \tfrac{1}{2}\omega_b)$ to $(\omega - \tfrac{1}{2}\omega_b)$, where ω_b is much less than ω. Let us consider the radiation received at two points P_1 and P_2 from a single point S_1 of the source and, for the moment, confine our attention to the two extreme frequencies. These will give beat waves as shown in fig. 4.12. From equation 4(29) we see that the beat wave maxima are separated in time by $2\pi/\omega_b$ and in space by $2\pi U/\omega_b$, where U is the group velocity. For our present problem U is almost equal to the phase velocity c, and we define $\lambda_b = 2\pi c/\omega_b$.

If the path difference $S_2P_1 - S_1P_2$ is near to an integral multiple of λ_b the two beat waves will be in phase. If a range of values of ω_b has to be considered, the beat waves are all in phase when $S_1P_1 = S_1P_2$. This equality of phase of the beat frequencies may be tested by allowing the radiation to fall on two photo-cells and passing the signals through two radio amplifiers into a "multiplier". The photo-cells and amplifiers respond to the beat frequencies (which may be of order 10^8 cycles per second), and the multiplier gives an output proportional to the integral of the product of the two signals which it receives. The integral is over a time long compared with the period of the beat waves and measures the cross-correlation† σ_{12} of the energy received at P_1 and P_2.

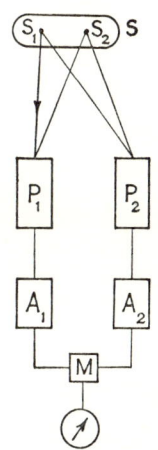

Fig. 5.24.—Intensity correlation interferometer (schematic diagram).

If
$$\sigma_{12}(\tau) = \frac{1}{T}\int_0^T E_1(t + \tau)\, E_2(t)\, dt$$

then, with a small source there will be some value of τ for which the normalized cross-correlation is unity.†

* See p. 497 of Reference 5.8.   † See § 18 of Appendix IVA.

8.—Let us now consider the joint effect of light from S_1 and S_2. A beat wave of frequency ω_b is partly due to the interaction of light of frequency $\omega + \frac{1}{2}\omega_b$ from S_1 with light of frequency $\omega - \frac{1}{2}\omega_b$ from S_2. This part will have different phases at P_1 and P_2, because we cannot move P_1 and P_2 so as to make $S_2P_1 = S_2P_2$ as well as $S_1P_1 = S_1P_2$. The phase difference corresponding to a path difference Δs is $\kappa \Delta s = (\omega/c)\Delta s$. This depends on the frequency. Thus the inequality of path implies an imperfect correlation of phases, as we have seen in §§ 1–5 above, and an imperfect correlation of intensity, because the phases of the beat waves at P_1 are not the same as at P_2. It is shown in Reference 5.9 that the cross-correlation of energy (σ_{12}) is very closely related to the cross-correlation of displacement (Γ_{12}), so that the arrangement shown in fig. 5.24 measures the coherence and, in principle, enables the diameters of stars to be measured.

9.—The following alternative description of the action of the intensity interferometer is instructive. The light received at P_1 from a very small source is an irregular wave-train (see fig. 5.25) and that received at P_2 is an identical wave-train, possibly with a time-delay. If P_1 and P_2 are moved (or alternatively

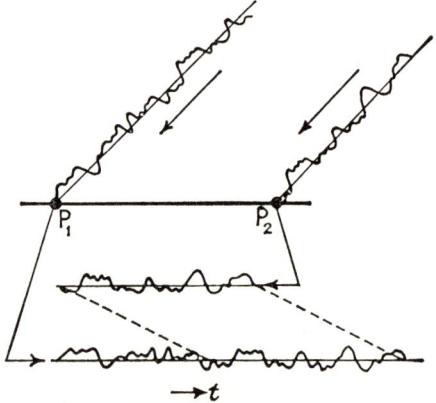

Fig. 5.25.—Wave trains received at P_1 and P_2 from a small source in the direction indicated

if a variable time-delay can be inserted into one of the amplifiers) the two wave trains can be brought into coincidence, and since they are similar the cross-correlation of the fluctuations is then unity. With an extended source, the phase differences between different components implies that the wave trains received at P_1 differ in shape from those received at P_2, and no shift along the time-axis will bring them into coincidence.

10.—The correlation interferometer constructed by Hanbury Brown and Twiss has the advantage over the Michelson stellar interferometer that large separations of the detectors are possible. It is not necessary to form a good optical image of the star, so that large mirrors of low quality may be used to focus roughly the light on to detectors of a few square centimetres in area. It is necessary to make the distances from P_1 and P_2 to the star equal within a small fraction of a " beat wavelength" (to within 20 cm.), whereas in the Michelson stellar interferometer the corresponding paths must be equal within a corresponding fraction of an optical wavelength.

The disadvantage of the correlation interferometer is that the desired signals have to be detected in the presence of a great deal of irregular disturbance (see Chapter XX). This confines the usefulness of an optical correlation interferometer to very bright stars. The situation in regard to radio stars is much more favourable.*

* See Reference 5.9.

CHAPTER VI

Diffraction

6.1. General Character of the Observations.
When a beam of light passes close to the edge of an opaque obstacle, propagation is not truly rectilinear. If certain conditions (which will be discussed later) are fulfilled, fringes are observed near the edge of the geometrical shadow, and it is found that some light penetrates into the shadow. Typical effects are shown in Plate III (p. 162). Phenomena of this type were first reported by Grimaldi (1618–63) and Hooke (1635–1703). Young (1773–1829) thought that the fringes were due to interference between a wave from the edges of the obstacle and the direct beam. Fresnel (1788–1827) showed that the fringes obtained with a razor edge were nearly the same as those obtained with a rounded edge. This was considered to have disproved Young's idea, since it was thought that the wave from a rounded edge would be much stronger than that from a razor edge. Fresnel calculated the distribution of light in the diffraction pattern by the mutual interference of Huygens wavelets from the unobstructed part of the wave and obtained results in general agreement with experiment. Kirchhoff (1824–87) justified Fresnel's assumptions by a mathematical analysis based on the wave equation. It has been shown* that the diffracted light can be separated into two parts, one of which appears to come from near the edges of the obstacle. Thus Young's idea is not irreconcilable with Fresnel's. There are some situations in which Young's method has advantages, though Fresnel's is more generally used.

6.2.—The name *diffraction* is given to all departures from rectilinear propagation of light. The most obvious diffraction effects are produced by opaque obstacles, although diffraction is also produced by obstacles which are not opaque. For example, diffraction fringes may be produced by air bubbles imprisoned in a lens. <u>Diffraction is produced by any arrangement which causes a change of amplitude or phase which is not the same over the whole area of the wavefront.</u> Diffraction thus occurs when there is any limitation of the width of a

---

* See § 6.10 and Reference 6.4.

(a) Fresnel diffraction at a straight edge.

(b) Interference fringes obtained with Fresnel biprism.

(c) Fresnel diffraction pattern (wide slit).

(d) Fresnel diffraction pattern (narrower slit).

(e) Fresnel diffraction pattern (very narrow slit).

(f) Diffraction pattern (needle).

(g) Diffraction pattern (wire).

(h) Diffraction pattern (fine wire).

(i) Fraunhofer diffraction pattern for small circular aperture showing the Airy disc.

(j) As (i) but with increased exposure to show outer rings.

(k) Enlargement of (j) for comparison with (l).

(l) Pattern due to two point sources which are just resolved (circular aperture).

(m) Fresnel diffraction obtained with point source and rectangular aperture whose shape is shown in bottom right-hand corner.

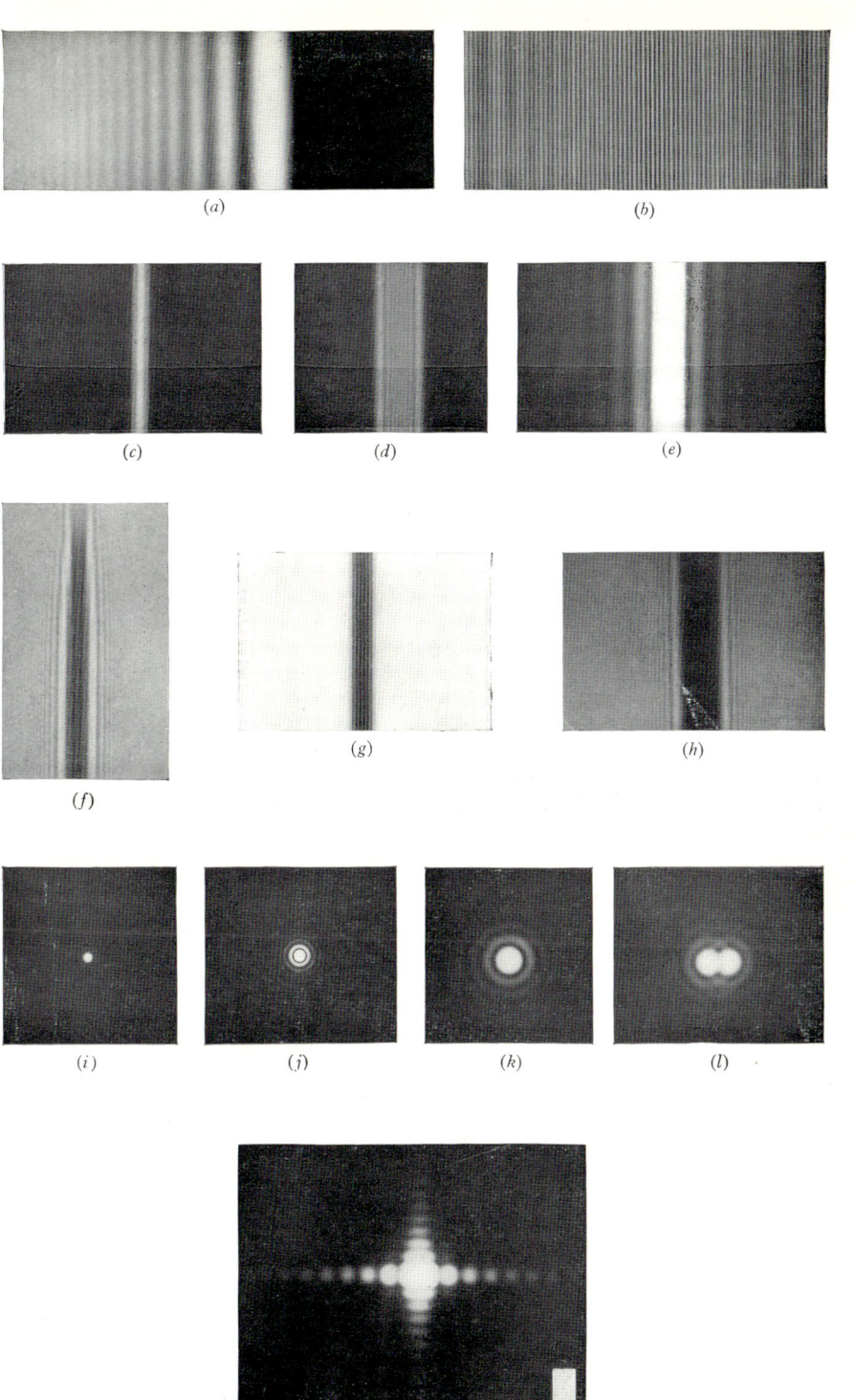

PLATE III

Facing p. 162

beam of light. In all optical experiments the width of the beam is limited by the dimensions of the apparatus, so that some diffraction is always present. Diffraction effects are often concealed by imperfections in optical images due to lens defects and in other similar ways. It is only when these other effects have been reduced by suitable design of apparatus that diffraction becomes of great importance. It then sets an inescapable limit to the sharpness of optical images and to the accuracy of certain types of measurement.

6.3. Fresnel and Fraunhofer Diffraction

Fig. 6.1 shows an arrangement in which a parallel beam of light passes through a slit in a screen S_1 (called the *diffraction screen*) and the light is received on a second screen S_2. Fig. 6.2 shows, in a general

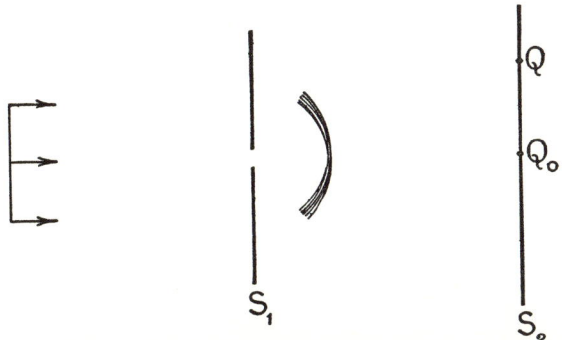

Fig. 6.1.—Diffraction of a parallel beam of light at a slit

way, the variation of illumination across the screen S_2 for different distances between S_1 and S_2. When the screens are very close (fig. 6.2a) the illumination is uniform within the geometrical image, and zero outside. Within the accuracy of observation we have rectilinear propagation. As the screen S_2 is moved away from S_1, there is a region in which the geometrical image is still easily recognizable although fringes appear on its edges (fig. 6.2b). This is known as the region of *Fresnel diffraction*. Now consider the arrangement shown in fig. 6.4, in which the slit source L_p is placed at the focus of L_1 and the screen S_2 at the focus of L_2. In the absence of diffraction, an image of L_p would appear on S_2. It is found that, when diffraction effects are small, the distribution of light on S_2 constitutes a fringed image of L_p. The distribution of light on S_2 is determined by the shape and size of the openings in S_1 (as well as by the shape and size of L_p) but it does not

164 DIFFRACTION

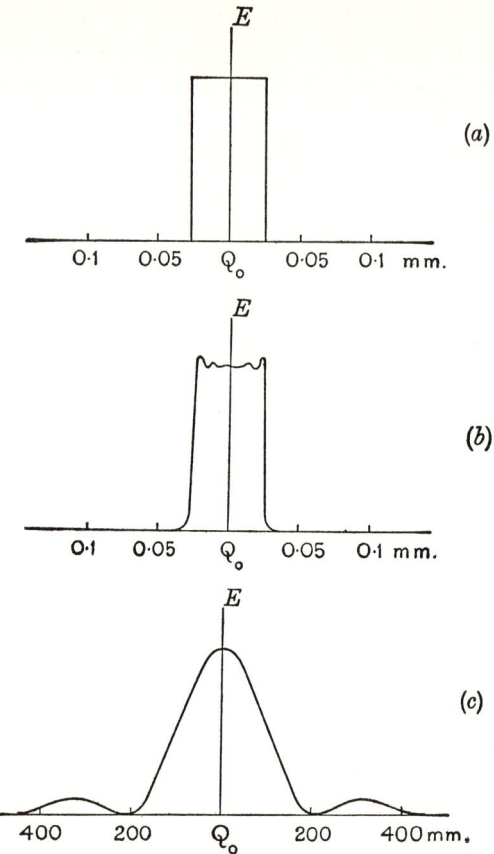

Fig. 6.2.—Variation of illumination across the screen S_2 in fig. 6.1 for slit 0·05 mm. wide: (a) when S_2 is in contact with S_1, (b) when S_2 is a few centimetres from S_1, (c) when S_2 is at 20 metres from S_1. A pattern similar to (c) is obtained with the arrangement shown in fig. 6.4.

represent the shape of these openings in any simple way. This type of diffraction is called *Fraunhofer diffraction*.* Note that in fig. 6.3 the distribution of illumination has no direct relation to the geometrical shape of two slits.

6.4.—Three regions are thus distinguished:

(1) Sharp images—effectively rectilinear propagation.
(2) Fringed image of the obstacle—Fresnel diffraction
(3) Fringed image of the source—Fraunhofer diffraction.

* J. Fraunhofer (1787–1826).

§ 6.4   FRESNEL AND FRAUNHOFER DIFFRACTION   165

Diffraction phenomena of the Fresnel type were studied in detail before the Fraunhofer phenomena. They are important in the historical development of the wave theory and still have some interesting ap-

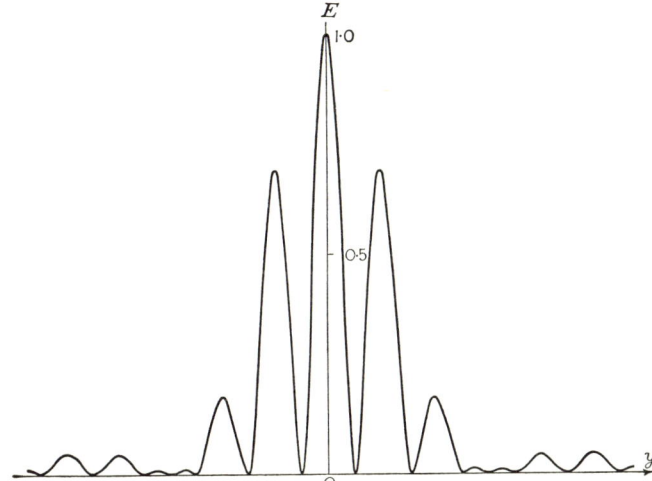

Fig. 6.3.—Distribution of illumination in Fraunhofer pattern due to two equal slits

plications. The Fraunhofer diffraction phenomena are of practical importance in connection with the general theory of optical instruments and the theory of diffraction gratings.

In the following paragraphs (§§ 6.5–30) we shall discuss Fresnel and

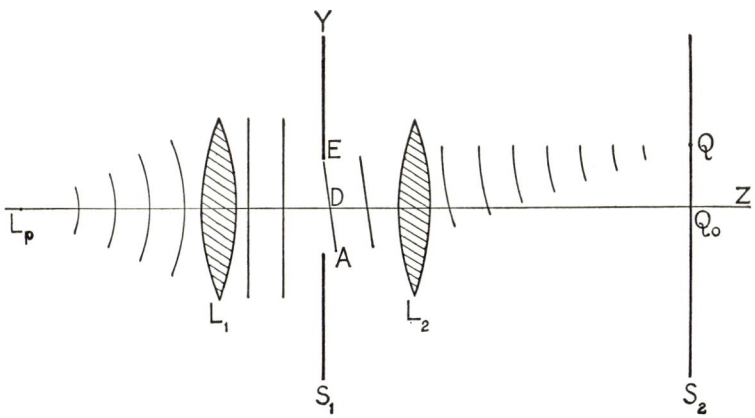

Fig. 6.4.—Arrangement for the production of Fraunhofer diffraction patterns

Fraunhofer diffraction using simple methods based on Huygens' principle. These methods yield approximate solutions of many practical problems and form an introduction to a more general theory based on an extension of the concept of wave groups discussed in Chapter IV. This general treatment is important in relating wave theory and quantum theory.

6.5. Development of Huygens' Principle.

It was shown in Chapter III that Huygens' principle, in its original form, was able to give a satisfactory account of the laws of reflection and of refraction. It enabled a series of wave surfaces to be constructed when one was given. Huygens' principle by itself was insufficient to

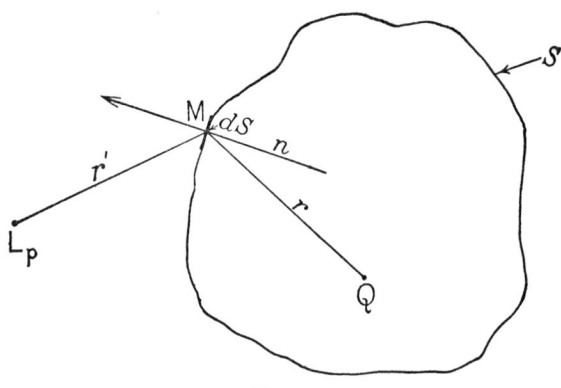

Fig. 6.5

enable the distribution of illumination in diffraction patterns to be calculated. Fresnel and his followers completed the Huygens' theory by assuming detailed properties for the wavelets. Fresnel was guided in his choice of assumptions by the requirement that, in the absence of obstacles, the wavelets must interfere in such a way that they reconstruct the forward wave, not only in regard to position but also as regards amplitude. Later Kirchhoff showed that it is unnecessary to use specific assumptions concerning the wavelets since the whole calculation can be made directly from the wave equation. The three stages are thus:

(i) *Huygens* expressed an intuitive rather than a logical conviction that a knowledge of the disturbance produced by a wave motion for all points on a suitably placed surface S at a time t_0 is sufficient to determine the disturbance at a point Q at a later time t (fig. 6.5).

§ 6.6   FRESNEL'S METHODS   167

(ii) *Fresnel* made detailed assumptions concerning the amplitude of a wavelet arriving at Q from an elementary area dS. He was then able to calculate the distribution of illumination in diffraction patterns. His results agreed with observations.

(iii) *Kirchhoff* showed that the effect of an elementary area can be derived from the wave equation without making special assumptions. He showed that the assumptions which had been made by Fresnel are satisfactory provided that neither the source nor the point Q is very near to the surface S and that St. Venant's hypothesis (§ 6.33) is accepted.

6.6. Fresnel's Methods.

Fresnel and his followers assumed that the amplitude at a point Q (fig. 6.5) due to the Huygens wavelets from an elementary area dS at M is proportional to AdS/r (where A is the amplitude at M) and to an *inclination factor* which depends on the angle between the radius vector r and the normal n to the wave surface. The total amplitude at Q is given by

$$\psi_Q = k \int \frac{\phi(n, r) A e^{-i\kappa r}}{r} dS, \qquad \ldots \quad 6(1)$$

where $\phi(n, r)$ is the inclination factor. The precise form of the function $\phi(n, r)$ is unimportant, provided that it decreases as the angle (n, r) increases. The factor $e^{-i\kappa r}$ takes account of the phase difference corresponding to the optical path MQ. The amplitude ψ_Q is, in general, complex. k is a constant of proportionality.

In addition to giving Huygens' theory a precise mathematical form, Fresnel devised two methods of carrying out the integration and obtained results in agreement with experiment. His methods of integration are: (*a*) the zone method—an ingenious geometrical device applicable to problems with circular symmetry,* and (*b*) the Fresnel integral—an analytical method of general application, but especially useful for diffraction apertures bounded by straight edges, such as rectangular slits (see Appendix VI D).

6.7. Fresnel Zones.

Let us suppose that the source is at a great distance from the plane OM, so that a plane wave is incident from the left as shown in fig. 6.6. Suppose that the illumination at a point Q is to be calculated and that O is the nearest point on the wavefront to Q. Let $OQ = r_0$. Then the

*See §§ 6.7–10 and Appendix VI C.

wavefront is imagined to be divided into a series of zones bounded by circles. M_1 and M_1' in the figure are points on the smallest of these circles, M_2 and M_2' on the second, and so on. The radii of the circles are

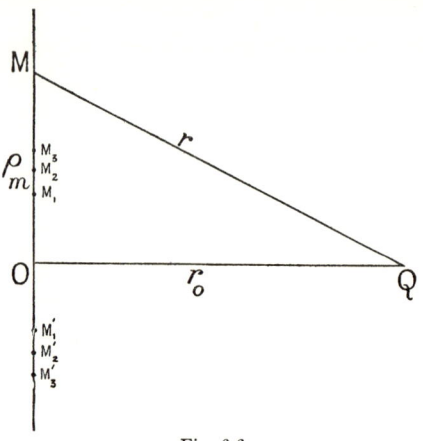

Fig. 6.6

chosen so that $M_1Q = r_0 + \lambda/2$, $M_2Q = r_0 + 2\lambda/2$, $M_3Q = r_0 + 3\lambda/2$, and so on. Then the radius (ρ_m) of the mth circle is given by

$$\rho_m^2 + r_0^2 = (r_0 + \tfrac{1}{2}m\lambda)^2,$$

or
$$\rho_m^2 \doteq \lambda m r_0, \qquad \ldots \ldots \quad 6(2)$$

provided that $m\lambda$ is small compared with r_0. The area of the mth zone is $\pi(\rho_m^2 - \rho_{m-1}^2) = \pi\lambda r_0$, so that <u>all zones have the same area</u>.

6.8.—We first calculate the effect at Q due to one zone and, for this purpose, divide the zone by a series of concentric circles into very small equal areas. Then, since $\phi(n, r)/r$ is nearly constant over one zone, the amplitudes at Q due to the infinitesimal areas are all equal while the phase advances uniformly from 0 to π. The resultant amplitude (see § 3.5) is $2/\pi$ times the amplitude which would be obtained if all elements were in the same phase, and the resultant phase is half-way between the extreme phases at the edges of the zone (i.e. it is a quarter-period behind the phase at the inner edge). The phases of the resultants of successive zones differ by a half-period, and they are therefore known as half-period zones.* Since the areas of the zones are equal and $\phi(n, r)/r$ decreases slowly as we go outwards from the centre, the contributions of successive zones to the integral of equation 6(1) form

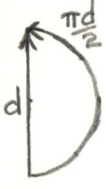

* They are also called " Fresnel zones " or, less commonly, " Huygens zones ".

§ 6.9   CIRCULAR APERTURE   169

This is considered in detail by Jenkins and White on p. 357.

a series whose terms slowly decrease in magnitude while alternating in sign. The sum of such a series is equal to half the first member. Thus the effect of the whole wave is $\frac{1}{2} \times 2/\pi = 1/\pi$ times the effect which would be produced by the first zone alone if all elements had the same phase. Since $r = r_0$ (approximately) the resultant is

$$\psi = \frac{1}{\pi} \int \frac{kA\,dS}{r} = \frac{kA\pi\lambda r_0}{\pi r_0} = k\lambda A. \quad \ldots \quad 6(3)$$

The phase is a quarter-period behind the phase of waves which reach Q from O, so that the resultant disturbance is

$$\psi_Q = k\lambda A \exp\left\{-i(\kappa r_0 + \tfrac{1}{2}\pi)\right\} = -ik\lambda A \exp(-i\kappa r_0). \quad 6(4)$$

But we know that the resultant for an unobstructed plane wave is $A \exp(-i\kappa r_0)$ and Fresnel therefore put $k = i/\lambda$, i.e. he assumed that the magnitude of k is $1/\lambda$ and that Huygens' wavelets start a quarter of a period in advance of the wave which they replace. These assumptions were introduced *ad hoc* to obtain the correct result for the unobstructed wave. With them Fresnel was able to calculate the patterns produced by many types of diffraction screens, and the agreement of his calculations with experimental observations constituted an important advance in wave theory.

6.9. Fresnel Diffraction at a Circular Aperture.

Certain results concerning the distribution of illumination in diffraction patterns may be obtained in a very simple and elegant way by use of the properties of the half-period zones. The calculation of the change of illumination along the axis when a plane wave is diffracted by a small circular aperture may be taken as an example.*

When the point under consideration is at a great distance from the aperture, the zones are very large, and only the wavelets from a small portion of the central zone are transmitted. These wavelets are in phase agreement, but their amplitude is proportional to $1/r$, so that the total effect is small. As the point of interest moves in towards the aperture, the zones shrink and the illumination gradually increases until the stage is reached where the first zone exactly fills the aperture. The amplitude is then twice that which would be produced at the same point if the screen were removed and the whole wave transmitted. The illumination is four times that given by the whole wave. If the point moves nearer to the aperture the illumination soon begins to decrease, and is zero when two zones fill the aperture. If the point is moved still nearer, the illumination goes through a series of maxima and minima. The minima occur when an even number of zones fills the aperture. The maxima are very near to the positions where an odd number of zones fills the aperture. The illumination reaches a constant value at points so near to the aperture that small irregularities in the shape of the aperture are

* Another example is discussed in Appendix VI C.

comparable with the width of the outermost zone transmitted. The positions of the maxima and minima are calculated by applying equation 6(2).

In order to calculate the amplitude at an axial point intermediate between a maximum and a minimum, it is necessary to estimate the effect of the portion of a zone which is not balanced. In doing this, it is not sufficient to assume that the effect is simply proportional to the area of the fraction. Allowance must be made for phase relations [Examples 6(iii) and 6(iv), p. 172.]

6.10 Fresnel Diffraction by a Circular Obstacle.

It is found that if a circular obstacle is placed at a moderate distance from a point source, the illumination at the centre of the geometrical shadow is the same as if the obstacle were removed. The following simple argument shows that this should be so.

Let SAO represent the path from S to O which just grazes the edge of the disc, and let SA_1O represent a path which is $\tfrac{1}{2}\lambda$, SA_2O a path

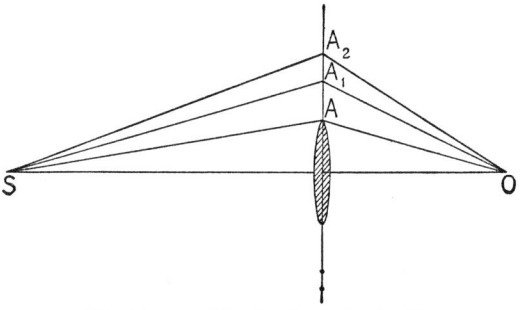

6.7.—Fresnel diffraction by a circular disc

which is λ longer, etc. A half-period zone will lie between the edge of the disc and a circle through A_1 (fig. 6.7), a second between this circle and one through A_2, and so on. In this way we construct a series of half-period zones beginning at the circumference of the disc. The resultant amplitude is equal to half that which would be produced by the first of this series of zones. If the point of interest is not too near the disc, the inclination factor may be ignored, and the amplitude is the same as that which would be produced by the whole wave. When Fresnel's paper on diffraction was presented to the French Academy, Poisson suggested that the above result was implied. He believed that he had disproved the whole theory by a *reductio ad absurdum*. The central bright spot in the shadow had indeed been observed by Delisle about half a century earlier, but his observation attracted little notice since it was not connected with any theory. His experiment was repeated by Fresnel and Arago in order to meet Poisson's criticism.

The bright central spot is observed only when the edge of the circular object is free from irregularities of a size comparable with the width of the first zone in the unobstructed portion of the wave. If the obstacle subtends a moderately large angle, either at the point of observation or at the source, the width of this zone becomes very small and the size of the irregularities which can be tolerated becomes very small. The phenomenon can be conveniently observed using a pinhole in front of the image of a Pointolite as source, and a small ball-bearing (about $\frac{1}{8}$ or $\frac{1}{4}$ inch diameter) as the obstacle. The ball-bearing may be attached to a piece of plate glass with a little wax. The source may conveniently be placed beside the obstacle and reflected in a mirror about four metres away. Very near to the obstacle the shadow is dark, owing to the effect of irregularities, but two or three metres away the central spot is clearly seen. Even if no irregularities were present, the illumination very near to the obstacle would be zero owing to the effect of the inclination factor.

In the above discussion of Fresnel diffraction it has been assumed that the fringes are received upon a screen or focused by an eyepiece. If the eye is placed in the plane of the screen and is focused upon the obstacle, the edges of the obstacle appear to be ringed with light. To observe this effect it may be necessary to use an artificial pupil, consisting of a pinhole, in front of the eye. Delisle's experiment shows this effect very well. This phenomenon is sometimes observed slightly before dawn. Provided that the atmosphere is really clear and steady, the edges of the branches of trees, etc., appear brilliantly lighted owing to the diffraction of light from the sun which is still below the horizon. This effect is clearly seen with the arrangement shown in fig. 6.7. The eye placed at O is focused on the plane $A\,A_1\,A_2$ and sees a narrow circle of light surrounding the obstacle. This observation is most simply understood in terms of the existence of an edge-wave as postulated by Young (see § 6.1 and Reference 6.4). Fresnel's treatment does not give any simple account of it.

EXAMPLES [6(i)–6(viii)]

6(i). Show that when the source is situated at a distance r' from a plane surface S, the radii of the circles which define the half-period zones, for an observer who is distant r_0 from the opposite side of the surface, are given by

$$\rho_m^2 \simeq m\lambda \frac{r_0 r'}{r_0 + r'}.$$

(Assume that ρ_m is small compared with both r_0 and r'.)

6(ii). Show that generally the curves which define the half-period zones are the intersections of an ellipsoid with the surface S (not necessarily plane). Show that the source and the point Q are the foci of the ellipsoids, and derive an equation for the mth ellipsoid referred to an origin placed half-way between the source L_p and Q.

[Equation of ellipsoid is $\dfrac{x^2}{A^2} + \dfrac{y^2}{A^2 - l^2} + \dfrac{z^2}{A^2 - l^2} = 1$,

where $2A = L_pQ + m\lambda/2$, and $2l = L_pQ$.]

6(iii). If ρ_1 is the radius of the first half-period zone, find the amplitude and phase of the resultant due to the portion of the zone within a circle of radius $f\rho_1$, where f is less than 1. Express the amplitude as a fraction of that due to the whole zone.

[Amplitude $= \sin f^2\pi/2$.   Phase $= f^2\pi/2$.]

6(iv). Derive a general formula for the resultant at Q due to an annulus between two radii ρ and ρ' which are within the same half-period zone. Express the amplitude as a fraction of that due to the whole zone.

$$\left[\text{Amplitude} = \sin\left(\frac{\rho'^2 - \rho^2}{2\lambda r_0}\right)\pi.\right]$$

6(v). A plane wave is incident upon a screen containing a circular aperture 1 mm. in diameter. Derive an expression for the distances of the maxima of the axial illumination (§ 6.9) and derive numerical results for the three maxima which are farthest from the screen. Assume a wavelength of 5000 Å.

[Axial maxima are at distances $50/(2n+1)$ cm., where n is an integer.]

6(vi). Using the data of the previous example, find the illumination at a point which is twice as far away (from the aperture) as the farthest maximum.

[$(8/\pi^2) \times$ illumination produced by unobstructed plane wave.]

6(vii). A point source of light is placed 50 cm. from a screen containing a circular aperture 0·5 mm. in diameter. Find the position of that maximum in the illumination (on the axis) which lies farthest from the aperture. Assume that the wavelength of the radiation is 5000 Å.   [17 cm.]

6(viii). A disc, which is 0·5 cm. in diameter and has irregularities of order 10 μ, is placed 1 metre from a point source. Assume that the central spot is visible when the irregularities do not cut into any zone to a depth equal to more than a quarter of its width, and calculate the shortest distance at which the central spot can be seen.   [67 cm.]

6.11. Fraunhofer Diffraction

At distances from a diffraction screen which are very large compared with the width of the screen, the Huygens wavelets may be treated as plane waves. If lenses are inserted, as shown in fig. 6.4, then the energy density at a point Q in the focal plane is proportional to the energy diffracted into a small solid angle including directions near to the line DQ. An eyepiece focused on this plane views a diffraction pattern in which every point represents a direction of diffraction. Wavelets reach Q with the phase relation which they had when they crossed the plane EDA perpendicular to DQ. The relative energy at Q is found by determining these phase differences and then forming a sum which is essentially similar to the integral of equation 6(1).

6.12. Diffraction Gratings.

An arrangement of similar diffracting elements with regular spacings constitutes a *diffraction grating*. We shall first consider linear gratings in which the diffracting elements consist of parallel lines ruled on glass or metal. These gratings may be used either in transmission (fig. 6.8a) or in reflection (fig. 6.8b). We shall begin by discussing gratings in which the diffracting elements (i.e. the clear spaces) are very small in ✓ comparison with the distance between them, so that there are only

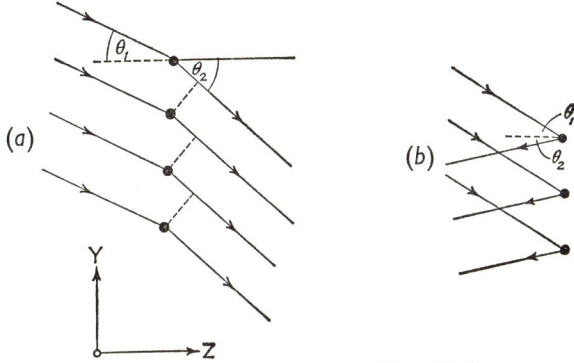

Fig. 6.8.—One-dimensional grating with small elements: (a) light diffracted forward, (b) light diffracted backward.

very small phase differences between wavelets arriving at a given point from different parts of the same element. This enables us to consider those features of the diffraction pattern which are determined by the geometrical arrangement of elements, i.e. by the co-operation of wavelets from different elements. We postpone discussion of the diffraction pattern due to a single element, although we shall see later that this is very important in relation to the quality of real gratings. *It is assumed that the illumination at all points on a grating is mutually coherent.** This is an essential requirement of the theory which follows.

6.13.—Suppose that the grating is in the XY plane with the lines parallel to OX (into the plane of the paper in fig. 6.8). Let $2e$ be the spacing and let the total number of lines be N. Consider the transmission grating (fig. 6.8a) and let the light be incident at an angle θ_1. The path difference for light diffracted at an angle θ_2 from two successive lines is

$$\Delta s = 2e(\sin \theta_2 - \sin \theta_1) = 2e(\beta_2 - \beta_1), \quad . \quad . \quad 6(5)$$

* See § 5.3.

where β_1 and β_2 are equal to $\sin \theta_1$ and $\sin \theta_2$ respectively. The phase difference for light of wavelength λ and wavelength constant κ is

$$\delta_\lambda = 2\pi\, \Delta s/\lambda = 2\kappa e(\beta_2 - \beta_1). \quad \ldots \quad 6(6)$$

Let $A(\lambda, \theta_2)$ be the amplitude of light of wavelength λ diffracted in the direction θ_2 from a single element acting alone. For the present, in accordance with § 6.36, we assume that A is nearly constant. The wavelets from different elements are in phase when

$$\Delta s = m\lambda \text{ or } \delta_\lambda = 2m\pi, \quad \ldots \quad 6(7a)$$

i.e.
$$\beta_2 - \beta_1 = \frac{m\pi}{\kappa e} = \frac{m\lambda}{2e}, \quad \ldots \quad 6(7b)$$

where m is an integer (positive, negative, or zero). The relative energy of the diffracted light then has a maximum value $N^2 A^2$ since all elements are in phase. The value $m = 0$ corresponds to ordinary transmission

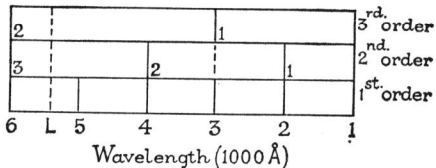

Fig. 6.9.—Overlapping orders. Spectra displaced vertically would in practice be superposed so that, for example, 1st order 5400 Å, 2nd order 2700 Å, and 3rd order 1800 Å coincide.

of an undeflected ray. If white light is used, the maxima for values of m other than $m = 0$ occur at different angles (θ_2) for different wavelengths, i.e. the light is spread into spectra. The value of m corresponding to a given spectrum is called the *order* of the spectrum. The spectra of different orders overlap to some extent, since if $\lambda''/\lambda' = m/n$ then the nth-order spectrum of λ'' coincides with the mth-order spectrum of λ' (see fig. 6.9).

6.14.—With the sign convention of § 7.4, the angle θ_2 in fig. 6.8b is negative, so that we must write

$$\Delta s = 2\kappa e(\sin \theta_2 + \sin \theta_1) = 2\kappa(\beta_1' + \beta_1). \quad \ldots \quad 6(8)$$

The zero-order spectrum then corresponds to $\theta_2 = -\theta_1$, i.e. to the ordinary laws of reflection.

If the media on the two sides of the grating are different (so that the wavelengths are different) then

$$\Delta s = 2(\kappa_1 \sin \theta_1 - \kappa_2 \sin \theta_2),$$

and the zero-order spectrum corresponds to

$$\kappa_1 \sin \theta_1 = \kappa_2 \sin \theta_2,$$

i.e. to Snell's law of refraction since $\kappa_2/\kappa_1 = b_1/b_2 = \mu_{12}$ (see § 3.13 and § 14.3).

6.15.—To find the energy in different directions, we apply equation 3(22) for the sum of N simple harmonic motions whose phases are in arithmetic progression. We have

$$E = \frac{A^2 \sin^2 N\delta/2}{\sin^2 \delta/2} = \frac{A^2 \sin^2\{N\kappa e(\beta_2 - \beta_1)\}}{\sin^2\{\kappa e(\beta_2 - \beta_1)\}}. \qquad 6(9)$$

E has a value $N^2 A^2$ when $\sin \kappa e(\beta_2 - \beta_1)$ is zero. These are principal maxima. The function is zero whenever the numerator vanishes but the denominator does not. This occurs when $N\kappa e(\beta_2 - \beta_1)$ is an integral multiple of π but $\kappa e(\beta_2 - \beta_1)$ is not, i.e. when the path difference between waves from the first and last elements is a multiple of π but not of $N\pi$. Thus there are $(N-1)$ minima between each of the principal maxima (for which all elements are in phase). There are also subsidiary maxima, approximately half-way between these minima, at angles where $N\kappa e(\beta_2 - \beta_1)$ is approximately equal to $(m + \tfrac{1}{2})\pi$ (where m is an integer but not a multiple of N). The form of the curve is shown in fig. 6.17a. When N is very large the principal maxima are very sharp, e.g. if there are 100,000 lines the principal maximum for 5000 Å. is clearly separated from that for 5000·1Å.

If the individual elements scatter equally in all directions, so that A is constant, then all the principal maxima have the same energy. In practice A is not constant, and spectra of some orders are much stronger than others. The way in which the function $A(\lambda_1 \theta_2)$ is determined by the shape of the groove will be discussed later (§ 6.19 and § 6.36).

6.16. Two-dimensional Gratings.

A series of similar apertures or obstacles arranged in a two-dimensional regular array, as shown in fig. 6.10, constitutes a two-dimensional grating. A set of such elements may be produced by

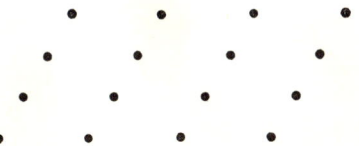

Fig. 6.10.—Two-dimensional grating.

ruling two sets of lines at an angle to one another. Nearly the same effect is obtained if light passes successively through two *crossed gratings*, i.e. two gratings almost in contact with the lines at an angle to one another.

Let us consider the case when the sets of lines are mutually perpendicular and are parallel to the OX and OY. Let the spacings be $2e_x$ and $2e_y$. Let α_1, β_1 be the direction-cosines of the incident beam and α_2, β_2 of the diffracted beam. Then we first sum for a strip parallel to the OX direction and then for all strips, to obtain, for the complex amplitude in direction α_2, β_2

$$a(\alpha_2, \beta_2) = A \left(\sum_{n_1=1}^{N_1} \exp in_1\delta_1 \right) \left(\sum_{n_2=1}^{N_2} \exp in_2\delta_2 \right), \quad 6(10)$$

where $\quad \delta_1 = 2\kappa e_x(\alpha_2 - \alpha_1)$ and $\delta_2 = 2\kappa e_y(\beta_2 - \beta_1), \quad 6(11)$
and N_1 and N_2 are the number of lines in the two directions. Each sum involves a calculation like that which led to equation 3(22) and we obtain, for the relative energy,

$$E(\alpha_2, \beta_2) = A^2 \left[\frac{\sin N_1\kappa e_x(\alpha_2 - \alpha_1)}{\sin \kappa e_x(\alpha_2 - \alpha_1)} \cdot \frac{\sin N_2\kappa e_y(\beta_2 - \beta_1)}{\sin \kappa e_y(\beta_2 - \beta_1)} \right]^2 \quad 6(12)$$

A is now a function of α_2 and of β_2.

When both δ_1 and δ_2 are integral multiples of 2π the energy reaches a maximum equal to $N_1^2 N_2^2 A^2$. When only one of them is integral, very much weaker maxima are obtained. Thus the principal maxima occur only when both α_1 and α_2 are integral multiples of 2π. One set (corresponding to $\delta_2 = 0$) lie along the x axis and another ($\delta_1 = 0$) along the y axis. Other spectra lie diagonally, pointing at the zero order which is in the direction α_1, β_1.

6.17. Moiré Fringes.

Now suppose that two similar gratings are placed in contact with the lines intersecting at a *small* angle ψ, as shown in fig. 6.11. Then the combination is nearly equivalent to a two-dimensional grating of the type discussed in the preceding paragraph. The spacing of the elements in the X' direction is very close ($= 2e/\cos \psi$) and in the Y' direction is much wider ($= 2e/\sin \psi$). (Note that X' and Y' are nearly, but not quite, perpendicular.) The separation of spectra in the X' direction is wide and in the Y' direction is very narrow, so that all the principal maxima lie near to directions parallel to the Y' axis. If conditions are such that the spectra are drawn out into lines, then sharp fringes nearly parallel to the Y' axis are obtained. These are known as *moiré fringes*. The sharpness of the fringes depends on the shapes of the grooves, and the direction depends on the exact relation of the two gratings (see Reference 6.3). The above discussion applies to fringes seen under the conditions of observation normally used for Fraunhofer diffraction.

The moiré fringes produced by the superposition of two gratings which are imperfect (either because the lines are not quite straight or the interval not quite constant) are distorted. A grating may be tested by superposing it on a perfect grating and viewing the moiré fringes.

If two gratings are superposed so as to show the moiré fringes and one is moved a distance x (perpendicular to its rulings), the moiré fringes move a distance

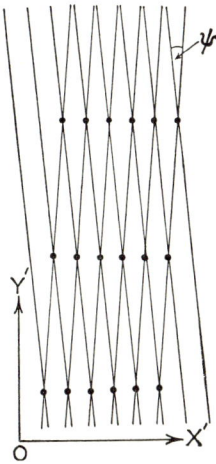

Fig. 6.11.—Crossed gratings at small angle showing moiré pattern.

$y = x/\psi$. The movement of the fringes can be made 100–1000 times as fast as that of the grating by adjusting ψ. It is possible to attach one grating to the base and the other to the carriage of a travelling microscope and to count the passage of the moiré fringes across the field of an auxiliary microscope. This count may be made automatically by photo-electric cells. Since one moiré fringe passes every time the carriage moves through one grating interval, the distance moved (expressed as a multiple of a grating interval) can be read on a counter. The fringes thus form a measuring scale. Several methods of measurement and control based on this principle have been developed by J. Guild* and collaborators.

6.18. Three-dimensional Gratings.

Von Laue realized that the atoms in a crystal form a regular array in three dimensions whose spacing (of order 1 Å.) is suitable for giving diffraction patterns with X-rays. These patterns may be used for investigating the crystal structure as well as for studying X-rays. Let us consider an orthorhombic crystal in which the axes (OX, OY, and OZ) are mutually perpendicular, and which contains only one type of atom (fig. 6.12). Let α_1, β_1, γ_1 be the direction-cosines of the incident beam and α_2, β_2, γ_2 of the diffracted beam. If the number of atoms along the three directions is N_1, N_2, N_3 respectively, we obtain maxima with energies pro-

* See Reference 6.23.

portional to $N_1^2 N_2^2 N_3^2 A^2$ in directions for which δ_1, δ_2, and δ_3 are integral multiples of 2π, where $\delta_1 = 2\kappa e_x(\alpha_2 - \alpha_1)$, etc. These directions are specified by

$$\alpha_2 - \alpha_1 = \frac{h_1 \lambda}{2e_x}; \quad \beta_2 - \beta_1 = \frac{h_2 \lambda}{2e_y} \text{ and } \gamma_2 - \gamma_1 = \frac{h_3 \lambda}{2e_z}, \quad . \quad . \quad 6(13)$$

where $2e_x$, $2e_y$, and $2e_z$ are spacings in directions parallel to OX, OY, and OZ respectively. h_1, h_2, and h_3 are integers. The distribution of diffracted energy is given by an expression similar to equation 6(12). A, which represents the amplitude of the radiation scattered from a single atom, is called the *atom form factor*.

These equations must be taken in conjunction with the relation

$$\alpha_2^2 + \beta_2^2 + \gamma_2^2 = 1. \quad . \quad . \quad . \quad . \quad . \quad . \quad 6(14)$$

We now have four equations and only three unknowns, so that if λ is fixed there is usually no strong diffraction. If however " white " radiation containing a range of wavelengths is used, then " Laue spots " are obtained corresponding to different integral values of h_1, h_2, h_3. The wavelength selected in this way is not the same for all spots.

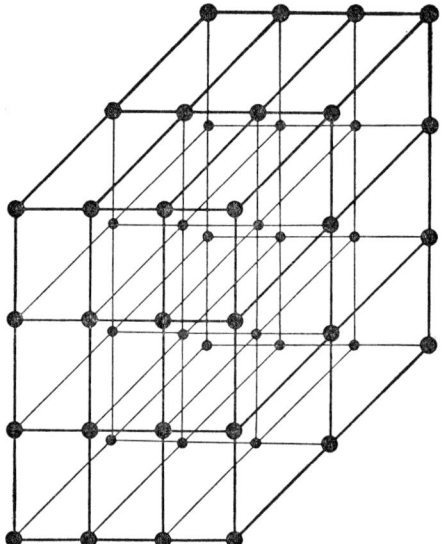

Fig. 6.12.—Simple three-dimensional grating (orthorhombic crystal).

If λ is fixed, the four equations 6(13) and 6(14) can still be satisfied by choosing a suitable angle of incidence. This is done in the Bragg method, which is based on the fact that certain sets of parallel planes contain many atoms and may be regarded as reflecting planes (fig. 6.13). In order that the wavelets from successive planes may reinforce one another it is necessary to have

$$4e_0 \sin \chi = m\lambda, \quad . \quad . \quad . \quad . \quad . \quad . \quad 6(15)$$

where χ is the angle between the direction of incidence and the scattering planes, and $2e_0$ is the distance between successive planes. From fig. 6.13 we see that each plane of atoms may be treated as a linear grating.*

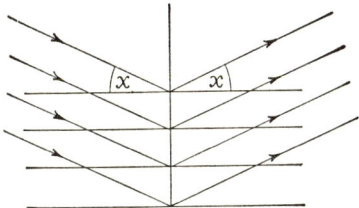

Fig. 6.13.—Reflection at an array of equi-spaced planes.

Reflections at the angle given by equation 6(15) may be obtained by rocking a single crystal so that different crystal planes come successively into the correct orientation. Another method is to use a powdered crystal as shown in fig. 6.14.

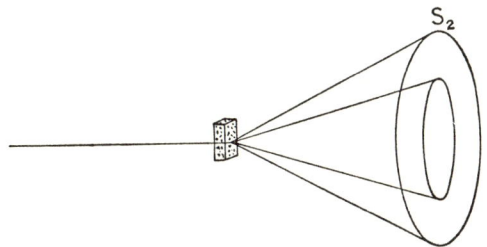

Fig. 6.14.—Diffraction by crystalline powder.

Some small crystals are then correctly orientated. Each plane gives rise to a cone of rays and hence to a ring on a plate placed at S_2. A pattern of this type is shown in Plate Vh (p. 746) which is a photograph obtained with electron waves.

6.19. The Form Factor.

Fig. 6.15

The angular distribution of light scattered from a single element will be discussed in detail later. We here consider in an elementary way some points which are important in the design of optical diffraction gratings. It is convenient to start by discussing a one-dimensional grating consisting of alternate clear and opaque strips (fig. 6.15). Suppose that the width of one clear region is $2d$. Then any one strip may be divided into a large number of equal infinitesimal areas by imaginary lines parallel to the grating ruling. The wavelets from these areas form a series of equal amplitude and with phase difference passing uniformly from 0 to $2\kappa d(\beta_2 - \beta_1)$.

---

* Equation 5(15b) which deals with successive reflections from parallel thin films is related to equation 6(15), but in equation 5(15b) θ is the angle between the normal to the reflecting planes and the direction of incidence.

180 DIFFRACTION

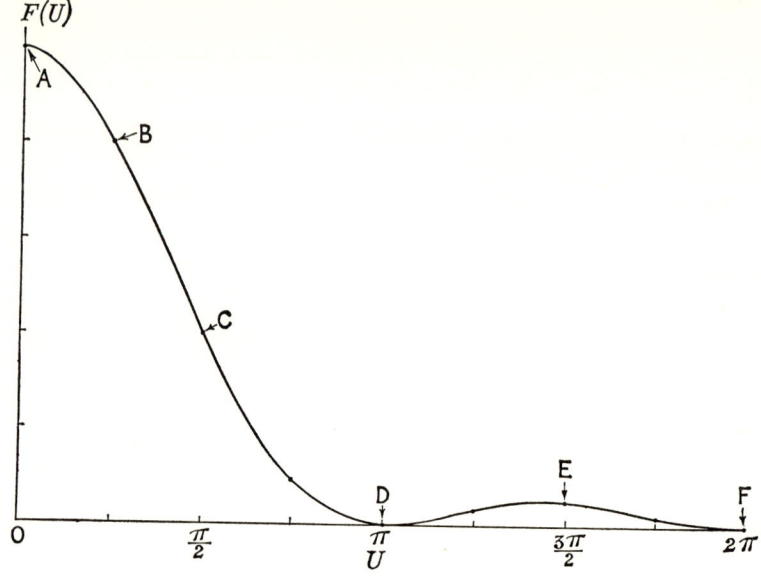

Fig. 6.16a.—The function $F(U)$

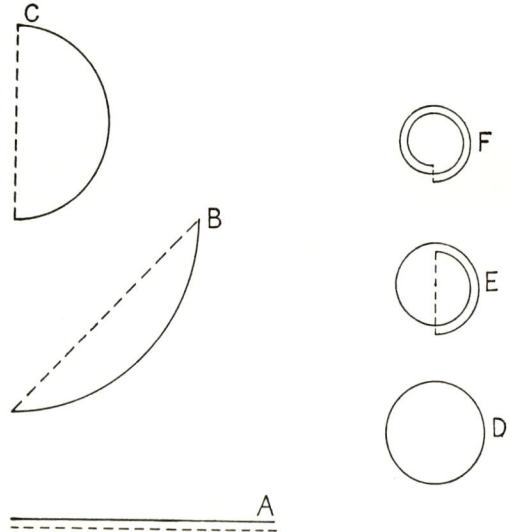

Fig. 6.16b.—Vector diagrams corresponding to the points indicated on fig. 6.16a

§ 6.20   THE FORM FACTOR   181

Then, using equation 3(16), we have for one element

$$A^2 = A_0^2 \left[\frac{\sin \kappa d(\beta_2 - \beta_1)}{\kappa d(\beta_2 - \beta_1)} \right], \quad \ldots \quad 6(16)$$

where A_0 is the value of A when $\beta_2 - \beta_1 = 0$, i.e. for a direction in which wavelets from all parts of the slit are in phase.

The energy diffracted in a given direction by a grating of N elements of width $2d$ with a spacing $2e$ between centres (see fig. 6.16) is obtained by substituting from 6(16) into 6(9), i.e. it is of the form

$$E = A_0^2 \frac{\sin^2 U}{U^2} \frac{\sin^2 NW}{\sin^2 W} = F(U) f(NW), \quad . \quad 6(17)$$

where

$$W = \kappa e(\beta_2 - \beta_1) = \frac{2\pi}{\lambda} e(\sin \theta_2 - \sin \theta_1), \quad . \quad 6(18a)$$

and

$$U = \kappa d(\beta_2 - \beta_1) = \frac{2\pi}{\lambda} d(\sin \theta_2 - \sin \theta_1). \quad . \quad 6(18b)$$

The form of the function $\sin^2 U/U^2$ is shown in fig. 6.16a. It has a single principal maximum equal to 1 and much smaller subsidiary maxima $(2/3\pi)^2$, $(2/5\pi)^2$, etc., i.e. approximately ·04, ·016, etc. The function $f(NW)$ was discussed in § 6.15. It is illustrated in fig. 6.17a, b. The product (E) is shown in fig. 6.18.

6.20.—The relation between $f(NW)$ and $F(U)$ may be seen from the vector diagrams. When there are a finite number of elements whose phases are in arithmetic progression, the resultant falls at first as the common difference of phase increases from zero. The resultant falls to zero when the phase diagram closes as shown in C and D of fig. 6.17b and reaches a subsidiary maximum when the condition shown in B is reached. When the common difference increases to 2π all elements are again in phase, and a new principal maximum is obtained. In this case the total phase difference for light from the two edges of the strip is finite, and there is a continuous variation across the strip. It was necessary to divide the strip into infinitesimal elements with an infinitesimal difference of phase between successive elements. This infinitesimal difference can be zero, giving the strong zero-order maximum, but it can never reach the finite value 2π, so there are no other principal maxima. When the difference of phase between light from the two edges of the strip is a multiple of 2π the

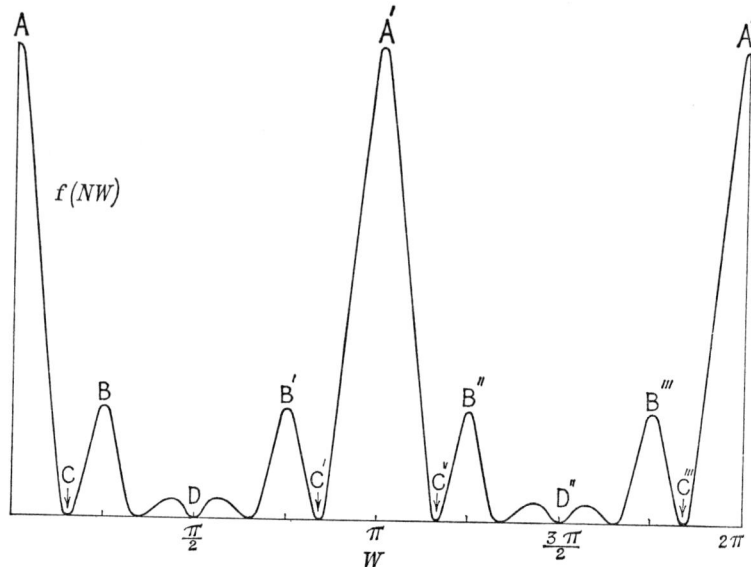

Fig. 6.17a.—The function $f(NW)$

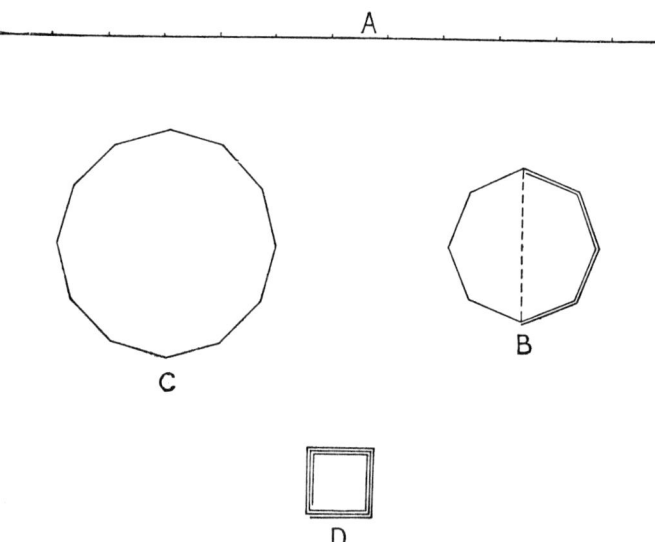

Fig. 6.17b.—Vector polygons corresponding to the points indicated on fig. 6.17a. (Note that the vector polygons for A', and A'', etc., are the same as those shown for A, B, etc.)

§ 6.20   THE FORM FACTOR   183

TABLE 6.1.

$F(U)$

Principal maximum	When $U = 0$,	$F(U) = 1.$
Secondary maxima	When $U \doteqdot \left(\dfrac{2m+1}{2}\right)\pi,$	$F(U) = \dfrac{1}{\pi^2}\left(\dfrac{2}{2m+1}\right)^2.$
Minima	When $U = m\pi,$	$F(U) = 0.$

$f(NW)$

Principal maxima	When $W = 0$ or $m\pi,$	$f(NW) = 1.$
Secondary maxima	When $W \doteqdot \left(\dfrac{2m+1}{2N}\right)\pi,$	$f(NW) \doteqdot \dfrac{1}{\sin^2 W}.$
Minima	When $W = \dfrac{m}{N}\pi,$	$f(NW) = 0.$
	$\left(\text{except } \dfrac{m}{N} \text{ integral}\right)$	

m stands for an integer (other than zero) and the sign $\doteqdot$ means "is *approximately* equal to".

resultant is zero as shown at D and F in fig. 6.16. When it is an odd multiple of π, a subsidiary maximum is obtained, as shown at E (see Table 6.1).

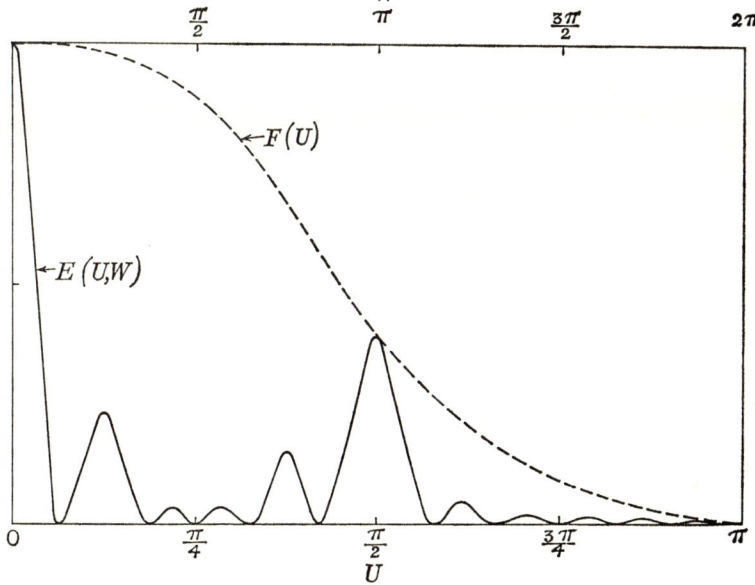

Fig. 6.18.—The distribution of light diffracted by a grating for which spaces and lines are of equal width ($l = 2d$)

6.21. Distribution of Energy among the Principal Maxima.

The mth principal maximum occurs when $\kappa e(\beta_2 - \beta_1) = m\pi$, and since $f(NW) = 1$ the energy is

$$E_m = A_0^2 \left[\frac{\sin \pi\, md/e}{\pi\, md/e}\right]^2. \quad \ldots \ldots \quad 6(19)$$

At the centre of the diffraction pattern there is complete agreement of phase, as there would be if the grating were removed, but the amplitude is reduced in the ratio d/e by the interposition of the opaque part of the grating. Hence, if we write E_T for the energy when the grating is removed then $A_0^2 = (d^2/e^2)E_T$ and

$$\frac{E_m}{E_T} = \frac{1}{m^2\pi^2} \sin^2\left(\frac{\pi\, md}{e}\right). \quad \ldots \ldots \quad 6(20)$$

Since the sine can never exceed 1, the maximum light in the first-order spectrum is $1/\pi^2$ or approximately one-tenth, and in the second-order is about one-fortieth and so on, i.e. the spectra are all weak compared with the central image and their strength rapidly decreases as m increases.

6.22. Gratings Ruled on Glass or Metal.

For the measurement of wavelengths of spectrum lines, it is desirable to produce spectra of high dispersion. Since some of the lines are very faint, it is also desirable that a high proportion of the light received by the spectroscope or spectrograph should go into one spectrum. When light is dispersed by a prism, all the light goes into one spectrum, but it is not possible to obtain very high dispersion in this way. Gratings with a very close spacing (of the order of a few wavelengths) give a very high dispersion, but, if the grating is formed of alternate opaque and transparent strips, only a small fraction of the incident light is found in any one spectrum. The only practical way to obtain improvement is to depart from the simple grating of alternate clear and opaque strips, and to alter the *unit* of the grating in such a way as to make the maximum of $F(U)$ coincide with one of the lateral maxima of $f(NW)$. In the case of reflecting gratings this may be done by altering the shape of the groove.

6.23.—The following quotation from Lord Rayleigh's article on "The Wave Theory of Light" (*Encyclopædia Britannica*, 1888; *Scientific Papers*, Vol. III, p. 108) is very interesting in view of later developments:

"If it were possible to introduce at every part of the aperture of the grating an arbitrary retardation, all the light might be concentrated in any desired spectrum. By supposing the retardation to vary uniformly and continuously we fall upon the case of an ordinary prism; but there is then no diffraction spectrum in the usual sense. To obtain such it would be necessary that the retardation should gradually alter by a wavelength in passing over any element of the grating, and then fall back to its previous value, thus springing suddenly over a wavelength. It is not likely that such a result will ever be fully attained in practice; but the case is worth stating, in order to show that there is no theoretical limit to the concentration of light of assigned wavelength in one spectrum."

Fig. 6.19 shows a section of a reflecting grating of the type suggested by Rayleigh. Suppose each elementary facet makes an angle

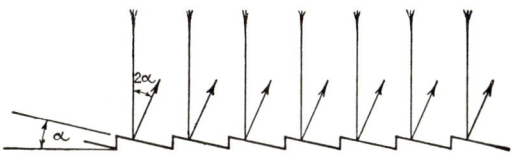

Fig. 6.19.—Reflecting grating suggested by Rayleigh

α with the plane which defines the macroscopic surface of the grating. When the light is incident in a direction normal to this plane, the maximum illumination for one element of the grating considered by itself is found in a direction making an angle 2α with the normal. If, for a given wavelength λ, a principal maximum of $f(NW)$ occurs in

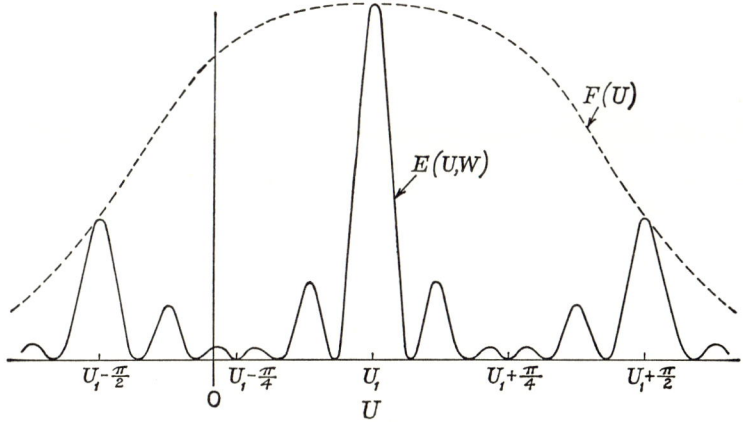

Fig. 6.20.—Distribution of light for the grating of fig. 6.19

that direction, then most of the light will be thrown into this maximum. The relation between $E(U, W)$ and $F(U)$ has been changed from that shown in fig. 6.18 to that shown in fig. 6.20.

6.24.—The original gratings made by Fraunhofer consisted of fine parallel wires. He also made gratings by ruling parallel lines on smoked glass. Either of these methods gives a grating of alternate light and dark spaces. At the time when Rayleigh wrote what has been quoted above, Rowland had succeeded in ruling gratings on metal and glass, using a diamond point and an accurately constructed ruling engine. When the gratings were ruled on speculum metal, up to 100,000 lines could be ruled before the ruling point broke down, and the spacing could be made as close as 15,000 lines to the inch. Each unit in the pattern was then about 3 wavelengths wide. The form of the groove cut was not under control and varied from one specimen to another, according to the shape of the diamond point. It was known that some gratings gave a fairly high concentration of the light in one or two orders, but always a great deal of the light was found in the undispersed central image. Investigation showed that the ruling point, when working at its best, did not remove any metal but created depressions and elevations which approached, though not very closely, the pattern described by Rayleigh. The only effective control was in regard to the depth of the groove, since the shape of the point was regarded as unalterable.

6.25. Echelette Gratings.

In 1910, R. W. Wood succeeded in producing gratings with grooves of controlled shape. They were ruled on gold-plated copper plates using the natural edge of a selected carborundum crystal as the ruling point. The angle between the planes forming the edge is 120°. In the following year, Wood and Trowbridge made similar gratings with a diamond ground to the desired angle by Brackett. These gratings were of a coarser structure than those made by Rowland. They were suitable for the production of infra-red spectra and for a practical study of the effect of different orientations of the groove angle. For a wavelength of about 30,000 Å. they concentrated nearly all the energy into one or two orders on one side of the central image. They were called *echelette* gratings because they were regarded as intermediate between ordinary gratings and the echelon gratings devised by Michelson which will be described in § 6.28. Copies of the original gratings could be made by flowing collodion on to the copper plates, allowing it to harden, and then stripping it. The material removed was mounted on glass plates and sputtered with gold. The copies so made were better than the originals because the copper plates were not perfectly flat, whereas the copies became flat when the collodion was pressed down on to optically flat glass plates.

For optical gratings the corresponding problem was not solved until

1935. By then, it had been found possible to deposit highly reflecting films of aluminium on to glass plates by evaporation in vacuum. When the vacuum is sufficiently good and other technical points are controlled, the films are durable and adhere to the glass so strongly that the material is "moulded" rather than removed by the ruling point. Using diamond points of controlled form and orientation, R. W. Wood* has succeeded in ruling gratings with 15,000 lines to the inch, in which 80 per cent of the light of the green mercury line (5461 Å.) is concentrated in the first order. The process is sufficiently under control so that the light can be concentrated in first, second or higher order as desired. These gratings have already proved very useful in obtaining spectra of faint stars and nebulæ. They are called *blazed* gratings.

With normal incidence the maximum concentration of light is obtained for only one wavelength. By altering the angle of incidence, the wavelength which gives maximum concentration can be altered. The reason for this may be seen from the following relations:

If α is the angle between the facets and the macroscopic surface, and θ is the angle between the incident beam and the normal to the macroscopic surface, then the maximum concentration occurs in a direction β given by

$$\beta = \theta + 2\alpha, \qquad \ldots \ldots \ldots \quad 6(21)$$

while the mth principal maximum for wavelength λ occurs in a direction θ_m given by

$$2e(\sin \theta_m - \sin \theta) = m\lambda. \qquad \ldots \ldots \quad 6(22)$$

If $\theta_m = \beta$ when $\theta = 0$ for wavelength λ, concentration will occur in the mth order of λ when incidence is normal. By altering θ a little, it is obviously possible to make $\theta_m' = \beta$ for some neighbouring wavelength λ'.

6.26. Methods of Manufacturing Gratings.

In the ruling engines constructed by Rowland the grating blank was fixed to a carriage which could be moved forward by turning a screw. The ruling point traversed the blank in a direction at right angles to the direction of motion of the carriage. After a line was ruled, the point was lifted and returned to its original position, while the carriage was advanced by giving the screw a predetermined fraction of a complete turn. In this way the spacing of the rulings could be made very much less than the pitch of the screw.

In an ideal grating every ruling is identical in depth and shape, and the distances between successive rulings are constant to within a small fraction of the grating interval. Since the accuracy desired is very much better than that normally obtained from a screw-cutting lathe, it

---

* Reference 6.6. See also Reference 6.7.

is not remarkable that all gratings produced by this method show appreciable errors and some have very serious defects. The errors include:

(a) *Lack of sharpness of the spectrum lines* due to a variety of causes including a gradual variation in grating interval (possibly produced by imperfect temperature control) or imperfection in the optical quality of the blank.

(b) *Rowland ghosts.* Rowland ghosts are spurious satellites, i.e. weak lines spaced at short intervals from strong lines in the spectrum. They are due to long-range periodic errors usually caused by defects in the screw or its bearings.

(c) *Lyman ghosts.* Lyman ghosts are spurious lines appearing at wavelengths $m\lambda/n$ (where m and n are small integers and $m < n$). These are due to short-range periodic errors (e.g. every fifth line slightly displaced has the effect of superposing a " grating " of spacing five times the true spacing and gives a " ghost " whose apparent wavelength is $\lambda/5$). This kind of error is due to some regularly repeated source of vibration.

Many attempts have been made to reduce or to eliminate the effect of errors in the screw. One method is to attach one plate of an interferometer to the carriage and the other to the main structure of the engine. The ruling of the lines is monitored by a photo-electric control which determines the position of the carriage by observing the interference fringes.

A grating of about 15,000 lines to the inch would be produced if a line were ruled every time 6 fringes pass, and the photo-electric control is capable of locating the fringe maxima to within a few hundredths of a fringe. Unfortunately this method does not eliminate all errors due to temperature variation and to imperfect rigidity of the machine. It introduces a new error because the fringe separation is altered by variations in barometric pressure. Several attempts to rule good gratings this way failed, but Harrison and co-workers have succeeded in developing the method so that large optical gratings substantially better than those obtained with a good ruling engine are produced.*

Another method which eliminates the effect of periodic errors of the screw has been developed at the National Physical Laboratory,† using a device due to Merton. A high-quality lathe is used to cut a very fine " primary " thread upon an accurately cylindrical rod. This rod is then mounted coaxially with a second cylinder, and the two rotated slowly. The movement of a resilient nut, lined with pith and gripping the thread upon the first cylinder, is conveyed to a diamond

---

* References 6.13 and 6.14.   † Reference 6.16.

tool which bears upon the second cylinder (fig. 6.21). The tool thus cuts upon the second cylinder a "secondary" thread free from the periodic errors of the primary thread by reason of the averaging effect of the resilient nut.

The secondary thread is next coated with a thin layer of plastic material and, after this has set to a hard film, it is cut parallel to the

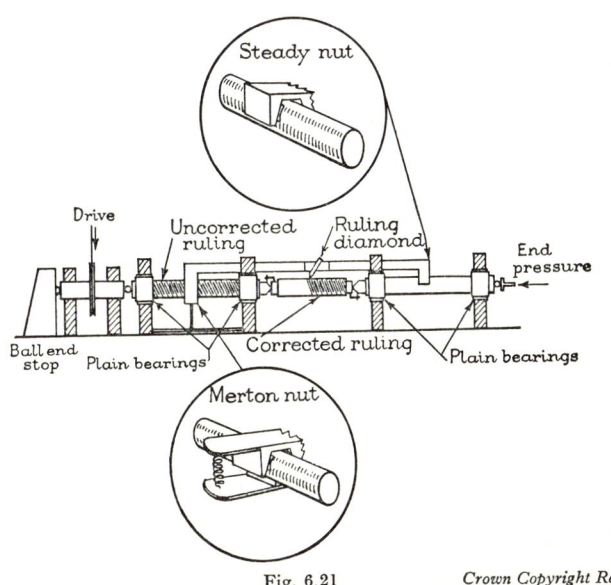

Fig. 6.21   *Crown Copyright Reserved.*

axis, removed from the cylinder, and applied to a thin layer of soft gelatine upon an optically flat surface. Here it remains until the gelatine is dry and hard, after which it can be peeled off, leaving in effect a flattened copy of the secondary thread in the hardened gelatine. This copy is itself used to generate further plastic copies which can be coated with aluminium by vacuum evaporation and used as reflection gratings.

Gratings can be produced in this way with spacings up to 7500 lines per inch. They have been found suitable for work in the infra-red region and for use as scales of measurement in moiré fringe systems.

6.27. Amplitude Gratings and Phase Gratings.

When light passes through a grating consisting of alternate clear and opaque strips, there is a periodic variation of amplitude across the emergent wavefront. An ideal reflecting grating produces periodic variations of phase (i.e. periodic variations of shape in the wave surfaces) and no variations of amplitude. A transmission grating giving variations of phase is obtained if one side of a sheet of plastic material is moulded to obtain the shape shown in fig. 6.19, the other side remaining plane.

In discussing the theory of diffraction and the formation of optical images* it is convenient to divide gratings into *amplitude gratings*, which change only the amplitude, and *phase gratings*, which change only the phase. It must, however, be understood that all real gratings produced by ruling lines on glass or metal change both amplitude and phase. It is further convenient to imagine a *sinusoidal displacement grating* such that, when a plane wave is incident normally, the transmitted or the reflected light is represented by equation 3(64). In a similar way, a *sinusoidal phase grating* produces sinusoidal variations of phase.

To obtain the distribution described by 3(64), it is necessary to have a sinusoidal variation of transmission, together with a reversal of phase, whenever $\sin \kappa_y y$ passes through zero. The distribution of energy corresponding to 3(64) is $E = 4a^2 \sin^2 \kappa_y y = 2a^2(1 - \cos 2\kappa_y y)$. This may be regarded as the difference of a constant term and a term which varies sinusoidally with spatial frequency $2\kappa_y$.

6.28. Echelon and Echelle Gratings.

If the angle at which light is incident on a grating is fixed ($\theta_1 =$ constant), then $d\theta_2/d\lambda$ may be called the *angular dispersion*. Equation 6(7b) shows that

$$\cos \theta_2 \frac{d\theta_2}{d\lambda} = \frac{m}{2e} = \frac{mN}{W}, \quad \ldots \ldots \quad 6(23)$$

where W is the width of the ruled area. Thus for a given width of ruling the angular dispersion is proportional to the product mN if we disregard the slowly varying factor $\cos \theta_2$. It will be shown later that the sharpness of the primary maxima (and hence the power of the grating to separate wavelengths which are nearly equal) is also proportional to mN. This product should therefore be made fairly large.

Ruled gratings of the type so far considered have N up to about 10^5 and are used in first, second, or third orders† so that mN is about

---

* See Chapter VIII. † Higher orders (in the range 10–15) are now often used.

3×10^5. The *echelon diffraction grating* shown in fig. 6.22a has about 30 elements ($N = 30$) and works in a very high order ($m = 35,000$); the echelle grating shown in fig. 6.22b operates with N about 10^3 and

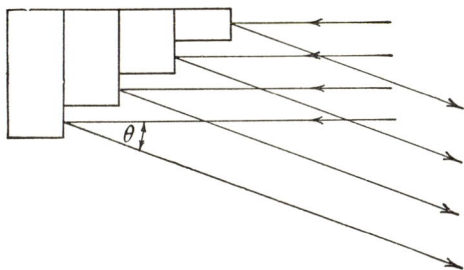

Fig. 6.22a.—Michelson-Williams reflecting echelon.

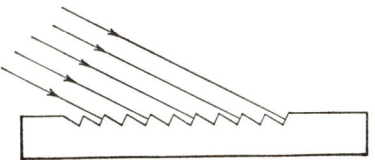

Fig. 6.22b.—Echelle grating.

m also about 10^3. For each of these instruments mN is about a million. Whereas the Rowland diffraction grating instrument is complete in itself, the echelon and the echelle need an auxiliary instrument to separate the orders unless they are being used to study the structure of a single line which can be isolated by filters (see § 9.44).

6.29.—The original echelon designed by Michelson in 1898 was used with transmitted light. Fig. 6.22a shows the reflecting echelon which is an improvement designed by Williams* in 1933. It is constructed by making a number of fused-quartz plates with accurately plane-parallel surfaces and all of equal thickness to within 0.1λ. The plates are cleaned and placed in contact. On heating to a temperature far below the melting-point, the surfaces adhere, and after cooling can be separated only with considerable force. There is extremely little reflection from the interface, and the surfaces are therefore said to be in optical contact. The final effect is similar to that which would be produced if the whole etalon could be carved out of a solid block of quartz. The faces of the steps are coated with aluminium by evaporation in vacuum.

The necessity of manufacturing a large number of plates of equal thickness to within 0.1λ makes the echelon very expensive. The echelle grating (see fig. 6.22b), designed by Harrison in 1949, is made by a special ruling engine. This process is much less costly than that which produces an echelon.

* See Reference 6.8.

6.30. Theory of the Echelon and of the Echelle.

Let us first consider the reflecting echelon. Suppose that the light is incident normally and consider the diffraction in a direction θ. If t is the thickness and $2e$ is the width of a step, the phase difference between the beams from successive steps is (fig. 6.22a)

$$\delta = \frac{2\pi}{\lambda} n_a(t + t\cos\theta - 2e\sin\theta),$$

where n_a is the refractive index of air.

When θ is very small this may be written

$$\delta = \frac{2\pi}{\lambda} n_a(2t - 2e\theta).$$

The variation of illumination with θ is given by an expression which is the product of two factors corresponding to $f(NW)$ and $F(U)$ of § 6.19.

Principal maxima of the function corresponding to $f(NW)$ occur when

$$m\lambda = n_a(2t - 2e\theta),$$

and the angle between the maxima of order m and $(m+1)$ is $\lambda/2e$ approximately (since n_a is nearly unity).

The function corresponding to $F(U)$ is

$$\left(\sin\frac{2\pi e\theta}{\lambda}\right)^2 \bigg/ \left(\frac{2\pi e\theta}{\lambda}\right)^2.$$

It is zero when $\theta = \pm\lambda/2e$ and nearly all the light is concentrated within these limits. If $2n_a t = m\lambda$, principal maxima of the function corresponding to $f(NW)$ occur at $\theta = 0$, $\pm\lambda/2e$, $\pm 2\lambda/2e$, ..., etc. The illumination is high for the central maximum, and zero or nearly zero for all the other maxima. If $2n_a t$ is not an integral number of wavelengths, two maxima, separated by an angle $\lambda/2e$ and situated between the limits $\theta = +\lambda/2e$ and $\theta = -\lambda/2e$, are seen. These are of equal magnitude when they occur at $\theta = \pm\lambda/4e$.

The condition in which only a single maximum appears is called the *single-order position*. The condition giving two equal maxima may be called the *symmetrical position*. The necessary control to attain either the single-order or the symmetrical position as desired may be obtained by placing the echelon in an airtight box and adjusting the pressure so as to alter n_a.

§6.31 THEORY OF DIFFRACTION

The echelle grating (fig. 6.22b) is essentially an echelon with a very large number of small steps. Because the ruling process does not give perfectly flat steps, the concentration of light for the echelle is not quite so good as for the echelon; the best concentration so far achieved with an echelle gives about one-third of the light in one order. This is sufficient for many purposes.

EXAMPLES [6(ix)–6(xvii)]

6(ix). Derive an equation giving the exact positions of the lateral maxima of $F(U)$. [$\tan U = U$.]

6(x). Solve the equation mentioned in example (ix) graphically and determine the value of U at which the first lateral maximum of $F(U)$ occurs. Compare the value of $F(U)$ at this maximum with its value when $U = 3\pi/2$.
[Maximum of $F(U)$ when $U = 2\cdot 86\pi/2$, at which $F(U) = 0\cdot 0472$. When $U = 3\pi/2$, $F(U) = 0\cdot 0451$.]

6(xi). Show that as $N \to \infty$ the form of $f(NW)$ becomes identical with that of $F(U)$. Examine what happens to the different maxima of $f(NW)$.
$\left[\text{Put } f(NW) = \left[\dfrac{(\sin NW)/NW}{(\sin W)/W}\right]^2,\text{ and let } N \to \infty \text{ while } NW \text{ remains finite.}\right]$

6(xii). How many subsidiary maxima of $f(NW)$ lie between the mth and $(m+1)$th principal maxima? [$N-2$.]

6(xiii). Draw graphs for $F_a(U) = \sin U/U$ and for $f_a(NW) = \sin NW/(N \sin W)$ (when $N = 4$), and compare them with corresponding graphs for $F(U)$ and $f(NW)$. The functions $F_a(U)$ and $f_a(NW)$ represent amplitudes.

6(xiv). Show that when the relation between d and e is such as to give as much light as possible in the first order, the brightnesses of all even orders are zero.

6(xv). What ratio of e to d makes the mth order (a) as bright as possible, and (b) of zero brightness? [(a) $2m$, (b) m.]

6(xvi). Show that if d is very small compared with e, all the maxima of low orders tend to the same brightness.
$\left[\dfrac{f_m}{f_T} = \dfrac{d^2}{e^2}\dfrac{\sin^2(\pi md/e)}{(\pi md/e)^2} \to \dfrac{d^2}{e^2} \text{ if } \dfrac{md}{e} \ll 1.\right]$

6(xvii). If the refractive index of air is 1·00029 for 5893 Å. at S.T.P., calculate the change in pressure required to pass from the single-order to the symmetrical position with an etalon of step 2 millimetres. [193 mm.]

6.31. General Theory of Diffraction.

The distribution of energy in a diffraction pattern may be obtained, in principle, by finding a solution of the appropriate wave-equation, subject to boundary conditions corresponding to physical conditions at the surface of the diffracting screen. The mathematical difficulties of this procedure are very serious, and an exact solution has been completely worked out for only one special case. Sommerfeld* solved the equations of the electromagnetic field for plane waves diffracted at the edge of a thin perfectly reflecting screen under the conditions of Fresnel diffraction. His results agree with experimental observations. The mathematical device used by Sommerfeld is not generally applicable, but other methods have been used to obtain somewhat less rigorous solutions for particular problems.†

6.32. Kirchhoff's Analysis.

Kirchhoff applied Green's theorem to solutions of the scalar wave-equation. He showed that the disturbance at a point Q (fig. 6.5) may be calculated when the disturbance at all points on a surface S (which completely surrounds Q) is known. This analysis is given in Appendix VI A, where the following equation is derived:

$$\psi_Q = \frac{i\kappa}{4\pi} \int \frac{A' \exp\left[-i\kappa(r+r')\right]}{rr'} (\cos n, r - \cos n, r')\, dS, \quad 6(24)$$

where A' is the strength of the source at L_p, n is the outward-drawn normal from the surface. The formula is valid when r and r' are large compared with the wavelength. The surface must either completely enclose the source or completely enclose the point Q. This result justifies Huygens' belief that the disturbance at Q is related to that on a wavefront in advance of Q. It gives Huygens' principle a satisfactory relation with the wave equation and makes it more definite by giving a formula for calculating ψ_Q. It may be shown that the detailed assumptions made, somewhat empirically, by Fresnel are also justified.

For a spherical wave $A' e^{i\kappa r'}/r'$ may be put equal to a new constant A, since all points on the wavefront have the same amplitude. The factor $(\cos n, r - \cos n, r')$ has the necessary properties to be the inclination factor. It decreases slowly from the value 2 as the angle of inclination (n, r) increases from zero. The factor i is equivalent to the quarter-period advance of phase which was postulated by Fresnel. Thus, under the conditions discussed in § 6.6, equation 6(24) reduces to 6(1).

6.33. St. Venant's Hypothesis.

Kirchhoff's analysis applies to an integral taken over the whole of an unbroken surface which surrounds Q, i.e. it gives the effect of the unobstructed wave. It does not show that, when an obstacle is inserted, the effect at Q may be calculated by taking the integral over the

* See References 6.1 and 6.2. † See p. 553 of Reference 6.1.

unobstructed part of the wavefront. St. Venant suggested that this assumption should be made on the grounds (a) that it is plausible, and (b) that it leads to results which are in agreement with experiment. This assumption is in fact made implicitly or explicitly in nearly all calculations on diffraction.

St. Venant's hypothesis cannot be exactly correct because, if it were, the values of $\partial \xi/\partial y$, etc., at the edge of an opaque obstacle would be infinite, and this would be inconsistent with the wave equation. However, the assumption does lead to satisfactory results except when the width of the aperture is less than the wavelength (see § 6.56).

6.34. Extension of the Concept of a Wave Group.

In Chapter IV it was shown that a train of waves of finite length does not constitute a pure simple harmonic wave, but can be analysed by Fourier's theorem into a set of simple harmonic waves of different wavelengths. When the wave train is fairly long, the effective range of wavelength is small and the system is called a *wave group*. In a similar way, we shall now show that a beam of light which is of finite width cannot be represented by a single plane wave, but may be regarded as the resultant of a system of plane waves travelling in different directions. When the width of the beam is very large in comparison with the wavelength, the effective angular spread is small, and the waves form a group of plane waves. All beams of light which occur in real problems are limited both in the direction of propagation and in the two transverse directions. There are certain problems for which the effects due to the limitation in the direction of propagation are unimportant. It is then sufficient to assume for the time being that the wave train is infinitely long in the z direction, which we take to be the centre of the small solid angle which contains the beam. This implies that we have a simple harmonic wave of one sharply defined frequency. In order further to simplify the initial stages of our calculation we consider, for the present, a beam which is limited in the y direction and unlimited in the x direction.

6.35.—An unlimited plane wave propagated in a direction perpendicular to the x axis and making an angle θ with the z axis may be represented by
$$a \exp i(\omega t - \kappa y \sin \theta - \kappa z \cos \theta),$$

which may be written
$$a \exp i(\omega t - \kappa_y y - \kappa_z z), \quad \ldots \quad 6(25)$$

where
$$\kappa_y = \kappa \sin \theta \quad \text{and} \quad \kappa_z = \kappa \cos \theta. \quad \ldots \quad 6(26)$$

Consider a group of waves whose directions lie within the range of angles which correspond to values of κ_y between $(\kappa_y - \tfrac{1}{2}d\kappa_y)$ and $(\kappa_y + \tfrac{1}{2}d\kappa_y)$. An amplitude $a(\kappa_y)\,d\kappa_y$ is related to this wave group (cf. § 4.19). Hence, if $d\xi$ is the resultant disturbance for the infinitesimal group, we have

$$d\xi = a(\kappa_y)\exp i(\omega t - \kappa_y y - \kappa_z z)\,d\kappa_y. \quad \ldots \quad 6(27)$$

Consider a system of waves whose mean direction is along the z axis, and which lies within the range of θ corresponding to $\kappa_y = -\Delta$ to $\kappa_y = +\Delta$.

The resultant disturbance for $t = 0$ and $z = 0$ is

$$\xi_0(y) = \int_{-\Delta}^{\Delta} a(\kappa_y)\exp(-i\kappa_y y)\,d\kappa_y. \quad \ldots \quad 6(28)$$

If it is understood that $a(\kappa_y) = 0$ for all values of κ_y outside the range $\pm\Delta$, which corresponds to the angular spread of the beam, no alteration is caused by extending the limits of integration to infinity; thus we may write

$$\xi_0(y) = \int_{-\infty}^{\infty} a(\kappa_y)\exp(-i\kappa_y y)\,d\kappa_y. \quad \ldots \quad 6(29)$$

By Fourier's theorem this relation implies that

$$a(\kappa_y) = \frac{1}{2\pi}\int_{-\infty}^{\infty} \xi_0(y)\exp(i\kappa_y y)\,dy. \quad \ldots \quad 6(30)$$

For a strictly parallel beam travelling in the direction of the z axis, $a(\kappa_y)$ would be zero except when $\kappa_y = 0$; 6(29) shows that $\xi_0(y)$ would then be independent of y. The displacement would then be the same at all points on the y axis and the beam would be infinitely wide in the y direction. If the beam is not strictly parallel, but $a(\kappa_y)$ is given, then the disturbance at different points on the y axis for $t = 0$ can be calculated from 6(29).

If, for example, $a(\kappa_y) = A$ when κ_y is between $\pm\Delta$, and zero outside this range,* then

$$\xi_0(y) = \frac{2A\sin y\Delta}{y}. \quad \ldots \ldots \quad 6(31)$$

From this equation we see that $\xi_0(y)$ has appreciable values only when

---

* See Appendix IV B, equation 4(88). Remember that the mean value of κ_y, corresponding to κ_m, is zero.

§ 6.36   BEAM OF FINITE WIDTH   197

y is in the range π/Δ to $-\pi/\Delta$; if Δ is very small the beam *must* be very wide. If Δ is fairly large, then the main energy of the beam may be confined within a narrow range of y.

6.36. Beam of Finite Width—One Dimension.

Let us now assume that we are given that $\xi_0(y) = A$ when y is between $-d$ and $+d$, and that $\xi_0(y) = 0$ outside this range. The beam has constant amplitude on the line $y = 0$ over a range which is physically small, though still large compared with the wavelength. Equation 6(30) then gives

$$a(\kappa_y) = \frac{A}{\pi} \cdot \frac{\sin \kappa_y d}{\kappa_y}. \qquad \ldots \ldots \quad 6(32)$$

If E is the ratio of the energy in the direction defined by κ_y to the energy in the direction of the z axis [for which $\kappa_y = 0$ and $(\sin \kappa_y d)/\kappa_y = d$], we have

$$E = \left\{\frac{\sin \kappa_y d}{\kappa_y d}\right\}^2 = \left\{\frac{\sin[(2\pi d \sin \theta)/\lambda]}{2\pi d \sin \theta/\lambda}\right\}^2 \ldots \quad 6(33)$$

From 6(33) we see that if d is very large compared with λ, the value of E is small except when θ is small. The beam is then nearly a parallel beam. As d decreases, the energy is effectively spread over a wider and wider range of angle. The width of the beam and the angular spread are connected by a definite mathematical relation.*

Note that equation 6(16) agrees with equation 6(33) in the case of normal incidence.

6.37.—In the preceding paragraphs we have considered a single-slit aperture in an infinite screen. We may now discuss a more general problem by imagining that a beam of coherent light of unit amplitude is incident upon a "screen" which lies in a surface of constant phase (we choose this phase as zero phase). The screen is specified by stating that the disturbance on the far side of the screen is $\xi_0(y) \exp i(\omega t - \kappa_z z)$. If the screen produces variations of amplitude, but not of phase, $\xi_0(y)$ will be real. If it produces variations of phase but not of amplitude, $\xi_0(y)$ will be a complex quantity whose modulus is the same for all values of y. In general, there will be variations both of amplitude and of phase, so that $\xi_0(y)$ may be written $\xi_0(y) = A \exp i\delta$, where

---

* The relation we have derived applies when a plane wave is incident upon the slit. This gives the *minimum* spread of waves emerging from the slit. A greater angular spread will be obtained if converging or diverging waves are incident.

both A and δ are functions of y. If A is a periodic function of y and δ is a constant, we have a sinusoidal amplitude grating (§ 6.27). If δ is a periodic function and A is a constant, then we have a sinusoidal phase grating. The general Fourier transform analysis of $\xi_0(y)$ is equivalent to regarding any real screen as a superposition of a number of sinusoidal amplitude and phase gratings (see § 8.36).

This method of calculating diffraction patterns may be considered in the following way. The distribution $\xi_0(y)$ on the plane immediately to the right of the diffraction screen was, in fact, produced by the screen operating on a plane wave. However, exactly the same distribution might have been produced, without the screen, by a certain system of plane waves incident from the left and advancing in different directions (§ 3.31). An observer on the right cannot, from observations of the diffraction pattern alone, determine how the distribution $\xi_0(y)$ arose. Therefore he observes that system of plane waves which would have produced this distribution $\xi_0(y)$ if they had passed uninterrupted across the plane $y = 0$.

Note that a system of waves cannot contain any terms corresponding to $\kappa_y > \kappa$. If the structure of the diffraction screen is such that the Fourier transform of $\xi_0(y)$ gives non-zero values for $a(\kappa_y)$ when $\kappa_y > \kappa$, then the above discussion does not apply. We shall see later that this happens when $\xi_0(y)$ changes much in distances of order $\lambda/2\pi$. These conditions will be considered in § 6.55.

6.38.—The Fourier transform of a sinusoidal distribution of amplitude which extends from $y = -\infty$ to $y = +\infty$ corresponds to two beams of light travelling in directions for which $\sin\theta = \pm\kappa_y/\kappa$ (see § 3.31). An infinitely wide sinusoidal amplitude grating thus has only two side spectra, each consisting of a parallel beam. If the grating extends from $y = -D$ to $y = +D$ (where $\kappa_y D$ is very large so that the width of the grating is large compared with the grating interval), there are still only two side spectra, but the two beams are not strictly parallel. When the distribution in the plane $z = 0$ is regarded as due to the interaction of beams of finite width, we need to allow for the spread of these beams according to equation 6(16). The side spectra are then not infinitely sharp but cover a range of angles.

When a diffraction aperture is of finite width it is sometimes convenient to use a Fourier series rather than a Fourier integral to represent the diffracted light. This gives the directions of the principal maxima and the total energy in one of these maxima. In order to investigate the sharpness of the maxima it is necessary to use Fourier transforms to allow for the finite width of the aperture.

6.39. Diffraction with a Two-dimensional Screen.

The Fourier theorem may be extended so that for a two-dimensional screen we may write

$$a(\kappa_x, \kappa_y) = \frac{1}{4\pi^2}\int_{-\infty}^{\infty}\int_{-\infty}^{\infty} \xi_0(x, y) \exp i(\kappa_x x + \kappa_y y) \, dx \, dy, \quad 6(34)$$

where $\kappa_x = \alpha\kappa$ and $\kappa_y = \beta\kappa$; α and β are direction-cosines. If we put

$$a(\kappa_x, \kappa_y) = C + iS, \quad \ldots \quad 6(35)$$

where C and S are real functions of κ_x and κ_y, then the ratio of the flux of radiation in the direction defined by κ_x and κ_y to that in the centre of the pattern ($\kappa_x = \kappa_y = 0$) is

$$E(\kappa_x, \kappa_y) = \frac{C^2 + S^2}{C_0^2 + S_0^2}. \quad \ldots \quad 6(36)$$

If the diffraction screen is symmetrical with regard to both the X and Y axes (ξ_0 an even function of x and y) then $S = 0$ and equation 6(34) reduces to

$$a(\kappa_x, \kappa_y) = \frac{1}{4\pi^2}\int_{-\infty}^{\infty}\int_{-\infty}^{\infty} \xi_0 \cos(\kappa_x x) \cos(\kappa_y y) \, dx \, dy, \quad 6(37)$$

and in this case $E = C^2/C_0^2$.

The pattern for a beam whose cross-section is a rectangle with sides $2d_x$ and $2d_y$ is obtained by putting $\xi_0 = A$ over the range 0 to d_x and 0 to d_y in 6(37) and integrating. We have

$$E = \left[\frac{\sin(\kappa_x d_x)\sin(\kappa_y d_y)}{\kappa_x \kappa_y d_x d_y}\right]^2. \quad \ldots \quad 6(38)$$

The distribution of illumination on the screen S_2 (fig. 6.4), when a point source of light is used with a rectangular slit aperture in S_1, is given by equation 6(38). If the screen S_2 is distant z_1 from the lens L_1 and if x_1 and y_1 are given by $2\pi x_1/\lambda z_1 = \kappa_x$ and $2\pi y_1/\lambda z_1 = \kappa_y$, then all portions of the wave whose direction of propagation is defined by κ_x and κ_y are focused at a point Q whose co-ordinates are x_1 and y_1. The distribution of illumination on the screen is given by

$$E(x_1, y_1) = \left\{\frac{\sin\left(\frac{2\pi}{\lambda}\frac{d_x}{z_1}x_1\right)}{\frac{2\pi}{\lambda}\frac{d_x}{z_1}x_1}\right\}^2 \left\{\frac{\sin\left(\frac{2\pi}{\lambda}\frac{d_y}{z_1}y_1\right)}{\frac{2\pi}{\lambda}\frac{d_y}{z_1}y_1}\right\}^2 \quad \ldots \quad 6(39)$$

The illumination is zero whenever $d_x x_1/(2\lambda z_1)$ or $d_y y_1/(2\lambda z_1)$ is a whole number (other than zero). Thus the diffraction pattern contains two sets of mutually perpendicular lines on which the illumination is zero. Regions of maximum illumination lie between these lines.

The pattern is shown in Plate III*m* (p. 162). It will be noticed that the long side of the rectangles in the pattern corresponds with the short side of the aperture. If the aperture is a very long vertical slit, the horizontal lines in the pattern are so close that they become confused. The resulting pattern is similar to that shown in Plate III*e*.

6.40.—The above discussion refers to the pattern produced when a point source illuminates a slit aperture. Now suppose that a slit aperture is illuminated by a slit source, and consider the diffraction patterns formed by two small regions A and B of the source. If the two slits are accurately parallel, the diffraction patterns due to light from A and B will be almost exactly the same. Since the light from A is not coherent with that from B there is no interference, and the energy at any point due to A and B acting jointly is just the sum of the energies when they act separately. Thus the pattern obtained with the slit source is the same in form as that obtained with a point source, but the illumination is increased at every point in a common ratio. Note that if the slits are not *accurately* aligned the pattern is badly blurred.

6.41 Diffraction at a Circular Aperture.

In view of the symmetry of the aperture, equation 6(37) may be used. The integral is to be evaluated over the area of a circle whose radius we shall take to be R. It is sufficient to investigate the variation of illumination along any radius from Q_0; we therefore choose the radius through Q_0 parallel to the x axis, for which $\kappa_y = 0$. Equation 6(37) is integrated over the region covered by the aperture, the limits of integration for y being $\pm(R^2 - x^2)^{1/2}$:

$$C = \frac{A}{4\pi^2} \int_{-R}^{R} \int_{-(R^2-x^2)^{1/2}}^{(R^2-x^2)^{1/2}} dy \cdot \cos(\kappa_x x)\, dx \quad \ldots \ldots \quad 6(40)$$

$$= \frac{A}{2\pi^2} \int_{-R}^{R} (R^2 - x^2)^{1/2} \cos(\kappa_x x)\, dx. \quad \ldots \ldots \quad 6(41)$$

If we put $x = R \cos \chi$ and $\rho = \kappa_x R$, then

$$C = \frac{AR^2}{2\pi^2} \int_0^\pi \sin^2 \chi \cos(\rho \cos \chi)\, d\chi. \quad \ldots \ldots \quad 6(42)$$

Bessel's integral of order unity is defined by the equation

$$J_1(\rho) = \frac{\rho}{\pi} \int_0^\pi \sin^2 \chi \cos(\rho \cos \chi)\, d\chi. \quad \ldots \ldots \quad 6(43)$$

§ 6.41   CIRCULAR APERTURE   201

This expression cannot be integrated in the form of a finite algebraic expression, but values have been calculated by series and tables are available. From 6(42) and 6(43) we have

$$C = \frac{AR^2}{2\pi} \cdot \frac{J_1(\rho)}{\rho}, \qquad \ldots \ldots \ldots \quad 6(44)$$

and, using the fact that $J_1(\rho)/\rho$ tends to the value $\tfrac{1}{2}$ when ρ tends to 0, we have

$$E(\rho) = 4\left(\frac{J_1(\rho)}{\rho}\right)^2, \qquad \ldots \ldots \ldots \quad 6(45)$$

$$E(x_1) = 4\left\{\frac{J_1\left(\dfrac{2\pi}{\lambda} \cdot \dfrac{Rx_1}{z_1}\right)}{\dfrac{2\pi}{\lambda} \cdot \dfrac{Rx_1}{z_1}}\right\}^2 \qquad \ldots \ldots \quad 6(46)$$

$E(x_1)$ is the illumination at a distance x_1 from Q_0. It is computed by calculating the value of ρ in terms of x_1, z_1, and R, and then referring to the tables. The result is shown graphically in fig. 6.23 and a picture of the diffraction pattern is shown

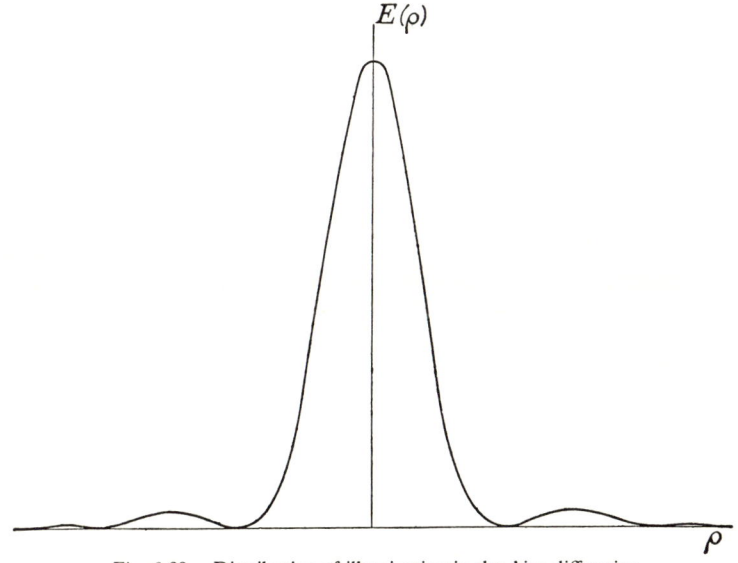

Fig. 6.23.—Distribution of illumination in the Airy diffraction pattern for a circular aperture

in Plate IIIk (p. 162). The pattern consists of a bright central disc surrounded by a series of alternate bright and dark rings. The radii corresponding to maxima and minima are given in Table 6.2, which shows also the values of the maximum illumination. It may be seen that all except the innermost rings are very weak. Computation shows that 84 per cent of the whole light is concentrated in the central disc. This is known as Airy's disc, after Sir G. B. Airy (1801–92), who first made a general investigation of this problem.

TABLE 6.2

Ring number	Radius (in units of $z_1\lambda/2R$)		Maximum illumination (relative to centre)
	Dark ring	Bright ring	
1	1·22	1·64	0·0174
2	2·23	2·69	0·0041
3	3·24	3·72	0·0016
4	4·24	4·72	0·0008
5	5·24	5·72	0·0004

6.42. Diffraction by a Number of Similar Apertures.

In §§ 6.12–6.30 we discussed the diffraction patterns produced by a number of similar apertures or diffracting elements arranged in a regular way. We showed that the illumination at any point in the pattern could be expressed as the product of a factor F, which is equal to the illumination which would be given by any one element acting alone, and a factor f which depends on the arrangement of the elements. We shall now show that this proposition is true for any system of similar elements (which are similarly orientated) even when they are irregularly arranged. We shall also show that for perfectly random arrangements the average value of the factor f is simply equal to the number of apertures. The distribution of illumination in the pattern due to a number of irregularly arranged apertures may thus be expected to be similar to that obtained in the pattern due to a single aperture.

6.43.—Let O_1, O_2, O_3, etc. (fig. 6.24), be a series of points, one in each of the apertures, and let each be similarly placed with respect to its aperture. Regard these as a series of local origins and let the co-ordinates of a point in a given aperture (referred to its own local origins be (x', y'). Let the co-ordinates of O_1, O_2, etc., referred to a given co-ordinate system lying in the diffraction screen be (X_1, Y_1), (X_2, Y_2), etc. Let (x, y) be the co-ordinates of any point, in any aperture, referred to the main co-ordinate system. Then we have, for the fth aperture,
$$x = X_f + x' \text{ and } y = Y_f + y'. \quad \ldots \quad 6(47)$$

Let $\xi_0(x', y')$ represent the disturbance over any one aperture.

When these values are inserted in 6(34) we obtain

$$a(\kappa_x, \kappa_y) = \frac{1}{4\pi^2} \sum_{g=1}^{N} \int_{-\infty}^{\infty} \int_{-\infty}^{\infty} \xi_0(x', y') \exp i[\kappa_x(x' + X_f) + \kappa_y(y' + Y_f)] \, dx' \, dy'. \quad 6(48)$$

§ 6.44 RANDOM ARRANGEMENT

The factors containing X_g and Y_g may be taken outside the integral sign so that

$$a(\kappa_x, \kappa_y) = \frac{1}{4\pi^2} \sum_{g=1}^{N} \exp i(\kappa_x X_g + \kappa_y Y_g) \int_{-\infty}^{\infty} \int_{-\infty}^{\infty} \xi_0(x', y') \exp i(\kappa_x x' + \kappa_y y') \, dx' \, dy'. \qquad 6(49)$$

If $\qquad A = \dfrac{1}{4\pi^2} \displaystyle\int_{-\infty}^{\infty} \int_{-\infty}^{\infty} \xi_0(x', y') \exp i(\kappa_x x' + \kappa_y y') \, dx' \, dy', \qquad 6(50)$

and $\qquad B = \displaystyle\sum_{g=1}^{N} \exp i(\kappa_x X_g + \kappa_y Y_g) = \sum_{g=1}^{N} \exp i\delta_g, \qquad \ldots \quad 6(51)$

then the relative energy is

$$E = AA^*BB^*, \qquad \ldots \ldots \quad 6(52)$$

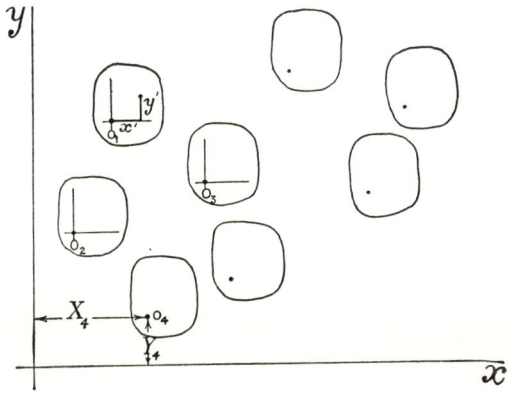

Fig. 6.24

i.e. the relative energy is given by the product of the factor $F = AA^*$ which depends solely on the property of the individual aperture or diffracting element and $f = BB^*$ which depends solely on the arrangement or spacing of the elements. These are known as the *form factor* and the *structure factor* respectively in discussion of crystal structure in relation to X-ray diffraction. The factors $F(U)$ and $f(NW)$ obtained in § 6.19 are special cases appropriate to a one-dimensional grating.

6.44. Random Arrangement.

The factor f represents the resultant for a number of simple harmonic motions whose amplitudes are all equal but whose phases are given by $\delta_1, \delta_2,$ etc.

We have

$$f = BB^* = \left(\sum_{g=1}^{N} \exp i\delta_g\right)\left(\sum_{g=1}^{N} \exp -i\delta_g\right). \qquad 6(53)$$

The summation will include N terms, each equal to unity, and a double summation of terms such as $\exp i(\delta_r - \delta_s)$. If the apertures are irregularly arranged these terms are as likely to be positive as negative, and when N is very large their average value is zero. The most probable value of f is therefore N. The distribution of light for N randomly arranged elements is just N times the distribution (F) obtained for a single element.

6.45.—Rayleigh[*] discusses in detail the resultant of N vibrations with arbitrary differences of phase. If we imagine that p trials are made with different random arrangements of phases, then the average value of f in equation 6(53) approaches N more and more closely as p becomes very large. However, the chance of a value materially different from N *in a single trial* is independent of N and is not small. For example the chance of a value less than $0·6N$ is $0·45$, and the chance of a value greater than $1·5N$ is $0·22$. In the problem of photometric summation (§ 5.1) the shortest normal period of observation covers a large number of random rearrangements of phase, and the chance of a significant deviation is small. In the problem considered in § 6.44 we deal with a single trial, and in this case there is a considerable chance of a departure from the average value. This consideration applies also to the diffraction of X-rays by liquids and amorphous solids, though the arrangement of atoms in a liquid or solid is never completely random. In a glass, for example, there are small regions of local order. Even in a liquid the distances between different atoms vary over only a narrow range.

6.46. Babinet's Theorem.[†]

Suppose that the diffraction screen S_1 is removed from the apparatus shown in fig. 6.4. Then the pattern formed on the screen S_2 will consist of the central image of the source together with very faint fringes due to diffraction at the edges of the aperture (i.e. at the edges of the lenses). Now suppose that two diffraction screens S_1' and S_1'' have the property that the clear regions in S_1' exactly correspond with the opaque regions in S_1'' and *vice versa*. These screens are said to be *complementary* screens.

If $a'(\kappa_y)$ is the energy diffracted in the direction κ_y when S_1' is in place, $a''(\kappa_y)$ when S_1'' is in place, and $a(\kappa_y)$ when both screens are removed, then

$$a' + a'' = a. \qquad\qquad 6(54)$$

If for any direction $a(\kappa_y) = 0$, then $a' = -a''$ and the two complementary screens give the same energy. This theorem is due to J. Babinet (1794–1872).

---

[*] See Reference 6.5. [†] The theorem is often called "Babinet's *Principle*".

When both S_1' and S_1'' are removed to leave a wide circular aperture, nearly all the light is concentrated in a small Airy disc. It is often stated that this implies that the diffraction patterns of complementary screens are *approximately* the same at all points except very near the centre. This addendum to the Babinet theorem is not generally true—as may be seen by taking a speck of dust 3μ in diameter on one of the lenses to constitute S_1'; the complementary screen S_2'' is then opaque except for a pinhole of 3μ in diameter. The speck of dust has very little effect on the pattern formed by the lenses alone, while the pinhole spreads the light over a considerable angle. Returning to equation 6(54), we see that a' is approximately equal to $-a''$ when a is small compared with a' or a'', i.e. the amount of light diffracted in a given direction in the absence of S_1' and S_2'' must be small compared with the amount of light scattered *in the same direction* when S_1' or S_1'' is inserted. It is not sufficient for a to be small compared with $a(0)$. In practice, this implies that the patterns produced by the complementary screens are *approximately* the same when (i) each screen obstructs an appreciable fraction of the area, and (ii) the apertures in at least one of the screens are widely distributed over the area. If these conditions are not satisfied, then the light in the diffraction pattern with one screen will be concentrated near the centre. In the outer parts of the field either $a'(\kappa_y)$ or $a''(\kappa_y)$ will then be small, and they are not necessarily of the same order of magnitude [see Examples 6(xviii) and 6(xx)].

EXAMPLES [6(xviii)–6(xx)]

6(xviii). Find expressions for the distribution of energy diffraction pattern due to (*a*) a diffraction aperture consisting of a very wide slit of width $4D$ (where D is of order 1 cm.), (*b*) a wire of width $4d$ (of order 0·1 mm.) placed centrally within the wide slit, and (*c*) the screen complementary to (*b*). Find the ratio of the energies for (*b*) and (*c*), and show that this ratio is 1 when $2\kappa_y D = \pi$.

$$\left[(a)\ \left(\frac{\sin 2\kappa_y D}{\kappa_y}\right)^2,\quad (b)\ 4\left(\frac{\sin \kappa_y(D-d)\cos 2\kappa_y(D+d)}{\kappa_y}\right)^2\right.$$

$$\left.(c)\ \left(\frac{\sin 2\kappa_y d}{\kappa_y}\right)^2.\ \text{See equations 6(9) and 6(32).}\right]$$

6(xix). Suppose that the wide slit of the previous example is filled with a grating consisting of N alternate slits of width $2d$ (order of 0·01 mm.) with distances $2e$ between centres. Find the ratio of intensity for this and the complementary grating.

6(xx). Calculate the radius of the Airy disc when $\lambda = 5000$ Å. and (i) $R = 1$ cm., $z_1 = 1$ metre; (ii) $R = 3$ mm., $z_1 = 50$ cm.; (iii) $R = 1\mu$, $z_1 = 1$ metre (one micron = $1\mu = 10^{-6}$ metre).

[(i) $3{\cdot}05 \times 10^{-3}$ cm., (ii) $5{\cdot}08 \times 10^{-3}$ cm., (iii) $30{\cdot}5$ cm.]

6.47. Diffraction by a Number of Circular Apertures or Obstacles.

The discussion of §§ 6.42–6.44 shows that the diffraction pattern due to a large number of *irregularly arranged* circular apertures is similar to that calculated for a single circular aperture and consists of a central bright disc surrounded by a series of alternate light and dark rings. The application of Babinet's principle shows that the diffraction pattern due to a set of irregularly arranged dark obstacles is similar except for a very small region in the centre. Diffraction rings of this type may sometimes be seen surrounding street lights, when small water-droplets are present in the atmosphere. They may also be formed by small particles on the surface of the eye. Under suitable meteorological conditions, the moon is seen to be surrounded by halos owing to diffraction by large numbers of small ice crystals in the upper atmosphere (though not all lunar and solar " halos " are formed in this way).

6.48 Young's Eriometer.

It is possible to apply this result to measure the diameters of small particles such as blood corpuscles. A simple apparatus for carrying out the experiment is formed by taking a sheet of metal and drilling about 12 holes, each of 1 millimetre diameter, at equal intervals round a circle of diameter 15 centimetres. A hole of 3 millimetres diameter is drilled in the centre of the circle (fig. 6.25). A source of roughly monochromatic light (such as a sodium lamp or a filament lamp with a green filter) is placed behind the screen. A microscope slide containing the corpuscles, or a piece of glass dusted with lycopodium powder, is held close to the observer's eye. Looking through the glass he sees the central hole surrounded by a series of light and dark rings. By adjusting his distance from the screen he may bring one of the rings into coincidence with the circle defined by the small holes. If the distance from the screen

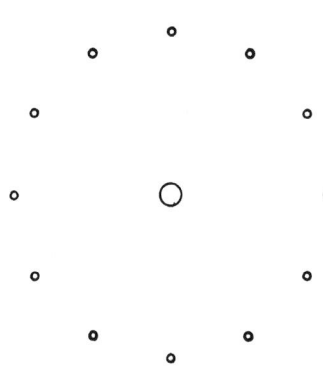

Fig. 6.25.—Young's Eriometer

is then measured, the diameter of the particles on the slide is obtained by reference to Table 6.2 (p. 202). This device is known as Young's Eriometer.

The diameters of blood corpuscles from one individual are not all exactly equal, but are distributed about a mean. This reduces the sharpness of the diffraction rings. Even with this limitation, readings of the diameter of a given ring on one specimen are reproducible to within 3 per cent, and it is easy to detect any variation from the norm which is sufficiently large to be of clinical importance.

6.49. The Angular Power Spectrum.*

We showed in Appendix IV B that, when the profile $\xi(x)$ of a wave is known, the *power spectrum*, i.e. the distribution of energy among different frequencies, may be calculated in either of two ways:

(i) By using equation 4(12) to calculate the complex amplitude distribution function $a(\kappa)$ and then calculating $a(\kappa)\, a(\kappa)^* = |\,a(\kappa)\,|^2$.

(ii) By calculating the auto-correlation function†

$$\rho(\alpha) = \frac{\int_{-\infty}^{\infty} \xi(x)\, \xi^*(x+\alpha)\, dx}{\int_{-\infty}^{\infty} \xi(x)\, \xi^*(x)\, dx},$$

and then calculating the Fourier transform of $\rho(\alpha)$, i.e.

$$\frac{E(\kappa)}{E} = \frac{1}{2\pi} \int_{-\infty}^{\infty} \rho(\alpha)\, e^{-i\kappa\alpha}\, d\alpha.$$

where E is the total energy (see §§ 16 and 17 of Appendix IV B).

Similarly there are two ways of calculating the angular power spectrum $E(\kappa_y)$ when the function $\xi_0(y)$ corresponding to a given diffraction screen is known. The relation between these two methods is shown in fig. 6.26. Note that in passing from the profile to the power spectrum by either path, there are two steps. One of these is reversible and the other is not reversible. If the profile is known then both the real amplitude *and the phases* of the Fourier components may be calculated. In passing from the complex amplitude to the power spectrum, knowledge of the phases is rejected. In a similar way, knowledge of the phases is eliminated in passing from the profile to the auto-correlation function. Thus the same auto-correlation function is obtained for all profiles corresponding to a given power spectrum,

---

* See Reference 6.12.   †See §17 of Appendix IVB

i.e. to a given set of real amplitudes but with different phase relations. Both methods of calculating the angular power spectrum may be extended to two dimensions.

For example, consider the diffraction of light from a one-dimensional diffraction grating which moves in a direction parallel to a line through

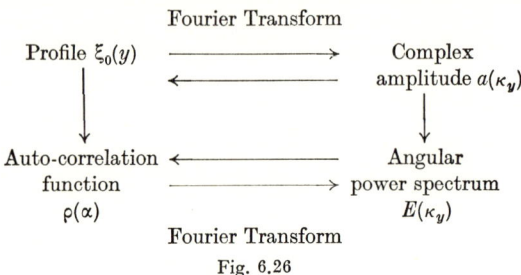

Fig. 6.26

the elements (OY in fig. 6.8). The auto-correlation function does not depend on the instantaneous position of the grating, so that the energy diffracted in a given direction does not change when the grating moves. Reference to equation 6(9), or simple argument based on fig. 6.8, confirms this conclusion and also shows that the phase of the spectrum of order m changes by $2\pi m(h/2e)$ when the grating moves through a distance h, i.e. there is a phase change of $2\pi m$ when the grating moves through a distance equal to the grating interval.

6.50. Diffraction of Light by Sound Waves.

When a beam of sound waves is propagated through a medium, as shown in fig. 6.27, alternate compression and rarefaction produces

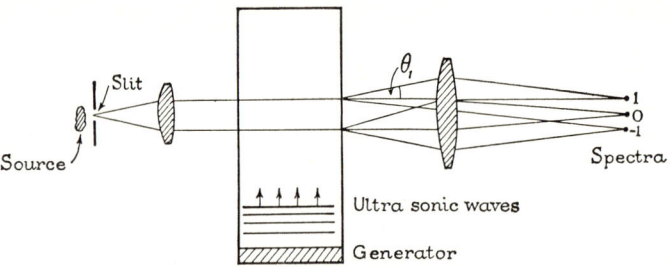

Fig. 6.27.—Diffraction of light by ultrasonic waves.

regular variation of optical density. The progressive sound waves have the same effect on a beam of light (incident normal to the direction of propagation of the sound waves) as a moving phase-grating. The grating interval is equal to the wavelength (λ_s) of the sound waves. If λ_s is large compared with the optical wavelength (λ), the diffraction maxima are obtained in directions θ_m for which

$$\theta_m = m\frac{\lambda}{\lambda_s}, \qquad \ldots \ldots \quad 6(55)$$

where m is an integer (positive, negative, or zero). The existence of diffraction of light by sound waves was predicted by Brillouin in 1921, but the phenomenon was not observed* until 1932. The wavelength of audible sound waves is inconveniently large, and ultrasonic waves of frequencies of order 10^7 cycles per second and of wavelengths of order 10^{-2} centimetre have been used by Parthasarathy† for a detailed investigation. Under this condition λ_s/λ is approximately 2×10^2, and the first-order maximum is diffracted through an angle of about 10 minutes. The equivalent grating moves through a distance equal to the grating interval in a time equal to $1/\nu_s$ where ν_s is the frequency of the sound waves. From the discussion at the end of the preceding paragraph it follows that the phase of the mth spectrum is advanced by $2\pi m\nu_s$ per second, i.e. the frequency of light in the mth spectrum is $\nu + m\nu_s$. The frequency change, which may be regarded as a Doppler effect, is too small to be observed directly, since ν_s/ν is of order 10^{-8}.

When the light is not incident normally, the problem can no longer be regarded as one-dimensional. It is necessary to consider the general equation for propagation of waves in a medium whose refractive index is a function both of position and of time. The directions of the principal maxima are not very different from those given by elementary theory, but the calculation of the relative energies involves an elaborate mathematics of approximation.‡ Diffraction is also obtained with stationary sound waves.

6.51. Diffraction by Irregular Screens.

Suppose that we have a number of ground-glass screens all made by the same process, e.g. on the same machine and with the same type of grinding paste. Then the detailed structure of each screen will be different, but the auto-correlation function for all the screens will be nearly the same. A certain average auto-correlation function will be characteristic of the process. The angular distribution of the light scattered by different screens, from a parallel beam incident at the same angle, will differ very little from that calculated using this average

---

* See p. 591 of Reference 6.1. † See p. 605 of Reference 6.1.
‡ See p. 596 of Reference 6.1.

auto-correlation function. Suppose that a certain process produces screens whose average auto-correlation function is

$$\overline{\rho(\alpha)} = \rho_0 \exp\left(-\frac{\alpha^2}{2e^2}\right). \quad \ldots \quad 6(56)$$

Such a screen would have irregularities of all sizes and shapes, but since $\bar{\rho}$ is nearly 1 when α is much less than e, there cannot be much variation of ξ in a distance much smaller than e (e.g. in a distance $0\cdot 3e$). The Fourier transform of equation 6(56) leads to the power spectrum

$$E(\kappa_y) = \rho_0 \int_{-\infty}^{\infty} \exp -\left(\frac{\alpha^2}{2e^2} + i\kappa_y \alpha\right) d\alpha. \quad \ldots \quad 6(57)$$

The integration is similar to that considered in § 14 of Appendix IV B, except that α is now the variable. The integration yields

$$E(\kappa_y) = E(0) \exp\left(-2e^2 \kappa_y{}^2\right). \quad \ldots \quad 6(58)$$

When $2e^2\kappa^2 \ll 1$, i.e. when e is smaller than $\lambda/2\pi$, $E(\kappa_y)$ is nearly constant.

We then have $\quad E(\kappa_y)\, d\kappa_y = E(0)\, d\kappa_y.$

Let $E(\theta)\, d\theta$ be the energy in the range of angles between θ and $\theta + d\theta$; then

$$E(\theta)\, d\theta = E(\kappa_y)\, d\kappa_y$$

$$E(\theta) = E(\kappa_y)\frac{d\kappa_y}{d\theta} = P \cos\theta, \quad \ldots \quad 6(59)$$

where $P = \kappa E(0)$ is a constant.

Thus, for a sufficiently finely ground screen, the energy per unit solid angle in a direction making an angle θ with the surface (see fig. 10.15) is proportional to $\cos\theta$. Such a screen obeys Lambert's law for a perfectly diffusing screen (see § 10.27).

6.52. Fresnel Diffraction.

Following the method of Huygens, Fresnel analysed the light leaving the diffraction screen into a series of spherical wavelets whose mutual interference generated the diffraction pattern. This method was found to be most convenient and simple for calculating the distribution of light on a plane at a finite distance from the diffraction screen (fig. 6.1). It is also possible to apply the method which we have so far used for Fraunhofer diffraction to the problems considered by Fresnel. Suppose that the Fourier transform is used to analyse the

§ 6.53   RECONSTRUCTION FROM A HOLOGRAM   211

light crossing the diffraction screen (situated in the plane $z = 0$) as was done in §§ 6.34–37.

$\xi_0(y)$ is represented by a set of plane waves, the amplitude distribution being given by equation 6(30). The disturbance at a point (y_1, z_1) is then given by

$$\xi(y_1, z_1) = \int_{-\infty}^{\infty} a(\kappa_y) \exp\{-i(\kappa_y y_1 - \kappa_z z_1)\} d\kappa_y$$

$$= \int_{-\infty}^{\infty} a(\kappa_y) \exp -i(\kappa_y y_1 - \delta_1) d\kappa_y, \quad \ldots \ 6(60)$$

where $\delta_1 = \kappa_z z_1 = (\kappa^2 - \kappa_y^2)^{\frac{1}{2}} z_1.$ . . . . . 6(61)

Thus, provided that $a(\kappa_y)$ is zero for values of $\kappa_y > \kappa$ (see § 6.37 and § 6.55), the plane waves are recombined on the plane $z = z_1$. Their amplitudes are the same as on $z = 0$ but the relative phases are different. It follows that the auto-correlation coefficient for the distribution of light on $z = z_1$ is the same as that on $z = 0$. Thus *the auto-correlation coefficient for a Fresnel pattern is the same as that for the diffraction screen which produces it.** This conclusion is indeed obvious since the angular power spectrum does not change as the wave advances.

6.53. Reconstruction of a Picture from a Hologram.

The discussion of the preceding paragraph shows that, in general, it is impossible to reconstruct an object from a photograph of its Fresnel diffraction pattern, because the photograph does not contain information about phases. It has been shown by Gabor† that approximate reconstruction of an object which diffracts only a small fraction of the incident light is possible. Suppose that an object OO′ (fig. 6.28a) is illuminated by a coherent light so that a Fresnel diffraction pattern, called a *hologram* is formed in the plane HH′. This hologram is photographed and a positive transparency is produced. Then, on removing the object and using a lens together with this transparency, as shown in fig. 6.28b, a reconstructed picture of the object is obtained at II′.

Suppose that the light received at a given point H_0 on the hologram is represented by the vector AC in fig. 6.28c. This may be regarded as the resultant of (i) that part of the incident light which is transmitted unchanged by the object (represented by the vector AB which is of unit length), and (ii) light scattered from the object (represented by BC which is of length a). This has suffered a phase-change δ. The energy of the light falling on the photographic plate is proportional to $E = AR^2 =$

* See figure 3 of Reference 6.9.   † See Reference 6.22.

$(1 + a \cos \delta)^2$, which is approximately equal to $1 + 2a \cos \delta$ when a is small. If the photographic material is processed so that the overall* value of the constant γ (see § 10.14) is 2, then the energy passing through the transparency at the point H_0 is proportional to E^2, i.e.

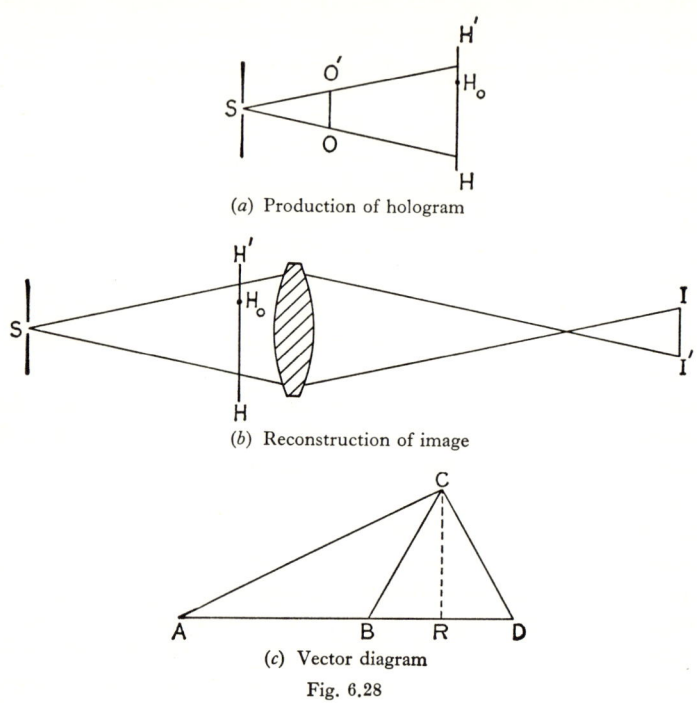

(a) Production of hologram

(b) Reconstruction of image

(c) Vector diagram

Fig. 6.28

it is approximately proportional to $(1 + 2a \cos \delta)^2$ and the amplitude is proportional to $(1 + 2a \cos \delta)$, i.e. to AD, where RD = BR. The vector AD may be regarded as the resultant of AC (derived from the real object) and CD (equal to BC but with opposite phase difference from AB) scattered by an imaginary object in another plane. The reconstructed picture in the plane I′I (conjugate to OO′) is an image of the real object together with an out-of-focus image of the imaginary object. It is possible to arrange that the image of the imaginary object is so much out of focus that it does not interfere with discrimination of detail in the real object—or to place a stop so as to reduce the amount of light in the second " image ".

* i.e. the slope of a curve which relates the transmission of the positive print to the original exposure.

§ 6.54 RECONSTRUCTION FROM A HOLOGRAM

The above method of reconstruction was proposed by Gabor* who wished to use it in the following way. The hologram was to be produced by an electron microscope and the reconstruction by an optical lens. Since the form of the diffraction pattern is determined by d/λ, where d is a parameter defining the effective size of the object, the reconstructed picture will be magnified in the ratio λ_0/λ_e where λ_0 is the optical wavelength and λ_e is the electron wavelength. This ratio is of order $10^5:1$. It was hoped to make a microscope which would combine some of the advantages of the extremely short electron wavelength (see § 8.23) with the high quality of optical lenses of moderate aperture. Technical difficulties prevented the realization of this development, but Gabor was able to produce very good reconstructed images when light was used both for making the hologram and for the reconstruction.

6.54.—The experimental data obtained from X-ray diffraction give an angular power spectrum and do not reveal phases. From them it is possible to determine the auto-correlation function of the scattering elements, and this is obtained by the Patterson series method of calculation. It is not, in general, possible to deduce the structure of the crystal from X-ray data alone, but X-ray measurements taken together with other chemical and physical data usually lead to a satisfactory analysis of the crystal structure. There are certain special cases when X-ray data alone may give the whole or nearly the whole solution.†

Optical diffraction may be used to assist X-ray crystal analysis by the following method which is due to Lipson.‡ When an X-ray diffraction pattern has been obtained, it is possible to calculate lattice parameters for the crystal. Then taking into account chemical and other evidence several structures may appear possible. Analytical methods may be used to calculate the diffraction pattern for each postulated structure, in order to see which one agrees most closely with the X-ray pattern which has been obtained. This lengthy process may be avoided by using the apparatus shown in fig. 6.29. Holes are punched in a thin card to represent the different scattering units of a postulated structure. The diffractometer forms a Fraunhofer diffraction pattern of the " card ". This may then be compared with the X-ray pattern. The differences between the optical and the X-ray patterns may indicate how the assumed structure must be altered in order to obtain an optical diffraction pattern more like the X-ray pattern. The dif-

---

* See Reference 6.22 and p. 452 of Reference 6.1.
† See Reference 6.15 and p. 457 of Reference 6.1. ‡ See Reference 6.11.

fractometer thus serves both as a rapid analogue computer and also as a means of assisting the investigator to visualize closer approximations to the correct structure.

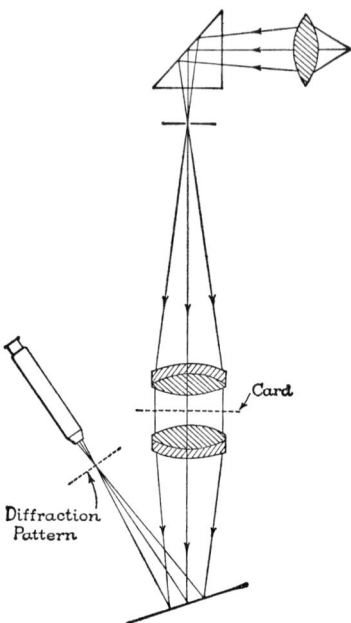

Fig. 6.29.—Lipson diffractometer

6.55. Evanescent Waves.

Consider a sinusoidal distribution of displacement (§ 3.31 and § 6.37) represented by

$$\xi = a \cos \kappa_y y \exp i(\omega t - \kappa_z z). \qquad \ldots \quad 6(62)$$

In order that the wave equation 2(38) shall be satisfied, we require

$$\frac{\omega^2}{b^2} = \kappa_z^2 + \kappa_y^2 = \kappa^2$$

or
$$\kappa_z = (\kappa^2 - \kappa_y^2)^{\frac{1}{2}}. \qquad \ldots \ldots \quad 6(63)$$

The distribution of amplitude over any plane for which z is constant is $a \cos \kappa_y y$, i.e. it is of spatial frequency κ_y. When κ_y is less than κ, this distribution is propagated in the OZ direction with a velocity ω/κ_z. Now suppose that a distribution for which $\kappa_y > \kappa$ could be established. κ_z would then be imaginary. Let $\mu = i\kappa_z$, where μ is real. Then equation 6(62) is replaced by

$$\xi = ae^{-\mu z} \cos \kappa_y y \exp i\omega t, \qquad \ldots \quad 6(64)$$

i.e. no wave is propagated in the OZ direction. Instead the disturbance dies away rapidly.* For example, if $\kappa_y^2 = 2\kappa^2$, then $\mu = \kappa$. The amplitude then falls to $1/e$ in a distance $\lambda/2\pi$ and, for optical wavelengths, to a very small value in a few microns. A disturbance of this type is called an *evanescent wave*. It may be shown by an extension of the discussion of § 14.16 that this kind of wave does not involve any transport of energy.

The Fourier analysis (equation 6(29)) of the function $\xi(y)$ corresponding to a diffracting screen may include terms corresponding to spatial frequencies higher than κ. These spatial frequencies are not represented in the diffracted light and we shall see later (Chapter VIII) that they cannot be reproduced in any image which may be formed by an optical system.

6.56. Diffraction by a very narrow Slit.

Consider a slit of width $2d$. From equation 6(32), we see that when $\kappa_y d \ll 1$, $a(\kappa_y)$ approaches a constant value Ad/π. We may imagine an arrangement in which A increases and d decreases without limit in such a way that Ad/π has the finite value A'. Then since $a(\kappa_y)$ is independent of κ_y, the light is radiated uniformly in all directions as from a line source. If $\kappa_y d \ll 1$, then $a(\kappa_y)$ still has the value A' when $\kappa_y > \kappa$. Evanescent waves are produced. These waves carry no energy, though they are formally included in the Fourier analysis of the function $\xi(y)$.

A function which is indefinitely large in an indefinitely narrow range, so that its integral remains finite (in the way described above) is called a *Dirac delta function*. The above discussion implies that the Fourier transform of a delta function is a constant for all values of the frequency. If the energy were distributed over an infinite range of frequency, then the energy in any finite frequency interval would be infinitesimal. In any real physical problem, something intervenes to limit the effective frequency range. In the optical problem considered in § 6.55, the transport of energy is limited to the range $0 < \kappa_y < \kappa$.

The above discussion of diffraction by a very narrow slit is incomplete because we have not so far considered any precise type of wave. If light is represented by transverse electromagnetic waves, it is necessary to consider the direction of the electric vector in this problem.† The electromagnetic theory must also be used for the theory of diffraction by small conducting spheres.‡ The equations, developed by Mie, reduce to a simple form obtained by Rayleigh§ when the spheres are small compared with the wavelength.

---

* Mathematically there is also a term with a positive exponential but, in the situation considered, physical boundary conditions make this term zero.

† See p. 553 of Reference 6.1. ‡ See p. 630 of Reference 6.1. § See §§ 15.45–8.

6.57. Rectilinear Propagation.

We shall now consider wave propagation when the ratio of the wavelength to the size of the spaces in a diffraction screen or to the size of an obstacle becomes indefinitely small, e.g. for a slit when $\kappa d \gg 1$. We shall see that when the limit is approached—either under the conditions of Fraunhofer diffraction or under those of Fresnel diffraction—we come to phenomena which are adequately described in terms of rays which, in a homogeneous medium, are straight lines.

Consider a diffraction grating in which the diffracting elements are much larger than the spaces between them. Then nearly all the energy

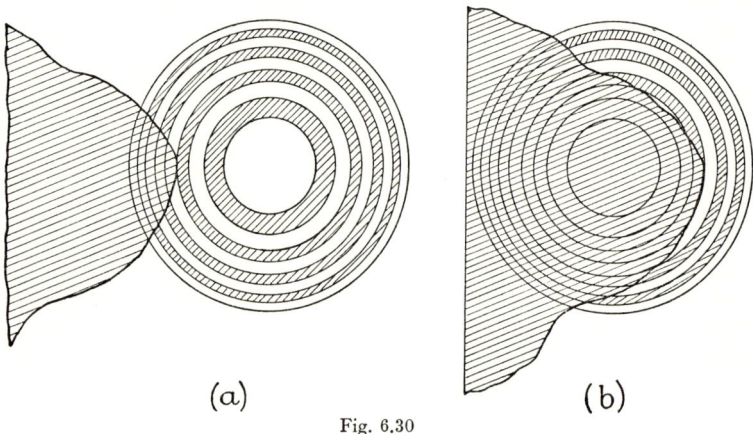

Fig. 6.30

is in the spectrum of zero order. If the ratio λ/e becomes very small ($\kappa e \gg 1$), the maximum becomes sharper so that, in the limit, as $\lambda/e \to 0$ the energy travels within an indefinitely small range of angles whose centre is the direction of the maximum of zero order. In § 6.14 we saw that this direction corresponds to the normal law of reflection if reflecting elements are used and to Snell's law for transmitting elements. Thus, in the limit of an indefinitely wide slit, light is propagated in the direction required by ray theory.

Our previous discussion of Fresnel theory shows that, for objects such as a slit or a straight edge diffraction effects are confined to a small region near the edge of the geometrical shadow. We shall now show that this restriction applies when the object is of irregular shape. Fig. 6.30 shows a system of half-period zones, partially obscured by an obstacle. In the absence of the obstacle, the amplitude at a point Q, for which the zones are drawn, is the sum of a series of terms alternately positive and negative, and gradually decreasing in magnitude. We have seen that the sum of such a series is equal to half that of the first term, and is independent of the exact rate at which the higher terms decrease. When the obstacle is in the position shown in fig. 6.30a, Q is outside the geometrical shadow by a distance equal to about three times the radius of the first zone. The only effect of the obstacle is to make the higher terms in the series decrease more rapidly than before. The resultant is nearly the same as that obtained in the absence of the obstacle. If the obstacle is moved into the position shown in fig. 6.30b, Q is inside the shadow, and the same distance as before from the edge. The resultant is the sum of a series of terms which are alternately positive and negative, and decrease gradually to zero at both ends. The sum of such a series is nearly zero. Thus for both the positions of the obstacle, the illumination is that given by the laws of geometrical optics.

Diffraction effects occur only when either:
(a) the edge of the obstacle is in, or near, the central zone; or
(b) the obstacle has a special shape so that its boundary follows the edges of one zone.

In either of these cases, the series is interrupted sharply at a certain term, and the resultant amplitude depends greatly on whether it is interrupted at an odd- or even-numbered term. The circular obstacle and aperture are the only simple arrangements in which the boundary may follow the edge of a zone.

6.58. Fermat's Principle.

Fermat (1601–65) suggested that the time taken by light to travel from one point on a ray to another is less than the time which would be required for transit between the same points by any neighbouring path. He regarded this " principle " as an example of the essential economy of nature! He showed that his statement is true for rays which have been reflected or refracted at plane surfaces.* Later investigation has shown that the principle as stated by Fermat is not always true when rays are reflected or refracted by curved surfaces. The principle has been modified and is now stated in the following way: " The difference between the time required for light to travel along the ray (i.e. the actual path) differs only by the second order of small quantities from the time required for light to travel along any neighbouring path." An alternative statement is: " For the true path, the first variation of the path length (measured in wavelengths)

* Essentially the same idea, in relation to *reflection* at plane surfaces, had been suggested by Hero of Alexandria (150 B.C.).

is zero." In the notation of the calculus of variations, these statements become

$$\delta \int_A^B \frac{ds}{b} = 0, \qquad \ldots \ldots \quad 6(65)$$

and

$$\delta \int_A^B \frac{ds}{\lambda} = 0. \qquad \ldots \ldots \quad 6(66)$$

A third form is

$$\delta \int_A^B n \, ds = 0, \qquad \ldots \ldots \quad 6(67)$$

where ds is an element of length along the path, b is the speed of light, and n the refractive index appropriate to the place where the element is situated. These forms may be seen to be equivalent by applying equations 2(25) and 3(31). The principle, stated in any of these ways, applies to rays which are reflected or refracted at plane or curved surfaces, and to rays which pass through a medium in which the refractive index varies continuously from point to point.

6.59.—We shall now show that the principle is obeyed in two simple cases: (i) rectilinear propagation in one uniform medium, (ii) refraction at a plane surface.

(i) *Propagation in a Uniform Medium.*

We know that the ray from A to C is a straight line ABC joining those points (fig. 6.31a). A neighbouring path is AB'C, and this path differs from the actual

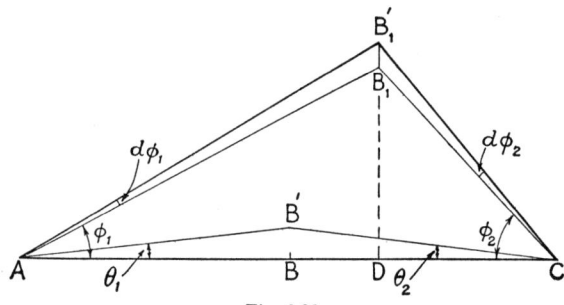

Fig. 6.31a

path by $AB'(1 - \cos \theta_1) + B'C(1 - \cos \theta_2)$. If θ_1 and θ_2 are small quantities, the difference is approximately $\frac{1}{2}(AB \cdot \theta_1^2 + BC \cdot \theta_2^2)$. If θ_1 and θ_2 are infinitesimal quantities, the path difference is of the second order of small quantities. Note that a similar proposition does not apply to a path such as AB_1C. If $AB_1'C$ is a path near to AB_1C, the difference of path is approximately

$$\Delta s = \left\{ \frac{AD}{\cos \phi_1} + \frac{DC}{\cos \phi_2} \right\} - \left\{ \frac{AD}{\cos (\phi_1 + d\phi_1)} + \frac{DC}{\cos (\phi_2 + d\phi_2)} \right\} \cdot \quad 6(68)$$

$$= \frac{AD \tan \phi_1}{\cos \phi_1} d\phi_1 + \frac{DC \tan \phi_2}{\cos \phi_2} d\phi_2. \qquad \ldots \ldots \quad 6(69)$$

§ 6.59   FERMAT'S PRINCIPLE   219

ϕ_1 and ϕ_2 have the same sign and Δs is of the *first* order of small quantities unless $\tan \phi_1/\cos \phi_1$ and $\tan \phi_2/\cos \phi_2$ are themselves infinitesimal. They vanish only for the ray ABC. Thus this path has a special property [stated in equation 6(65)] which does not apply to any other path.

(ii) *Refraction at a Plane Surface.*

Consider the path difference between PQR and PQ'R (fig. 6.31b) which are neighbouring rectilinear paths from P to R, giving slightly different angles of

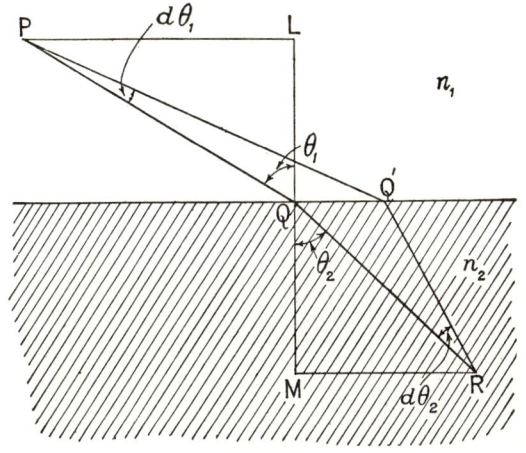

Fig. 6.31b

refraction at the surface between two media of indices n_1 and n_2. For the path PQR the value of the integral of equation 6(67) is

$$n_1(\text{PQ}) + n_2(\text{QR}) = \frac{n_1(\text{QL})}{\cos \theta_1} + \frac{n_2(\text{QM})}{\cos \theta_2}, \quad \ldots \quad 6(70)$$

and for the path PQ'R it is

$$\frac{n_1(\text{QL})}{\cos (\theta_1 + d\theta_1)} + \frac{n_2(\text{QM})}{\cos (\theta_2 + d\theta_2)}. \quad \ldots \quad 6(71)$$

The difference is

$$\Delta s = \frac{n_1(\text{QL}) \sin \theta_1}{\cos^2 \theta_1} d\theta_1 + \frac{n_2(\text{QM}) \sin \theta_2}{\cos^2 \theta_2} d\theta_2. \quad \ldots \quad 6(72)$$

But

$$(\text{QQ}') \cos \theta_1 = (\text{PQ}) d\theta_1 = \frac{\text{QL}\, d\theta_1}{\cos \theta_1}. \quad \ldots \quad 6(73)$$

Hence

$$\text{QQ}' = \frac{(\text{QL})\, d\theta_1}{\cos^2 \theta_1}, \quad \ldots \quad 6(74)$$

and similarly

$$\text{QQ}' = -\frac{(\text{QM})\, d\theta_2}{\cos^2 \theta_2}. \quad \ldots \quad 6(75)$$

Thus the path difference is equal to

$$\Delta s = \text{QQ}'(n_1 \sin \theta_1 - n_2 \sin \theta_2), \quad \ldots \quad 6(76)$$

and this difference vanishes if, and only if

$$n_1 \sin \theta_1 = n_2 \sin \theta_2, \quad \ldots \quad 6(77)$$

i.e. if Snell's law is obeyed.

6.60.—When the rays of light emitted by a point source are reflected or refracted at a suitably curved surface, they converge towards a real or virtual image. In general, lenses or mirrors with spherical surfaces do not produce perfect images. The refracted or reflected

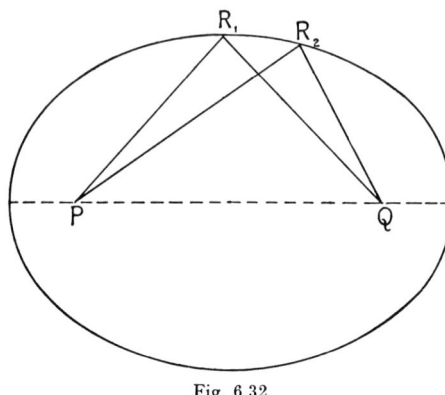

Fig. 6.32

rays from a point source pass near to a certain point, and the deviations are called *aberrations*. It is, however, possible to calculate certain surfaces for which all the rays from a certain object point P pass through an image point Q. A surface of this type has the property that the sum of the optical paths from P to R, and from R to Q, is

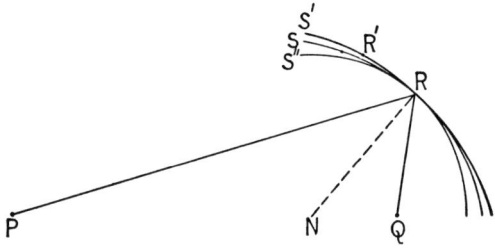

Fig. 6.33

constant if R is any point on the surface. When the points P and Q are situated in a medium of constant refractive index, an ellipsoid (formed by revolving an ellipse whose foci are P and Q about the line PQ) brings all the rays from one point to meet at the other (fig. 6.32). The sum (PR + RQ) is constant. If a surface S' of larger radius of curvature touches the correct aspherical surface S at R (fig. 6.33), a ray from P which strikes S' at R is reflected to Q, because the direction of the ray reflected at this point depends only on the angle between the incident ray PR and RN, which is the normal to the plane tangential to all three surfaces. If the radius of curvature of S' is greater than that of S, the optical path P to R, plus the optical path R to Q, is less than a path which goes from P to Q via a point R' which is on S' and near to R. If the radius of curvature of S'' is less than that of S, then the path from P to Q via R is a maximum. In either case equation 6(65) is satisfied.

6.61. Gouy's Experiment.

Suppose that a point source of light is placed at P and that systems of half-period zones are constructed on the surfaces S' and S'' by an observer at Q. For the surfaces S' and S'' the centre of the zone system will be at R, but for S' the central zone will be the zone of minimum path, and for S'' the central zone will be the zone of maximum path. No zone can be constructed on S since all paths from P to Q via S are equal.* The phase of the resultant wave reaching Q from P via S' is the same as the mean phase over the central zone drawn on S', i.e. it is a quarter-period *behind* the phase of the wave from R. Similarly the phase of the wave received at Q from P via S'' is a quarter-period *ahead* of the phase of the wave from R. These phase differences were demonstrated experimentally by Gouy† and others. The experimental arrangement is shown in fig. 6.34. A parallel beam of *white* light is reflected from a plane mirror M_1 and a curved mirror M_2. The curved mirror focuses the light at Q. It has a greater radius of curvature than the correct aspherical surface corresponding to Q' (since a mirror of smaller radius would be needed to focus the light at Q'). It is of smaller radius of curvature than the correct surface corresponding to Q''. The plane mirror is of greater radius of curvature than the correct surface for all three points.

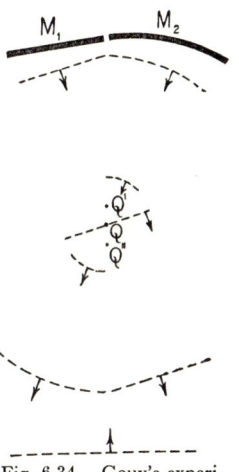

Fig. 6.34.—Gouy's experiment

Now suppose that the mirror M_1 is tilted slightly so as to allow interference fringes to be observed on a small screen placed near Q. When the screen is placed at Q', both beams have been reflected from a surface whose radius of curvature is higher than that of the correct surface. The fringe system should therefore have a white centre at the point where the paths are geometrically equal. When it is placed at Q'', the beam from M_1 has been reflected at a surface of higher radius of curvature than the correct surface, and that from M_2 has been reflected at a surface of lower radius of curvature. There should therefore be a half-period difference of phase so that the fringe system should show a dark centre. These effects were observed.

---

* In a certain sense every point on S may be regarded as the centre of a zone system for which the central zone is of infinite area. The whole surface S then covers only an infinitesimal fraction of the central zone.

† Reference 6.17.

6.62. Relation between Wave and Ray Optics.

Fermat's principle is connected both to wave and to ray optics, and clarifies the relation between them. Suppose that equation 6(65) is satisfied for a given path between two points A and B. Then the phase difference between waves arriving at B from A by this path and by neighbouring paths is vanishingly small. Such waves have agreement of phase at B, and energy will travel from A to B if no obstacle is placed on or near a path defined by 6(65). This is just the definition of a ray adopted in Chapter I. This concept may be expressed slightly differently by considering the half-period zones.

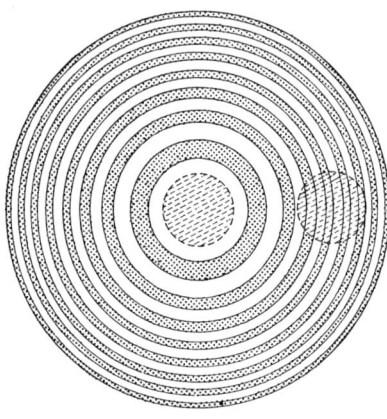

Fig. 6.35

Suppose that the half-period zones have been drawn on any surface intersecting any chosen line drawn from A to B, and suppose an imaginary cylindrical tube, whose cross-section is smaller than the area of the central zone, surrounds the line. This tube cuts the surface in a small circle. If the chosen line intersects the zone system at the centre, the phases of the unobstructed wavelets are all very nearly the same. If, however, it intersects at some point not very far out in the zone system (fig. 6.35), wavelets from a similar area surrounding the point of intersection have widely different phases. If this is the only clear path, very little energy travels from A to B. From this point of view the ray is defined as the locus of the centre of the half-period zone systems on all surfaces which lie between A and B.

6.63 Rays and Wave Normals.

Equation 6(65) is obeyed by paths taken along wave normals provided that the media are isotropic, though they need not necessarily be homogeneous, i.e. the speed of light may vary from point to point, but at any one point it must be independent of the direction of propagation. A wave surface may be defined by putting the phase (at a given time)

§ 6.64   RAYS IN RELATION TO WAVE GROUPS

$\phi(x, y, z)$ equal to some parameter χ (§ 2.13). Suppose light travels from a source placed at a point A, situated on the wave surface defined by $\phi = \chi_1$, to a receptor placed at B, situated on the wave surface defined by $\phi = \chi_2$. Imagine an infinite series of intermediate wave surfaces to be constructed. Provided that the wave surfaces are continuous, successive surfaces are nearly parallel curves, and a path which follows the wave normal is clearly defined. For such a path, the integral of equation 6(67) becomes

$$\int n \, ds = \chi_2 - \chi_1. \qquad \ldots \ldots \quad 6(78)$$

In general, a path which is near to this path will be parallel to it part of the way, but will include some portions which lie near to the original path but inclined to it at small angles. These portions will give contributions to the integral equal to $n \, ds/\cos \alpha$, where α is the small angle between the path defined by 6(67) and the varied path. These contributions will differ from the corresponding terms in 6(78) by quantities of the second order. Thus Fermat's principle applies to a path defined by the wave normal. *In isotropic media*, the wave normals and the rays coincide.

6.64   Rays in Relation to Wave Groups.

It was shown in Chapter IV that even " monochromatic " light must be represented by a wave group. In order to show that Fermat's principle applies under practical conditions, it is therefore necessary to show that the above results apply to wave groups. This problem has been investigated* and it has been shown that:

(i) In a dispersive medium the energy in a wave group travels along the ray defined by applying equation 6(67), inserting the values of n appropriate to the mean wavelength.

(ii) The group travels along this ray with the group velocity given by inserting the mean wavelength in equation 4(34).

6.65. Fermat's Principle as a General Statement of the Laws of Ray Optics.

Fermat's principle includes and summarizes the following laws of ray optics:

(i) *Rectilinear propagation* in a medium of constant refractive index.

(ii) *The laws of reflection and refraction* of rays at surfaces where the index changes discontinuously.

---

* See Reference 6.20.

(iii) *Curvilinear propagation* in a medium where the index varies continuously along a path for which 6(67) is satisfied.

(iv) *The law of reversibility of path* according to which any line which is a possible path for light energy travelling in one direction is also a possible path in the reverse direction.

The last of these relations is implied in equations 6(65) because, if the variation of the integral is zero when the limits are A to B, it is also zero when they are interchanged to become B to A. It is important to recognize that *all* the above relations apply only under the limiting conditions of ray optics.

REFERENCES

6.1. BORN, M. and WOLF, E.: *Principles of Optics* (Pergamon Press, London).
6.2. SOMMERFELD, A.: *Optics* (Academic Press, New York).
6.3. GUILD, J.: *The Interference of Crossed Gratings* (Oxford University Press).
6.4. RUBINOWICZ: *Nature*, 1957, Vol. 180, p. 160.
6.5. RAYLEIGH: *Scientific Papers*, Vol. III, p. 52.
6.6. WOOD: *J.O.S.A.*, 1944, Vol. 34, p. 509.
6.7. BABCOCK: *J.O.S.A.*, 1944, Vol. 34, 1.
6.8. WILLIAMS: *Applications of Interferometry* (Methuen). See also Brit. Pat. 315234.
6.9. BOOKER, RATCLIFFE and SHINN: *Phil. Trans. Roy. Soc.*, 1950, Vol. 242, p. 579.
6.10. SAWYER: *Experimental Spectroscopy* (Prentice-Hall).
6.11. HANSON, A. W., LIPSON, H., and TAYLOR, C. A.: *Proc. Roy. Soc.* A, Vol. 218, p. 371.
6.12. RICE, S. O., *Bell System Technical Journal*, 1944, Vol. 23, p. 282; and 1945, Vol. 24, p. 46.
6.13. HARRISON, G. R., STURGIS, N., BAKER, S. C., and STROKE, G. W.: *J.O.S.A.*, 1957, Vol. 47, p. 15.
6.14. HARRISON, G. R., DAVIS, S. P., and ROBERTSON, H. J.: *J.O.S.A.*, 1953, Vol. 45, p. 835.
6.15. LIPSON, H., and COCHRAN, W. A.: *The Determination of Crystal Structures* (Bell).
6.16. HALL, R. G. N., and SAYCE, L. A.: *Proc. Roy. Soc.* A, 1952, Vol. 215, p. 536.
6.17. GOUY: *Ann. de Chimie et de Physique*, 1891, Ser. VI, Vol. 24, p. 145.
6.18. RAYLEIGH: *Scientific Papers*, Vol. III, p. 112.
6.19. RAYLEIGH: *Scientific Papers*, Vol. III, p. 128.
6.20. KEMBLE: *Foundations of Quantum Mechanics*, Chap. II, Sec. 12 (McGraw-Hill).
6.21. DYSON, J.: *Proc. Roy. Soc.* A, 1958, Vol. 248, p. 93.
6.22. GABOR, D.: *Proc. Phys. Soc.* B, 1951, Vol. 64, p. 449.
6.23. GUILD, J.: *Diffraction Gratings as Measuring Scales* (Oxford University Press).
6.24. BAKER and COPSON: *The Mathematical Theory of Huygens' Principle* (Oxford University Press).

APPENDIX VI A

KIRCHHOFF'S DIFFRACTION FORMULA *

1.—Consider a simple harmonic wave represented by

$$\xi = \psi(x, y, z)e^{i\omega t}, \quad \ldots \ldots \ldots \quad 6(79)$$

where ψ is a function of position (not of time) which gives the form of the wave surfaces, e.g. for plane waves ψ has the form

$$\psi = \exp i\kappa(lx + my + nz), \quad \ldots \ldots \quad 6(80)$$

and there is a corresponding form for spherical waves [2(56)]. We do not specify ψ at present, because we do not wish the analysis to be restricted to any particular

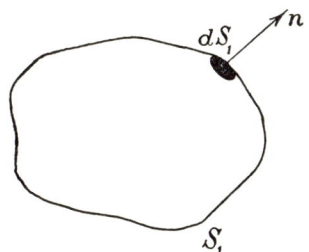

Fig. 6.36

type of wave surface. Inserting the value given by 6(79) in the wave equation [2(38)] and remembering that $\kappa b = \omega$, we see that ψ must satisfy the equation

$$\Delta \psi + \kappa^2 \psi = 0. \quad \ldots \ldots \ldots \quad 6(81)$$

Green's theorem states that if ψ_1 and ψ_2 are any two functions of position, then

$$\int (\psi_2 \Delta \psi_1 - \psi_1 \Delta \psi_2) \, d\tau = \int \left(\psi_2 \frac{\partial \psi_1}{\partial n} - \psi_1 \frac{\partial \psi_2}{\partial n} \right) dS_1, \quad \ldots \quad 6(82)$$

where the left-hand integral is taken over the volume enclosed by the surface S_1 (fig. 6.36) and the right-hand integral is taken over the surface. n is the *outward* normal from the surface. The theorem is valid provided that ψ_1 and ψ_2 do not have singularities within the volume.

2.—If ψ_1 and ψ_2 are two solutions of 6(81), then

$$(\psi_2 \Delta \psi_1 - \psi_1 \Delta \psi_2) = -\psi_2 \kappa^2 \psi_1 + \psi_1 \kappa^2 \psi_2 = 0, \quad \ldots \quad 6(83)$$

so that the left-hand side of 6(82) is zero. We now choose ψ_1 to be equal to ψ [i.e. to any unspecified solution of 6(81)] and ψ_2 to be equal to $e^{-i\kappa r}/r$. It may easily be verified that this function, which represents a spherical wave diverging from the origin, is a solution of 6(81). Inserting these functions for ψ_1 and ψ_2, we obtain

$$\int \left\{ \frac{e^{-i\kappa r}}{r} \frac{\partial \psi}{\partial n} - \psi \frac{\partial}{\partial n} \left(\frac{1}{r} e^{-i\kappa r} \right) \right\} dS_1 = 0, \quad \ldots \ldots \quad 6(84)$$

* See References 2.1 and 6.24.

provided that neither ψ nor $e^{-i\kappa r}/r$ have singularities within the volume enclosed by S_1. This condition prevents us from applying 6(84), directly, to a surface which includes the origin since $e^{-i\kappa r}/r$ has a singularity at the origin. Since we wish to deal with surfaces surrounding the origin, we now choose to let S_1 consist of two parts:

(i) The surface S in which we are chiefly interested, and
(ii) a small sphere S_0 surrounding the origin, which we take as the point P (see fig. 6.37).

The volume to which Green's theorem is now applied is that which lies between S and S_0, i.e. the origin is excluded from the domain of integration, and on S_0

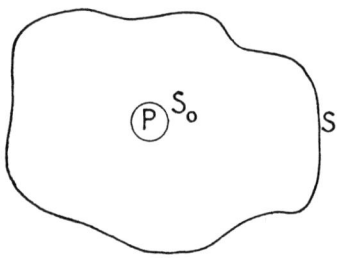

Fig. 6.37

the outward normal is directed towards P, i.e. $\partial/\partial n = -\partial/\partial r$ for this surface. That part of the integral in 6(84) which refers to S_0 may be written

$$-\int \left\{ \frac{e^{-i\kappa r}}{r} \frac{\partial \psi}{\partial r} - \psi \frac{\partial}{\partial r}\left(\frac{1}{r} e^{-i\kappa r}\right) \right\} r^2 \, d\Omega = -\int e^{-i\kappa r} \left\{ \psi + i\kappa r \psi + r \frac{\partial \psi}{\partial r} \right\} d\Omega, \quad 6(85)$$

where $d\Omega$ is an element of solid angle round the origin P. When $r \to 0$ the right-hand side of 6(85) tends to the value $-4\pi\psi_P$ and 6(84) becomes

$$\psi_P = \frac{1}{4\pi} \int \left\{ \frac{e^{-i\kappa r}}{r} \frac{\partial \psi}{\partial n} - \psi \frac{\partial}{\partial n}\left(\frac{e^{-i\kappa r}}{r}\right) \right\} dS. \quad \ldots \quad 6(86)$$

Thus, if we are given ψ and $\partial\psi/\partial n$ over the surface S, which encloses P, the value of ψ_P can be calculated. In the preceding discussion we have considered a surface which encloses the point of interest. It may also be shown that, if the values of ψ and $\partial\psi/\partial n$ are given for a surface which excludes the point P but includes all the sources of light, then ψ_P can still be calculated. Equation 6(86) is still valid but n is in this case the inward normal.

3.—Huygens assumed that, if we knew the disturbance on a certain surface, we could calculate the disturbance at a point in advance of the surface. The above analysis only partly supports this view. In the first place it appears that we need to know the disturbance on a given surface, and also to know $\partial\psi/\partial n$ (effectively to know the disturbance on a neighbouring surface). Also, since we assume that the frequency is given, the value of $\partial\psi/\partial t$ is implicitly involved. It should, however, be stated that $\partial\psi/\partial n$ and $\partial\psi/\partial t$ are not completely independent functions, and, for this reason, we shall be able to develop later an approximate form [6(90)] which depends only on ψ and comes near to Huygens' original idea.

KIRCHHOFF'S DIFFRACTION FORMULA

4.—Another way of considering the relation of Kirchhoff's formula [6(86)] to Huygens' principle is to introduce the idea of double sources. The amplitude at P due to a point source at O (distant r from P) is $Ae^{-i\kappa r}/r$. Now consider two sources of equal intensity and opposite phase separated by a short distance. Let the line of separation be n and the distance between the sources be dn. The line n is not, in general, coincident with OP. Then the amplitude at P due to the two sources acting together is

$$A \frac{\partial}{\partial n} \left\{ \frac{1}{r} e^{-i\kappa r} \right\} dn.$$

If the separation dn is allowed to diminish indefinitely while the product $A\,dn$ retains the finite constant value B, we arrive at the concept of a double source—closely analogous to an electric or magnetic doublet. This concept is of practical importance in sound. Huygens (and later Fresnel) replaced the wave at S by a series of elementary single sources distributed over S. Kirchhoff's formula [6(86)] allows us to express the effect of an element dS as equivalent to that of a single source of strength $-(\partial\psi/\partial n)\,dS$ plus a double source of strength $\psi\,dS$.

5.—It will be remembered that Huygens' concept applied to an advancing wave. We have, so far, assumed one frequency which implies a steady state (infinite wave train). To apply Kirchhoff's equation to an advancing group of waves in a non-dispersive medium we need only note that the form of 6(86) is such that we could use it to sum the effects at P of a series of waves of different frequencies. Since any pulse, or non-permanent wave, may be analysed by Fourier methods into a series of simple harmonic waves, the Kirchhoff method must apply to the pulse.

6.—*Approximate Form of Kirchhoff's Equation.*

Let us now consider the situation shown in fig. 6.38. O is a point source of light emitting spherical waves and S is a closed surface surrounding P. Consider

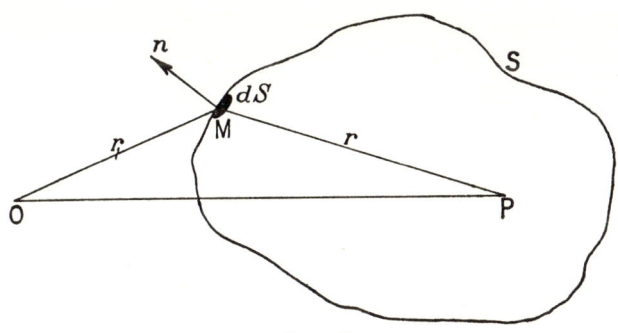

Fig. 6.38

an element dS situated at M, and let $OM = r_1$ and $PM = r$. The outward-drawn normal from S is n. The approximation now under discussion is valid when r and r_1 are both large compared with the wavelength, i.e. κr and κr_1 are large compared with unity. The disturbance at M may be represented by

$$\xi_M = \frac{a}{r_1} \exp i(\omega t - \kappa r_1), \qquad \ldots \ldots \quad 6(87)$$

so that
$$\psi_M = \frac{a}{r_1} e^{-i\kappa r_1}. \qquad \qquad \qquad 6(88)$$

Inserting this value of ψ_M for ψ in 6(86), we obtain

$$\psi_P = \frac{1}{4\pi} \int \left\{ \left(\frac{e^{-i\kappa r}}{r} \cos(n, r_1) \frac{\partial}{\partial r_1} \left[\frac{a}{r_1} e^{-i\kappa r_1} \right] \right) - \left(\frac{a}{r_1} e^{-i\kappa r_1} \cos(n, r) \frac{\partial}{\partial r} \left[\frac{e^{-i\kappa r}}{r} \right] \right) \right\} dS \qquad 6(89)$$

Differentiating term by term, and neglecting all terms in which the amplitude is of order $a/r_1 r^2$ or $a/r_1^2 r$, we have

$$\psi_P = \frac{1}{4\pi} i\kappa \int \left\{ \frac{a}{rr_1} e^{-i\kappa(r+r_1)} \left[\cos(n, r) - \cos(n, r_1) \right] \right\} dS. \qquad 6(90)$$

The terms neglected are less than the terms retained by factors of κr and κr_1, i.e. by factors of order r/λ. The expression 6(90) may therefore be used when both O and P are separated from the surface S by distances which are large compared with the wavelength.

APPENDIX VI B

The Concave Grating

1.—The properties of a grating ruled upon the surface of a concave spherical mirror were investigated by Rowland. He showed that light incident upon the grating from a suitably placed slit gives spectra which are focused upon a certain curve. We shall first show that spectra are formed and focused in this way and then discuss how concave gratings are used.

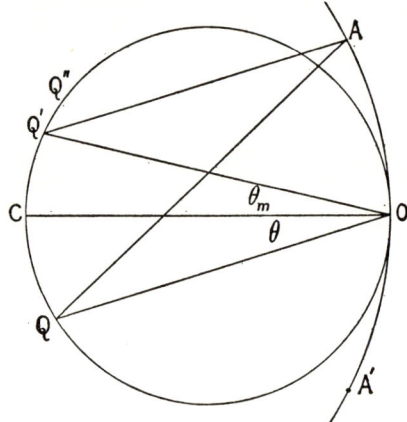

Fig. 6.39

Let AOA′ (fig. 6.39) be part of a section of a sphere whose centre is C. The region between A and A′ is ruled with lines which form the intersections of the sphere with a family of parallel planes which are normal to the plane of the paper and equidistant from one another. The common distance is $2e$ and $AA' = 4Ne$

THE CONCAVE GRATING

(where N is a large integer). Construct a circle with CO as *diameter* and let Q and Q′ be two points on this circle. Let us now find the difference of path for two paths from Q to Q′, i.e. $(QA + Q'A) - (QO + Q'O) = \Delta s$.

2.—Let $\quad QO = u; \quad Q'O = v; \quad CO = 2a;$

$\angle COQ = \theta; \quad \angle COQ' = \theta_m; \quad \angle OCA = 2\alpha.$

Then, from triangle QOA,

$$QA^2 = QO^2 + OA^2 - 2OA \cdot OQ \cos QOA. \quad \ldots \quad 6(91)$$

In fig. 6.40, M bisects the straight line OA and from this figure we see that angle $QOA = (\tfrac{1}{2}\pi - \alpha) + \theta$ and that $OA = 4a \sin \alpha$. Hence 6(91) gives

$$QA^2 = u^2 + 16a^2 \sin^2 \alpha - 8au \sin \alpha \sin (\alpha - \theta). \quad \ldots \quad 6(92)$$

With rearrangement of terms 6(92) becomes

$$QA^2 = (u + 2a \sin 2\alpha \sin \theta)^2 - 4a^2 \sin^2 2\alpha \sin^2 \theta + 8a(2a - u \cos \theta) \sin^2 \alpha. \quad 6(93)$$

The equivalence of 6(92) and 6(93) may be verified by expanding both expressions.

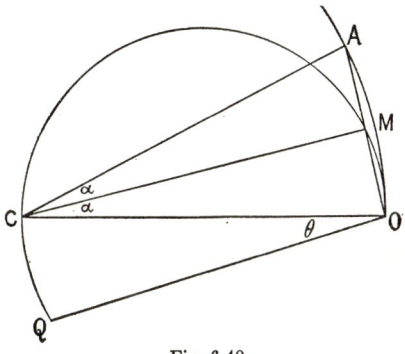

Fig. 6.40

Let us assume that α is a fairly small angle so that we may neglect terms of order α^4. We may then put $\sin^2 2\alpha = 4 \sin^2 \alpha$ and, to the same approximation, 6(93) gives

$$QA^2 = (u + 2a \sin 2\alpha \sin \theta)^2 - 2a(u - 2a \cos \theta) \sin^2 2\alpha \cos \theta. \quad 6(94)$$

Q is a point on the circle whose diameter is $2a$, so that $u = 2a \cos \theta$ and 6(94) gives

$$QA - u = 2a \sin 2\alpha \sin \theta. \quad \ldots \quad 6(95)$$

We may obtain a similar expression for $Q'A - v$ and hence

$$\Delta s = (QA - u) + (Q'A - v) = 2a \sin 2\alpha (\sin \theta - \sin \theta_m). \quad 6(96)$$

But, from the triangle A′CA,

$$4Ne = AA' = 4a \sin 2\alpha.$$

Hence the path difference $\Delta s = Nm\lambda$, if

$$2e(\sin\theta - \sin\theta_m) = m\lambda. \quad \ldots \quad 6(97)$$

This is equivalent to 6(22) since m may be either a positive or a negative integer.

3.—We have shown that the path difference for the two rays from Q to Q′ is proportional to the number of lines between A and O. When 6(97) is satisfied, the phase difference for light of wavelength λ increases by $2m\pi$ as we go from one line to the next. Thus the mth order for wavelength λ is focused at Q′. The same order for wavelength λ'' will be focused at some point Q″ on the same circle and near to Q′. If then a point source of light is placed at a point Q on the circle whose diameter is equal to the radius of the grating, and which touches the grating at its centre, the spectra will be focused along the circle. This circle is known as the " Rowland circle ".

4.—The above discussion is confined to rays in the plane of the paper. The focusing for these rays is very good since the terms of third order in α are zero. Further investigation shows that the rays which pass above and below the plane of the paper give an astigmatic image, i.e. a point source placed at Q gives rise to an image which is a line perpendicular to the plane of the paper, passing through Q′. The length of this line increases as the angle of incidence increases.

5.—A method of mounting a concave grating due to Rowland is shown in fig. 6.41. The mounting is designed to allow spectra of different orders or different

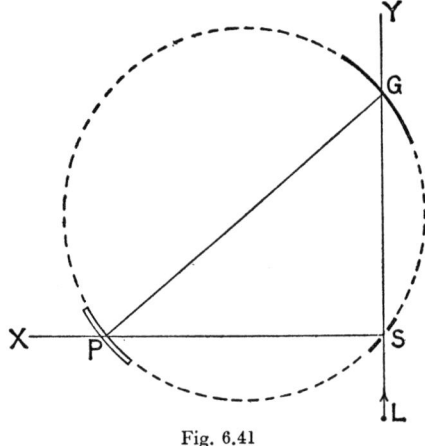

Fig. 6.41

parts of one spectrum to be photographed in turn, without moving the slit S or the source L. The grating G and the photographic plate P are placed on carriages which move along mutually perpendicular rails SX and SY. The two carriages are connected by a rod so that they always face one another, and so that the distance from the centre of the grating to the centre of the plate is equal to the diameter of the Rowland circle (i.e. to the radius of curvature of the grating).

THE CONCAVE GRATING

Thus θ_m is always zero and θ is varied by moving the carriages. Different spectra are then brought on to the plate and, if the grating and mounting are perfect, the instrument is always in focus.

6.—A large grating has a resolving power of order 250,000. To obtain sufficient dispersion to make this resolving power effective it is necessary to use a grating of about 6 metres radius of curvature. Smaller gratings are made with radii of curvature down to 1 metre. This is the smallest value normally used, partly because the photographic plate has to be bent to fit the Rowland circle. The space occupied by a large grating using a Rowland mounting is so large that it is difficult to maintain a constant temperature during the long exposures which are often required. The Rowland mounting is also rather expensive. For these

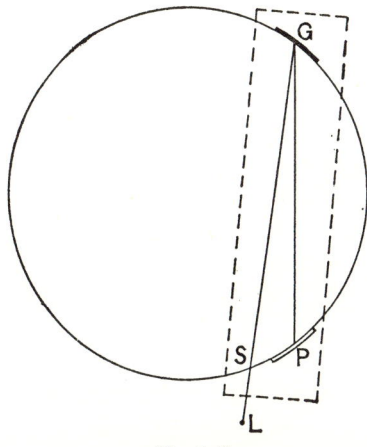

Fig. 6.42

and other reasons, alternative methods of mounting the grating have been devised. In one, due to Eagle, Q' is brought as close to Q as possible, i.e. the slit is placed beside the plate (see fig. 6.42). Sometimes it is placed below the plane of the paper, and the plate is a little above the plane of the paper. This means that the region between the dotted lines (fig. 6.42) can be enclosed in a box of reasonable size. Temperature control is relatively easy. This mounting has the advantage that it reduces θ_m and θ (which are of opposite sign) and so reduces the astigmatism.

A detailed account of methods of mounting gratings is given in Reference 6.10. It is possible to obtain automatic refocusing with mountings of this type, but the mechanical linkages (levers or cams) are more complicated than the simple arrangement used by Rowland.

APPENDIX VI C

THE ZONE PLATE*

1.—The resultant amplitude at a given point due to the whole wave-front from a small source has been shown to be approximately half of the amplitude produced by the first zone, because the effects of the odd-numbered zones are in opposition to those of the even-numbered zones. The resultant amplitude due to either the odd-numbered zones or to the even-numbered zones would clearly be much greater than that of the whole wave. This may be tested by making a diffraction screen in which one set of zones is covered by opaque material while the other is clear (fig. 6.43). Such an obstacle, called a *zone plate*, may be made by photographing

Fig. 6.43.—Zone plate

(on a reduced scale) a diagram prepared by drawing circles of radii proportional to the square roots of the natural numbers, and blackening alternate spaces. There is a practical limit to the number of rings which can be drawn, because the outer rings are very close to one another. Plates containing as many as 250 rings have been constructed. A still greater increase of illumination is produced if the phases of either the odd- or the even-numbered zones are retarded by half a period, so that the effects of all zones co-operate. These zone plates are called *phase-reversal zone plates*. R. W. Wood has succeeded in making zone plates of this type.

2.—A zone plate is capable of producing images like a lens or mirror. The exact theory of these images is complicated and not of great practical importance. A general discussion is, however, of some interest and may help in the understanding of the action of lenses and gratings. A perfect lens transforms a plane wave into a spherical wave whose centre of curvature is the focus. The lens introduces just those differences of phase which are required to make the wavelets, from all parts of the wavefront which it receives, arrive at the focal point in

* This Appendix follows the discussion of §§ 6.7 to 6.10.

THE ZONE PLATE 233

the same phase. The phase-reversal zone plate does not produce quite such a good effect because all the parts of one zone do not co-operate perfectly. The resultant amplitude due to a whole zone is only $2/\pi$ times that which would be produced if all parts of the zone co-operated exactly.

3.—Whereas a lens has only one focus (on each side), the zone plate has a series of foci and associated focal lengths. If the radius of the inner edge of the mth zone is ρ_m, and if the source is placed at a very great distance from the plate, the primary focus is found at a distance

$$f_1 = \frac{\rho_m^2}{m\lambda} \quad \ldots \ldots \ldots \quad 6(98)$$

[equation 6(2)]. A bright point of light will be found at this distance. With an ordinary zone plate having alternate clear and opaque spaces, the path difference between disturbances arriving from successive clear spaces at a point distant f_1 from the plate is λ. With the same plate the path difference between resultant disturbances arriving at a point $\frac{1}{2}f_1$ from successive clear spaces is 2λ. These resultants have agreement of phase, but each resultant is very small because the spaces now cover two half-period zones each. The resultant disturbances arriving at a point $\frac{1}{3}f_1$ have agreement of phase, the path difference being 3λ. Each space now covers three zones. Two of these oppose one another, but the unbalanced third zone gives an appreciable effect and the energy at this point is about one-ninth that of the energy at the primary focus. In a similar way, it may be shown that the zone plate has a series of foci at $f_1/5$, $f_1/7$, etc. There is also a series of foci on the opposite side of the plate, so that it is capable of acting as a concave lens. When the source is not placed at a very great distance from the plate, the relation between the distances of the source and image from the zone plate is similar to that obtained for a lens [equation 3(33)].

4.—In the above discussion, we have considered the relation between the zone plate and a lens. There is also a relation between the zone plate and the diffraction grating. Any small region of the plate is effectively a diffraction grating. The spacing of the lines in the small gratings which make up the zone plate varies systematically from point to point. The foci of the plate may be regarded as points where the directions corresponding to Fraunhofer diffraction spectra from different parts of the plate intersect. The primary foci correspond to the coincidence of first-order spectra, the secondary foci to the coincidence of second-order spectra, and so on. With a grating consisting of equal light and dark spaces, the spectra of even order are of zero brightness, and in a similar way the images corresponding to foci $f_1/2$, $f_1/4$, etc., are of zero brightness. The fact that the zone plate forms a *focused* image suggests that a grating in which the spacing increases at a suitable rate from the centre towards the ends, or from one end to the other, should have a similar focusing property. These effects have been observed by Mascart (1837–1908) and are discussed by Cornu and by Rayleigh.*

The theory of circular diffraction gratings (with a constant difference of radii) has been developed by Dyson who has used these gratings in devices for accurate alignment.†

* Reference 6.18. † Reference 6.21.

APPENDIX VI D

FRESNEL DIFFRACTION

1. Fresnel's Integrals.

The method of calculation which will now be developed is of general application and is particularly convenient in relation to obstacles or apertures bounded by two sets of lines which are mutually perpendicular (e.g. slits or wires). The treatment given is restricted to the case where the incident wave is a plane wave.

2.—Returning to equation 6(3) and putting $dS = dx_0\, dy_0$,

$$d\psi_Q = \frac{iA}{\lambda} \frac{\exp(-i\kappa r)}{r} dx_0\, dy_0, \quad \ldots \ldots \quad 6(99)$$

provided the angles involved are small so that the inclination factor may be neglected. If the apertures are in the screen S_1 and the point Q lies in screen S_2 of fig. 6.44, then the co-ordinates of Q will be (x_1, y_1, z_1), and the co-ordinates

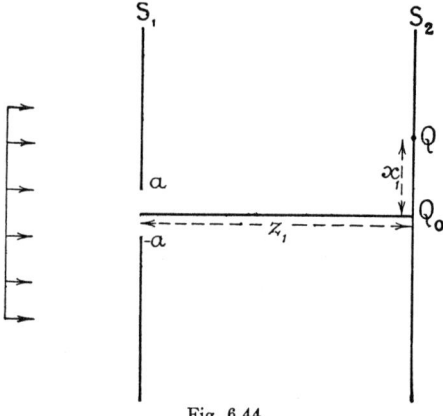

Fig. 6.44

of a point on the aperture will be $(x_0, y_0, 0)$. The distance of Q from a point on the aperture is given by

$$r^2 = z_1^2 + (x_1 - x_0)^2 + (y_1 - y_0)^2, \quad \ldots \ldots \quad 6(100)$$

and this leads to the approximation

$$r = z_1 + \tfrac{1}{2}\frac{(x_1 - x_0)^2}{z_1} + \tfrac{1}{2}\frac{(y_1 - y_0)^2}{z_1}. \quad \ldots \quad 6(101)$$

It is now assumed that the constant value z_1 may be used for r in the denominator of 6(99), but that the approximation 6(101) must be used in the exponential term. This is equivalent to assuming that differences of distances from different parts of the aperture to the point Q may be ignored when applying the inverse square law to determine the amplitude of the wavelets, but that they must be taken into account to the approximation implied in 6(101) when computing the effects of phase differences. In order to see that this procedure is reasonable, we take account of the fact that z_1 is always at least a few millimetres (i.e. several thousand wavelengths at least). Variations of a few wavelengths make nearly no difference to the amplitude, but a variation of $\frac{1}{2}\lambda$ is sufficient to reverse the sign of the factor which depends on phase difference. If we are concerned with relative illuminations, we may omit constant factors and write

$$\psi_Q = \int\int \exp\left[-\frac{i\kappa}{2z_1}\{(x-x_0)^2 + (y-y_0)^2\}\right] dx_0\, dy_0. \quad . \quad 6(102)$$

The integral is to be taken over the areas of the apertures in the screen. St. Venant's hypothesis (§ 6.33) is assumed to apply. In the case of diffraction at a slit aperture, equation 6(102) contains the product of two integrals one of which is

$$\psi_{Qx} = \int_{a_1}^{a_2} \exp\left[-\frac{i\kappa}{2z_1}(x-x_0)^2\right] dx_0, \quad \ldots \quad 6(103)$$

where the lines $x_0 = a_1$ and $x_0 = a_2$ are the edges of the slit. Let us introduce a new variable v, defined by

$$\sqrt{\frac{\kappa}{2z_1}}(x-x_0) = \sqrt{\frac{\pi}{\lambda z_1}}(x-x_0) = \sqrt{\frac{\pi}{2}}v. \quad \ldots \quad 6(104)$$

We then have
$$\psi_{Qx} = \int_{v_1}^{v_2} \exp\left(-\tfrac{1}{2}i\pi v^2\right) dv, \quad \ldots \quad 6(105)$$

and the variation of illumination in the x direction is given by

$$E(x) = \psi_{Qx}\psi_{Qx}{}^* = C_F{}^2 + S_F{}^2, \quad \ldots \quad 6(106)$$

where
$$C_F = \int_{v_1}^{v_2} \cos\left(\tfrac{1}{2}\pi v^2\right) dv,$$
and
$$S_F = \int_{v_1}^{v_2} \sin\left(\tfrac{1}{2}\pi v^2\right) dv.$$
$$\quad \ldots \quad 6(107)$$

The functions C_F and S_F are known as Fresnel's integrals.

It is necessary to resort to special series to obtain the values of these integrals between finite limits.* When the limits of integration are $\pm\infty$, the value of either integral is $\pm\tfrac{1}{2}$. On account of the rapid variation of sign, the part of the range for which v exceeds a fairly small integer (e.g. 10) contributes little to the integral.

3. Cornu's Spiral.

The following geometrical method of using the integrals was devised by Cornu. Suppose that a curve is plotted with $u = C_F$ and $w = S_F$ (the limits of integration being 0 and v) as abscissæ and ordinates (fig. 6.45). The square of the length of a line joining two points defined by v_1 and v_2 is equal to the sum of the squares of the integrals, and is therefore proportional to the energy of the light diffracted in the corresponding direction. The direction of this line also gives the phase

* Methods of evaluating the integrals have been studied by Fresnel, Knockenhauer, Cauchy, Gilbert and Lommel (see Reference 6.19).

of the resultant vibration. Let s be the length, measured along the curve, from O to a given point A and let $\mathscr{I}$ be the angle which the tangent to the curve at A makes with the axis of u. Then

$$(ds)^2 = (du)^2 + (dw)^2 = (\cos^2 \tfrac{1}{2}\pi v^2 + \sin^2 \tfrac{1}{2}\pi v^2)(dv)^2 = (dv)^2.$$

Hence
$$s = v \quad \ldots \ldots \ldots \quad 6(108)$$

(the constant of integration being zero since $s = 0$ when $v = 0$). Let

$$\left. \begin{array}{l} \mathscr{I} = \tan^{-1}\dfrac{dw}{du} = \tfrac{1}{2}\pi v^2, \\[4pt] \mathscr{I} = \tfrac{1}{2}\pi s^2. \end{array} \right\} \quad \ldots \ldots \quad 6(109)$$

i.e.

Then the curvature,

$$\frac{\partial \mathscr{I}}{\partial s} = \pi s. \quad \ldots \ldots \ldots \quad 6(110)$$

The last two equations show that, when $s = 0$, both $\mathscr{I}$ and $\partial \mathscr{I}/\partial s$ are zero, so that the curve touches the u axis at the origin. From this point it proceeds in the positive direction of s as a curve of continually increasing curvature, i.e.

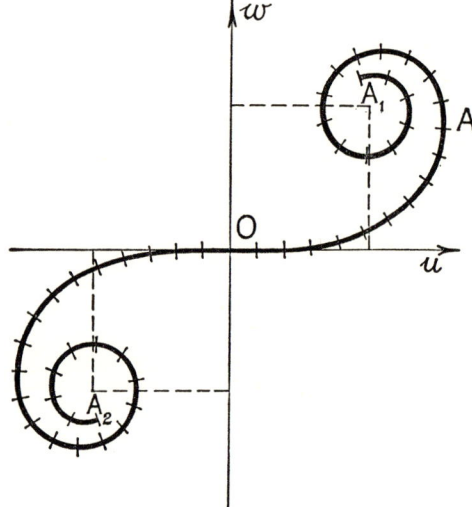

Fig. 6.45.—Cornu's spiral

it forms a spiral whose successive turns enclose one another. The curve continually approaches the asymptotic point A_1 ($u = \tfrac{1}{2}, w = \tfrac{1}{2}$) which corresponds to $v = \infty$. A similar branch in the negative direction revolves about the point A_2 ($-\tfrac{1}{2}, -\tfrac{1}{2}$) as shown in fig. 6.45.

4. Diffraction at a Straight Edge.

The Cornu spiral may be applied to determine the variation of illumination near the boundary of the shadow of a straight edge. We may imagine the point

DIFFRACTION AT A STRAIGHT EDGE

Q to be initially in the lighted region and remote from the edge of the geometrical shadows. The limits of integration are then so wide that the line whose square represents the illumination has to be drawn between two points which are extremely near to the asymptotic points of the spirals. As Q moves towards the geometrical shadows, one end of this line remains fixed very near to the asymptotic point, since on one side the wavefront is unbounded. The other end moves along the spiral from the asymptotic point towards O. At first this produces very little effect on the resultant illumination because the convolutions of the spiral lie within a narrow radius. As Q comes near to the edge of the geometric shadow, the point on the spiral moves on curves of large radius; the illumination oscillates between values larger and smaller than that which would be obtained if the whole wave were unobstructed. When Q is very near the edge of the geometrical shadow, the illumination decreases sharply as the representative point moves along the last half-turn of the spiral before reaching O. From this stage onward there are no further fluctuations in the illumination; it decreases smoothly and fairly rapidly to an insignificant value. Thus the last fringe is found slightly outside the geometrical shadow and there are no fringes within the shadow. The general system of fringes is shown in Plate IIIa, p. 162.

The above discussion suffers from the defect that we have included a portion of wavefront corresponding to large angles of diffraction, whereas the equations from which the spiral was constructed are exactly valid only for small angles of diffraction. The effect of zones remote from the centre is very small. The factors we have omitted would, if included, merely deform the spiral a little in the region where it is near the asymptotic point. If it is desired to remove the formal inconsistency, we may suppose that we consider the diffraction at one edge of a very wide slit.

CHAPTER VII

Optical Instruments: Coaxal Systems of Lenses and Mirrors

7.1 Formation of Images.

Let us consider the formation of the image of an object situated in the plane OPQ by an optical system S (fig. 7.1). The light from a small area situated at P may be represented by spherical waves W_1, W_2 with their centre at P. The optical system has two effects on these waves: (a) to change their shape as described in §§ 3.14–15, and (b) to restrict them at the edges. The change of shape constitutes the focus-

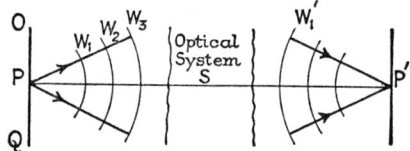

Fig. 7.1.—Formation of an image. Wave surfaces and rays.

ing property of the system since the emergent waves converge, more or less perfectly, on some point P'. The restrictions of the wavefront at the edges of stops or of optical components lead to diffraction. The spreading of light in this way sets an ultimate limit to the performance of optical instruments, and in high-quality instruments this limit is closely approached. We shall discuss this effect in Chapter VIII.

In an isotropic medium the rays are wave normals (§ 6.63). If diffraction effects are excluded, each element of the wavefront is propagated (with the appropriate phase velocity b) along its wave normal. The change in the shape of the wavefront by the action of an optical system may equally well be described as changes in the directions of the rays by refraction or reflection at surfaces. The two descriptions are equivalent. If the spherical waves W_1 emitted from a point P pass through the system and emerge as spherical waves W_1' with centre at P', then we say that P' is conjugate to P or that P' is a *perfect geometrical image* of P. All the rays which initially came from P pass finally through P', which is the centre of the sphere of which they are wave normals. It is convenient to use the nomenclature of ray theory to discuss the focusing properties of optical systems, but it is desirable to keep in mind the associated wavefronts in view of later developments.

In wave optics it is, in principle, necessary to consider a source as having a finite area, even though the area may be small. The energy is proportional to the area and must vanish if the area vanishes. Rays of light may, however, be regarded as diverging from, or converging to, a mathematical point, and we therefore speak of *point sources* or *point images*. It is possible to treat a real source as a point source within the approximation of ray optics when its largest linear dimension is small compared with its distance from the optical system. A star which is physically large is a point source for ray optics.

7.2. Coaxal Systems with Spherical Surfaces.

Most lenses and mirrors have surfaces which are exactly or nearly spherical. A coaxal optical system may be formed by mounting a number of these components so that the centres of curvature of the

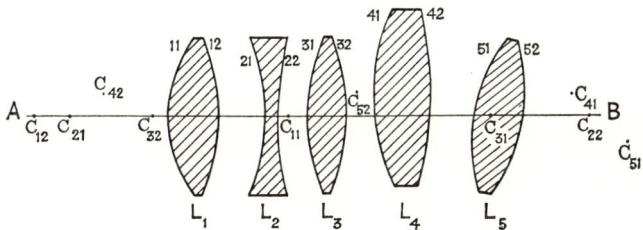

Fig. 7.2.—*Alignment of Lenses.* C_{11}, etc., are the centres of curvature of the corresponding surfaces. L_1, L_2, L_3 form a concentric system (centres all on the line AB). L_4 is displaced from the axis and L_5 is tilted.

surfaces lie on the same straight line (fig. 7.2). Systems may be non-coaxal either because a lens is displaced transversely or because one is tilted, or by a combination of these errors.

The term *coaxal system* is also applied to systems which have smooth surfaces which are not spherical but are symmetrical about an axis. Our discussion is, however, confined to systems with spherical surfaces. Systems which include a reflection at a plane mirror may still be regarded as coaxal; the axis then consists of two straight lines which would become collinear if one of them was reflected in the mirror.

In the manufacture of optical instruments machines are used to provide edges which facilitate the mounting of the components to form coaxal systems. Fig.

7.3a shows a lens whose edges are cylindrical; the axis of the cylinder is the line joining the centres of curvature of the two surfaces. Fig. 7.3b shows this lens mounted in a cell which could be screwed into a tube so that a coaxal system is formed with other similar components. When the lenses are very small, as in

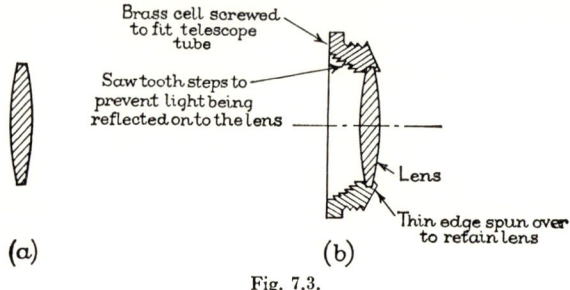

Fig. 7.3.
(a) Lens after it has been " centred ". (b) Lens in cell.

high-power microscope objectives, the alignment has to be very accurate, and it is undesirable to disturb it by taking the unit to pieces. The exact alignment of lenses on optical benches is more difficult and much more important than students usually realize. A good method of alignment is described in Reference 7.5.

7.3. Paraxial Rays.

When a spherical wave is incident upon a coaxal optical system the emergent wave is a smooth surface, though it is not, in general, exactly spherical. The rays do not meet exactly in a point. It is convenient to start by considering the behaviour of the parts of the wavefront which are near the axis, i.e. to consider rays which make small angles with the axis. These are known as *paraxial rays*. Since the emergent wavefront is smooth, a sufficiently small region near the axis can be replaced by a tangent sphere of equal curvature (fig. 8.13). The wave normals of this sphere meet in a point, so the paraxial rays from the point P (fig. 7.1) meet in the point P′, which is said to be the paraxial-ray* image of P.

We start by considering the rays near the axis (and the associated part of the wavefront) because these give " perfect " geometrical images. The geometrical image obtained in this way would be of little practical importance if the actual wavefronts were very different from spheres. In fact, they are so nearly spherical that it is a reasonable approximation to replace the whole wavefront over a considerable area by the tangent sphere and to work out the focusing properties of the system in this way. The departures of the wavefront from sphericity (called *aberrations*) are discussed in Chapter VIII.

---

* The first systematic and reasonably complete discussion of the formation of images by paraxial rays is due to C. F. Gauss (1777–1855). This discussion is therefore sometimes called Gaussian Optics.

It might appear that although this approximation is reasonable for one reflection or refraction at a spherical surface, it must fail when an optical system has a large number of surfaces. This is not so because, in good optical systems, the designer has arranged that the aberrations due to one surface are partially compensated by those due to others. Thus the wave may become more nearly spherical as it encounters the later surfaces.

7.4. Sign Convention and Notation.

In this book we adopt the convention of signs in which the direction of the incident light is positive. In all relevant diagrams the light is incident from the left and signs both for horizontal and for vertical directions are the same as in the Cartesian co-ordinate system. The direction of a ray AB is from A to B, and if l is the distance AB, then the distance BA is $-l$. The radius of curvature of a surface is measured from the pole to the centre, so that a surface which presents a convex surface to the incident light has a positive radius of curvature.

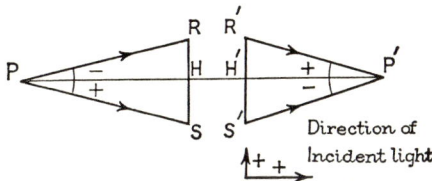

Fig. 7.4.—Sign convention

To find the sign of an angle between a ray and the axis, complete a triangle such as PRH in fig. 7.4. The angle is positive if its tangent is positive, lengths being measured from the corner where the right angle is situated. Thus in fig. 7.4 HR is positive and HP is negative, so RPH is negative and other angles are as marked. Lengths, angles, etc., which apply to the image are distinguished by a prime; unprimed letters apply to the object space.

7.5.—Let α be the angle between a ray and the axis. Then, for rays sufficiently near the axis, we may write

$$\sin \alpha = \tan \alpha = \alpha \quad \text{and} \quad \cos \alpha = 1. \qquad . \quad . \quad 7(1)$$

It is assumed that this approximation is valid for all angles which appear in the paraxial-ray theory, including the angles of incidence and of reflection or refraction at the spherical surfaces.*

---

* For convenience of drawing, the angles shown in diagrams are much larger than those to which paraxial-ray theory applies.

Thus the law of refraction,
$$n' \sin i' = n \sin i, \qquad \ldots \ldots 7(2)$$
is replaced by
$$n'i' = ni. \qquad \ldots \ldots \ldots 7(3)$$
Taking account of the sign convention (see figs. 7.4 and 7.5) the law of reflection for rays making small angles with the axis may be derived by putting $n' = -n$ in equation 7(3), so that we have
$$i' = -i, \qquad \ldots \ldots \ldots 7(4)$$
i.e. *reflection may be regarded as equivalent to refraction from a medium of index n to one of index $-n$.*

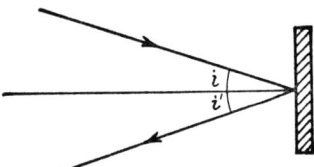

Fig. 7.5.—Reflection at a plane surface

7.6. Refraction at a Spherical Surface.

Consider the ray MNP incident upon the spherical surface NA whose centre of curvature is C, and let NP' be the refracted ray (fig. 7.6). Then, using the notation indicated on the figure, we obtain from 7(3)

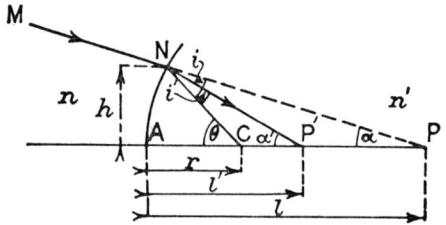

Fig. 7.6.—Refraction at a spherical surface (all lengths and angles are positive)

$$n(\theta - \alpha) = n'(\theta - \alpha'), \qquad \ldots \ldots 7(5)$$
so that
$$n'\alpha' - n\alpha = (n' - n)\theta, \qquad \ldots \ldots 7(6)$$
or
$$n'\alpha' - n\alpha = \left(\frac{n' - n}{r}\right)h = Fh, \qquad \ldots 7(7)$$

where $F = (n' - n)/r$ is a constant whose dimensions are (length)$^{-1}$. It is called the *power* of the surface.

Equation 7(7) may also be written

$$\frac{n'}{l'} - \frac{n}{l} = \frac{n'-n}{r} = F. \qquad \ldots \ldots \quad 7(8)$$

Now equation 7(8) does not contain i or h. Therefore all rays initially directed towards P will, after refraction pass through P'. We therefore say that P' is a "perfect ray-image" of P.

Note that the whole of the preceding discussion could be stated in terms of wavefronts, leading to the conclusion that a beam of light, which before encountering the surfaces is represented by spherical waves whose centre is at P,

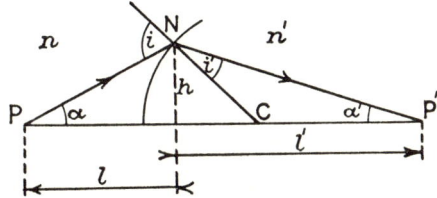

Fig. 7.7.—Refraction at a spherical surface (distance of object from surface is negative)

will after passing the surface be represented by approximately spherical wave surfaces centred on P'. More exactly we should say that the wavefronts in the second medium are not quite spherical, but that the tangent sphere at the origin has its centre at P'.

EXAMPLE [7(i)]

Verify that all angles and lengths in fig. 7.6 are positive. Refer to fig. 7.7. Decide the sign of each length and angle, and verify that 7(7) and 7(8) still apply.

In fig. 7.8 let P and P' be conjugate points in respect of refraction at the spherical surface AB whose centre is at C. If the line PCP' be

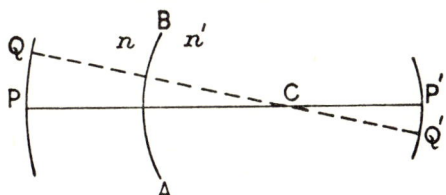

Fig. 7.8.—Conjugate planes

rotated about a line through C to the position QCQ', all that has been proved for the two points P and P' will also be true of Q and Q'. Thus Q and Q' are conjugate points, and the two small portions of spheres have the property that every point on one is conjugate to a point on the other. To the approximation now considered these two small areas may be replaced by tangent planes. These are called *conjugate planes*. So long as only one surface is considered, the tangent planes may touch the spheres at any pair of conjugate points. If, however, a system with more than one surface is considered, the tangent planes must be normal to the axis.

7.7. Magnification Relation.

In fig. 7.9 let y be the height of the object PQ and y' of its image P'Q'. Let PNP' be a ray from P to P' whose initial and final inclinations to the axis are α and α'. The law of refraction for paraxial rays reduces to $ni = n'i'$, so that

$$\frac{ny}{l} = \frac{n'y'}{l'}, \qquad \ldots \ldots \quad 7(9)$$

and
$$\frac{nyh}{l} = \frac{n'y'h}{l'}, \qquad \ldots \ldots \quad 7(10)$$

i.e.
$$ny\alpha = n'y'\alpha'. \qquad \ldots \ldots \quad 7(11)$$

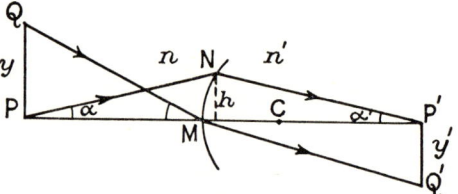

Fig. 7.9.—Magnification relation

If a ray encounters a series of surfaces $1, 2, 3, \ldots, f$, this relation may be applied to each refraction in turn, so that

$$ny\alpha = n'y'\alpha' = n''y''\alpha'', \text{ etc.,} \qquad \ldots \quad 7(12)$$

or, we may apply equation 7(11) to the system as a whole with the understanding that n, y, α refer to the first and n', y', α' to the final medium.*

We define
$$M_T = \frac{y'}{y} \quad \text{and} \quad M_\alpha = \frac{\alpha'}{\alpha}, \qquad \ldots \quad 7(13)$$

---

* Equation 7(12) was discovered independently by several writers including Huygens (1690) and C. Smith (1738). It is often called the Lagrange or the Helmholtz relation.

where M_T is called the *transverse magnification* and M_α is called the *angular magnification*, and 7(12) gives

$$M_T = \frac{n}{n'} \cdot \frac{1}{M_\alpha} \qquad \ldots \ldots \quad 7(14)$$

From the figure we see that y' is proportional to y, i.e. M_T is independent of y. If the object is a geometrical figure drawn on a plane through P normal to the axis, then the image is a geometrically similar figure on a parallel plane through P'.

7.8. Maxwell's Conditions.

J. C. Maxwell (1831–79) stated three conditions which should be satisfied by an optical system in order that it should be " perfect " in regard to ray-optics. These are:

(1) All rays from a point on an object which enter the optical system should be made to pass (really or virtually) through a single image point.
(2) If the object lies in a plane perpendicular to the axis of the system, then the image should lie in a parallel plane.
(3) The image should be geometrically similar to the object, i.e. the magnification should be constant for any one pair of conjugate planes.

We have shown that the image-object relation is perfect in the above sense for refraction at a single spherical surface. With a number of coaxal surfaces the image formed by the nth surface may be regarded as the object for the $(n+1)$th surface. Since each image-object relationship is perfect, the relationship between the image finally formed by the system as a whole and the original object must be perfect in the above sense. It may be shown that if the object-image relation is perfect for two pairs of conjugate planes, then it is perfect for all pairs of conjugate planes.

7.9. Cardinal Points.

It will be shown below that a coaxal system, however complicated, may be specified by four parameters (or three in addition to the ratio of the indices of refraction for the initial and final media). When these parameters are known it is possible to calculate the position of the plane conjugate to any given plane, and the magnification. For many purposes it is convenient to choose, as the four parameters, the positions of the two focal points and two principal points which will be defined below.

We shall commence by considering a *dioptric* or transmitting system of lenses such that a parallel incident beam emerges as a convergent or divergent beam and, for generality, we assume that the initial and final media are different. The theory so developed requires minor modification to apply to the following types of systems:

(i) *Dioptric* systems with initial and final media the same (§ 7.15).
(ii) *Catadioptric* (or reflecting) systems (§ 7.16).
(iii) *Telescopic* systems for which a parallel incident beam produces a parallel emergent beam (§ 7.20), i.e. the focal planes are at infinity.

7.10. Focal Points and Principal Points.

The plane conjugate to a plane at an indefinitely great distance from the system in a positive direction is called the *first focal plane*, and the point in which it cuts the axis is called the *first focal point* (F). In a similar way the *second focal plane* is conjugate to a plane infinitely distant in the negative direction.

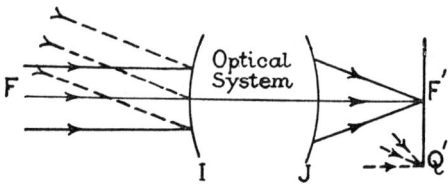

Fig. 7.10.—Focal planes (I and J are the initial and final surfaces of the system)

Light from an infinitely distant object may be represented by plane parallel wavefronts or by a parallel bundle of rays. When the object is on the axis, the rays are parallel to the axis and come to a focus at a focal point. When the distant object is off-axis, the parallel bundle of

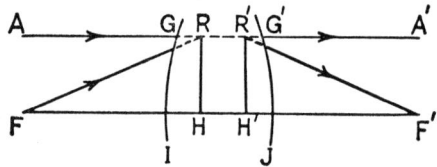

Fig. 7.11.—Principal planes

rays makes an angle with the axis and comes to a focus at some other point Q′ in the focal plane (see fig. 7.10).

Consider a system whose focal points are F and F′ (fig. 7.11). Let FG represent a ray which is incident on the system at G and emerges at G' along the line G'A', which must be parallel to the axis since F is a focal point. Let the initial and final directions meet in R. Consider a second ray incident parallel to the axis along the direction AR. This must pass through F' after emerging from the system. Let R' be the intersection of its initial and final directions.

Two rays initially directed towards R emerge in directions which meet at R' and, since two rays define a point, R' and R are conjugate points. The planes RH and R'H' (normal to the axis) are conjugate and, since RH = R'H', they are *conjugate planes of unit positive magnification*. They are known as *principal planes* and the points in which they cut the axis are called *principal points* (H and H'). The intersection of the initial direction of a ray from F with its emergent direction is in the *first principal plane*, and similarly the intersection of a ray directed towards F' with its original direction is in the *second principal plane*.

The distance HF from the first principal plane to the first focal point is called the *first focal length* (f) and the *second focal length* (f') is the distance H'F'. It is important to note that these distances are measured *from* the principal points *to* the corresponding focal points. In the case shown in the figure f is negative and f' is positive.

7.11. Construction of Images.

When the positions of the focal points and principal points for a given optical system are known, either by calculation or by experiment, it is possible to find the size and position of the image of a given object,

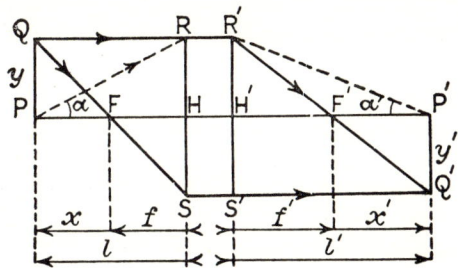

Fig. 7.12.—Construction of image when cardinal points are in order FHH'F'

even though details of the curvatures of refracting surfaces are not known. In fig. 7.12, let PQ be the object. Draw a ray from Q parallel to the axis and extend it, if necessary, until it cuts the second principal plane in R'. The final direction of this ray must pass through R', because the initial direction was through R, and must also pass through

F′, because the initial direction was parallel to the axis. Therefore its direction is R′F′. Similarly the ray QF is prolonged to meet the first principal plane in S. This must emerge parallel to the axis through S′. Prolong the two rays until they intersect in Q′, which is therefore the image of Q. A perpendicular from Q′ on to the axis gives P′, which is the image of P.

In general, the rays pass *virtually* and not *really* through R and R′. The actual refractions or reflections occur elsewhere. Note also that if a point source of light were placed at R (in a case such as that shown in fig. 7.11) we should not obtain

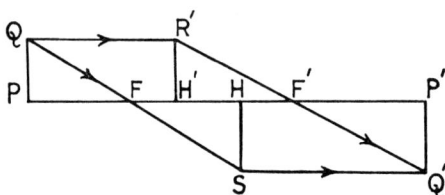

Fig. 7.13.—Construction of image when H′ is between F and H

an image at R′. The rays must enter from the left and be directed towards R before they have encountered *any* of the lenses, and they give an image at R′ after passing through the *whole* system.

It is easiest to develop the formulæ by reference to systems in which the cardinal points are in the order shown in figs. 7.11 and 7.12. It should however be understood that this is only one of many possibilities. The construction of the image when the order is FH′HF′ is shown in fig. 7.13.

7.12. Calculation of Image Position and Size.

The geometrical method described in the preceding paragraph is the same as that used in elementary geometrical optics for constructing the image formed by a thin lens. The planes of unit positive magnification for a thin lens coincide with the lens. We shall now show that algebraic formulæ for finding the position of and size of the image are similar to the well-known formulæ for thin lenses, provided that any distance which was measured from the thin lens is now measured from the appropriate principal point (i.e. H for distances to the object or to F and H′ for distances to the image or to F′).

Using the notation of fig. 7.12, and considering the similar triangles HSF and RSQ, we obtain

$$\frac{f}{l} = \frac{\text{HS}}{\text{RS}} = \frac{y'}{y' - y},$$

i.e. $$\frac{f}{l} = -\frac{y'}{y - y'}. \qquad \ldots \ldots \quad 7(15)$$

§ 7.12 IMAGE POSITION AND SIZE

Similarly
$$\frac{f'}{l'} = +\frac{y}{y-y'}. \quad \ldots \ldots \quad 7(16)$$

(Note the signs: f, l and y' are negative, and f', l' and y are positive in the diagram.)

From equations 7(15) and 7(16) we obtain

$$\frac{f}{l} + \frac{f'}{l'} = 1, \quad \ldots \ldots \quad 7(17)$$

and
$$\frac{f}{f'} = -\frac{ly'}{l'y}. \quad \ldots \ldots \quad 7(18a)$$

The ray from P directed towards R (dotted in fig. 7(12)) emerges in the direction R'P' and $HR = H'R' = PQ$, so that

$$l\alpha = l'\alpha' = y, \quad \ldots \ldots \quad 7(18b)$$

and using 7(18a) and 7(18b), together with the magnification equation 7(12), we obtain

$$-\frac{n}{f} = +\frac{n'}{f'} = +F. \quad \ldots \ldots \quad 7(19)$$

The constant F is called the *power* of the system.

From 7(14) and 7(18b) we have

$$M_T = \frac{y'}{y} = \frac{nl'}{n'l}. \quad \ldots \ldots \quad 7(20)$$

Equations 7(17) and 7(20) give the position and size of the image when the principal points and the focal points are known. If x and x' are the distances of two conjugate planes from the corresponding focal planes, we obtain, by considering the similar triangles FHS and FPQ and the corresponding triangles on the other side,

$$M_T = \frac{y'}{y} = -\frac{f}{x} = -\frac{x'}{f'}. \quad \ldots \ldots \quad 7(21)$$

so that
$$xx' = ff', \quad \ldots \ldots \quad 7(22a)$$

or
$$xx' = -\frac{nn'}{F^2}. \quad \ldots \ldots \quad 7(22b)$$

Equation 7(22a) is known as *Newton's equation*.

EXAMPLES [7(ii)–7(v)]

7(ii). A system of lenses in air is of power F and the distance HH' is d. Find the distance between two conjugate planes of unit negative magnification ($M_T = -1$).
$$[d + 4/F.]$$

7(iii). A system of lenses in air, of power F, forms an image of magnification M_1. The lens system is moved along its axis through a distance x in the direction of the incident light, and the object is moved so that the image is in the same plane as before. The magnification is now M_2. Derive an expression for the power of the system. $[M_2 - M_1 = Fx.]$

7(iv). A thin lens of power F forms an image in the plane $x = g$ of an object situated in the plane $x = 0$. Derive an expression for the magnification (M_T).
$$\left[2 - M_T - \frac{1}{M_T} = Fg. \right]$$

7(v). Using the result of the preceding example show that $dg/dM_T = 0$ when F is chosen so that $M_T = 1$. If F is fixed at 0.05 cm.$^{-1}$, what are the greatest and least values of g when the lens is moved so that M_T varies from $2/3$ to $3/2$.
[At both extremes $g = 83$ cm. At the centre of the range, when $M_T = 1$, $g = 80$ cm.]

7.13. Nodal Points.

Two conjugate points on the axis having *unit positive angular magnification* are called *nodal points*. Any ray which, before entering the system, is directed towards the first nodal point (N) will emerge with its final direction *parallel to its original direction* and passing through the second nodal point (N').

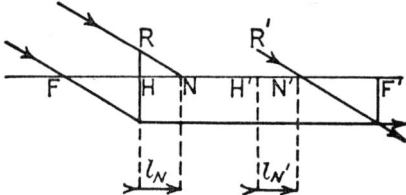

Fig. 7.14.—Nodal points

In fig. 7.14, RN is an incident ray and R'N' the corresponding direction of emergence. Since these are parallel and H'R' = HR, the distances l_N and l_N' of the nodal points from the corresponding principal points are equal. Equation 7(17) then gives

$$l_N = l_N' = f + f', \quad \ldots \ldots \quad 7(23a)$$

§ 7.13   NODAL POINTS   251

and, if x_N and $x_N{'}$ are the distances of the nodal points from the corresponding focal points,

$$x_N = l_N - f = f' \text{ and } x_N{'} = f, \quad \ldots \ldots \quad 7(23b)$$

in agreement with 7(22a).

If z and z' are the distances of two conjugate planes from the corresponding nodal points, then, from the figure,

$$M_T = \frac{y'}{y} = \frac{z'}{z}. \quad \ldots \ldots \quad 7(24)$$

Consider an object at a very great distance from an optical system which subtends an angle $\omega = y/z$. The image is formed in the second focal plane whose distance from the corresponding nodal plane is

$$f' - (f + f') = -f,$$

$$\therefore \omega = -\frac{y'}{f} \text{ or } \frac{n\omega}{y'} = F. \quad \ldots \ldots \quad 7(25)$$

This equation is sometimes used to define the power. If length is measured in centimetres, the power is in (centimetres)$^{-1}$. If length is measured in metres, the power is in *dioptres* (D).

From the various relations which have been derived it is clear that if the focal points and the two focal lengths are given, then the positions of the nodal points and principal points can be derived. There are only four independent data.

EXAMPLES [7(vi) and 7(vii)]

7(vi). Show that the transverse magnification for planes through the nodal points is n'/n and that the angular magnification for the principal planes is the same.

7(vii). Show that

$$zz' + z'f' + zf = 0, \quad \ldots \ldots \quad 7(26a)$$

and that

$$\frac{1}{n'z'} - \frac{1}{nz} = \frac{1}{nf'} = -\frac{1}{n'f} \quad \ldots \ldots \quad 7(26b)$$

[Substitute $z = x - f'$, etc., in Newton's equation.]

7.14.—Suppose that a beam of light parallel to the axis is incident from the left (fig. 7.15a) and is focused at F'. Now let the system be rotated about a point O on the axis through a small angle θ. The incident beam will now come to a focus at a point G' (fig. 7.15b) which is in the focal plane because the beam is parallel. Also the ray AN which is incident through N must emerge parallel to its original direction and so as to pass through both N' and G'. Its image will be situated at a distance $g\theta$ from its original position, where $g = $ N'O is the distance

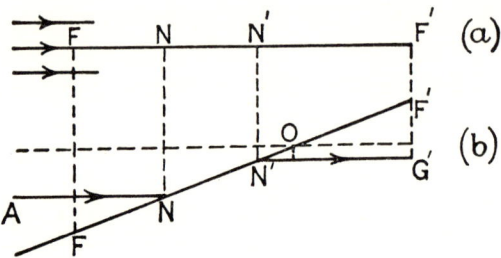

Fig. 7.15.—(a) Incident light parallel to axis. (b) Situation after the optical system has been rotated about O.

of the centre of rotation from the second nodal point. Thus if the centre of rotation is at N', the image does not move. This special property of the nodal points is not possessed by any other axial points or by other points in the conjugate planes through the nodal points.

EXAMPLE [7(viii)]

Find the principal points, nodal points, and focal points of a single refracting surface of radius 20 cm. (fig. 7.9) separating air and glass of index 1·5. [The principal points coincide with each other and with the surface, and the nodal points are at the centre of curvature. The foci may be obtained by putting first l and then $l' = \infty$ in equation 7(8). They are at -40 and $+60$ cm. from the surface.]

7.15. Transmitting Systems with Initial and Final Media the Same.

These systems (including, of course, systems of lenses in air) have the following special properties which may be obtained by putting $n' = n$ in the preceding equations:

(i) $-f = f' = \dfrac{n}{F}$, ... 7(27a)

or $\quad -f = f' = \dfrac{1}{F}$ (for a system in air). . . . . . 7(27b)

(ii) $\dfrac{\alpha'}{\alpha} = \dfrac{y}{y'}$ . . . . 7(28a)

or $\quad M_\alpha = \dfrac{1}{M_T}.$ . . . . 7(28b)

§ 7.16   REFLECTING SYSTEMS   253

(iii) The nodal points coincide with the corresponding principal points (see equations 7(23) and 7(27)).

(iv) Equations 7(17) and 7(22) reduce to

$$\frac{1}{l'} - \frac{1}{l} = F = \frac{1}{f'} = -\frac{1}{f}, \qquad \ldots \ldots \quad 7(29)$$

and $xx' = -f^2 = -f'^2.$ . . . . 7(30)

For a very thin lens, the two principal and the two nodal points coincide with each other and with the lens.

7.16. Catadioptric or Reflecting Systems.

An optical system which returns an axial ray along the axis is called a *catadioptric system*. The simplest system of this type is the concave mirror (fig. 7.16). There is one focus F conjugate to the plane

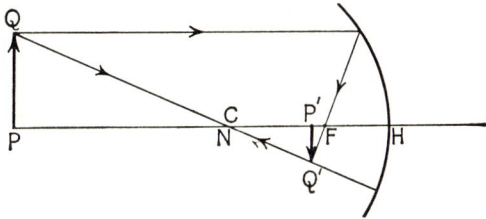

Fig. 7.16.—Principal, focal, and nodal points for catadioptric system (single mirror)

at $-\infty$. The two principal points coincide with each other and with the mirror. The two nodal points coincide with each other and with the centre of curvature, as may be seen by considering the rotational property (§ 7.14).

We have $HF = +f = \dfrac{1}{F},$ . . . . 7(31a)

and $HN = +2f = \dfrac{2}{F}.$ . . . . . 7(31b)

By putting $n' = -n$ in 7(19), 7(22b), 7(25), etc., we see that these properties apply more generally. Also from 7(19) we obtain $f' = f$.

$$\frac{1}{l'} + \frac{1}{l} = \frac{1}{f} = F. \qquad \ldots \ldots \quad 7(32)$$

$$xx' = f^2. \qquad \ldots \ldots \ldots \quad 7(33)$$

The difference of sign in 7(32) and 7(33) as compared with 7(29) and 7(30) corresponds with the physical fact that a lens system of zero power (e.g. a plate of glass) does not deviate rays of light, whereas a mirror of zero power (i.e. a plane mirror normal to the axis) rotates the axial ray through an angle π.

When a system includes lenses as well as a plane or spherical mirror, the above discussion applies to a ray which has encountered each refracting surface twice. For example, if some lenses and a mirror are placed below the surface of a liquid, so as to form a coaxal system with the axis vertical, the formulæ apply when both object and image are in air. More complicated relations are involved if one is in air and the other in the liquid.

7.17. Calculation of Positions of Cardinal Points.

It is convenient to divide this calculation into two stages: (*a*) development of a formula for the power of the system as a whole, and (*b*) calculation of the distances of the foci from a physically defined point such as the outer surface of one of the lenses. When the power is known, the focal lengths are given by equation 7(19), so the principal points can be located with respect to the corresponding foci. Equation 7(23) enables the nodal points to be found.

7.18. Formulæ for the Power.

Suppose a ray encounters a series of refracting surfaces at heights h_1, h_2, etc. Then repeated use of equation 7(7) gives

$$n'\alpha' - n\alpha = \sum_s F_s h_s, \qquad \ldots \ldots \quad 7(34)$$

where n' and α' refer to the image, and n and α to the object.

When the incident ray is parallel to the axis, $\alpha = 0$ and equation 7(34) reduces to

$$\alpha' = \frac{1}{n'} \sum_s F_s h_s. \qquad \ldots \ldots \quad 7(35a)$$

But from § 7.13 and fig. 7.17 we see that

$$\alpha' = \frac{1}{n'} F h_1, \qquad \ldots \ldots \quad 7(35b)$$

where F is the power of the whole system.

Combining equations 7(35a) and 7(35b) we obtain

$$F = \frac{1}{h_1} \sum_s F_s h_s. \qquad \ldots \ldots \quad 7(36)$$

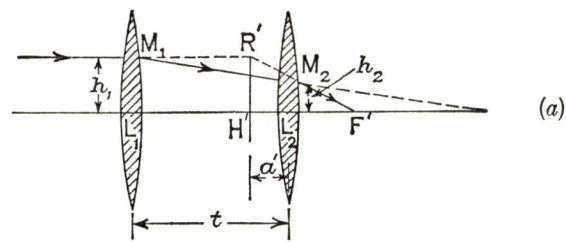

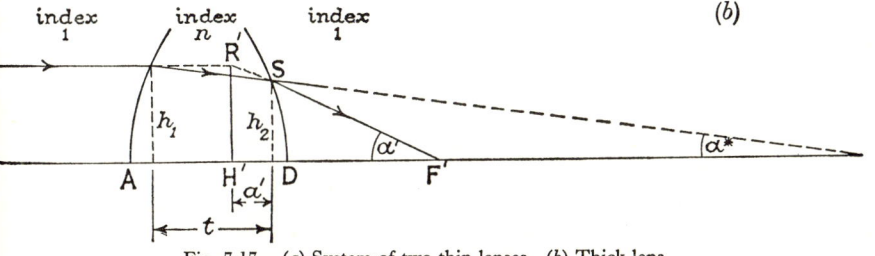

Fig. 7.17.—(a) System of two thin lenses. (b) Thick lens.

We now apply this relation to special cases:

(i) For a thin lens, of index n in a medium of index 1, with surfaces whose radii are r_a and r_b, we have $h_1 = h_2$. When equation 7(8) is combined with equation 7(36) we obtain

$$F = (n-1)\left(\frac{1}{r_a} - \frac{1}{r_b}\right) = (n-1)k, \qquad \ldots \quad 7(37)$$

where k is the algebraic sum of the curvatures of the two surfaces.

(ii) For two thin lenses of powers F_1 and F_2 separated by a distance t (see fig. 7.17a) in air, we have

$$h_2 = h_1 - F_1 t h_1 = h_1(1 - F_1 t), \qquad \ldots \quad 7(38)$$

and equation 7(36) then gives

$$F = F_1 + F_2 - F_1 F_2 t. \qquad \ldots \ldots \quad 7(39)$$

(iii) For a thick lens (fig. 7.17b) we have

$$h_2 = h_1\left(1 - \frac{F_1}{n} t\right), \qquad \ldots \ldots \quad 7(40)$$

using equation 7(7) to find the angle α^*.

Equation 7(36) then gives

$$F = F_1 + F_2 - \frac{F_1 F_2}{n} t, \qquad \ldots \quad 7(41a)$$

where F_1 and F_2 are the powers of the two surfaces.

Inserting values from equation 7(7), we have, for surfaces of radii r_a and r_b,

$$F = (n-1)\left(\frac{1}{r_a} - \frac{1}{r_b} + \frac{n-1}{n} \frac{t}{r_a r_b}\right). \qquad . \quad 7(41b)$$

7.19. Positions of Foci.

(i) For a thin lens the planes of unit *positive* magnification coincide with the lens, and the foci are therefore distant f and $-f$ from the lens.

(ii) For a combination of two thin lenses, we have from the similar triangles F'R'H' and F'M$_2$L$_2$, in fig. 7.17a,

$$\frac{a'}{\text{H'F'}} = a'F = \frac{h_1 - h_2}{h_1},$$

where $F = 1/\text{H'F'}$ is the power of the system as a whole and $a' = \text{H'L}_2$.

Using equation 7(38) we obtain

$$a' = \frac{F_1}{F} t. \qquad \ldots \ldots \quad 7(42)$$

(iii) Similarly for a thick lens

$$a' = \frac{F_1 t}{nF}, \qquad \ldots \ldots \quad 7(43)$$

where F is the power of the lens and F_1 is the power of the first surface.

Equation 7(42) gives the distance of H' from L$_2$ in fig. 7.17a and equation 7(43) gives the distance of H' from D in fig. 7.17b. The distance of H from L$_1$ in fig. 7.17a or from A in fig. 7.17b may be found in a similar way.

7.20. Telescopic Systems.

From 7(39) we see that when two thin lenses are separated by a distance $f_1 + f_2 = 1/F_1 + 1/F_2$, the combination has zero power. Its focal length is infinite. The well-known astronomical telescope (fig. 7.18a) and the Galilean telescope (fig. 7.18b) are systems of this type. A beam of light incident parallel to the axis emerges parallel to it, but in general the width is changed. There is a single transverse magnification M_T for all conjugate planes, including the planes at infinity which are conjugate to one another. A parallel beam of light incident at an angle to the axis emerges as a parallel beam, making a different angle to the axis (fig. 7.18). Formulæ involving focal lengths and powers are inappropriate, but the magnification relation (equation 7(12)) is still valid, and the relation $M_T = 1/M_\alpha$ applies to a refracting telescope for which the initial and final media are the same. The relation $M_T = -1/M_\alpha$ applies to a reflecting telescope.

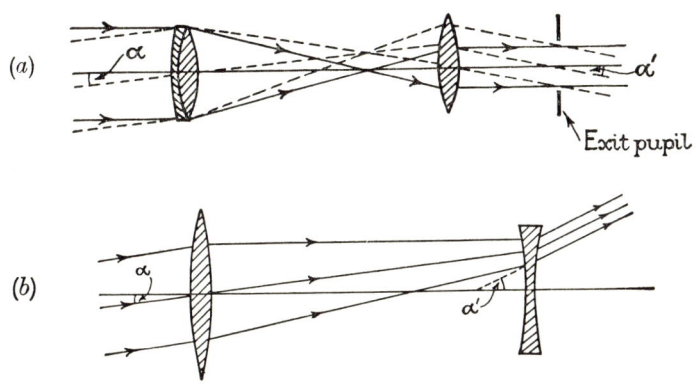

Fig. 7.18.—Telescopes: (a) astronomical, (b) Galilean

A telescopic system is obtained when any two non-telescopic systems are placed on one axis, so that the first focal point of one coincides with the second focal point of the other. From fig. 7.18a we see that

$$M_\alpha = -\frac{F_2}{F_1} = -\frac{f_1}{f_2}, \qquad \ldots \quad 7(44)$$

where F_1 is the power of the first lens (which is called the objective) and F_2 is that of the eyepiece.

7.21.—A non-telescopic system which receives two beams of light from two stars forms two image points in its focal plane. The separation of these image points is proportional to the angle between beams of light from the stars. The constant of proportionality has the dimension of a length and is equal to $f' = n'/F$, and this constant characterizes the system. A telescopic system receiving light from two stars forms images at an infinite distance. The angle which the images subtend is proportional to the angle subtended by the objects. The ratio is a pure number, and in equation 7(44) it is expressed as the ratio of two lengths. This ratio characterizes the telescopic system. All telescopic systems may be divided into two non-telescopic systems. There are trivial exceptions, e.g. a plane mirror normal to the axis could be described as a telescope of magnification -1.

7.22. General Note on Calculations for Coaxial Systems.

When only two components are involved, it is often simplest to obtain the position and size of image by elementary methods without using the general theory. Newton's formula (equations 7(22)), the deviation equation (7(7)) and the power equation (7(39)) are very useful. It often helps to consider a selected ray which, at some stage, is parallel to the axis.

EXAMPLES * [7(ix)–7(xv)]

7(ix). A lens of power 10 D intersects the axis at $x = 0$ and one of power -8 D does so at $x = 5$ cm. Find the power and the principal points of the system. Calculate the telephoto magnification M_{T_e} (see § 7.37).

[Power = 6 D. F, H, H', F' at -23.3, -6.6, -3.3 and $+13.3$ respectively. $M_{T_e} = 2.0$.]

7(x). An eyepiece (see § 7.32) consists of a lens of focal length 6 cm. at $x = 0$ and a similar lens at $x = 4$. Find the focal length and the positions of the principal points and foci.

[$f' = 4\frac{1}{2}$ cm. F, H, H', F' at $-1\frac{1}{2}$, $+3$, $+1$ and $+5\frac{1}{2}$ respectively.]

7(xi). If the nearest distance of distinct vision is 30 cm., what is the magnification of this eyepiece? (see § 7.31). If it is used with a telescope, where should the focal plane of the objective be situated and where should cross-wires be placed?

[Both coincide with F.]

7(xii). An eyepiece consists of a lens of focal length 6 cm. at $x = 0$ and one of focal length 3 cm. at $x = 4$. The latter is nearer the eye. Find the focal length and the positions of principal points and foci.

[$f' = 3.6$ cm. F, H', H, F' at 1·2, 1·6, 4·8, 5·2 respectively.]

7(xiii). Where should cross-wires be placed and where should the focal plane of an objective be situated?

[Since the eyepiece is negative, cross-wires are viewed through the eye lens alone and should be placed at its focus, i.e. at $x = 1$. Focal plane of object glass should be at F, i.e. at $x = 1.2$.]

7(xiv). Use Newton's Formula to check the answers to examples 7(ix), 7(x) and 7(xii).

* For further examples on lens systems see FINCHAM: *Optics* (Hatton Press, 1936).

[Note that, for example in 7(x), rays from the focus of the field lens are parallel to the axis between the lenses and therefore converge on the second focus of the eye lens.]

7(xv). Show that the focal length of the compound microscope shown in fig. 7.27 is $-f_e f_0/g$. In what plane should the object be placed if the image is to be at ∞ ?

[Object is distant $-f_0'(f_0' + g)/g$ from the objective. Use equation 7(39) with $t = f_e + f_0 + g$.]

7.23. Chromatic Aberration.

Since all optical glasses are dispersive media, the deviation of a ray at the surface of a lens varies with the wavelength. Within the approximation of paraxial-ray theory each wavelength forms a perfect image, but the images for different wavelengths do not coincide either

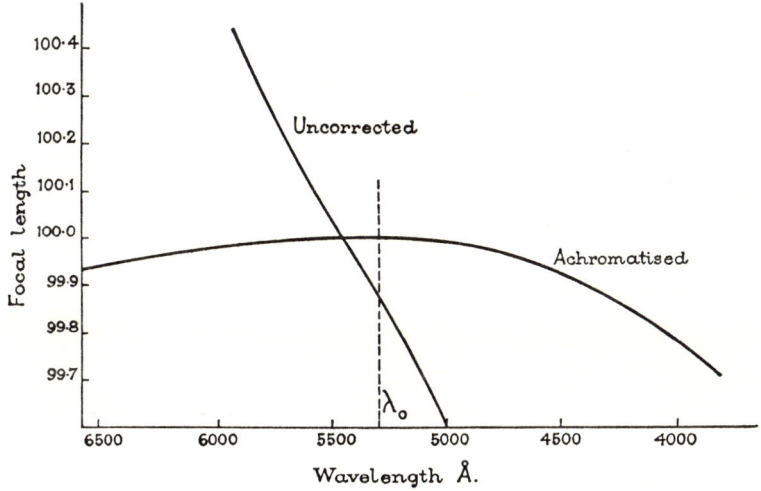

Fig. 7.19.—Achromatic combination

in position or in size. When white light is used, coloured fringes appear at the boundaries between light and dark regions in an image. The displacement of images along the axis is known as *longitudinal* (or axial) *chromatic aberration*, and the variation in image size is called *transverse* (or lateral) *chromatic aberration* or *chromatic difference of magnification*. The main effects of chromatic aberration are included in paraxial-ray theory and are therefore discussed in this chapter; some additional effects, obtained with lenses of wide aperture, are described in § 8.32.

It is possible to design a combination of two lenses of power F_c so that $dF_c/d\lambda$ is zero for some chosen wavelength λ_0 (see fig. 7.19).

A combination which has this property is said to be *achromatic*, and the residual effects at wavelengths remote from λ_0 are called the *secondary spectrum*. It will be shown in the next paragraph that two thin lenses, made from the same glass, form an achromatic combination if their separation is half the sum of the focal lengths, and also that an achromatic doublet may be made by using two thin lenses of different materials in contact.

By using more than two materials it is possible to obtain combinations for which $dF_c/d\lambda$ is zero for more than one wavelength. Microscope objectives corrected in this way (and also corrected at two wavelengths for spherical aberration) are described as *apochromatic*. By using two materials whose dispersion curves have a favourable relation, it is possible to approach these properties closely. These semi-apochromatic objectives may be constructed by combining lenses of glass and of fluorite.

7.24. Achromatic Systems.

Before considering achromatic-lens systems, it is desirable to note that mirror systems are entirely free from chromatic error. They are particularly advantageous in the infra-red region, where the loss by reflection is small and where a wide range of wavelength is involved. Large telescopes are usually reflectors. Microscopes for the visible region are usually refracting systems, but high-quality reflecting microscopes are now being used for ultra-violet, visible, and infra-red regions.

For two thin lenses in contact ($t = 0$) we obtain from equations 7(37) and 7(39)
$$F_c = (n_1 - 1)k_1 + (n_2 - 1)k_2, \quad \ldots \ldots \quad 7(45)$$
and $dF_c/d\lambda$ is zero if
$$k_1 \frac{dn_1}{d\lambda} = -k_2 \frac{dn_2}{d\lambda}. \quad \ldots \ldots \quad 7(46)$$

Equations 7(45) and 7(46) may be regarded as simultaneous equations for k_1 and k_2 when F_c is fixed and the glasses have been chosen.

Substituting from equation 7(46) into 7(45) we have
$$F_c = (n_1 - 1)\left(1 - \frac{\nu_1}{\nu_2}\right)k_1, \quad \ldots \ldots \quad 7(47)$$
where
$$\nu_1 = \frac{1}{n_1 - 1}\frac{dn_1}{d\lambda} \text{ and } \nu_2 = \frac{1}{n_2 - 1}\frac{dn_2}{d\lambda}.$$

If ν_1 and ν_2 had the same value for all optical materials (as Newton supposed), there would be no possibility of making an achromatic doublet in this way. In fact optical glasses with values of ν covering a range of 2 to 1 are readily available, and achromatic combinations without excessively high values of k_1 and k_2 (i.e. without very high curvatures) are possible. Equation 7(46) implies that k_1 and k_2 must be of opposite sign, i.e. one lens must be positive and the other **negative**.

Since the lens surfaces have four radii of curvature, the design is not completely fixed when k_1 and k_2 have been determined. The remaining freedom of choice is used by the designer to reduce the other aberrations (especially spherical aberration and coma). He may also decide to make two faces match, so that the lens may be cemented to reduce internal reflection.

7.25.—For two lenses of the same material separated by a distance t equations 7(37) and 7(39) give
$$F_c = (n-1)(k_1 + k_2) - (n-1)^2 k_1 k_2 t, \quad \ldots \quad 7(48)$$
and $dF_c/d\lambda = 0$ if
$$k_1 + k_2 = 2(n-1)k_1 k_2 t$$
and, substituting $1/f = (n-1)k$, we obtain
$$2t = f_1 + f_2. \quad \ldots \ldots \ldots \quad 7(49)$$

This relation is exactly true at one wavelength only, because f_1 and f_2 depend on the wavelength.

The equality of focal lengths at two wavelengths does not necessarily imply that the images are coincident either in position or in size, because the cardinal points for different wavelengths may not coincide. When two thin lenses are in contact the principal planes are not very far from the centre of the lens pair, and the variation of their positions with wavelength is very small. Thus agreement of the power for different wavelengths implies elimination of both longitudinal and transverse chromatic effects. With two separated lenses of the same glass, longitudinal chromatic aberration remains even when equation 7(49) is satisfied, although the chromatic difference of magnification is removed.

7.26. Stops.

Stops are often inserted in optical systems to exclude or trap scattered light which lies entirely outside the paths of the rays which contribute to the image. The lens hood of a camera has this effect. Stops of this type are particularly important in grating spectrographs where spectra of orders other than the one being observed are incident on the sides of the cover and may be scattered on to the plate unless they are trapped. This use of stops is of great practical importance but, since the optical principles involved are very simple, we shall not discuss it further.

Let us now consider the restriction of the rays which form an image either by diaphragms which have been inserted for this purpose or by the edges of optical components. Either form of restriction may be called a stop.

7.27. The Aperture Stop.

For a given pair of conjugate points (P and P' in fig. 7.20) the angular diameter $2\alpha_0$ of the cone of rays which forms the image is restricted either by the size of one of the components or by a diaphragm S_0 as shown in the figure. A simple optical system is shown, but the following discussion applies to more complicated systems if it is understood that L_1 stands for all lenses which precede S_0 and L_2 for all lenses which follow S_0. (It also applies, with small alterations, to systems in which the cone of rays which pass S_0 just passes a second diaphragm.)

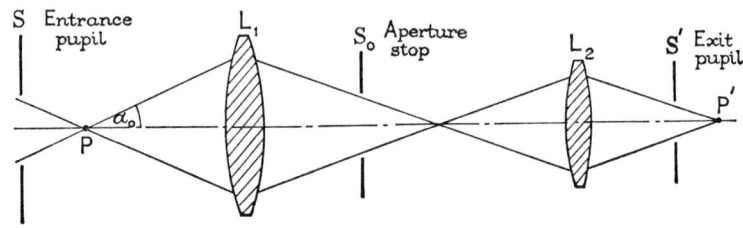

Fig. 7.20.—Field stop

The diaphragm S_0, which forms the effective restriction, is called the *aperture stop*; its image S formed by L_1 is called the *entrance pupil* and its image S′ formed by L_2 is called the *exit pupil*. S and S′ are conjugate in respect of the lens system as a whole. The ray which passes from P to P′ through the centre of the aperture stop (and therefore through the centres of S and S′) is called the *chief ray* or *principal ray*. In a telescope, the objective usually constitutes the aperture stop and, since there are no lenses preceding it, is also the entrance pupil, In an astronomical telescope the exit pupil is as shown in fig. 7.18a. and in a visual instrument is made to coincide approximately with the entrance pupil of the eye. The latter is near to the iris diaphragm which forms the aperture stop of the eye. For a telescope or a camera used to focus distant objects the relative aperture is the ratio of the focal length to the diameter of the entrance pupil. This is called the *f*/number. In a microscope the aperture is usually determined by the first lens of the objective (see § 8.21).

7.28. **The Field Stop.**

If a stop Σ_0 is placed in a telescope as shown in fig. 7.21 its edges, which are focused by the eyepiece, sharply delimit the available field of view. All rays (which pass the object glass) from a point whose intermediate image is within Σ_0 also pass the eyepiece. All rays from a point whose intermediate image is outside Σ_0 are stopped. Σ_0 is called the *field stop*; its image Σ formed by all preceding components is called the *entrance window,* and its image Σ' formed by the following system is called the *exit window*. In the telescopic system shown, the entrance and exit windows are at infinity; the angular diameter of the entrance window is called the *angular field of view*.

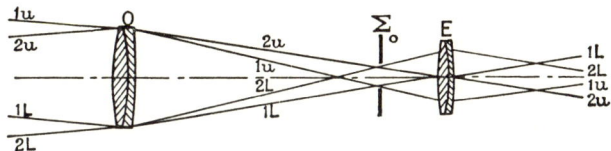

Fig. 7.21.—Aperture stop: the rays 1u, 1L and 2u, 2L are from stars whose primary images fall just inside the field stop.

The case illustrated in fig. 7.21 is a special one; unless a stop has been deliberately inserted to give sharp edges to the field, the cone of rays forming the image decreases gradually as the object point moves off-axis. This effect is known as *vignetting*. It is usual to regard a point as within the field of view if its chief ray passes through the system. For a given pair of conjugate planes, one diaphragm or the edge of one lens restricts this field of view, and this is regarded as the field stop. Note that in this situation some light from points outside the " field of view " does reach the observer.

7.29. The Field Lens.

In the telescope shown in fig. 7.22a, the field is restricted by the edge of the eye-lens E. The insertion of a lens L_F increases the available field (fig. 7.22b) and, if its focal length is correctly chosen, its edges become the field stop. A lens which functions in this way is

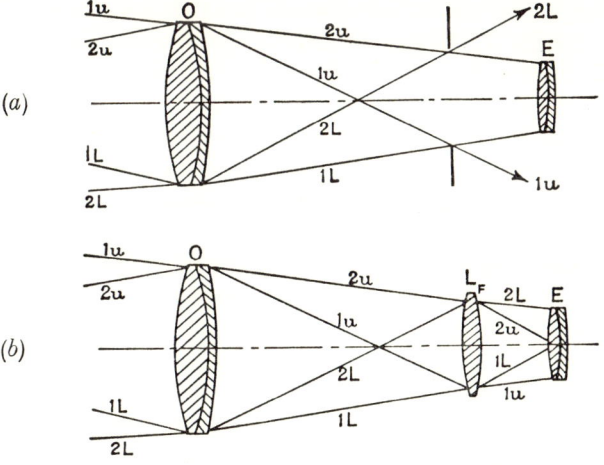

Fig. 7.22.—Field lens: (a) rays 1u and 2L miss the eyepiece, (b) the lens L_F deviates these rays so that they enter the eyepiece

called a *field lens*. It does not alter the aperture or the magnification of the system, which is still determined by the diameter of the objective, but it changes the size and position of the exit pupil.

In certain instruments, e.g. the cystoscope, an image-forming system is severely restricted by the necessity of passing the light through a long narrow tube or through a series of small stops. In this situation, field lenses and image-forming lenses may be used alternately as shown in fig. 7.23. in which L_1, L_3, L_5, etc.,

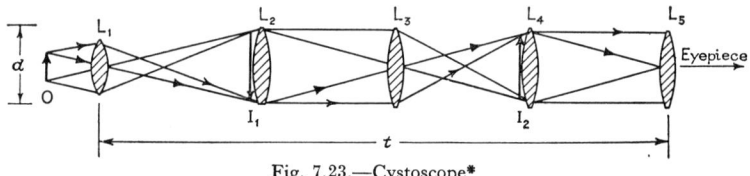

Fig. 7.23.—Cystoscope*

form successive images of the object O. Lenses L_2, L_4, etc., are field lenses. Note that L_3, L_4, L_5 together form a telescope of unit magnification. Periscopes and cystoscopes use systems of this kind. The magnification of the image I_N viewed by the ocular is much less than that which would be formed by a telescope having an objective of diameter d and a tube length t. Since the light accepted from a given small area of the object is the same, the image is much brighter. The field of view is much greater. The advantage to be gained from anti-reflecting surfaces in a system of this type is very large. Another method of conveying an image along a tube is described in Appendix VII A.

7.30. The Eye.

The optical system of the eye (fig. 7.24) consists of the cornea, the aqueous humour, the crystalline lens, and the vitreous humour. The refractive index for the aqueous humour and the vitreous humour does not differ much from that for water (1.33). The index of the lens varies from 1·38 at the surface to 1·41 at the centre. The main refracting power is in the cornea (40 D); the lens contributes about 23 D. The refracting system of the unaccommodated eye may be represented to a first approximation by a single spherical surface of power 60 D separating air from a medium of index 1·33. The eye is not strictly a coaxal system but as a second approximation (which is adequate for most purposes) it may be represented by a coaxal system.†

Accommodation of about 4 D, enabling the observer to focus objects at 25 cm. is available to most young observers. This adjustment is made mainly by altering the shape of the anterior surface of the lens. The iris diaphragm forms an aperture stop which is adjusted

---

* For a discussion of alternative systems see p. 242 of Reference 6.1.

† The constants of this system are given in Chapter XIV of Reference 7.3.

(by involuntary action in response to changes in illumination) from about 2·5 mm. to 8 mm., i.e. a change of nearly ten to one in area. The retina is a mosaic of fine nerve endings which are essentially part

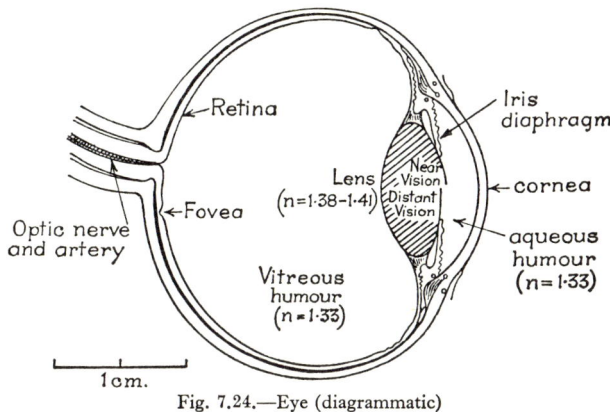

Fig. 7.24.—Eye (diagrammatic)

of the brain. Photochemical changes produced in these receptors by changes of illumination produce electrical pulses which pass along the associated nerve fibres to the cortex.

7.31. Magnifiers and Oculars.

The size of an image on the retina is proportional to the angle which it subtends at the first nodal point of the eye. The advantage gained by using a magnifying system is measured by the ratio of this angle when the object is seen through the magnifying system to its value when the object is seen by the naked eye. When the object is a star field and the magnifying system is a telescope, this ratio is simply the angular magnification of the telescope. When the magnifying system is a short-focus lens, an object of height y being placed at the focus, the angle subtended is y/f. The corresponding condition for the naked eye is for the object to be situated at the nearest distance of distinct vision. Call this distance d (measured from the nodal point). Then the magnification* is d/f. The value of d for a young observer with normal sight is about 25 cm.

The detailed design of magnifying lenses involves a compromise between the elimination of aberrations, high magnification, good conditions of illumination, etc. Some magnifiers which have been widely used are illustrated in fig. 10H of Reference 7.6.

* The magnification of an eyepiece is often called its " power ".

7.32.—Oculars or eyepieces are designed for magnifying an intermediate image formed by the objective of a telescope or microscope. In the *negative eyepiece*, the intermediate image is formed within the

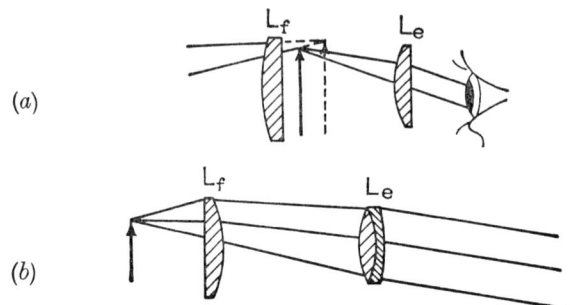

Fig. 7.25.—Eyepieces: (a) negative (Huygens), (b) positive (Kellner)

ocular, as shown in fig. 7.25a. In the *positive eyepiece* the intermediate image is external (fig. 7.25b). This type of ocular may be used as a magnifier for real objects.

The eyepiece designed by Ramsden consists of two lenses, L_f and L_e in fig. 7.26, of equal focal length and separated by a distance f (i.e. half the sum of the focal lengths). The aerial image which is being magnified must coincide with L_f which acts entirely as a field lens. L_e alone is responsible for the magnification.

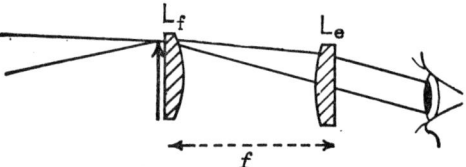

Fig. 7.26.—Ramsden eyepiece

The crosswire or graticule must be in contact with L_f. This is mechanically inconvenient, and also any speck of dust on L_f is in focus. It is therefore usual to reduce the distance between the components, so that the eyepiece is positive (fig. 7.25b). This sacrifices some of the chromatic correction, but in the form designed by Kellner this is restored by using an achromatic doublet as eye-lens. The lens L_f now contributes something to the magnification but still acts also as a field lens.*

7.33. The Compound Microscope.

A microscope consists of a compound objective of very short focal length f_o and an ocular of focal length f_e (fig. 7.27). The distance g

* For a more detailed discussion of oculars see Reference 7.2 or 7.6.

between the back focus of the objective and the front focus of the eyepiece is always positive and is called the *optical tube length*. It is usually 160 mm. It may be shown (Example 7(xv)) that the focal length of the combination is $f_e f_o /g$, and the magnification M is therefore

$$M = \left(\frac{g}{f_o}\right) \cdot \left(\frac{d}{f_e}\right). \quad \cdots \cdots \quad 7(50)$$

The first factor gives the magnification of the intermediate image and the second is the magnification of the eyepiece.

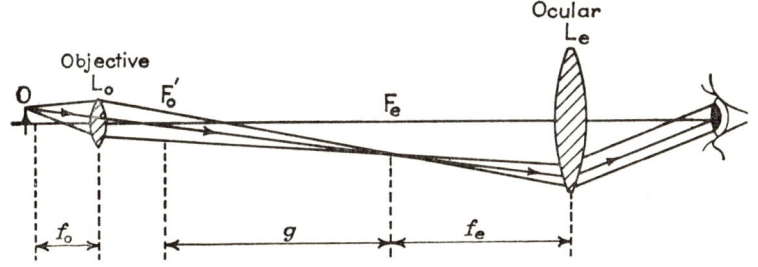

Fig. 7.27.—Compound microscope

7.34. The Reflecting Telescope.

Nearly all modern large telescopes are reflecting. It is a good deal easier to support a mirror from the back than to mount a large lens so that it does not deform under its own weight. Chromatic aberration

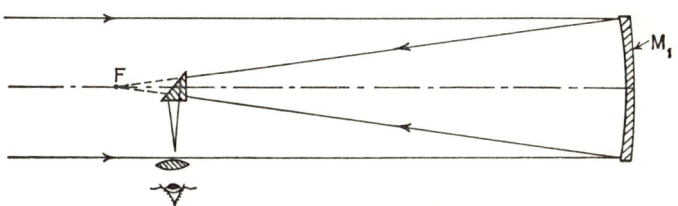

Fig. 7.28.—Newtonian reflector

is avoided, and other aberrations are more easily corrected. Usually the main mirror is a paraboloid, and light from a star on axis is directed towards a primary focus at F (fig. 7.28). In the Newtonian telescope a small mirror is placed as shown in order to allow the image to be viewed through an eyepiece without obstructing much of the primary mirror.

The largest telescope now in existence is at Mount Palomar (California). Its mirror is 200 inches in diameter and has a focal length of 666 inches ($f/3\cdot 33$). It is nearly always used as a camera, and for photographing faint objects the plate is placed at the primary focus. A five-fold magnification is obtained with the mounting shown in fig. 7.29a and a nine-fold magnification with that shown in fig. 7.29b.

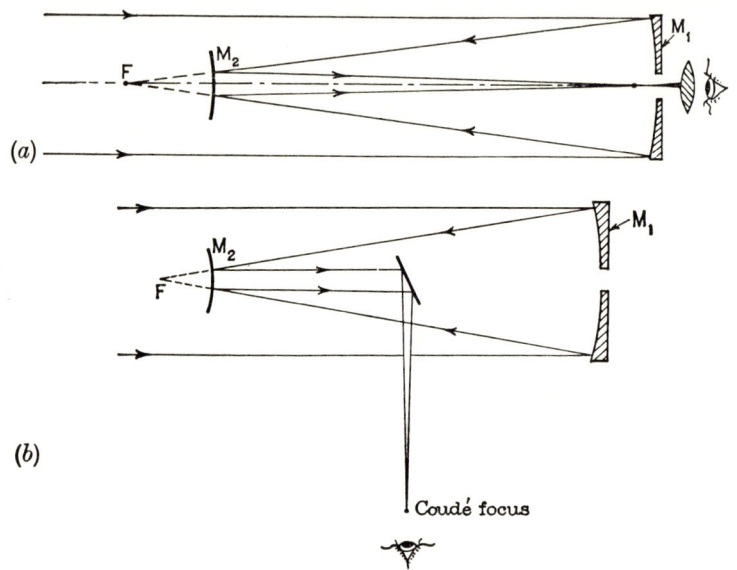

Fig. 7.29.—(a) Cassegrain mounting. (b) Coudé focus

7.35. Mirrors, and Prisms used as Mirrors.

When a beam of light is incident upon a mirror at an angle i, it is deviated through an angle $2i$. If the beam is reflected twice (in the same plane) by two mirrors whose normals intersect at angle α, the angle of incidence for the second mirror is $(i - \alpha)$ and the total deviation $\delta = 2i - 2(i - \alpha) = 2\alpha$ and is thus independent of the angle of incidence. In many optical instruments a solid block of glass is used to give two total reflections and so deviate all rays through the same angle.

Fig. 7.30 shows (a) the Porro prism ($\alpha = \pi/2$; $\delta = \pi$), (b) the pentagonal prism ($\alpha = \pi/4$; $\delta = \pi/2$), (c) the rhomboid ($\alpha = 0$) which displaces rays without deviation.

The Porro prism reverses the image in the plane of reflection only. In a pair of prism binoculars two Porro prisms invert the image in both planes, so that the

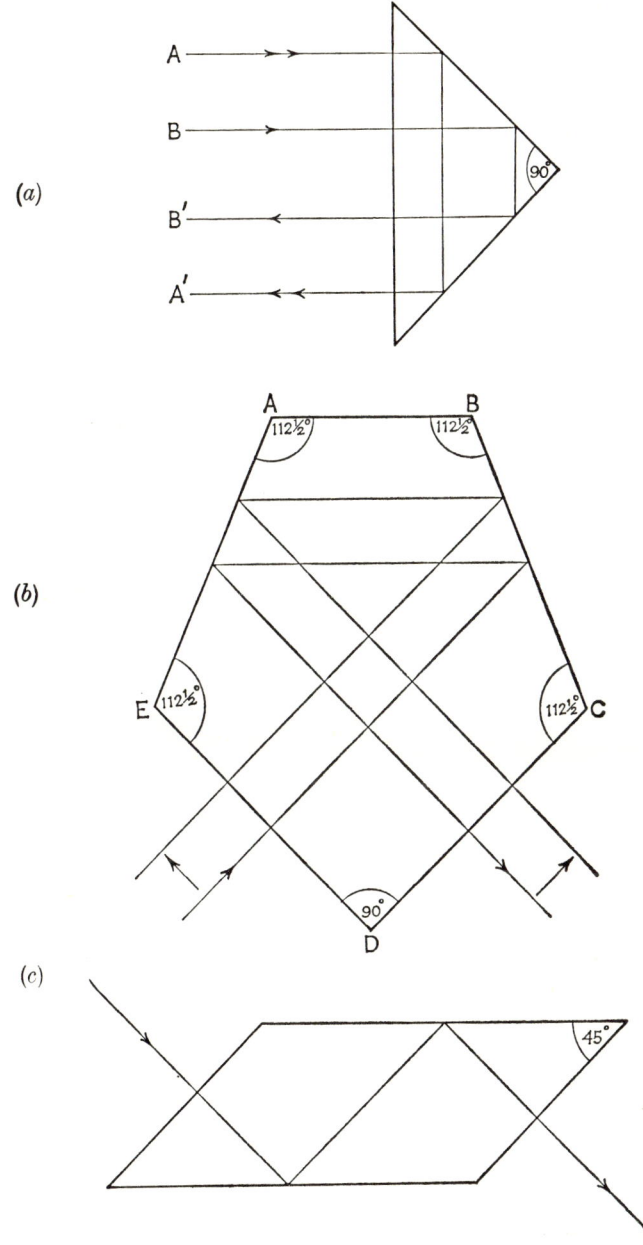

Fig. 7.30.—(a) Porro prism, (b) pentagonal prism, (c) rhomboid prism

viewer sees an erect image. The Dove prism (fig. 7.31) rotates the image as shown in the figure without deviating the beam. The roof prism both deviates the beam (through a right angle) and rotates the image.

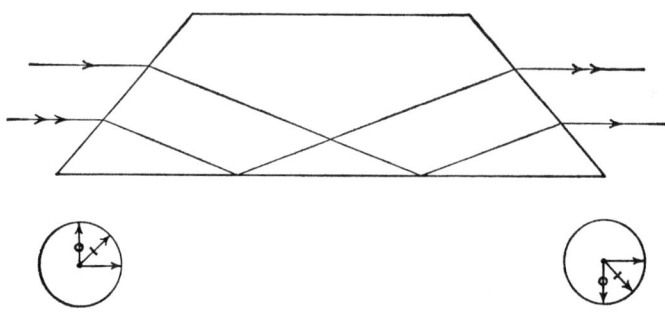

Fig. 7.31.—Dove prism

The use of a glass prism in this way gives greater mechanical stability, and the preservation of surfaces is easier than with the equivalent set of mirrors. There is, however, some chromatic aberration for rays which do not enter and leave normal to the prism faces, and some loss of optical quality due to inhomogeneity of the glass. For some laboratory applications an arrangement of front-surface mirrors is better.

7.36. Constant-deviation Monochromator.

In studying fluorescence (and in many other experiments) it is desirable to illuminate a specimen with light of different wavelengths in turn, without moving either the source of light or the specimens. This is made possible by a constant-deviation monochromator (fig. 7.32). The light is both dispersed and reflected in the single piece of glass (Pellin-Broca prism) which is equivalent to two 30° prisms (ABE and BCD) and to a mirror AD. As the block is rotated, successive wavelengths pass out through the slit S_2. When the prism is rotated, the angles of incidence and of emergence remain equal. Effectively, the light which emerges through S_2 has passed through a 60° prism in the position of minimum deviation.

7.37. Telephoto Lenses and Zoom Lenses.

The photographic camera in its simplest form consists of a single lens with a variable-aperture stop and a shutter close to the lens (fig. 7.33a). The plate, or film, forms the field stop and also the exit window. Compound lenses are used to correct aberrations so as to give a high aperture and a wide field. For example, a fairly good modern camera lens would give an 80° field with an aperture of $f/3.5$. For a camera

§ 7.36 CONSTANT-DEVIATION MONOCHROMATOR 271

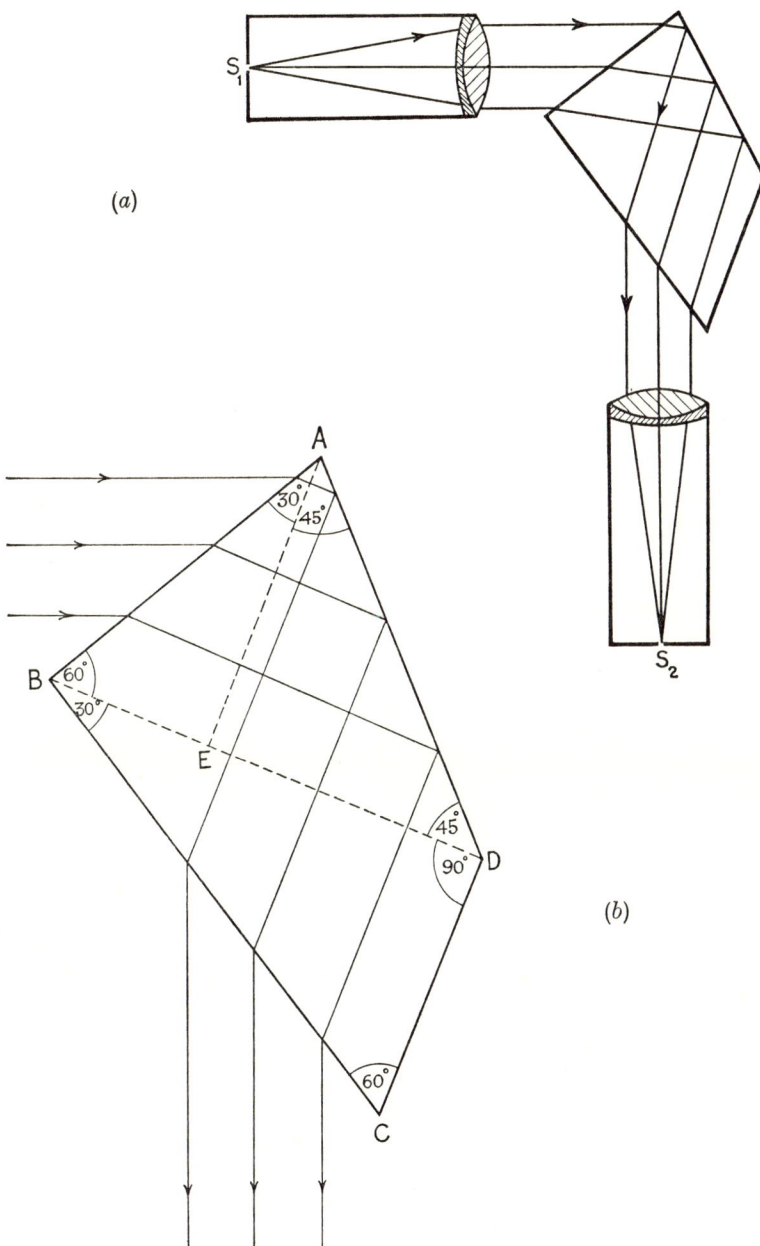

Fig. 7.32.—(a) Monochromator, (b) Pellin-Broca prism

of the type shown in fig. 7.33a, the height of the image of a distant object is proportional to the focal length, and the length of the camera is approximately equal to this focal length. The size of the picture may be increased by using an enlarger, but only within certain limits. For the best results, it is necessary to start with a picture of reasonable size, and this requires a focal length larger than a convenient length for the camera. The telephoto lens (fig. 7.33b) consists of a combination

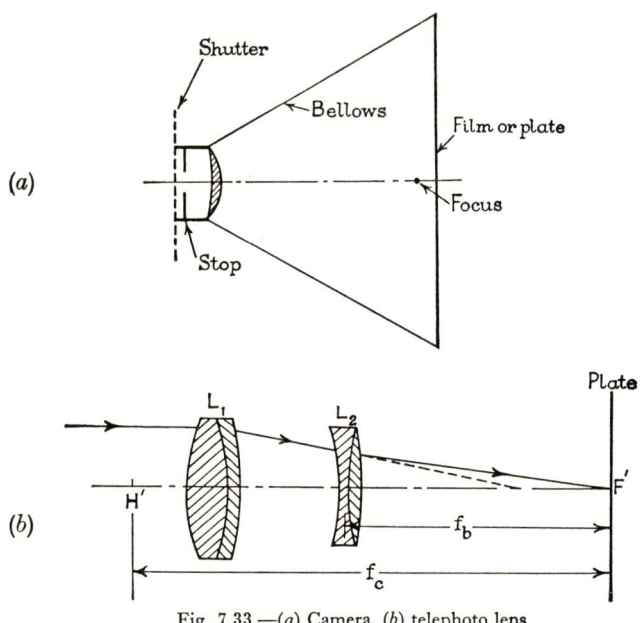

Fig. 7.33.—(a) Camera, (b) telephoto lens

of a positive lens with a weaker negative lens which is nearer the plate. For this combination, the principal point H' is on the side of the lens remote from the plate. The distance from L_2 to the plate, called the *back focal length* (f_b) is much less than the focal length (f_c) of the combination. The ratio f_c/f_b is called the *telephoto magnification* (M_{Te}). Telephoto lenses for which $M_{Te} = 2$ are commonly used, and good lenses with M_{Te} up to 5 are obtainable. Both the positive and the negative components are corrected for chromatic aberration, and the system as a whole is corrected for the geometrical aberrations.

7.38.—In photography for cinema or television it is sometimes desired to pass from a distant view to a " close-up " continuously and without allowing the picture to go badly out of focus. The " zoom " lenses, designed for this purpose, are combinations whose focal length is changed by altering the positions of some of the components in such a way that the distance of the image from the fixed components is unchanged while M_T changes from a value near unity to a much higher value. The ratio of magnifications is called the *zoom ratio*.

One zoom lens design depends on the result of Example 7(v) that $dg/dM = 0$ when $M = \pm 1$, where g is the distance from object to image. By forming an intermediate image and moving one component through the field lens position (in which it coincides with the intermediate image) its effect on the overall magnification may be varied from 2/3 to 4/3 (corresponding to a zoom ratio of 2) without serious loss of focus (see Example 7(v)). For larger zoom ratios a small adjustment of focus is needed, and this may be obtained by moving another component. The zoom lenses used in cinema and television must have high aperture and good correction, and the cost is correspondingly high.

7.39. Projection Systems.

The projection lantern and the photographic enlarger differ from optical systems previously described in that they provide illumination for a semi-transparent object as well as forming an image (fig. 7.34a).

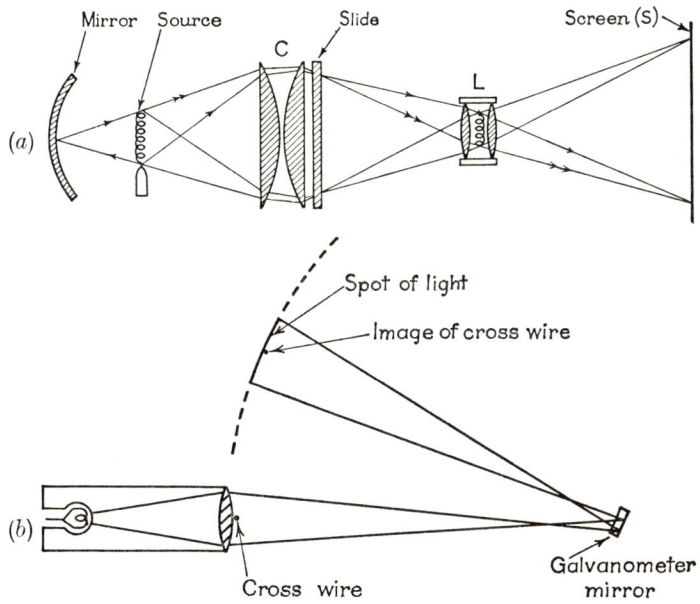

Fig. 7.34.—(a) Projection lantern (distance LS is about 30 times larger than shown), (b) galvanometer system

The condenser C forms an image of the source within the projection lens L. This allows an efficient use of the light from the source, because all light which passes through the object ultimately reaches the image (apart from small losses due to reflection, etc., in the projector). The ordinary galvanometer mirror and scale is a catadioptric projection system (fig. 7.34b). The source should be focused on the galvanometer mirror which forms the aperture stop of the system.

REFERENCES

7.1. CONRADY, A. E.: *Applied Optics and Optical Design* (Dover).
7.2. LONGHURST, R. S.: *Geometrical and Physical Optics* (Longmans Green).
7.3. EMSLEY, H. H.: *Visual Optics* (Hatton).
7.4. STRONG, J.: *Concepts of Classical Optics*.
7.5. TAYLOR, C. A., and THOMPSON, B. J.: *J. Sci. Inst.*, 1957, Vol. 34, p. 439.
7.6. JENKINS, F. A., and WHITE, H. E.: *Fundamentals in Optics* (McGraw-Hill).

APPENDIX VII A

FIBRE OPTICS

1. **The " Light Pipe ".**

Light may be conveyed along a cylindrical rod of transparent material with small loss by successive internal total reflections as shown in fig. 7.35. When the index exceeds $\sqrt{2}$ (critical angle $> 45°$) all the light incident upon one plane end emerges through the other, provided that the rod is straight, the material perfectly homogeneous and transparent, and the surface smooth and clean. Traces

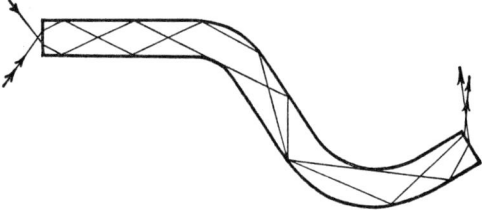

Fig. 7.35.—Transmission of light in a glass rod

of grease on the surface produce a considerable loss of light. If the rod is strongly curved some light is lost because some rays are incident at angles less than the critical angle. This loss can be calculated, but the loss observed in practice is appreciably greater than that calculated because of the effect of inhomogeneity. The loss becomes serious if the radius of curvature is less than about twenty times the diameter of the rod. Curved rods may be used for conveying light to a detector from a place where direct observation would be difficult or dangerous (e.g. from a strongly radioactive body which must be shielded on all sides).

2. Image Formation.

If a bundle of plastic threads is wound on a former in a regular way, and is subsequently cut, a series of parallel fibres is produced. If one end of this system is placed in contact with a self-luminous object, such as the screen of a cathode-ray tube, an image is formed at the other end. Since the whole hemisphere of rays is transmitted, the image is brighter than that obtained with a conventional lens system, provided that the fibres are homogeneous and very transparent. In a similar way the bundle of fibres can also transmit an image projected by a lens on to one end. The path can be curved and the bundle twisted, provided that the ordering of the fibres at the ends is not changed. The fineness of detail which can be conveyed is determined by the diameter of the fibres, unless this diameter is made comparable with the wavelength. If it is as small as this, the fibres function as wave guides (§ 3.31). If light is transmitted from one fibre to another at points of contact, the image will suffer loss of contrast. To prevent this loss fine fibres of a high-index glass coated with a thin layer of a low-index glass have been developed. A summary of the applications of this method is given in Appendix N of Reference 7.4.

CHAPTER VIII

Defects of Optical Images

8.1.—The defects of optical images are due to three main causes:
(i) Aberrations.
(ii) Diffraction.
(iii) Parasitic light.

Parasitic light or *veiling glare* is produced by internal reflections at the surfaces of lenses and by scattering of light by dust particles or small bubbles in the glass. The reflected light can be greatly reduced by the use of anti-reflecting films. Dust particles on internal surfaces can be eliminated by hermetically sealing portions of an instrument. The effect of parasitic light on image quality and loss of detail associated with properties of the detector (e.g. the grain structure of a photographic emulsion) are discussed in Chapter XX.

8.2.—Up to a certain point in the history of optical instrument design, imperfections of image due to aberrations were so large that any additional unsharpness due to diffraction was negligible. In many modern spectrographs, telescopes, and microscopes, imperfections of image due to causes other than diffraction have been made very small so that, when the instrument is used under precisely the conditions for which it was designed, diffraction forms a practical, as well as a theoretical, limit. In the design of these instruments, effects due to aberrations and to diffraction must be considered together. In our discussion of these effects it is convenient to start by considering the effect of diffraction on the image of an object which consists of two adjacent point sources (or line sources). From this we pass to a more general discussion of the unsharpness of optical images due to diffraction, and are able to develop a logical method of assessing the quality of an optical image. This method is later used in relation to images affected both by aberration and by diffraction.

8.3. Limit of Resolution.

As explained in § 6.60, an ideal optical system provides a set of optically equal paths from an object point to an image point. In accordance with Fermat's principle, a set of equal optical paths may be represented by a set of rays from an object point which pass through the optical system and meet at the image point. The image is then perfect from the point of view of geometrical optics. It does not, however, form an exact representation of the object. The image of a point object is not a point but a diffraction pattern. The ideal optical system arranges that all portions of the wave which pass through the system arrive at the image point in phase agreement. To form a perfect image, it would also be necessary to arrange that, at every other point in the image plane, the waves interfered to produce zero illumination. The theory of Fraunhofer diffraction is an expression of the fact that no optical system of finite aperture can achieve this result. No optical system transmits the whole wave emitted by the object and there is therefore always some diffraction. When the aperture is circular, the image of a point source consists of the Airy disc and the surrounding ring pattern (§ 6.41). When the angular separation of two point sources (e.g. two stars seen through a telescope) is sufficiently great, the diffraction patterns which form the images do not effectively overlap. Such images are said to be "resolved". On the other hand, if the angular separation of the two objects is much less than the angular radius of the Airy disc, the two images will be superimposed to such an extent that they cannot be clearly distinguished from an image due to one object alone. Such images are "unresolved".

8.4. The Rayleigh Criterion.

From the above discussion, it is clear that the condition under which the images are seen separately cannot be defined with precision. If two object points, initially very close together, could be moved apart slowly, there would be (i) a condition under which a person observing the image thought there was only one point, and (ii) a condition under which he could see two points clearly separated. These two conditions would be separated, not by a definite boundary, but by an intermediate region in which the observer suspected the existence of two points, but could not be sure that there were two, and could not determine their relative positions. In the first stage of the study of this phenomenon, it is desirable to adopt some arbitrary criterion which gives a mathematically defined boundary between resolution and non-resolution. Rayleigh* suggested the following criterion. Two images are regarded as just resolved when the central maximum in the diffraction pattern due to one is situated at a point

* Reference 8.1.

corresponding to the first minimum in the diffraction pattern due to the other (Plate III*l* (p. 162) and fig. 8.1). Images which have a smaller separation are unresolved.

This criterion enables quantities called the *limit of resolution* of a telescope, microscope, or spectrograph to be defined in such a way that they form useful measures of the performance and can be computed when the optical dimensions of the instrument are known.

When the limit of performance of an instrument is set by diffraction, no advantage is gained by increasing the magnification. If an image is

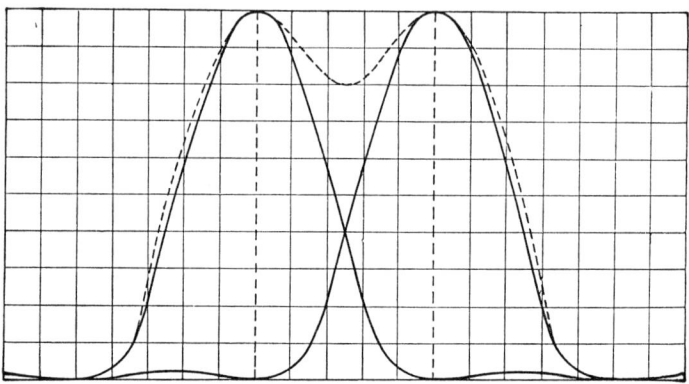

Fig. 8.1.—Energy distribution at the Rayleigh limit for two similar images. (Full lines show the distributions due to the separate sources; the dotted line shows the distribution when both act together.)

magnified, the width of the diffraction pattern increases in proportion to the magnification, because Fraunhofer diffraction effects have a constant *angular* width. There is, in general, an optimum magnification.

8.5. Limit of Resolution for a Telescope.

The limit of resolution for a telescope may be determined by applying Airy's results for diffraction at a circular aperture. It is shown in § 6.41 that the angular radius (θ) of the first dark ring in the diffraction pattern is given by

$$\sin \theta = 1 \cdot 22 \frac{\lambda}{d}, \quad \ldots \ldots \quad 8(1)$$

where d is the diameter of the lens.

The angle involved is usually small enough for θ to be used in place of $\sin \theta$, so that $1 \cdot 22 \lambda/d$ is then the angular separation of two stars which are just resolved. Taking $\lambda = 5500$ Å. (corresponding to the middle of the visible spectrum), putting d in centimetres and θ in minutes of arc, we have

$$\theta = \frac{0\cdot231}{d}. \qquad \ldots \ldots \ldots 8(2)$$

Thus a telescope with an object glass 10 centimetres in diameter will separate two stars whose angular separation is $0\cdot023' = 1\cdot4''$. The angular diameters of stars range up to about $0\cdot05$ seconds of arc. The diameter of the image is thus always a small fraction of that of the Airy disc and the star is effectively a point source.

8.6.—An approximate value for the limit of resolution for a lens covered with a rectangular aperture may be obtained by direct application of the Rayleigh criterion. In fig. 8.2 let AB and AB′ represent two wave surfaces received from two very distant objects O and O′. The angle $\alpha = \angle BAB'$ is the angular separation of the objects. All parts of the wavefront AB reach a certain point P in the

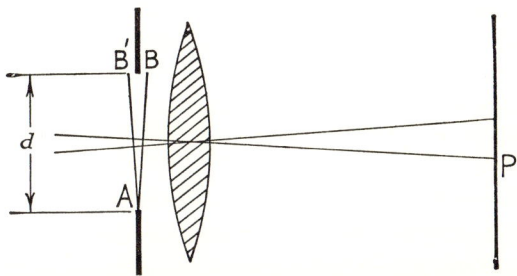

Fig. 8.2.—Limit of resolution for a telescope objective

focal plane of the lens with phase agreement. This point is the centre of the diffraction pattern formed by the point source O. If $BB' = \lambda$, the phases of the wavelets arriving at P from O′ will range uniformly over a period. Their resultant is zero (see § 3.5). Thus the Rayleigh criterion indicates that the minimum angle of resolution is λ/d. In making this calculation we have assumed that the line of separation is parallel to one side of the aperture and have neglected certain small effects (due to the finite length of the other side). It will be noted that the result obtained differs from that given by equation 8(1) only by the factor $1\cdot22$.

EXAMPLES [8(i)–8(iii)]

8(i). Find the minimum angle of resolution (a) for a telescope with a mirror of 200 in. diameter, (b) the lens of the eye when the pupil is 3 mm. diameter. Assume $\lambda = 5500$ Å.   [(a) 0·00045 minute, (b) 0·77 minute.]

8(ii). Find the distance between the images of two stars which are just resolved by a lens of focal length 3 m. and diameter 10 cm. Take $\lambda = 5500$ Å.
[0·02 mm.]

8(iii). Assuming that the length of the exposure does not matter, obtain an expression for the optimum value of the size of the hole in a pinhole camera.

[The diameter of the image of a point source estimated by geometrical optics increases as the diameter of the hole increases. If, however, the hole is made very small, the size of the image is determined by the diameter of the Airy disc. This latter is *inversely* proportional to the diameter of the hole. The optimum condition is attained when both sources of " unsharpness " are equal. If d is the diameter of the pinhole, this happens when $\frac{1}{2}d = 1\cdot 22(\lambda/d)f$, where f is the distance of the plate from the pinhole and the object is assumed to be at an infinite distance. Show that when the object is at a distance u, the optimum diameter of the pinhole is $\{2\cdot 44\lambda uf/(u+f)\}^{\frac{1}{2}}$. This problem has been investigated in detail by Rayleigh. (See Reference 8.2.)]

8.7. Limit of Resolution for the Eye.

A theoretical limit of resolution for the eye may be calculated by inserting the diameter of the pupil in equation 8(1). The average diameter of the pupil in full daylight is about 2·5 millimetres, and the corresponding minimum angle of resolution (for light of wavelength 5500 Å.) is $2\cdot 7 \times 10^{-4}$ radian or 56 seconds of arc. Practical tests show that people with good sight can, under the most favourable conditions of observation, distinguish two point sources of light when the separation is a little less than one minute of arc. Thus under these conditions the ability of the eye to distinguish detail in an object is almost entirely determined by diffraction. If the pupil of the eye is made larger, either by the use of drugs or by lower illumination, the practical limit of resolution is no longer equal to the theoretical value calculated from 8(1). This is because lens aberrations and the structure of the retina then have important effects. Average laboratory conditions of observation are not ideal, and it is reasonable to assume a limit of resolution for point objects of about $3\cdot 4 \times 10^{-4}$ radian or 1·25 minutes of arc for laboratory work. If the point objects are situated at the nearest point of distinct vision (25 centimetres), the minimum linear separation required is a little less than a tenth of a millimetre. Objects which are separated by 0·2 millimetre are resolved comfortably.

8.8. Useful and Empty Magnification.

If the image formed by a telescope or microscope is not magnified enough, some detail of the object which is resolved by the instrument may not be seen by the eye. The detail may be correctly represented in the image formed by the instrument, but its size in that image may be so small that it cannot be resolved by the eye. For this reason it is desirable that the image shall be of sufficient size to make the smallest detail resolved by the instrument occupy a space of about 0·2 millimetre in the image seen by the eye. Magnification which gives an image up to this size is called *useful magnification*. Any magnification in excess is called *empty magnification* since it does not reveal any fresh detail in the object. Empty magnification is undesirable because it is usually accompanied by an increase in lens aberration and a reduction in the illumination of the field. The maximum useful magnification is therefore usually the optimum magnification. When an image is formed by a single lens, the resolving power depends on the diameter, and the size of the image depends upon the focal length. We have seen in § 8.5 that a lens whose diameter is 10 centimetres will resolve two stars whose angular separation is 1·4 seconds of arc. The distance between the images of these stars is equal to $6·7 \times 10^{-6}$ times the focal length of the lens. Thus, if no eyepiece were used, it would be necessary to have a lens of 30 metres focal length in order to obtain optimum viewing conditions. This length is so great that it is convenient to use an objective of much smaller focal length (say 3 metres) and then to use a magnifying eyepiece to view the image.

When an object is to be photographed, full detail will be represented in the photograph only if the distance between the images of points which are just resolved exceeds the spacing of the grains in the photographic plate. For certain plates, with a fairly coarse grain, the desirable size of image is about the same as that given in § 8.7. When fine-grain emulsions are used it is possible to use much lower magnification. The resulting photograph must, however, be viewed under magnification in order that the eye may perceive all the detail which is represented therein.

8.9. Resolving Power of a Prism Spectroscope.

When a line spectrum is formed by a spectroscope or spectrograph, the dispersing system (i.e. the prism or grating) forms an image of the slit corresponding to each line. Neighbouring lines give rise to images whose angular separation is small. Lines will be separated only if the angular separation of their images exceeds the limit of resolution of the telescope. The resolving power of a spectroscopic instrument is defined to be equal to $\lambda/\Delta\lambda$ when lines whose wavelengths are λ and $(\lambda + \Delta\lambda)$ are just resolved. Fig. 8.3 shows a simple prism spectroscope. Light from the slit S is collimated by the lens L_1 and plane waves (with wave surfaces parallel to AB) fall upon the prism LMN. The rays are refracted by different amounts in passing through the prism and the emergent wave surfaces are parallel to CE for wavelength λ, and to CE′ for wavelength λ'. The lens L_2 focuses the wavefront CE at Q and CE' at Q'. The thickness of the base of the prism is t_p and the refractive index of the material is μ for λ and μ' for λ'. The light is supposed to be restricted by a rectangular aperture whose width (CE) is equal to d. By Fermat's principle the total path from S

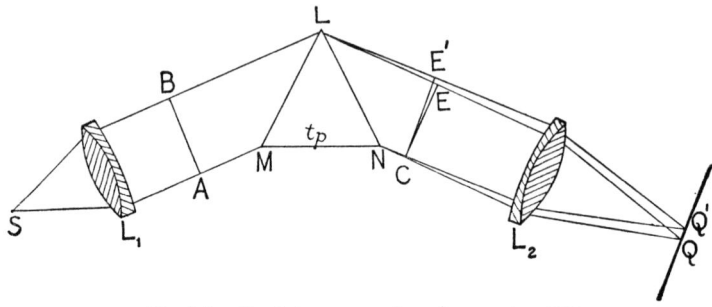

Fig. 8.3.—Resolving power of a prism spectroscope

to Q is the same for all rays of one wavelength, and the focal properties of the lenses imply that the paths S to A and S to B are equal. Similarly the paths C to Q and E to Q are equal. Hence we have for wavelength λ

$$BL + LE = AM + \mu(MN) + NC, \qquad 8(3)$$

and similarly for λ'

$$BL + LE' = AM + \mu'(MN) + NC. \qquad 8(4)$$

Hence
$$LE - LE' = (\mu - \mu')\,MN = t_p(\lambda - \lambda')\frac{d\mu}{d\lambda}. \qquad 8(5)$$

The angle between the emergent wave surfaces is $(LE - LE')/d$ and the minimum angle which the telescope can resolve is λ/d. Hence the two wavelengths are just resolved if

$$\frac{\lambda}{d} = (\lambda - \lambda')\frac{t_p}{d}\cdot\frac{d\mu}{d\lambda}, \qquad 8(6)$$

and the minimum difference of wavelength for resolution is given by the relation

$$R_p = \frac{\lambda}{\Delta\lambda} = t_p\frac{d\mu}{d\lambda}. \qquad 8(7)$$

It will be seen that although the resolving power of the prism is determined by reference to the aperture of the telescope, the thickness of the base of the prism is the only geometrical factor in the final result. This is so because the wavelength resolving power is determined partly by the aperture and partly by the angular dispersion. When the prism is not completely filled with light, t_p must be put equal to the difference of thickness at the places where the extreme rays traverse the prism. The resolving power is slightly different when the rays are restricted by a circular stop. This case has been treated by Struve, who has also considered the effect of finite length of the slit. In practice the stop is often approximately elliptical in shape.

8.10. Resolving Power of a Grating Spectroscope.

Suppose light of wavelengths λ and $(\lambda + \Delta\lambda)$ is diffracted in a certain direction θ by a grating containing N lines and of total width D. Then the path difference between portions of the wavefront which reach the focal point from opposite ends of the grating is $D \sin \theta$. If this direction corresponds to the principal maximum of order m for wavelength λ, and to one of the two neighbouring minima for $(\lambda + \Delta\lambda)$, then
$$mN\lambda = D \sin \theta = (mN - 1)(\lambda + \Delta\lambda),$$

and hence
$$R_g = \frac{\lambda}{\Delta\lambda} = mN. \quad \ldots \ldots \quad 8(8)$$

The above method of calculating the resolving power shows the similarity between the action of the grating and that of the prism. The result might also have been obtained directly from Table 6.1 (p. 183).

8.11.—Gratings up to 10 inches wide with 15,000 lines per inch have been constructed. A large grating thus has a resolving power of 150,000 in the first order. It is often practicable to use the third-order spectrum* in which the resolving power is nearly half a million, i.e. at 5000 Å. two lines whose wavelengths differ by 0·01 Å. can just be separated. The resolving power of prisms of convenient size is very much lower. It varies a good deal with wavelength and with the type of glass as well as with the thickness of the base. A flint glass prism of 5 centimetres base gives a resolving power of about 5000 at 6000 Å. and of about 12,000 at 4500 Å. A quartz prism of 5 centimetres base has a resolving power of 2000 at 6000 Å. and of 75,000 at 2000 Å. Owing to the very high dispersion of quartz in the ultra-violet, large quartz prisms have a resolving power which is not greatly inferior to that of a grating in the region 2500 Å. to 1850 Å. The prism instrument has the advantage that there is only one spectrum and no overlapping of orders.

* In some applications orders in the range 10–15 are now used.

8.12. The Rayleigh Limit of Aberration.*

In calculating the limits of resolution, no account was taken of imperfections of image due to imperfect *definition* in the instrument. It was assumed that all rays from the object points passed through the corresponding image points and hence that all optical paths from an object point to a corresponding image point were equal. In practice, this condition is not fulfilled exactly. It is therefore desirable to estimate how great the departures from this condition may become before they begin to reduce the sharpness of the image by a detectable amount. Rayleigh suggested that defects of image caused by inequalities of path up to a quarter of a wavelength should be small in comparison with the inescapable unsharpness due to diffraction, and that if the phase of the wavelets arriving from any part of the wavefront differed from that of the resultant by more than a quarter-period, then the image would be noticeably improved by correcting the corresponding part of the optical system. This estimate of the permissible tolerance may be applied to calculate limits for spherical and for chromatic aberration. It may also be used to estimate tolerances in the working of optical surfaces and in the homogeneity of optical materials (see §§ 9.11 and 9.12). It is now known that the permissible tolerance is not the same for all parts of a lens, and may be greater or less than the Rayleigh value. This value still forms a good initial working estimate.

EXAMPLES [8(iv)–8(x)]

8(iv). Calculate the resolving power of a prism of rocksalt of 4 cm. base at 4000 Å., 5000 Å., and 6000 Å., given the following data:

λ (Å.)	μ
6708	1·5400
6438	1·5412
5461	1·5477
4861	1·5537
4047	1·5665
3034	1·5988
2144	1·6737

[8600; 4400; 2500].

8(v). Derive an expression for the resolving power of a material which obeys Cauchy's law of dispersion (see § 3.18). When $A = 27 \times 10^{-5}$ and $B = 5·0 \times 10^{-11}$, plot a curve for the resolving power against wavelength of a prism whose base thickness is 6 cm. $\left[R_p = \dfrac{2t_p AB}{\lambda^3}. \right]$

* Reference 8.3.

8(vi). Using the data given in Example 8(iv), derive values for A and B applicable to the region 4000 Å. to 6000 Å. Hence, using the formula derived in Example 8(v), check the results calculated in Example 8(iv).

$$[A = 0.525; \ B = 1.30 \times 10^{-10}.]$$

8(vii). The ruled space on a grating is as wide as the base of a 60° rocksalt prism. It has the same resolving power in the first order as the prism has at 5000 Å. Calculate the size of the grating interval. $[9.1 \times 10^{-4} \text{ cm.}]$

8(viii). Show that if the diameter of the objective of a telescope is equal to that of the central half-period zone, little advantage is gained by using a lens because the telescope would function like a pinhole camera. Show that the useful length of the "pinhole telescope" tube increases in proportion to the square of the diameter of the "objective". Show that for a hole of 0·1 in. diameter the useful length is about 10 ft. and for one of 4 in. diameter the appropriate focal length is 3 miles!

[The useful length is that which gives the maximum useful magnification (see § 8.8)].

8(ix). Applying the limit stated in § 8.12, show that the depth of focus of a lens of diameter d (when the object is very far from the lens) is

$$\delta f = \frac{4f^2 \lambda}{d^2}. \qquad \ldots \ldots \ldots \quad 8(9)$$

[Assume that all the paths to the true focus are equal. Calculate the difference of path between a ray passing through the centre and one coming from the edge of the lens to a point distant δf from the true focus and situated on the axis of the lens. The calculation is given by Rayleigh.*]

8(x). Show that, if a prism and a grating have equal resolving powers at wavelength λ, then (assuming Cauchy's law, § 3.18) $2t = mn\lambda^3/AB$.

8.13. Purity of a Spectrum obtained with White Light

Suppose that a vertical slit is placed in the spectrum of a white-light source formed by means of a prism or grating spectroscope, and that the light which passes through the slit is examined in a second spectroscope of higher dispersion and resolving power. It is found that the light transmitted by the first instrument covers a certain range of wavelength. When the slit is fairly wide the range of wavelength is approximately proportional to the width of the slit. When this width is gradually decreased, the range of wavelength transmitted reaches a constant value not dependent on the width of the slit, which then affects only the total amount of light transmitted. This constant minimum range of wavelength is an inverse measure of the *purity* of the spectrum. If the instrument is free from aberrations, it is determined by the resolving power. Each wavelength in the light incident upon the first spectroscope forms a Fraunhofer diffraction pattern of the slit. The light of any one wavelength is spread over a finite region

* Reference 8.4.

in the spectrum. Consequently, the light reaching any one point in the spectrum is not entirely of one wavelength, but includes a range of wavelengths. The range of wavelength reaching a given point (with appreciable energy) is of the order of $2\Delta\lambda_R$, where $\Delta\lambda_R$ is the minimum wavelength difference which can be resolved. The purity of the spectrum is inversely proportional to $\Delta\lambda_R$ and is proportional to the resolving power. Thus a *pure spectrum* in which every point corresponds to one and only one wavelength, is an ideal concept which cannot be realized in practice. An instrument of infinite resolving power would be required to produce such a spectrum. In any actual spectrum the light passing any given point is represented by a wave group, not by an infinitely long simple-harmonic wave train. The effective number of wavelengths in the wave train produced by putting a very narrow slit into the spectrum is approximately $\lambda/\Delta\lambda_R$, i.e. it is equal to the resolving power of the instrument (see § 4.21 and also Appendix IV B, §§ 10–14).

8.14.—In the two preceding paragraphs we have assumed that white light may be " analysed " by Fourier's methods into components of different wavelengths. As explained in § 4.33, it was at one time contended that white light " consisted " of a series of irregular pulses, and the validity of analysis was questioned. It is of historical interest to see how the formation of a spectrum with white light can be discussed without analysis. The formation of monochromatic light from an irregular pulse by a grating is explained on the assumption that each clear space of the grating transmits a single small pulse. At a given place in the spectrum these pulses arrive at regular intervals. These intervals correspond to the differences of path from the different elements to the given point, and in a first-order spectrum the path differences between paths from successive spaces are equal to the wavelength whose principal maximum is situated at the given point. Thus a disturbance of the frequency corresponding to that wavelength is produced. Also the number of waves in the wave train is equal to the number of elements in the grating, i.e. to the resolving power of the grating in the first order. The formation of an approximately simple-harmonic wave train in this way has been compared to the reflection of an irregular noise, such as a handclap, from a flight of steps. An observer situated in a suitable position hears, as an echo, not the original sound but a definite note produced by the successive arrivals of reflections from the different steps. Rayleigh* has considered the problem of how a prism which possesses no periodic structure of its own may yet give rise to regular trains of waves.

8.15.—In Chapter V it was shown that in general interference fringes are obtained with white light only when the path difference is small (or when some special achromatizing arrangement is used). It was stated that, if a spectroscope is placed to receive light from a point corresponding to a high order of interference, channelled spectra may be obtained even though no interference effects can be observed with a nonselective receptor. Obviously the " bands " will be observed

* Reference 8.5.

§ 8.16 RESOLVING POWER—ETALON

only if the wavelength difference between successive maxima is greater than the minimum difference resolved by the spectroscope. From equations 5(17) and 5(18) we see that the wavelength difference is λ/n, where n is the order of interference at the point from which light is taken. It follows that the bands are seen only when the resolving power is greater than the order of interference.

8.16. Resolving Power of the Fabry-Pérot Etalon.

The energy distribution in the pattern produced by this instrument is given in equation 5(14) and is shown graphically in fig. 8.4. The distribution differs from that given by a diffraction grating in that the subsidiary maxima of the diffraction pattern have been smoothed out. Reference to the theory of the etalon (§ 5.26) shows

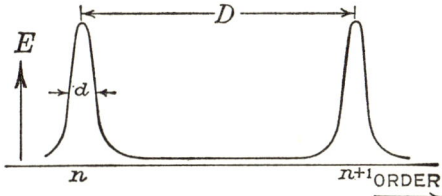

Fig. 8.4.—Energy distribution in Fabry-Pérot pattern

that this occurs because the interfering beams from the etalon are of gradually decreasing amplitude, whereas those from the grating are of equal amplitude. From equation 5(14) it is possible to calculate the difference in wavelength between two lines when there is a " 20 per cent dip " in the pattern which they jointly produce. Reference to equation 5(12) shows that the whole scale of the pattern (including this critical distance) is inversely proportional to $2e/\lambda$ (where e is the separation of the plates). The resolving power ($\lambda/\Delta\lambda$) is thus proportional to the separation, i.e. to the order of interference. The resolving power also depends, in a rather complicated way, on the reflection coefficient of the plates. It is possible to regard the series of beams produced by the etalon as equivalent to a certain number of beams of *equal* amplitude. The equivalent number N is defined by the relation $N(2e/\lambda) = R$, where R is the resolving power of the etalon. N is equal to the number of steps in a reflecting echelon which would give the same resolving power and the same order of interference. The equivalent number N is a function of the reflection coefficient. It can be calculated from 5(14), but the calculation is not very simple and graphical methods of computation are useful. Some results calculated by Hansen[*] are shown in fig. 8.5. The theoretical resolving power

---

[*] Reference 8.7.

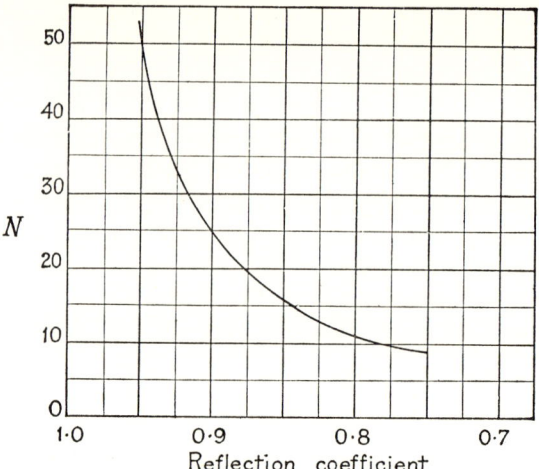

Fig. 8.5.—Resolving power of Fabry-Pérot etalon (theoretical)

will be obtained in practice only if the plates are plane to within a deviation of order λ/N, i.e. for high-reflection films $\lambda/50$.

Fig. 8.6 shows the results of some measurements for films of different

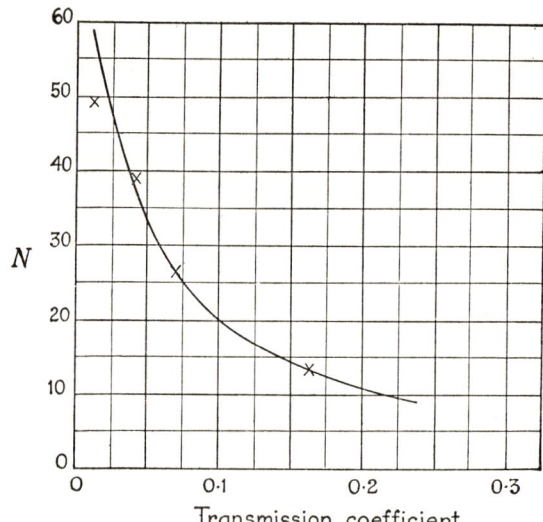

Fig. 8.6.—Resolving power of Fabry-Pérot etalon (crosses represent experimental results; the line represents theoretical values, calculated for an absorption of 4 per cent).

transmissions.* These results cannot be directly compared with the calculated values because the absorption is not known exactly. They do, however, show that very sharp fringes, i.e. very high effective reflection coefficients, can be obtained and they agree with the calculated values of N if we assume an absorption of about 4 per cent. It may be seen that the resolving power increases rapidly as the reflection coefficient increases. If, however, the thickness of the film is increased beyond a certain point in order to increase the reflection coefficient, the amount of light transmitted becomes inconveniently small. There is thus an optimum thickness of film for practical purposes. In practice films of reflection coefficient about 0·85 are used for measurement in the visible region of the spectrum.

8.17. Resolving Power of a Microscope.

In the preceding discussion of resolving power it has been assumed that the light from the two objects is non-coherent, so that the illumination at any point due to the two sources acting jointly is the sum of the illuminations due to the separate sources (see § 5.2). This assump-

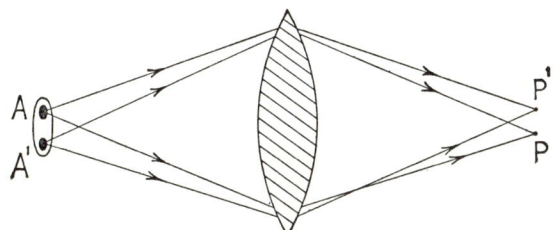

Fig. 8.7.—Illumination of an object by a condenser

tion is clearly justified when the two objects are stars, and when they are images of a slit formed by light of slightly different wavelength. When a microscope is focused on a self-luminous object (such as the incandescent filament of an electric light), the radiation from different parts of the object is non-coherent. An object which is not self-luminous must be illuminated by a source of light and no real source is confined to a mathematical point. A condenser is used to form a more or less sharply focused image of the source in the object plane. Owing to diffraction, a point P of the object receives light from a finite area (A) of the source (see fig. 8.7). The light vector at P is the resultant of wavelets from all parts of A. Similarly, the light vector at P' is the

* Reference 8.8.

resultant of wavelets from an area A'. If the source is sharply focused, and if P and P' are well separated, the areas A and A' do not overlap, and the light at P' is not coherent with that at P. In considering the performance of microscopes, we are usually concerned with points which are close together, and the areas A and A' then overlap to a considerable extent so that the light is at least partially coherent. When P and P' are so close that they are just resolved, the light is effectively coherent. We shall consider the resolution of two objects (a) when the light is completely non-coherent, and (b) when it is completely coherent. Condition (a) applies to self-luminous objects. The illumination of ordinary microscopic objects is not completely coherent, but under practical conditions it may be assumed that the illumination at two points which are just resolved is coherent.

8.18. Resolution with Non-coherent Illumination.

When the illumination is non-coherent, the calculation of the minimum distance between two points whose images are just resolved differs very little from the corresponding calculation for the telescope. For a rectangular aperture the result may be obtained in the following

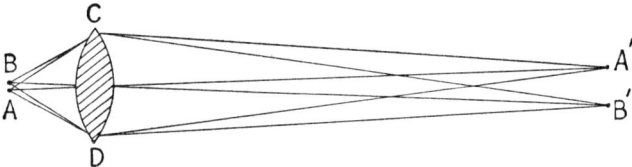

Fig. 8.8.—Resolving power of the microscope

way. Let A and B (fig. 8.8) be two points in the field of a microscope which is represented in the diagram by the lens CD. Let A' and B' be the image points corresponding to A and B which are at equal distances from the axis of the lens CD. Then all paths from A to A' are equal and the extreme difference of paths from A to B' is equal to 2(AC–AD). From the geometry of the figure, this difference is equal to 2AB sin α, where α is half the angle subtended at the object by the microscope objective. This extreme difference of path is equal to the wavelength (λ') when the distance between the objects is equal to $\lambda'/(2 \sin \alpha)$. The entire difference of path is situated in the medium between the objective and the object. Let μ be the refractive index of this medium (with respect to air) and λ the wavelength of the light (in air). Then the distance between points which are just resolved (according to the Rayleigh criterion) is given by

$$y = \frac{\lambda'}{2 \sin \alpha} = \frac{\lambda}{2\mu \sin \alpha}. \qquad \ldots \quad 8(10)$$

When the aperture is circular, the size of the Airy disc has to be calculated, allowing for the fact that the object is near to the lens. When this is done,* the distance between two points which are just resolved is found to be about 20 per cent greater than that given by 8(10).

8.19. Abbe Theory.

The theory of resolution with coherent illumination was developed by Ernst Abbe (1840–1905). His work was of great importance in the development of modern high-power microscopes. It leads to a general

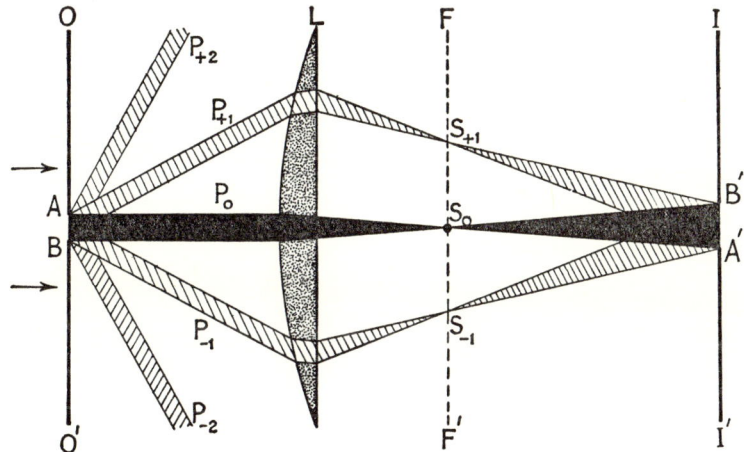

Fig. 8.9a.—Formation of images by the microscope

method of assessing the performance of lens systems. This method is applicable, with appropriate modifications, both for coherent and for non-coherent illumination.

Let us first consider the formation of the image of a plane grating which is illuminated with a coherent beam of light in a direction parallel to the axis of the lens L (fig. 8.9). A Fraunhofer diffraction pattern is formed in the focal plane of the lens (FF'). The same light which

---

* See RAYLEIGH: *Journal of Royal Microscopical Society*, 1903, Vol. 23, p. 460. Rayleigh does not quite complete the computation, but the result follows from his equations 17–21.

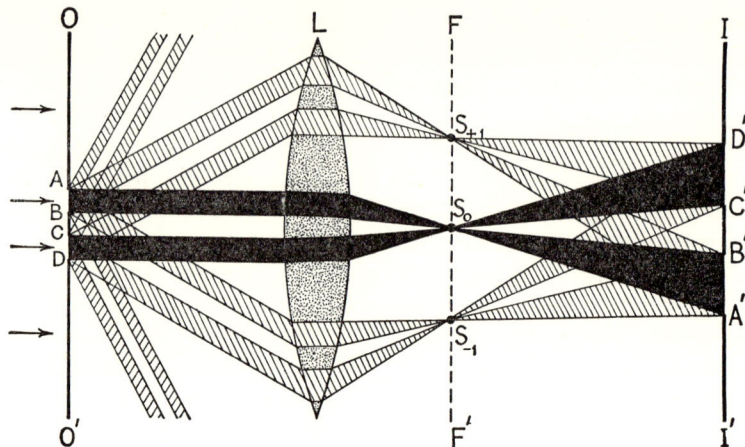

Fig. 8.9b.—Formation of images by the microscope

forms the diffraction pattern on FF' gives a focused image on II'. In figs. 8.9a and 8.9b we show the rays corresponding to light which forms the principal maxima in the diffraction pattern. For simplicity only the rays from one space are shown in fig. 8.9a and from two spaces in fig. 8.9b. In fig. 8.10 the grating is assumed to have a large number

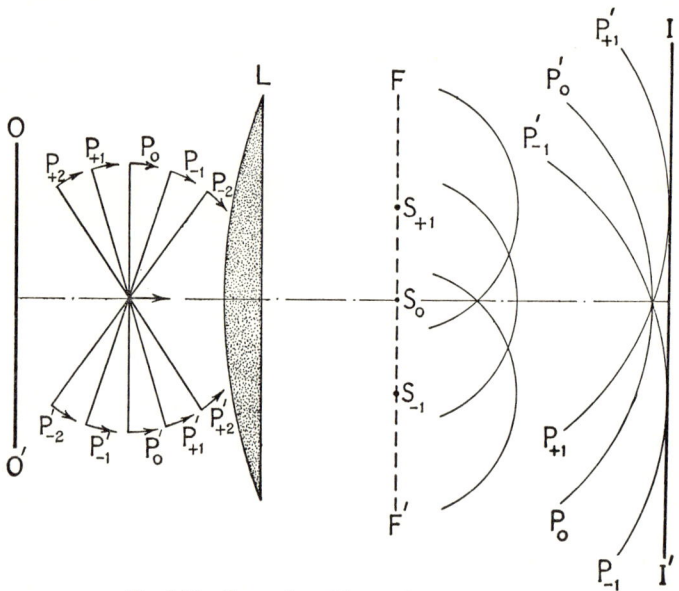

Fig. 8.10.—Formation of images by the microscope

of lines and the diffracted light is represented by the wavefronts P_0, P_{-1}, P_{+1}, etc. These plane waves become approximately spherical waves, centred on S_0, S_{-1}, S_{+1}, after passing the lens L. They interfere to form the focused image on the plane II'. These diagrams are useful in helping to form a mental picture of the way in which the lens forms both a Fraunhofer diffraction pattern in the plane FF' and an image in the plane II', but it must be understood that they show only the most important rays and wavefronts. The diffracted light is not confined to the rays shown and does not all pass through the points S_0, S_{-1}, S_{+1}. Since, however, a large part of the energy does pass near to these points, we may regard the light as divided into a set of spectra represented by the plane wavefronts, provided that we understand that the spectrum of each order includes all the energy passing near to S_0, S_{-1}, S_{+1}, etc.

8.20.—Abbe's theory is based on the fact that an observer viewing the plane II' from the right can obtain information about the object on the plane OO' only through light which has passed the plane FF', i.e. through the light included in the spectra. He says that, if some of the spectra corresponding to waves P_0, P_{-1}, P_{+1}, etc., are not transmitted by the instrument, then the image will correspond to a grating for which the absent spectra have zero energy. To take an extreme case, suppose that only the spectrum of zero order is transmitted. This maximum would be given by a wide aperture, uniformly illuminated, in the plane OO'. Accordingly the observer sees uniform illumination on the image plane. The central maximum alone gives no resolution of detail.

Pursuing this idea Abbe suggested that, if the aperture of a microscope is not sufficiently wide to include all the diffraction spectra from an object, details in the object may be absent and, under certain conditions, false detail may appear. This last conclusion was strongly resisted by microscopists. Abbe proved his case by a long series of experiments in which he inserted stops into the microscope so as to exclude certain spectra, and showed that false detail appeared. For example, suppose that the object is a grating with a spacing of a few wavelengths and that the clear spaces are fairly narrow. Several spectra contain appreciable energy and stops may be inserted to cut out the spectra of odd orders. The remaining spectra correspond to an object of half the spacing and the image plane contains an image in which each true line appears to be divided into two. When a microscope is working at a high numerical aperture, very small errors in focus will cause some of the spectra to fall on to stops. This may not only lead to loss of detail but may also cause the appearance of false detail. This point is of some practical importance because with certain types of object it is not possible to know when the object is truly in focus. The assumption that the best focus is the one which shows the most detail is not always justified.

A. B. Porter gave a striking practical demonstration of the effect of obstructing some spectra using a piece of wire gauze of about 0·3 millimetre spacing. The gauze G (fig. 8.11) forms a series of spectra in a rectangular pattern. These spectra are formed on a screen S_1 very

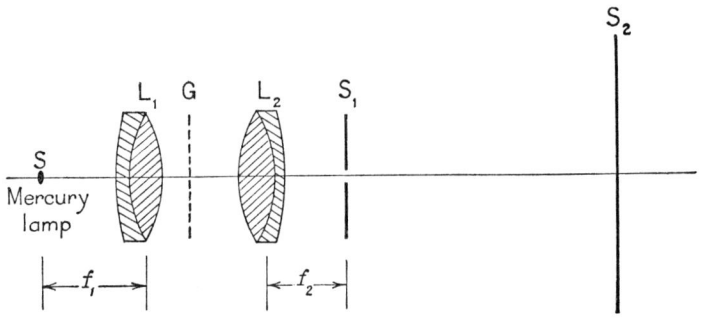

Fig. 8.11.—Porter's experiment (L_1 acts as a condenser. L_2 gives spectra on S_1 and image on S_2)

close together, and by cutting small holes in the screen different sets of spectra may be allowed to pass. An image is formed by the lens L_2 on the screen S_2. If a slit is used to exclude all the spectra except those on a horizontal line through the central image, then only vertical wires are seen. If the slit is turned through a right angle, then only the horizontal wires are seen. Perhaps the most striking effect is produced by using two slits in the form of a cross. If this is set with its lines at 45° to the lines of the gauze, it allows the diagonal spectra to pass. The eye then " sees " the gauze but with its lines turned through 45°.

8.21.—We have considered Abbe's theory in its application to objects which have a periodic structure. We obtained a limiting distance of resolution by considering the angular separation of the " spectra " produced by a grating of alternate transparent and opaque spaces. The principal maxima occur in directions given by $\sin \theta = n\lambda'/y$ when the source of illumination is a parallel beam of light travelling in the direction of the axis of the microscope, where y is the distance between successive lines of the grating, λ' is the wavelength between the grating and objective, and λ the corresponding wavelength in vacuum. We assume that the points are not resolved unless at least two spectra enter the microscope. This will occur only if

$$y > \frac{\lambda'}{\sin \alpha}, \quad \text{i.e.} \quad y > \frac{\lambda}{\mu \sin \alpha}. \qquad \ldots \quad 8(11)$$

When the illumination is at an angle θ', the spectra occur in directions given by

$$\sin \theta - \sin \theta' = \frac{n\lambda'}{y}$$

if the illumination is such that the direct light (spectrum of zero order) and the first-order spectrum on one side just enter the microscope, then $\alpha = \theta = -\theta'$ and

$$y > \frac{\lambda}{2\mu \sin \alpha}. \qquad \ldots \ldots \quad 8(12)$$

Thus, according to the Abbe theory in its simplest form, the minimum distance between resolved points is reduced by a factor of two when oblique illumination is substituted for axial illumination.* This conclusion is verified approximately by experiment. Following Abbe, the number $\mu \sin \alpha$ is called the *numerical aperture* (N).

8.22.—The following account of the delineation of detail in an image formed by a microscope was given by Johnstone Stoney† in the course of an exposition of the Abbe theory. We may imagine the object plane to be crossed by a series of fine gratings set at various angles to one another. The amount of light in the different gratings varies in such a way that together they make up an approximation to the pattern of light in the object plane. Each grating is approximately reproduced (on an enlarged scale) in the image plane if the corresponding spectra are collected. The finest grating for which this can occur is one whose spacing is given by 8(11) or 8(12), according to the type of illumination. Accordingly the image includes only such details as can be formed by the superposition of gratings of this (or greater) spacing. Obviously, the order of magnitude of the detail which can be seen clearly is given by 8(11) or 8(12). If the object is of low contrast, resolution will be more difficult than if it is " black on white ". It will be understood that there is no limit to the smallness of an object which can be seen when sufficient light is available. Objects whose sizes are much smaller than the limit of resolution can be seen

---

* For a detailed investigation of the effect on the resolving power of the direction of illumination, see Reference 8.15.

† Reference 8.6.

by the light which they scatter, but they are seen as discs of light. No detail is observed, and in so far as one of these discs has a defined boundary its limits are defined by 8(11) or 8(12) and not by the size of the object.

8.23. Optimum Magnification.

The above discussion may be extended to a system of magnification M by introducing for the image plane a co-ordinate system whose unit is $1/M$ times that of the co-ordinate system in the object plane. The limit of resolution is independent of the magnification except in so far as $\sin \alpha$ is altered if the object moves with respect to the optical system. Other things being equal, it is likely that aberrations will increase if extremely high magnification is attempted. There is therefore an optimum magnification for a microscope which is to be used visually.

With a dry lens, the maximum value of the numerical aperture is 1·0, and values up to 0·95 have been attained. Oil-immersion objectives with numerical apertures up to 1·45 have been constructed. The minimum distance between points which are just resolved is thus $2·9 \times 10^{-5}$ centimetre for a dry lens and $1·9 \times 10^{-5}$ centimetre for an oil-immersion lens using oblique illumination and a wavelength of 5500 Å. The *maximum useful magnification* (see § 8.8) is thus about 800 for a dry lens, and 1200 for an oil-immersion lens.

It is possible to reduce the limit of microscopic resolution by photographing the object with ultra-violet radiation of wavelength about 2200 Å. The limit of resolution is then about 1000 Å. or 0·1 μ. The microscope and slides must be constructed of materials transparent to radiation of this wavelength and the optical system must be specially corrected for the wavelength used. The photograph may be enlarged to give an overall magnification of about 3000. Very much higher magnifications have been obtained using electron microscopes. In these instruments the effective wavelength may be of the order of 0·1 Å., but the numerical aperture of models so far available is very low, being only of the order of 0·01. The theoretical limit of resolution is thus of the order of 10 Å. The useful magnification is in the region of 300,000. There are many difficulties in connection with the use of these instruments, and many technical problems concerning the preparation of specimens and the interpretation of results remain to be solved. Further discussion of these matters is outside the scope of this book.*

8.24. Ray Theory and Wave Theory of Aberrations.

Consider the formation of the image of a point O on the axis of a thin lens of large aperture. When the angles of refraction are calculated exactly (without the approximations of equation 7(1)) it is found that the emergent rays do not meet in a point but form a bundle

* Reference 8.12.

as shown in fig. 8.12. The emergent wavefront (calculated by drawing rays through the lens and computing optical paths) is not spherical. In ray theory the deviation of any ray from the Gaussian image point (obtained by tracing paraxial rays) constitutes its aberration. The

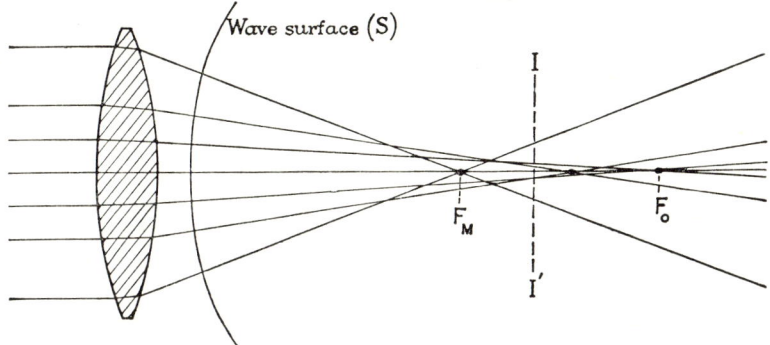

Fig. 8.12.—Positive spherical aberration (ray diagram)

distance $F_0 F_M$ in fig. 8.12 is called the longitudinal spherical aberration. In wave theory the aberration is described by an *aberration function W*, which is the distance (measured along a ray) between the actual wave-surface and a *reference sphere*. The sphere which touches

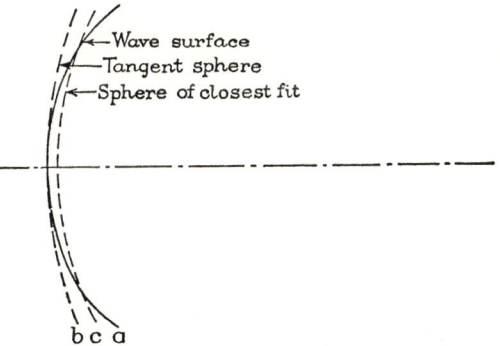

Fig. 8.13.—Positive spherical aberration: (*a*) wave surface, (*b*) tangent sphere at axis, (*c*) sphere of closest fit. Note that centre and radius of (*a*) both differ from those of (*c*). Either (*b*) or (*c*) may be chosen as reference sphere.

the surface at the axis, and whose centre is the Gaussian image point, may be taken as reference sphere, but sometimes it is convenient to choose some other sphere, e.g. the sphere which most closely fits the actual surface (see fig. 8.13). The aberration along a given path may be expressed as a multiple of the wavelength.

When the aberration function W is known, the distribution of light in the image plane may be calculated using Kirchhoff's equation (§ 6.32). The first calculations of this type were due to Rayleigh (1879) and Strehl (1893).

8.25.—The ray theory and the wave theory of aberration are related through Fermat's principle since, if all emergent rays meet in a point, the corresponding paths from object point to image point are equal and the emergent wave-front is a sphere. At one time lens designers considered only the rays. In fig. 8.12 there is a moderately well-defined constriction of rays in the region of the plane II'. The intersection of limiting rays with this plane is called the *circle of least confusion*. The distribution of light across this plane may be estimated from the concentration of rays (if the lens is divided by a single grid into equal small areas and one ray is drawn through each). This method gives the designer useful information when the circle of confusion is large compared with the Airy disc but can be misleading when the optical system is so good that the loss of detail due to diffraction is comparable with the loss due to aberration.

8.26. Theory of Aberrations.*

The detailed theory of aberrations involves laborious algebra, and it is easy to lose sight of the physical principles. In the following paragraphs wave theory is used with a minimum of formulæ to classify the aberrations, and the effects (on the image) of different types of aberration are described.† Let P'Q'T' be the image (calculated from paraxial optics) of a linear object PQT (fig. 8.14). Consider a path from Q to Q' which intersects the emergent wavefront in A'. Let Q' be specified by $\sigma = \mathrm{P'Q'/P'T'}$ and A' by the co-ordinate ϕ (i.e. the angle between the plane A'Q'P' and the plane PP'Q') and the co-ordinate $r = h/h_0$, where h is the distance of A from the line OQ' and h_0 is the maximum value of h. Then the aberration function W will be a function of r, σ, and ϕ. When the aperture and the height of the image are not very large, W may be expanded in a power series. Symmetry considerations show that certain of the terms in a general power series do not occur, and that others are zero when the reference sphere is correctly centred. For example when $\sigma = 0$, the whole system is symmetrical about the axes, so that only even powers of r can occur. The term in r^2 is zero if the reference sphere is centred correctly, so

---

* §§ 8.26–8.43 may be omitted on first reading.
† For more detailed treatment see Reference 8.24.

that the aberrations depend on r^4, r^6, etc. It is found that, with a suitable choice of reference sphere, W may be written

$$W = (_0c_{40}\, r^4 + {}_1c_{31}\, \sigma r^3 \cos \phi + {}_2c_{22}\, \sigma^2 r^2 \cos^2 \phi \\ + {}_2c_{20}\, \sigma^2 r^2 + {}_3c_{11}\, \sigma^3 r \cos \phi) + {}_0c_{60}\, r^6 + \ldots, \text{etc.} \qquad 8(13)$$

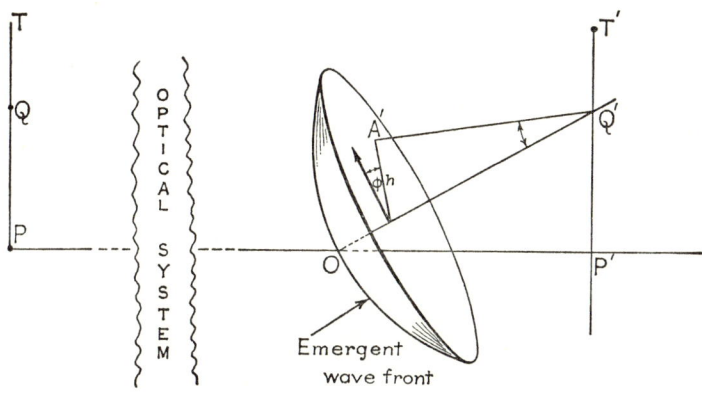

Fig. 8.14

In this equation, the subscripts of the coefficients correspond with powers of r, σ, and $\cos \phi$. Note that all terms are derived from the rotational invariants σ^2, r^2 and $r\sigma \cos \phi$ and that, for all terms in the bracket, the sum of the powers of r and σ is 4.

8.27. Spherical Aberration.

When $\sigma = 0$, the aberration reduces to

$$W = {}_0c_{40}\, r^4 + {}_0c_{60}\, r^6 + \cdots \qquad \ldots \quad 8(14)$$

This aberration, which is known as spherical aberration, does not depend on the distance of the image point from the axis. The aberration represented by the term $_0c_{40}\, r^4$ (which is dominant when the aperture is small) is called *primary spherical aberration*, that represented by the next term is called secondary spherical aberration, and so on. The primary aberrations are often called Seidel aberrations after Von Seidel who first investigated the ray theory of these aberrations. * The image formed is qualitatively similar to the Airy pattern

---

* Unfortunately Von Seidel's theory and the aberrations involved are sometimes called " third order " because they involve the θ^3 term in the expansion of sin θ.

obtained in the absence of aberration, but there is much less light in the centre, and rings of appreciable intensity extend farther out.*

8.28. Comatic Aberration.

The aberration represented by the term $_1c_{31}\,\sigma r^3 \cos\phi$ is called *primary coma*. Higher-order comatic aberrations are represented by other terms involving odd powers of $\cos\phi$. This aberration gives rise to flared images as shown† in fig. 8.15. It is the first aberration to

(a)   (b)   (c)

Fig. 8.15.—Comatic flare
(a) No aberration. (b) Small amount of coma. (c) Larger amount of coma.

manifest itself for objects a little off-axis, because it is the only one involving the first power of r.

It is possible to set a crosswire fairly accurately in the centre of an image which has been symmetrically broadened by spherical aberration. The effect of coma on the measurement of the separation of images in a photograph of a stellar field is much more serious because there is no identifiable centre in the comatic flare.

8.29. Astigmatism and Curvature of Field.

The aberration represented by $_2c_{22}\,\sigma^2 r^2 \cos^2\phi$ is known as *primary astigmatism*; higher orders are represented by other terms involving even powers of $\cos\phi$. This term (which depends on r^2) increases re-

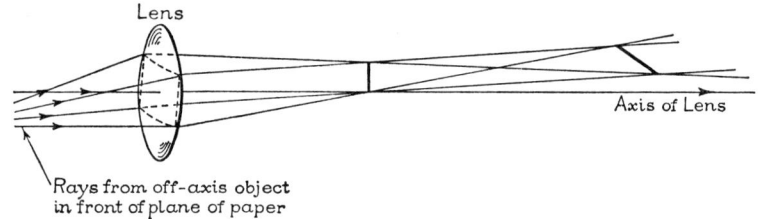

Fig. 8.16.—Focal lines (astigmatism)

lative to coma as r increases. It is shown in Reference 8.24 that a term involving r^2 corresponds to a change in curvature of the wavefront. It thus appears that when positive astigmatism is present, the

---

* For photographs of images with aberrations see Plate II (p. 48) of Reference 8.23.
† See also Plate III (p. 80) of Reference 8.23.

curvature of the wavefront in the *sagittal plane* (for which $\phi = 0$) is higher than the curvature in a *tangential plane* ($\phi = \pi/2$). If astigmatism alone is present the section of the wavefront in the tangential plane is a circle whose centre is at Q′, and we obtain a line focus in the Gaussian plane. The section of the wavefront in the sagittal plane has a higher curvature and comes to a line focus nearer to the lens (see fig. 8.16). Since the aberration is proportional to σ^2 (i.e. to the square of the distance of the image point from the axis) the distance of the

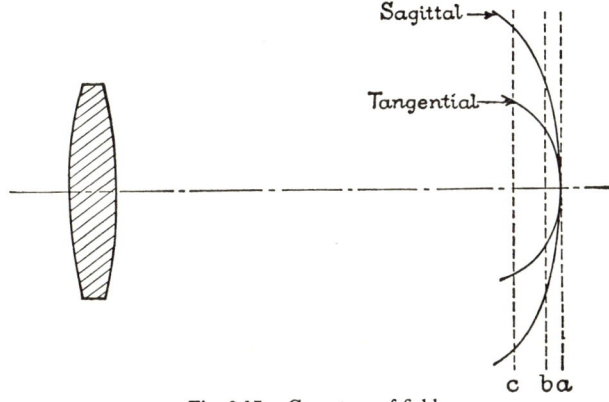

Fig. 8.17.—Curvature of field

sagittal focal line from the Gaussian plane increases as the image point moves away from the axis, i.e. the sagittal lines lie on a curved surface—as shown in fig. 8.17.

Astigmatism is nearly always accompanied by field curvature, which is represented by the term $_2c_{20}\,\sigma^2 r^2$. The additional curvature represented by this term applies equally to the sagittal and to the tangential foci; both line foci are on curved surfaces nearer to the lens than the Gaussian image plane (see fig. 8.17).

8.30.—The effect of astigmatism and field curvature may be seen by considering the images of the pattern shown in fig. 8.18. As a screen is moved towards the lens a clear image appears in the centre when it reaches the Gaussian image plane. When it has reached the position represented by b in fig. 8.17, the circle is in focus (see fig. 8.18b) because a slight spread in the tangential direction does not matter. The radial lines are clearest farther out where the plane cuts the curve of sagittal focus. When the plane is still nearer, a second circle and radials still further out come into focus.

DEFECTS OF OPTICAL IMAGES

It is possible to design a combination of lenses so that astigmatism is very small but field curvature remains. Both line foci come together to one true focus lying on a curved surface. The curvature which remains when the power is the same for both tangential and sagittal lines and for all zones of the lens is called *Petzval curvature*.* It may be shown that the difference between curvature in the tangential plane and the Petzval curvature is three times the difference between the curvature in the sagittal plane and the Petzval curvature.

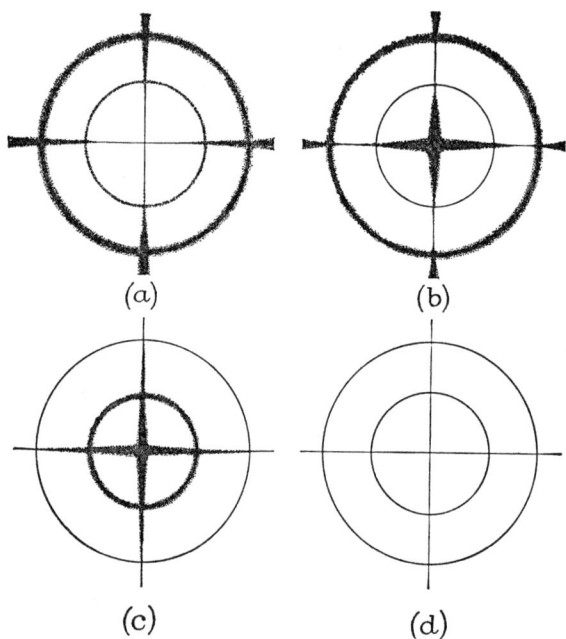

Fig. 8.18.—(d) is the object. (a), (b) and (c) show the images found in the planes a, b and c respectively, marked on fig. 8.17.

8.31. Distortion.

If all other aberrations have been eliminated and the term $_3c_{11}\,\sigma^3 r \cos\phi$ remains, the image point is well defined but is displaced from the Gaussian image point in a direction away from the centre by an amount proportional to the cube of its distance from the centre; so that when $_3c_{11}$ is positive, the effective magnification increases in the outer parts of the field to give *pin-cushion distortion* (fig. 8.19b). When the coefficient is negative we obtain *barrel distortion* (fig. 8.19a). Large amounts of distortion spoil an ordinary camera photograph, but small amounts are tolerated. However, in

* J. Petzval, Hungarian mathematician (1807–91).

survey measurements from aerial photographs correction for even small amounts of distortion is important.

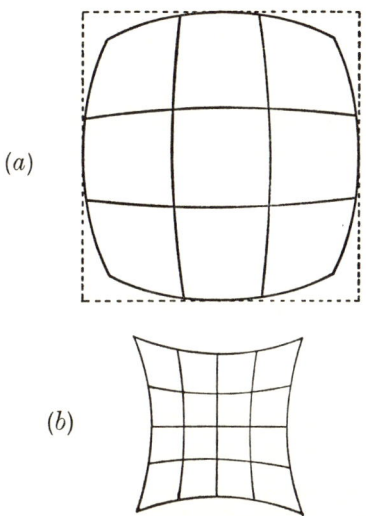

Fig. 8.19.—Distortion: (a) barrel distortion, (b) pincushion distortion

8.32. Chromatic Effects.

The chromatic aberration for paraxial rays has already been discussed (§ 7.23 ff.). The chromatic difference for marginal rays is not necessarily the same as that for paraxial rays. This effect may be treated as an additional chromatic aberration, so that the total chromatic aberration consists of a constant term plus terms which depend on r and σ. The constant term is the paraxial chromatic aberration. Alternatively, the additional effect may be regarded as chromatic variation of the Seidel aberrations (i.e. as a variation of the coefficients $_0c_{40}$, etc., with wavelength) so that we find, for example, that when spherical aberration has been corrected for one wavelength it is not necessarily corrected for all wavelengths. This chromatic effect is significant in high-power eyepieces and very important in high-power microscope objectives. An apochromatic objective is corrected for spherical aberration at two wavelengths.

8.33. Optical Transfer Function.

We now consider an assessment of optical systems based on an analogy with an electrical transmission system. A signal introduced at one end of a transmission system may be analysed by Fourier methods into a number of sinusoidal components of different frequencies. If the system is linear, each sinusoidal term in the input is reproduced in the output without distortion, but different frequencies are attenuated by different factors, so that the overall waveform which represents the output is usually different from that which represents the input. The curve of attenuation versus frequency is called the *frequency response function*.

In a similar way, light leaving the object plane may be analysed into a number of spatial frequencies (§ 3.31) each of which represents one of the " gratings " discussed in § 8.22. Provided that certain conditions (which will be discussed in Appendix VIII A) are fulfilled, each spatial frequency is transmitted without distortion. The curve of attenuation factor versus spatial frequency is called the *optical transfer function*. There is always a critical frequency above which the response is zero. Light corresponding to higher spatial frequencies is diffracted outside the optical system. The critical frequency is proportional to the numerical aperture. We shall see that the transfer function constitutes a better evaluation of the performance of the optical system than a statement of the resolving power.

8.34.—Suppose that the distribution of energy in the plane $z = 0$ immediately to the right of the object is, as shown in fig. 8.20,

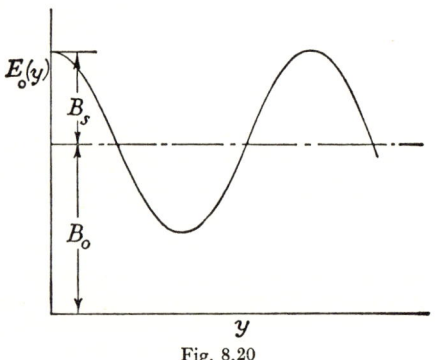

Fig. 8.20

$$E_0(y) = B(0) + B(s) \cos sy, \qquad \ldots \quad 8(15)$$

where s represents the spatial frequency. It is convenient to choose as unit of spatial frequency, the value $\kappa_c = N\kappa$ (where N is the numerical aperture); so that s is related to the spatial frequency κ_y by the equation

$$s = \frac{\kappa_y}{N\kappa} = \frac{\kappa_y}{\kappa_c}. \qquad \ldots \ldots \quad 8(16)$$

The distribution 8(15) represents a sinusoidal distribution of energy whose *contrast* is defined to be

$$A(s) = B(s)/B(0). \qquad \ldots \ldots \quad 8(17)$$

The total energy integrated over a whole number of "grating intervals" is proportional to $B(0)$.

The distribution of energy in the image plane is

$$E_i(y') = B'(0) + B'(s)\cos sy', \quad \ldots \quad 8(18a)$$

and the contrast is

$$A'(s) = B'(s)/B'(0). \quad \ldots \quad 8(18b)$$

Since we are not now concerned with the fraction of energy transmitted but only with the loss of contrast, we *normalize* both 8(15) and 8(18a), i.e. we divide through by appropriate constants to obtain

$$E_{ON}(y) = 1 + A(s)\cos sy, \quad \ldots \quad 8(19a)$$

$$E_{IN}(y') = 1 + A'(s)\cos sy', \quad \ldots \quad 8(19b)$$

or

$$E_{IN}(y') = 1 + D(s)A(s)\cos sy', \quad \ldots \quad 8(19c)$$

where $D(s)$ is the ratio of the contrast in the image to the contrast in the object. It is called the *optical transfer factor* for frequency s. In general many terms such as $A(s)\cos sy$ will be needed, and it may be necessary to use a Fourier integral (Appendix VIII A).

8.35.—In practice there is seldom complete phase coherence for all points in an object, and there is seldom complete non-coherence for points which are so close that they are just resolved in the image formed by a good lens.* Nevertheless, it is convenient to discuss the two extreme cases of complete coherence and complete non-coherence. Fig. 8.21a shows a system of illumination which gives a high degree of mutual coherence between light from different object points. Fig. 8.21b shows a system which gives a low degree of coherence for points which are resolved. Note that the arrangement shown in fig. 8.21a gives a high degree of coherence only when the hole in D is fairly small (see p. 522 of Reference 6.1).

For each kind of illumination, spectra are formed approximately in the plane FF', which is in the focal plane of the lens L_1 in fig. 8.21a and is the plane of the image of the condenser (formed by L_1) in fig. 8.21b. In a more elaborate optical system, the relevant plane is the plane of the exit pupil. When discussing the construction of the image, it is convenient to consider the spectra as localized on that reference sphere (see § 8.24) whose centre C is at the image point and which touches the

---

* See § 8.17.

plane of the exit pupil. For simplicity we discuss an image of unit magnification and consider only the variation of E_0 in one direction.

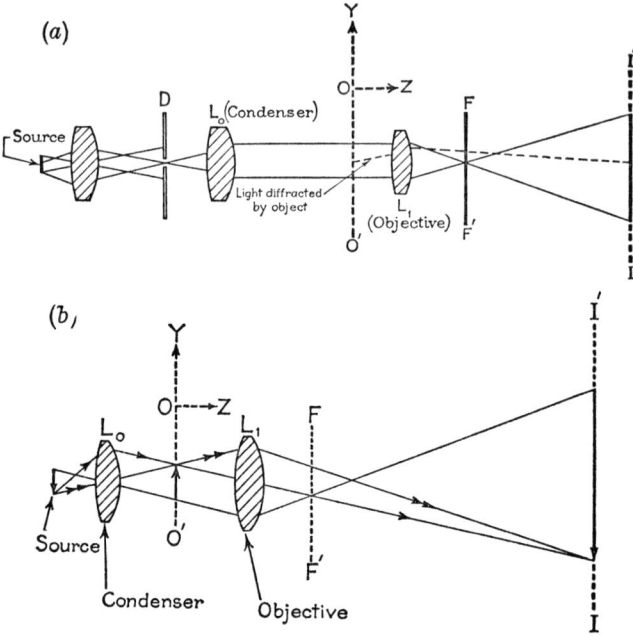

Fig. 8.21.—(a) Highly coherent illumination, (b) effectively non-coherent illumination

8.36. Coherent Illumination.

Suppose that the displacement in the plane $(z = 0)$ immediately to the right of the object is $\xi_0(y)$. In general, $\xi_0(y)$ is complex and we may put

$$\xi_0(y) = a(y) \exp i\delta(y), \qquad \ldots \qquad 8(20)$$

and the relative energy is

$$E(y) = \xi_0 \xi_0^*. \qquad \ldots \ldots \qquad 8(21)$$

If δ is constant for all values of y, then there are variations of amplitude in the plane $z = 0$ but no variations of phase. The object is then called an *amplitude object* and may be regarded as a superposition of a number of amplitude gratings (§ 6.37) whose constants are determined by taking the Fourier transform of $A(y)$. In a similar way, if A is constant and δ varies with y, we have variations of phase but not of amplitude. The object is a *phase object* and may be regarded as a superposition of a number of phase gratings. The structure of a phase object cannot be seen with the naked eye, but we shall see later that it can be made visible in the image (§ 8.44). A perfectly plane surface whose reflection coefficient varies from point to point (viewed by reflected light) is an amplitude object. A surface whose reflection coefficient is uniform but which is not perfectly flat constitutes a phase object.

For the present we consider that ξ_0 is complex and that both modulus and argument may be functions of y. Note that the following analysis, in terms of ξ_0, is significant only when the illumination is at least partially coherent because otherwise there is no permanent phase relation between light from different parts of the object.

It is necessary to distinguish between spatial frequencies in the energy distribution and spatial frequencies in the distribution of displacement. We denote the former by s and the latter by m, both being measured in the unit defined in § 8.34. As an example consider an object for which

$$\xi_0 = a_1 \cos m_1 y + a_2 \cos m_2 y, \quad \ldots \quad 8(22a)$$

where a_1 and a_2 are real.

Then

$$\begin{aligned}
E_0 &= \xi_0 \xi_0{}^* \\
&= a_1{}^2 \cos^2 m_1 y + a_2{}^2 \cos^2 m_2 y + 2a_1 a_2 \cos m_1 y \cos m_2 y \quad . \quad 8(22b) \\
&= \tfrac{1}{2}(a_1{}^2 + a_2{}^2) + \tfrac{1}{2}a_1{}^2 \cos 2m_1 y + \tfrac{1}{2}a_2{}^2 \cos 2m_2 y + \\
&\quad a_1 a_2 \{\cos (m_1 + m_2)y + \cos (m_1 - m_2)y\}. \quad \ldots \quad 8(22c)
\end{aligned}$$

Thus the values of s are 0, $2m_1$, $2m_2$, $m_1 + m_2$ and $m_1 - m_2$. In general E_0 contains the sum and difference of all spatial frequencies which occur in ξ_0.

8.37.—Consider an object, in the plane XY, illuminated by a coherent beam of light parallel to OZ, and suppose that the transmitted light is represented by

$$\begin{aligned}
\xi_0 &= 1 + \cos my \\
&= 1 + \tfrac{1}{2} \exp (imy) + \tfrac{1}{2} \exp (-imy) \quad . \quad . \quad 8(23a)
\end{aligned}$$

from $y = D$ to $-D$, where D is a large multiple of the grating interval.

Then
$$E_0 = 1\tfrac{1}{2} + 2 \cos my + \tfrac{1}{2} \cos 2my \quad . \quad . \quad 8(23b)$$

and
$$E_{0N} = 1 + \tfrac{4}{3} \cos my + \tfrac{1}{3} \cos 2my. \quad . \quad . \quad 8(23c)$$

Equation 8(23a) represents a cosinusoidal distribution of amplitude plus a constant term. Equation 8(23b) shows that, in the energy distribution, spatial frequencies $s_1 = m$ and $s_2 = 2m$ both appear, but the recognizable grating interval corresponds to $s_1 = m$. By applying the discussion of § 3.31 and § 6.38, we see that the diffracted light consists of a zero-order spectrum of unit amplitude and two side spectra each of amplitude $\frac{1}{2}$. Following § 8.19 we may regard these spectra as focused into three small sources* at the points S_0, S_+ and S_-

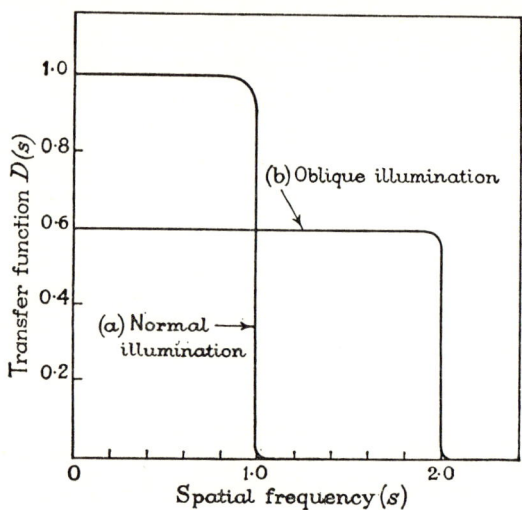

Fig. 8.22.—Optical transfer function (coherent illumination)

in the region of the exit pupil, and the image may be constructed by considering the interference of light from these sources (§ 8.38). A more complicated object may be represented by a series of terms similar to those in 8(23a), and the light corresponding to any one term will be focused into a small source near a point in the plane of the exit pupil.† Thus we have effectively a Fourier transform of the structure of the object in the region of the exit pupil. The condition that a spectrum shall pass through the system is $\kappa_y < \kappa_c$ (see § 8.21) and in our present units this implies $m^2 < 1$. Although the physical stop which limits the transmission is elsewhere, we may imagine a circular stop of unit radius in the plane of the exit pupil. We attach co-

* See fig. 8.23.
† For gratings with lines parallel to OY, the spectra all lie on a line parallel to OX. In general they may have any co-ordinates in the plane of the exit pupil.

ordinates* (u, v) to points in this plane. If the light is incident normally, zero-order spectra pass close to the point $(0, 0)$ and, if the structure has variations in the y direction but not in the x direction, other spectra are situated at points for which $u = 0$, e.g. at 0, m and 0, $-m$.

With normal illumination and an aberration-free lens, all frequencies up to $m^2 = 1$ are transmitted unchanged, and all higher frequencies are completely removed. The optical transfer curve is as shown in curve (a) of fig. 8.22.

8.38.—With coherent illumination incident at an angle θ to the normal, the zero-order spectrum moves from the centre to a point v_1, where $v_1 = \sin\theta/\sin\alpha$, and the side spectra move in a corresponding way so that one may be transmitted and not the other. When the extreme condition $v_1 = 1$ (see § 8.21) is reached, S_0 and S_- are transmitted if $m < 2$. Thus oblique illumination is an advantage for the higher frequencies but (owing to occlusion of one side spectrum) there is some reduction of contrast at all frequencies (fig. 8.22).

The reconstruction of the image may be carried out in the following way. Since all the spectra have real and positive amplitudes, they are all in phase and may be represented by 1, $\tfrac{1}{2}e^{imy}$ and $\tfrac{1}{2}e^{-imy}$. When all three are transmitted, the energy distribution on the image plane is

$$|1 + \tfrac{1}{2}e^{imy} + \tfrac{1}{2}e^{-imy}|^2$$
$$= (1 + \cos my)^2$$

in agreement with 8(23).

When only one side spectrum is transmitted, the energy is

$$(1 + \tfrac{1}{2}e^{imy})(1 + \tfrac{1}{2}e^{-imy})$$

$$E_i = \tfrac{5}{4} + \cos my \quad \ldots \ldots \quad 8(24a)$$

and
$$E_{iN} = 1 + \tfrac{4}{5}\cos my. \quad \ldots \ldots \quad 8(24b)$$

The transfer factor D_s for any frequency for which only one side spectrum is transmitted (obtained by comparing 8(24b) with 8(23 c)) is 0·6.

With normal illumination and both spectra transmitted, 8(23) represents the image as well as the object, so that a small amount of the spatial frequency $s = 2m$ is transmitted. The recognizable grating interval is, however, $2\pi/m$ and the image of a grating with a closer spacing than that corresponding to $m = 1$ would show no structure (i.e. the limiting value in ordinary units of length is given by 8(11)).

8.39. Effect of Aberration on Transfer Function (Coherent Light).

Assume that the aberration function W is known with respect to a reference sphere whose centre (C) is at the middle of the paraxial-ray

---

* In Reference 8.19, etc., u, v are used for co-ordinates in the object and x and y for those in the exit pupil.

image and which touches the exit pupil at S_0 (fig. 8.23). In the absence of aberration, the light from the three effective sources is in phase when it crosses the reference sphere, and the three spectra may be replaced by three cophasal sources placed at S_0, S_+ and S_- on the reference sphere. For normal illumination these sources are symmetrically placed, and the distribution of light on the image plane agrees with 8(23b) if $m < 1$.

Now suppose that aberration is present but that the system is symmetrical, so that the same aberration W is obtained for both the side spectra when the reference sphere passes through the spectrum of zero

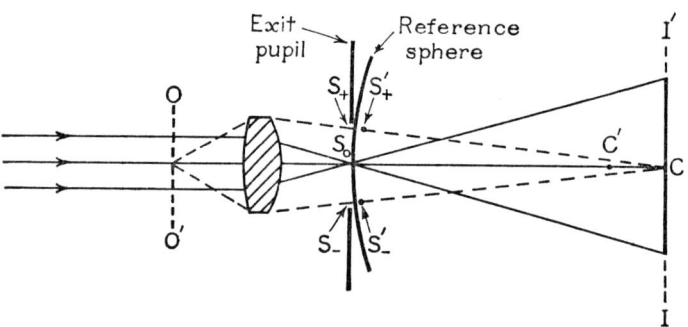

Fig. 8.23.—Formation of image when there is aberration. The distances S_+S_+' and S_-S_-' have been exaggerated for clarity of reproduction.

order. Then each of the side spectra has the same phase difference (κW) from the zero-order spectrum, and we have (when $m < 1$)

$$\xi_i = 1 + \tfrac{1}{2} \exp i(my + \kappa W) + \tfrac{1}{2} \exp i(-my + \kappa W), \quad 8(25a)$$

and $\quad E_i = 1\tfrac{1}{2} + 2 \cos \kappa W \cos my + \tfrac{1}{2} \cos 2my. \quad \ldots \quad 8(25b)$

Comparison with 8(23b) shows that the contrast has been reduced by the factor $\cos \kappa W$. For every frequency which is transmitted, the contrast is less than that obtained with a lens which has no aberration.

8.40.—When aberration is present the light is in phase on the deformed wave surface, and we may locate three small cophasal sources at S_0, S_+' and S_-'. The light from these three sources arrives in phase at that point C' on the axis which is the centre of the circle which passes through the three points. The intensity at that point is the same as that obtained at C when there is no aberration. A similar argument applies in relation to other points in the image, provided that the aberration varies only slowly across the field. Thus a nearly perfect image is obtained on a surface (which is nearly plane) displaced along the axis.

If oblique coherent illumination is used, the three sources S_0, S_+' and S_-'

are no longer symmetrically placed with respect to the axis. The centre C'' of the circle which passes through these points is off-axis. We still have a nearly perfect image, but there is displacement both parallel to the axis and at right angles to it.

8.41.—It thus appears that with coherent illumination a nearly perfect image of a single sinusoidal grating can be obtained (even though severe aberration is present) by altering the plane of focus. The displacement of the image from the Gaussian image plane varies with s, and usually varies rapidly when s is near the critical frequency, because aberration varies rapidly in the outer zones of the lens. Since the reproduction of fine detail involves transmission of a range of frequencies, a clear picture of an ordinary object with fine detail cannot be obtained by refocusing, though it is possible to improve the transmission of any given frequency by adjusting the focus. This discussion shows that a sinusoidal grating does not form a good test object for investigating the quality of a microscope objective which is to be used with coherent illumination.

In the above discussion we have not taken account of the fact that a phase difference of $2n\pi$ is equivalent to a phase difference of zero. When this is taken into account it is found that there is a series of planes in which a clear image of a single sinusoidal grating is obtained. If normal illumination is used, an undisplaced image is obtained when $W = 2n\pi$ and an image with reversed contrast when $W = (2n + 1)\pi$. This effect is sometimes called "spurious resolution".

8.42. Non-coherent Illumination.

The formation of the image with the system of illumination shown in fig. 8.21b may be related to the previous discussion by considering the lens L_0 as an effective source. Light from a very small area Q, which may be treated as coherent light, forms three "spectra" in the plane FF' if an object described by 8(19a) is used. The interference of the three corresponding effective sources gives the contribution of the small area at Q to the energy distribution on the image plane. Since light from different points in the effective source is non-coherent, the total energy at any point in the image plane is obtained by adding the *energy* (not the displacement) due to light from different parts of L_0.

If L_0 is uniformly illuminated, the zero-order spectra from different parts of L_0 exactly fill the exit pupil, i.e. they fill the circle of unit radius in the plane FF'. The side spectra fill two circles displaced from the centre (as shown in fig. 8.24), the displacement being proportional to s, and parts of these areas fall outside the exit pupil (i.e. the corresponding light misses the lens L_1). Thus, one or both of the side spectra, corresponding to illumination from certain areas of L_0 is lost even at low frequencies. The loss of the side spectra increases as s increases and the whole of the side spectra is lost when $s > 2$. The optical transfer curve for an aberration-free lens is shown in fig. 8.25b.

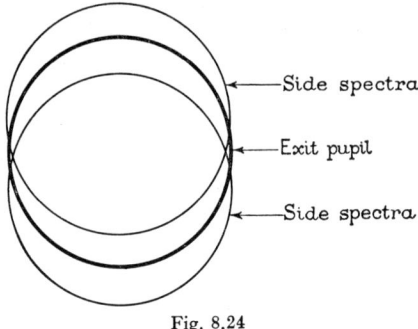

Fig. 8.24

Comparison of this curve with those shown in fig. 8.22 for normal and oblique coherent illumination shows that the best reproduction of detail can usually be obtained with suitably adjusted coherent illumination.

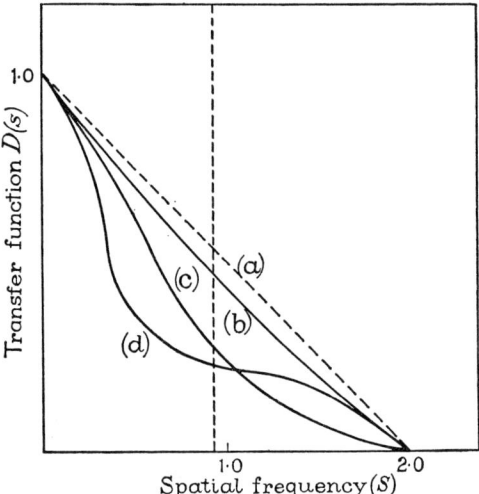

Fig. 8.25.—Optical transfer function (non-coherent illumination)

8.43. Effect of Aberration (Non-coherent Illumination).

The effect of aberration for a single spatial frequency is obtained by writing down an equation similar to 8(25) for the light from a small region of L_0 and calculating the resultant energy distribution on the image plane. It is then necessary to integrate over all that area of L_0 for which one or both side spectra are transmitted. The remaining area contributes only a uniform distribution of energy in the image plane.

§ 8.43 NON-COHERENT ILLUMINATION

Since W varies in a fairly complicated way, the resultant integration cannot, as a rule, be carried out explicitly, and recourse to electronic calculating machines is now usual. A few general points can be deduced without considering any detailed calculation:

(1). Equation 8(25) and the above discussion imply that the contrast in the image formed by an aberration-free lens is better, for every frequency, than the contrast obtained with a lens (of the same aperture) which suffers from aberration.

(2). The optical transfer curve depends on the choice of image plane, so that different parts of the structure may be made clear by refocusing.

(3). For frequencies near to the limit of resolution the side spectra pass through two small areas near to the edge of the lens L. Since the aberration is nearly constant over these small areas, the discussion of §§ 8.40–8.42 applies, and resolution can be obtained by altering the plane of focus. Thus a sinusoidal test grating which is just resolved does not form a good test object for assessing the effect of aberration.

(4). The best possible transmission for the high spatial frequencies is needed for the reproduction of fine detail. Sometimes the picture contains no fine detail, or the reproduction of fine detail may be prevented by effects which do not depend on the optical system (see (6) below). Transmission of lower frequencies then becomes important. Thus the transfer curve (d) of fig. 8.25 is more favourable than curve (c) when reproduction of fine detail is desired, but (c) will be more favourable when there is no fine detail. Thus, if spatial frequencies above 0·9 are not present, the portions of the transfer function curves to the right of the vertical dotted line are inoperative.

(5). The lenses represented by (c) and (d) have the same limit of resolution. The optical transfer curve contains more information than a statement of the limit of resolution and enables us to choose the better lens, taking account of the type of picture to be reproduced and of other circumstances. For any one lens we may choose the best plane of focus (see (2) above).

(6). An optical system is only one element in a transmission system. In a camera, for example, the reproduction of fine detail depends on the grain structure of the plate as well as on the camera lens. The contrast transfer factor for photographic material may be measured by photographing a set of interference fringes whose contrast is known either from calculation or by direct measurement using a photomultiplier, and then measuring the variations of density on the plate or film. The overall optical transfer factor for a camera is given (approximately) by the product $D_0(s)D_p(s)$, where D_0 is the factor of the lens and D_p is that of the photographic material.

Similarly in a television system, the spatial frequencies are transmitted to the screen of the camera and are converted to electrical frequencies by the scanning system. The electrical signals are transmitted through several stages of amplification and finally are converted back again into spatial frequencies in the picture-tube. The overall transmission is the product of several factors. The number of lines sets an upper limit to the frequency which is transmitted, and this limit is considerably less than that set by the resolving power of the camera lens. It is therefore desirable to use a lens which has good transmission at moderate spatial frequencies (fig. 8.25).

(7). When signals pass successively through several electrical amplifiers which are linear, the overall transmission factor may be obtained by simple multiplication. This is not true for successive transmission through optical components. One lens may correct the aberrations due to another, and the overall performance of a corrected system is often better than that of any of its components taken alone. Thus the transfer function for an optical system must be calculated for the system as a whole and cannot be derived in any simple way from the functions of parts of the system taken separately.

8.44. The Phase-contrast Microscope.

A transparent object produces differences of phase but not differences of amplitude in the incident beam, i.e. if the incident beam has unit amplitude and zero phase then the modulus of ξ_0 is unity but the argument is a function of y. The eye and all physical receptors can detect differences of energy but not differences of phase, so that light which has traversed a perfectly transparent object appears to be unchanged (apart from a small loss by reflection). In order to see a small transparent object such as an unstained bacterium, it is necessary both to magnify it and to convert differences of phase into differences of energy. Interferometric methods by which differences of phase may be made to produce differences of energy will be discussed in Chapter IX. We shall now describe the phase-shifting method developed by Zernike, which is used in the phase-contrast microscope. Phase changes cannot produce any observable effect except when the illumination is at least partially coherent, and for simplicity we assume that the illumination is perfectly coherent.

8.45.—If the light at two points y_1 and y_2 differs in phase but not in energy, then $\xi(y_1)$ and $\xi(y_2)$ may be represented by two vectors A_1B_1 and A_2B_2 (fig. 8.26) whose lengths are equal. Now suppose that some optical device is able to resolve the vector A_1B_1 into $(A_1C_1 + C_1B_1)$ and A_2B_2 into $(A_2C_2 + C_2B_2)$, and that a phase difference of $\pi/2$ may be inserted between A_1C_1 and C_1B_1 and between A_2C_2 and C_2B_2. This is equivalent, in the vector representation, to rotating one

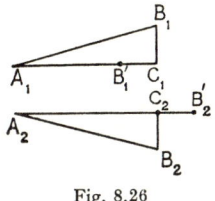

Fig. 8.26

of the vectors through $\pi/2$. If this is done and the pairs of vectors are recombined, the resultants are A_1B_1' and A_2B_2' and, since the energies are proportional to the squares of these lengths, there is a difference of energy where previously there was only a difference of phase.

8.46.—Suppose that a phase object for which $\xi(y) = 1$ for all values of y is viewed by a microscope. We have seen that light corresponding to different spatial frequencies is separated in the exit pupil of the objective and recombined in the image. In the simplest phase-contrast microscope, a thin transparent film covering a small area in the centre of the exit pupil of the objective is used to produce a phase difference of $\pi/2$ between the light $a(0)$ corresponding to a uniform background and the light $a(\kappa_y)$ corresponding to details of structure. From the discussion of the preceding paragraph, we should expect that, when the light is recombined to form the image, differences of energy at different points of the image plane will correspond with differences of phase in the object plane. We shall now show that this is so, and that it is possible in some situations to make differences of energy in the image directly proportional to differences of phase in the object.

8.47.—Consider an object for which $\xi = ae^{i\delta}$ where $\delta = f(y)$. Then the energy, which is proportional to $|\xi|^2$, is the same at all points in the object plane but the phase varies from point to point. If δ is small and $a = 1$, we may put

$$\xi_p = 1 + if(y). \quad \ldots \ldots \quad 8(26a)$$

Let us consider also two objects for which

$$\xi_+ = 1 + f(y) \qquad 8(26b)$$

and
$$\xi_- = 1 - f(y). \qquad 8(26c)$$

Then ξ_p represents a phase object, ξ_+ and ξ_- represent objects which absorb light in some areas more than others but which introduce no phase changes. ξ_+ and ξ_- are complementary in that the dark parts of the object represented by ξ_+ correspond with the light parts of that represented by ξ_- and vice versa. If $f(y)$ is real and does not contain any constant part, $a(0)$ is approximately the same for all three objects. The energy corresponding to any given spatial frequency is the same for all three objects since it is derived from the Fourier transform of $f(y)$. The only difference is that for the phase object the spectra are $\pi/2$ ahead of $a(0)$ (since $\exp(i\pi/2) = i$). Now suppose that a thin plate is introduced into the plane FF' so as to retard the phase in the centre by $\tfrac{1}{2}\pi$. Then the distribution of phases on FF' given by (a) with the plate is the same as that given by (b) without the plate. Thus the object (a) is visible when the plate is used (*positive phase-contrast*). If the phase in the centre is advanced by $\tfrac{1}{2}\pi$ the object (a) is again visible, but the regions which were dark before are now light (*negative phase-contrast*). Photographs showing positive and negative phase-contrast with transparent objects are given in Reference 8.10. In practice, to obtain good resolution, the object is illuminated with a hollow cone of light. The central image is then replaced by an annular ring on the plane FF'. It is usual to insert in this place a plate which has been coated with an annular ring of transparent material of optical thickness slightly less than $\tfrac{1}{4}\lambda$. The ring is applied by vacuum evaporation. It is thus necessary for the condenser and the phase plate to match one another.

8.48.—Phase contrast may be obtained with small modifications to an ordinary microscope, but a specially designed phase-contrast microscope is needed for the best results. The transmission of spatial frequencies and the limit of resolution is not affected, so that high magnification may be used. In one respect the phase-contrast microscope does not give a true representation of the object. Light corresponding to very low spatial frequencies overlaps the light corresponding to zero frequency. Thus some of the light corresponding to low frequencies passes through the phase plate, and no phase difference is introduced between this light and that corresponding to zero frequency. The differences of illumination corresponding to the lower spatial frequencies are thus smaller than they ought to be. Suppose for example that a phase object whose size is large compared with the limits of resolution is viewed with a phase-contrast microscope. The representation of the boundaries is correct because this derives from the higher frequencies, but the contrast in the central part is too low (fig. 8.27). The edges are

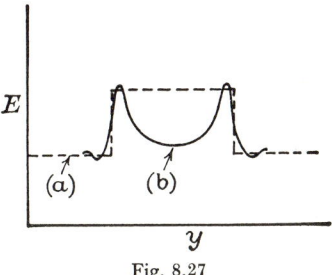

Fig. 8.27

thus " outlined ". This effect is not a serious disadvantage and indeed may help to make a faint object visible. It is however important that the user of a phase-contrast microscope should realize that the " line round the edge " in the image is an artifact. The phase-contrast method may also be applied to the microscopic examination of opaque objects. It then detects small deviations from flatness in a surface of uniform reflection coefficient.

8.49.—The phase-contrast method is not the only way of making transparent objects visible. If the central image is excluded by a stop (dark-ground illumination) or if all the light on one side of the centre is excluded (Schlieren method), then transparent objects become visible. Several devices of this type were known before the advent of phase-contrast methods.* Zernike gave the first really satisfactory theory of these methods, and his own phase-contrast device is the only one that makes contrasts in the image proportional to phase differences in the object plane. Zernike's method does this only when the phase differences are small. We can see that it will not work so well when phase differences are large by considering an object of many strips of equal area with a phase difference π between alternate strips. The energy in the central image is then zero and insertion of a central phase-plate is useless. When phase differences are fairly large (but not π), it is an advantage to be able to alter the energy of the central image as well as its phase. Devices which enable this to be done are available.†

---

* For interferometric methods see Chapter IX. † References 8.10 and 8.11.

REFERENCES

8.1. RAYLEIGH: *Scientific Papers*, Vol. I, p. 415.
8.2. *Ibid.*, p. 513.
8.3. *Ibid.*, p. 436.
8.4. *Ibid.*: Vol. III, p. 103.
8.5. *Ibid.*: Vol. V, p. 272.
8.6. JOHNSTONE STONEY: *Phil. Mag.*, 1896, Vol. 43, p. 332.
8.7. WILLIAMS, W. E.: *Applications of Interferometry* (Methuen).
8.8. BRIGHT, R. J., JACKSON, D. A., and KUHN, H.: *Proc. Phys. Soc.* A, 1949, Vol. 62, p. 225.
8.9. LINFOOT, E. H.: *Proc. Roy. Soc.* A, 1946, Vol. 186, p. 72.
8.10. TAYLOR, E. W., *Proc. Roy. Soc.* A, 1947, Vol. 190, p. 422.
8.11. OSTERBERG, H.: *J.O.S.A.*, 1947, Vol. 37, p. 726.
8.12. COSSLETT: *The Electron Microscope* (Oxford University Press).
8.13. RAYLEIGH: *Scientific Papers*, Vol. V, p. 118, 1903.
8.14. *Ibid.*: Vol. III, p. 123.
8.15. HOPKINS, H. H., BARHAM, P. M.: *Proc. Phys. Soc.* B, 1950, Vol. 63, p. 737.
8.16. RAYLEIGH: *Scientific Papers*, Vol. IV, p. 235.
8.17. SELWYN, E. W. H., and TEARLE, J. L.: *Proc. Phys. Soc.*, 1946, Vol. 58, p. 493.
8.18. DUFFIEUX, P. M.: *L'Intégrale de Fourier et ses applications à l'optique* (printed privately at Besançon, 1946).
8.19. HOPKINS, H. H.: *Proc. Roy. Soc.* A, 1953, Vol. 217, p. 408.
8.20. FELLGETT, P. B., and LINFOOT, E. H.: *Phil. Trans. Roy. Soc.* A, 1955, Vol. 247, p. 369.
8.21. WYNNE, C. G.: *Proc. Phys. Soc.*, 1959, Vol. 73, p. 777.
8.22. HOPKINS, H. H.: *Proc. Phys. Soc.*, 1956, Vol. 69B, p. 562.
8.23. LINFOOT, E. H., *Recent Advances in Optics* (Oxford University Press).
8.24. HOPKINS, H. H.: *Wave Theory of Aberrations* (Oxford University Press).

APPENDIX VIII A

OPTICAL TRANSFER FUNCTION

1. Historical.

The concepts discussed in § 8.20 were due to Abbe and were developed in mathematical form by Rayleigh* (1896). About fifty years later they became the basis of an assessment of optical systems. Selwyn† (who was principally concerned with contrast transfer) and Duffieux‡ (who considered the electrical transmission analogy) published their results soon after the end of the 1939–45 war. Hopkins§ has extended the basic theory, and he and pupils have contributed a great deal to practical applications. Fellgett and Linfoot|| have considered the relation with information theory (see Chapter XX). The following discussion is based on work by Hopkins and by Fellgett and Linfoot.

2. The Spread Function.

Consider the distribution of light from a small strip of width dy (centred at y) in the object plane. Aberration and diffraction will spread this light over the whole of the image plane but, with a moderately well-corrected and well-focused system, most of it will be near to the geometrical image. Let us assume that the aberration is uniform over the whole field. Then the illumination at a point y' in the image plane depends only on its distance from the geometrical image point y, and we may write for the illumination due to the strip at y,

$$dE_i(y') = E_0(y)\, \sigma(y - y')\, dy, \quad \ldots \ldots \quad 8(27a)$$

where σ is called the *spread function*. (The Airy diffraction pattern is the spread function for an aberration-free lens with a point source.) Integrating, we have

$$E_i(y') = \int_{-\infty}^{\infty} E_0(y)\, \sigma(y - y')\, dy. \quad \ldots \ldots \quad 8(27b)$$

We now use the Fourier integral to analyse $E_0(y)$ into a continuous set of spatial frequencies

$$E_0(y) = \int_{-\infty}^{\infty} A(s)\, \exp(isy)\, ds, \quad \ldots \ldots \quad 8(28)$$

where

$$A(s) = \frac{1}{2\pi} \int_{-\infty}^{\infty} E_0(y)\, \exp(-isy)\, dy. \quad \ldots \ldots \quad 8(29)$$

Using the definitions in the text we have

$$E_i(y') = \int_{-\infty}^{\infty} D(s)\, A(s)\, \exp(isy')\, ds, \quad \ldots \ldots \quad 8(30)$$

where $D(s)$ is the optical transfer factor.

---

* References 8.13 and 8.16.   † Reference 8.17.   ‡ Reference 8.18.   § Reference 8.19.
|| Reference 8.20.

Inserting the Fourier transform 8(28) in 8(27b) we obtain

$$E_i(y') = \int_{-\infty}^{\infty} \int_{-\infty}^{\infty} A(s) \exp(isy) \, \sigma(y - y') \, dy \, ds. \quad . \quad . \quad 8(31)$$

This may be rearranged to give

$$E_i(y') = \int_{-\infty}^{\infty} \int_{-\infty}^{\infty} \sigma(y - y') \exp\{is(y - y')\} A(s) \exp(isy') \, d(y - y') \, ds \quad 8(32)$$

which agrees with 8(30) if

$$D(s) = \int_{-\infty}^{\infty} \sigma(y - y') \exp\{is(y - y')\} \, d(y - y'), \quad . \quad . \quad . \quad 8(33a)$$

i.e. if

$$D(s) = \frac{1}{2\pi} \int_{-\infty}^{\infty} \sigma(y) \exp(isy) \, dy, \quad . \quad . \quad . \quad . \quad 8(33b)$$

so that $D(s)$ is the Fourier transform of $\sigma(y)$.

3. Isoplanatism.

If the aberration is the same over the whole of a finite patch, σ (and therefore $D(s)$) are constant over this patch, and the patch is said to be an *isoplanatism patch*. If the aberration is constant over the whole field, the system is said to be *strictly isoplanatic*, just as a lens system may be said to be *strictly achromatic* if the cardinal points are exactly the same for all wavelengths in the range considered. A system for which the aberration does not vary significantly in the range over which the spread function differs significantly from zero, may be said to be *isoplanatic*, just as a system for which $df/d\lambda = 0$ at some chosen wavelength is often called *achromatic*.

When a system is isoplanatic in the above sense (but not necessarily *strictly isoplanatic*) σ can still be unambiguously defined at any point in the field, even though the aberration varies considerably over the whole field. $D(s)$ can then be defined, for any point in the field, as the Fourier transform of σ. A spatial frequency s is not precisely defined unless the " grating " contains many intervals, and this constitutes a formal objection to giving $D(s)$ a " value at a point ". To avoid this difficulty we define $D(s)$ (the Fourier transform of σ) as the optical transfer factor which would be obtained if the aberrations were the same over the whole field as they are at the point under consideration.

4.—When the aberration is not the same over the whole field the optical system is not, strictly speaking, a linear transmission system. The method adopted in the preceding paragraph is similar to that used with a nearly linear electrical system in which a curve is replaced for certain purposes by the tangent at a point of interest. In general $\sigma(y)$ and therefore $D(s)$ depend on the orientation of the small line object with respect to a line joining its centre to the axis of the optical system. No new physical principle is involved in this complication which is considered in detail in Reference 8.20.

5. Coherent Illumination.

The distribution of displacement may be analysed in a similar way and we have

$$\xi_0(y) = \int_{-\infty}^{\infty} a_0(m) \exp(imy)\, dm, \qquad \ldots \ldots 8(34)$$

where
$$a_0(m) = \frac{1}{2\pi} \int_{-\infty}^{\infty} \xi_0(y) \exp(-imy)\, dy \qquad \ldots \ldots 8(35)$$

and
$$\xi_i(y) = \int_{-\infty}^{\infty} \tau(m)\, a_0(m) \exp(imy)\, dm. \qquad \ldots \ldots 8(36)$$

We have also a spread function ρ such that

$$\rho(y) = \int_{-\infty}^{\infty} \tau(m) \exp(imy)\, dy. \qquad \ldots \ldots 8(37)$$

If $\tau(m)$ is complex, the reproduction in the image involves a linear shift as well as a loss of contrast.

6. Periodic and Non-periodic Objects.

If ξ_0 can be expressed by a series

$$\xi_0(y) = \sum_m a_0(m) \exp imy, \qquad \ldots \ldots 8(38)$$

(where m is integral) then $\xi_0(y + 2\pi) = \xi_0(y)$ and the object is periodic with a repetition interval 2π. If the values of m are not all integral but are rational numbers so that there is a highest common factor r (which may be a small fraction), then the object is periodic with an interval $2\pi/r$. According to the discussion of § 4.18, the series on the right-hand side of 8(38) may be used to represent any periodic object or a non-periodic object in a finite range. It is convenient when there is a small number of terms with $a_0(m)$ significantly different from zero. Otherwise the Fourier transform 8(34) is more useful. In §§ 7 and 8 below we use 8(38) because this makes it easier to visualize the relation between the physical situation and the equations, but the results apply equally to an object represented by 8(34).

7. Relation between E and ξ.

For a periodic object, using 8(38), we may put

$$E_0(y) = \xi_0 \xi_0^* = \sum_m \sum_p a(m)\, a^*(p) \exp i(m-p)y, \qquad \ldots 8(39)$$

where m and p are not necessarily integral but have a common factor as explained in § 6. The terms may be regrouped to yield a summation equivalent to 8(28), and we then obtain

$$E_0(y) = \sum_s A(s) \exp(isy), \qquad \ldots \ldots 8(40)$$

where
$$A(s) = \sum_m a(m + \tfrac{1}{2}s) \, a^*(m - \tfrac{1}{2}s). \quad \ldots \quad 8(41)$$

The light in the image may be expressed in the form of a summation equivalent to 8(36), so that we obtain

$$D(s) \, A(s) = \sum_m \tau(m + \tfrac{1}{2}s) \, \tau^*(m - \tfrac{1}{2}s) \, a(m + \tfrac{1}{2}s) \, a^*(m - \tfrac{1}{2}s). \quad 8(42)$$

The summation must include those values of m for which the appropriate "spectra" pass through the exit pupil. By combining 8(41) and 8(42) we obtain

$$D(s) = \frac{\sum_m \tau(m + \tfrac{1}{2}s) \, \tau^*(m - \tfrac{1}{2}s) \, a(m + \tfrac{1}{2}s) \, a^*(m - \tfrac{1}{2}s)}{\sum_m a(m + \tfrac{1}{2}s) \, a^*(m - \tfrac{1}{2}s)}. \quad 8(43)$$

When the illumination is coherent, this expression cannot be simplified; $D(s)$ depends on the values of $a(m)$ (i.e. on the structure of the object) and is not a constant of the optical system. This is necessarily so because analysis of the energy $E_0(y)$ by means of 8(34) or 8(40) does contain information concerning the relative phases of light from different points in the object plane. This information is needed to construct the image since, with coherent illumination, light from different object points can interfere. Thus $\tau(m)$ and not $D(s)$ is the important constant in relation to the formation of an image with coherent light.

When the illumination is non-coherent there are no defined phase differences and the analysis of $E_0(y)$ contains all the necessary information. We shall now show that, for non-coherent objects, $D(s)$ is independent of the structure of the object.

8. Non-coherent Illumination.

Suppose that an object is illuminated with light which just fills the exit pupil which is a circle of unit radius. Light, initially directed to an infinitesimal area near to a point u_0, v_0 in the exit pupil, comes from an infinitesimal area of the source, and this light alone is coherent. If the spatial structure of the object includes a frequency m with lines parallel to OX, the light initially directed to u_0, v_0 will pass through the points $u_0, (v_0 + m)$ and $u_0, (v_0 - m)$.

We obtain a contribution to the sum on the right-hand side of 8(42) from the light initially directed to u_0, v_0 if the two points $u_0, (v_0 + m + \tfrac{1}{2}s)$ and $u_0, (v_0 + m - \tfrac{1}{2}s)$ both lie within the exit pupil, i.e. within the circle of unit radius (see fig. 8.28a in which O and O′ represent two possible directions of the incident light). Now consider two circles each of unit radius with centres displaced $\pm\tfrac{1}{2}s$ from the centre of the exit pupil (fig. 8.28b). If a point on the upper edge of the shaded area is represented by u_0, v_0 then $u_0, v_0 + \tfrac{1}{2}s$ will just lie within the exit pupil and $u_0, v_0 - \tfrac{1}{2}s$ will be well within. A little consideration shows that light directed to any point within this area will give a contribution to the right-hand side of 8(42). Light directed to any other point will not do so, because one or other of the terms $a(m + \tfrac{1}{2}s)$ or $a^*(m - \tfrac{1}{2}s)$ will be lost.

If there is no aberration, $\tau(m + \tfrac{1}{2}s) \, \tau^*(m - \tfrac{1}{2}s)$ is unity for a point within the shaded area and zero outside. Thus the value of $D(s)$ is simply the ratio of

NON-COHERENT ILLUMINATION 323

the shaded area to that of the circle of unit radius (which equals π). We obtain curve (b) of fig. 8.25. A small extension of the above argument indicates that when there is an aberration represented by W

$$D(s) = \frac{1}{\pi}\int \exp i\kappa(W_+ - W_-)\, dS \quad \ldots \ldots \quad 8(44)$$

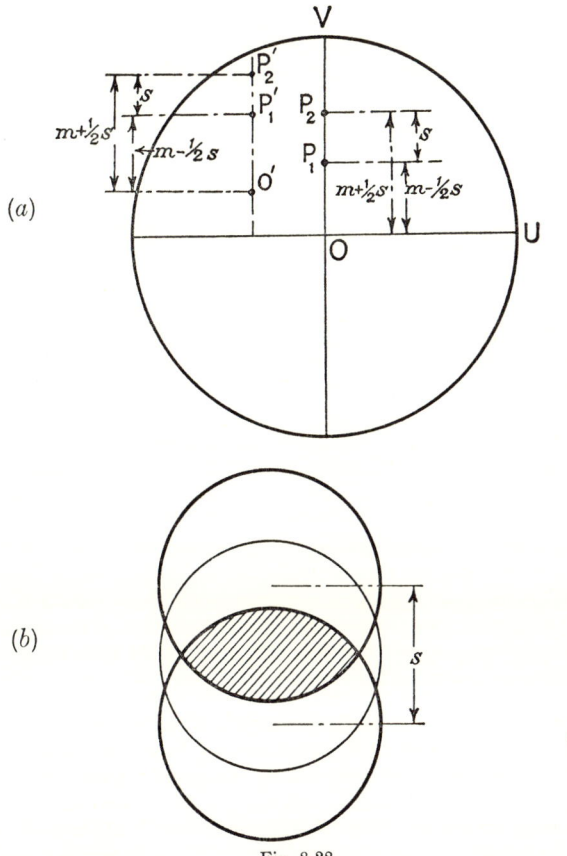

Fig. 8.28.

where W_+ and W_- are the values of the aberration function at $u, (v + \tfrac{1}{2}s)$ and $u, (v - \tfrac{1}{2}s)$ respectively, and the integral is to be taken over the shaded area in fig. 8.28b. Note that the size of the shaded area depends on s but not on m.

APPENDIX VIII B

1. Correction of Aberrations.

The general aberration function W cannot be expressed in analytic form. The design of a lens of given focal length, aperture, and field is therefore approached in the following way. The seven primary aberrations (i.e. the five Seidel aberrations and the two primary chromatic aberrations discussed in §§ 7.23 ff.) are first considered. General formulæ, even for them, are too difficult except for a few simple systems. The designer makes a first trial with a lens system whose components are usually chosen by reference to his experience of other lens systems. The seven primary aberrations are computed as functions of the radii of curvature of the lenses, the separations of surfaces, and the refractive indices. It is then usually possible to vary these parameters so that some of the primary aberrations are reduced to zero and the others to low values. The higher-order aberrations may then be estimated by ray tracing (i.e. calculating the exact paths of typical rays). The last, and most difficult problem, is to alter the parameters in such a way that the higher-order aberrations are removed without reintroducing significant primary aberrations. This is done by successive approximations.* In recent years the aim of many designers has been to find a method of programming a large electronic computer so that it carries through a series of calculations which converges certainly and rapidly. If this can be done, the computer, starting with a system which is moderately good, will fairly quickly calculate the parameters of a system which is the best possible development of the original system.† Very good image-forming properties may be obtained for one distance of the object from the system. It is however possible to design a lens system so that its properties are still good over a considerable range of object distances, e.g. an $f/4 \cdot 5$ camera lens of 10 cm. focal length may give good performance for object distances from 5 m. to infinity. The performance of systems of high magnification (microscope objectives) falls off very rapidly if the object distance departs from the distance for which they have been corrected.

2.—A lens system which is perfect in regard to ray optics (i.e. for which all paths through the system from an object point to an image point are nearly equal) is better in respect of every spatial frequency than a similar lens which is not perfect.‡ A lens system which is very bad by the criteria of ray optics also gives a poor response curve. These considerations justify the use of ray-optical calculations for nearly all lens-design problems. When it becomes necessary to decide between two designs, both of which are very good but not perfect by ray-optical criteria, it is necessary to calculate frequency-response curves. It may, for example, be shown that over a considerable range of frequencies a lens which is slightly over-corrected for spherical aberration (i.e. whose marginal rays come to a focus farther from the lens than the paraxial focus) is better than one which is slightly under-corrected.§

---

* It is also arranged that the residual primary and higher-order aberrations oppose one another if possible.
† See Reference 8.21.   ‡ See § 8.43.   § See Reference 8.22.

3. Aplanatic Systems—The Sine Condition.

Systems which are completely corrected for spherical aberration and coma are said to be *aplanatic*, and the pair of axial points (in whose neighbourhood spherical aberration and coma are zero) are called *aplanatic points*.

It may be shown* that if the relation

$$ny \sin \alpha = n'y' \sin \alpha' \qquad \ldots \ldots \quad 8(45)$$

is satisfied for all zones of a lens system, then coma is absent. This relation is known as the *Abbe sine condition*. There are some systems which satisfy this criterion exactly for one particular pair of points.

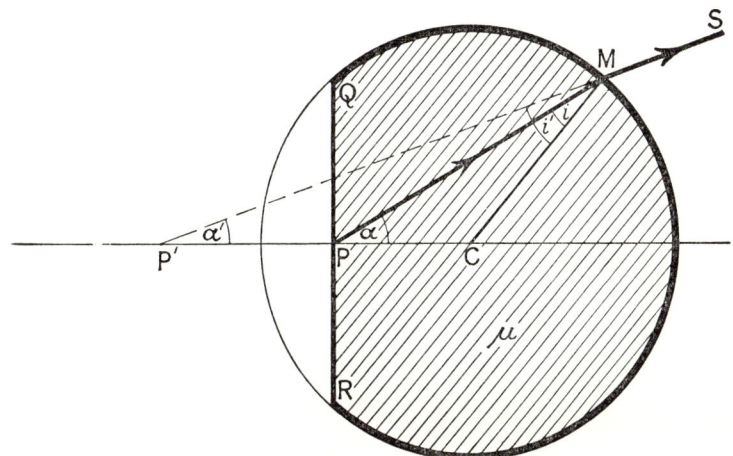

Fig. 8.29.—Aplanatic points of a sphere

In fig. 8.29, C is the centre of a glass sphere of radius r and index μ. It may be shown that if $CP = r/\mu$ and $CP' = \mu r$, then P and P' are conjugate points for which equation 8(45) is satisfied, and that these points are aplanatic. This property is sometimes used in the first element of a microscope objective. A sphere is ground and polished so as to give a flat surface through P (see fig. 9.18).

4. Use of Aspheric Surfaces—The Schmidt Camera.

Perfect imaging properties for a single point can usually be obtained with aspheric surfaces. Corrected optical systems have to form images over wide fields, and sometimes for a range of object distances from the system. It is difficult to design aspheric systems which are useful in these conditions. It is also difficult to make the lenses for an aspheric design, so the use of aspheric systems is restricted to special applications.

* See p. 279 of Reference 7.4.

326 DEFECTS OF OPTICAL IMAGES

The Schmidt camera (fig. 8.30) is based on a very successful use of a single aspheric surface. A paraboloid forms a perfect ray image of a star on axis, but the quality of the image rapidly deteriorates if the star moves off-axis. A spherical mirror may be supplemented by a corrector plate with one aspheric surface as shown in the figure. The plate is placed so as to include the centre of curvature of the mirror. The path differences $(\mu - 1)t$ produced by the corrector plate are

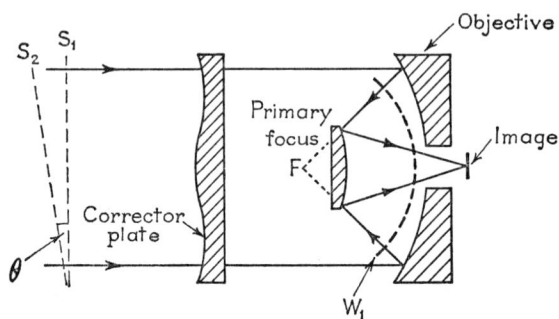

Fig. 8.30.—Schmidt camera

equivalent to a change in shape of the mirror. The shape of the aspheric surface may be chosen so that the plane wave S_1 is reflected as a perfectly spherical wave W_1. The system as a whole acts on S_1 as if it were a paraboloid with axis normal to S_1. The symmetry of the system is such that it acts on a wave S_2 incident at an angle θ to the axis as though it were a paraboloid normal to S_2. (The small differences of equivalent thickness—approximately proportional to $(1 - \cos \theta)$—do not spoil the focus though they give a curved field.) Thus a Schmidt camera of very high aperture gives good definition over a wide angular field and is suitable for photographing an extensive region of the sky on one plate.*

5. The Design of Simple Optical Systems.

The following advice is intended for a physicist who is not a specialist in technical optics, who may have to construct a simple optical system using components available in his laboratory. Two main requirements have to be satisfied (a) to produce a sufficiently *clear* image and (b) to produce a sufficiently *bright* image. This latter requirement usually makes it necessary to form images of the light source at certain points in the system. Some of the lenses which image the light source are placed near to the object or to an image of it, e.g. in a projection lantern the condenser is placed near to the slide and forms an image of the light source in the projection lens (fig. 7.34), i.e. these lenses act as field lenses (§ 7.29). In a cystoscope (fig. 7.23) repeated imaging of the source is needed.

Severe aberration is likely to occur when a bundle of rays suffers a large deflection at one spherical surface. The sharpness of the image formed by an optical system which has not been corrected by careful optical design is usually limited by aberration rather than by diffraction. If this is so, it is advantageous to place a stop over one of the lenses to reduce the aperture until the sharpness

---

* A detailed theory is given in Reference 8.23. See also Reference 6.1.

of the image is limited by diffraction—provided that the loss of light can be tolerated.

Aberrations are usually reduced when the deflection of a bundle of rays is distributed between two or more surfaces. It is, however, not desirable to increase unduly the number of lenses used, because of internal reflections. Also in an uncorrected system errors may be cumulative. The condenser system shown in fig. 7.34a distributes the deflection between four surfaces and is much better than that obtained by placing the flat sides inwards so that all the deflection occurs at two surfaces.

A camera lens or a telescope objective is designed to be used with one particular side facing the object. Usually the correct way is that which distributes the deflection of the rays nearly evenly between the two surfaces. In a system with several components, it may be easier and quicker to find the correct way by trial rather than by theoretical consideration.

Mirror systems have the great advantage that they do not suffer from chromatic aberration. In order to reduce other aberrations it is desirable to use spherical mirrors with the rays as near as possible to normal incidence. If the direction of the light as a whole is to be changed, it is usually best to insert an extra plane mirror.

Finally, correct alignment (§ 7.2) is of the greatest importance and is worth a good deal of care.

APPENDIX VIII C

Testing of Optical Components and Optical Instruments

1.—It is desirable to distinguish between a *working test* intended to assist the person who is polishing an optical component and a *performance test* designed to assess the quality of a completed component or instrument, although some tests are suitable for both purposes. Any test must be related to a criterion of assessment, and early methods of testing such as the Foucault test (first published in 1859) were related to ray optics. They were designed to test whether the first condition of Maxwell (§ 7.8) was satisfied, i.e. to see how nearly the rays forming an image of a point object were concurrent. About fifty years ago attention turned towards the shape of the wave surface emerging from an instrument. Instruments such as the Twyman-Green interferometer (§ 9.6) are designed to test these wave surfaces for sphericity or planarity.

Either of these tests may be used as a working test or as a performance test. It is likely that both of them will long continue to be used as working tests. It is probable that measurements of transfer function will gradually supersede them for assessing the overall performance of some instruments.

2. The Foucault Knife-edge Test.

Suppose that a lens L forms an image of a distant point source at P (fig. 8.31). If a knife edge is moved across the plane F_1F_2 in the direction indicated, it will first intercept the rays from the upper part of the lens, so that an observer looking through an erecting telescope T (which is focused on the lens L) will see a shadow moving from top to bottom. If the knife edge moves in the same direction across the plane G_1G_2, the shadow moves from bottom to top. By mounting the knife on a carriage so that its plane can be traversed in the axial direction by turning a micrometer screw, it is possible to locate the plane of best focus very accurately. If all rays meet in a point at P, then according to ray theory the whole lens should suddenly go dark when the knife edge is made to traverse the plane P_1P_2. If there is no plane for which this happens, then the appearance of the shadow as the knife edge traverses a plane very near P_1P_2 will indicate which parts of the lens need repolishing to improve the system.* An arrangement similar to that shown in fig. 8.31 is used for testing mirrors.

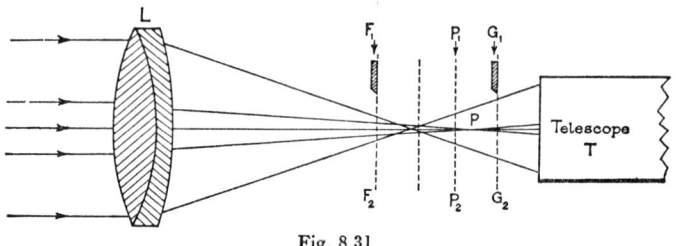

Fig. 8.31

The changes in the distribution of light as the knife edge is moved across a plane near to the plane of best focus have been discussed by Linfoot,† who has calculated the diffraction pattern to be expected for a perfect component and for a component with certain specified defects. He shows that (a) when a mirror is defective by more than a few wavelengths, the test gives correct information concerning the areas to be repolished; (b) the test is still useful for improving a surface which is correct to about 1λ, but the interpretation of the shadows is not as simple as ray theory suggests; (c) in particular, a perfect mirror will give a bright circle at the edge; this has sometimes been incorrectly interpreted to mean that the edge is "turned"; (d) the test is sensitive enough to detect imperfections of surface which are about $0{\cdot}03\lambda$ deep.

3. The Zernike Phase-contrast Test.

In the simplest phase-contrast microscope, a plane wavefront is incident upon a transparent object. The object produces differences of phase and deforms the

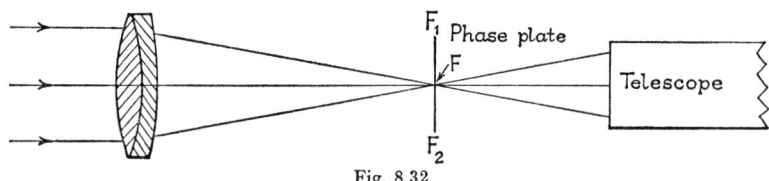

Fig. 8.32

surface of constant phase (i.e. the wavefront) from its original plan or form. When convergent light is used, the wavefront is originally spherical. In the arrangement shown in fig. 8.32 a point source is placed so that its image formed

* Simple empirical tests distinguish areas which are "high" from areas which are "low". Material must be removed from the "high" areas.
† References 8.9 and 8.23.

by the lens at the left is in the plane F_1F_2. If the lens is perfect the reflected wavefront is spherical, and an Airy diffraction pattern (§ 6.41) is formed in the plane F_1F_2. If the wave is not spherical there will be light outside the region of the Airy disc, corresponding to the deviations from sphericity, but an observer looking through the telescope T will see a uniformly illuminated field. If, however, a phase-retardation plate is placed at F, the differences of phase in the focal plane of the telescope become differences of illumination. The optical worker is usually seeking to detect departures from sphericity which are smooth and which extend over a considerable area. The light from such deviations passes very close to F, and it is therefore important that the phase-retardation plate shall not be too large. A diameter between half and two-thirds of that of the Airy disc is recommended. A detailed investigation of this method* shows that it is about as sensitive as the Foucault knife-edge test. When deviations from sphericity are small, its indications are more easily interpreted, and it has the advantage of using all the light.

4. Measurement of Optical Transfer Function.

The transfer function $D(s)$ may be obtained by measuring the spread function σ and then calculating the Fourier transform, using the inverse of equation 8(33b). This may be done by using a short and very narrow slit as object and then scanning the image with a photomultiplier covered with another very narrow slit. This is equivalent to the method of testing an electrical transmission line by applying a short impulse at one end and making a Fourier analysis of the signal received at the other. As explained in § 4 of Appendix VIII A, $D(s)$ depends on the orientation of the object slit, unless its centre is on the axis of a coaxal system. The slits must be so short that there is no appreciable variation over their length, and their width must be less than the resolution distance of the lens under test. The amount of light available is rather small.

If a photomultiplier, covered by a narrow slit, scans the image of a grating object of spatial frequency s at uniform speed, the output is a signal which varies sinusoidally with time, the temporal frequency being proportional to s. Several methods of measuring optical transfer depend on the conversion of spatial variations into temporal variations, and subsequent analysis by electrical circuits.

The discussion of § 7 of Appendix VIII A (and equation 8(44)) shows that $D(s)$ is proportional to the resultant of the interference between light in two images of the exit pupil which have been displaced sideways through a distance proportional to s. This result is the basis of a method of determining $D(s)$ using a wave-shearing interferometer (see § 9.51 and Reference 9.12).

APPENDIX VIII D

1. Talbot's Bands.

It was shown by Fox Talbot that when a thin plate of glass is inserted in a prism or grating spectroscope so as to cover one-half of the aperture of the lens of the telescope (see fig. 8.33), a series of bands appears in the spectrum. The bands are obtained only if the plate be inserted on the side of the lens towards the blue

* See Reference 8.9.

end of the spectrum.* Thus with a grating the bands appear in spectra on only one side of the central image. This is the same side as that on which the plate has been inserted. There is an optimum thickness of the plate which gives the clearest bands and, if the thickness exceeds twice this value, bands are not seen no matter how high the resolving power. It was originally suggested that the bands were due to a simple type of interference between light from the two halves

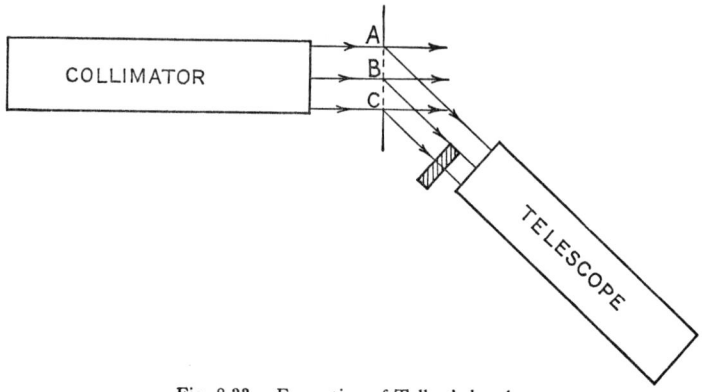

Fig. 8.33.—Formation of Talbot's bands

of the aperture. This explanation is not correct because the effect of the plate is not to produce two virtual sources but to displace part of the wave surface. Thus the problem is one of diffraction. The original explanation also fails to show why the fringes are found only when the plate is on one side of the aperture, and why there is an optimum thickness.

2.—A simple explanation of Talbot's bands may be based on the "irregular pulse" view of white light. In § 8.14 a grating of N lines was assumed to send a series of N wavelets to arrive successively and give rise to a vibration of wavelength λ at a certain point (P) in the spectrum. When the plate is inserted, two wave trains each $N\lambda/2$ in length will arrive at this point. One has arrived directly from the upper half of the grating (see fig. 8.33). The other has passed through the lower half of the grating and through the plate whose thickness we may put equal to t_g. Maximum interference will occur when the two wave trains completely overlap at the point P, i.e. when they start to arrive at that point simultaneously. If the plate were not present the one train would begin to arrive $N\lambda/2c$ seconds before the other. Owing to the presence of the plate it has to travel a distance t_g in a dispersive medium with group velocity U, while the other beam travels a distance t_g in air. We neglect the dispersion of air and put its refractive index equal to unity. The difference of time caused by the insertion of the plate is therefore (from 4(41))

$$\frac{t_g}{U} - \frac{t_g}{c} = \frac{t_g}{c}\left(\mu - \lambda\frac{d\mu}{d\lambda} - 1\right). \quad \ldots \quad 8(46)$$

* The plate may be inserted in various positions, either before or after the prism or grating. In the case of a liquid prism it may be inserted within the prism. It may also be inserted in front of the observer's eye so as to cover half the pupil. All these positions are equivalent, for our present purpose, to the one shown in fig. 8.33.

TALBOT'S BANDS 331

Thus for fringes of maximum visibility we must have

$$\tfrac{1}{2}N\lambda - t_g\left(\mu - \lambda\frac{d\mu}{d\lambda} - 1\right) = 0. \quad \ldots \ldots \quad 8(47)$$

When the above relation holds exactly the two wave trains interfere to produce a maximum at P. If the value of the left-hand side of 8(47), when λ' is substituted for λ, is $\tfrac{1}{2}\lambda'$, then for this wavelength the amplitude is zero. Thus the relation between the wavelengths corresponding to maxima and minima is given by

$$\tfrac{1}{2}N\lambda - t_g\left(\mu - \lambda\frac{d\mu}{d\lambda} - 1\right) = \tfrac{1}{2}(N-1)\lambda' - t_g\left\{\mu' - \lambda'\left(\frac{d\mu}{d\lambda}\right)' - 1\right\}, \quad 8(48)$$

where μ' and $(d\mu/d\lambda)'$ are the values corresponding to λ'. Over short ranges of the spectrum we may neglect the difference between μ and μ', and we then have

$$\frac{\lambda' - \lambda}{\lambda'} = \frac{1}{N} \quad \ldots \ldots \ldots \quad 8(49)$$

for the wavelength difference between a maximum and a minimum. If the thickness of the plate has some value between zero and twice the value given by 8(47), the wave trains partly overlap and some fringes are present, though the visibility is very low when t_g is near one of the extreme values. When, however, t_g is greater than twice the value given by 8(47), the wave trains from the part AB of the grating will have passed P before that from BC has commenced to arrive. No fringes will then be produced. Also no fringes will be produced if the plate is placed so as to retard the part AB of the wave train coming from AC. This part is already retarded with respect to the part BC before the plate is inserted and further retardation obviously does not produce interference.

3.—If we consider the problem from the point of view of the Fourier analysis, equation 6(30) may be integrated between limits corresponding to the two halves of the grating, the appropriate retardation being introduced. The integration is carried out for one wavelength, and then the resulting expression integrated over all wavelengths. This process is rather lengthy but it does give a complete solution, including the energy distribution both for the simple case considered in § 2 and for cases where the plate covers more or less than half the aperture, etc. Detailed treatments have been given by Airy, Stokes and Struve.*

EXAMPLES [8(xi)–8(xiii)]

8(xi). Write down equations for the passage of a wave group first through a prism (of base thickness t_p and refractive index μ_p) and then through a plate (of thickness t_g and refractive index μ_g). The plate covers half the prism. Consider in order the cases where (1) neither material is dispersive, (2) the prism material is non-dispersive and the plate is not, (3) both materials are dispersive and have

* A summary of Airy's analysis and full references are given by Rayleigh (Reference 8.14).

different indices and dispersions. Show that the condition for maximum clearness of Talbot's bands in the third case is

$$\left(\mu_p - \lambda \frac{d\mu_p}{d\lambda} - 1\right)\tfrac{1}{2}t_p - \left(\mu_G - \frac{\lambda\, d\mu_G}{d\lambda} - 1\right)t_G = 0, \qquad 8(50)$$

and that the results for the other two cases are the same as those obtained by putting one or both of the quantities $d\mu_G/d\lambda$ and $d\mu_p/d\lambda$ equal to zero in 8(50).

8(xii). Baden-Powell obtained bands by inserting a thin plate of dispersive material in a liquid prism, the length of the plate being half the height of the prism. Derive an expression for the maximum clearness of the bands. Under what conditions must the plate be placed (a) to touch the apex of the prism and (b) to touch the base of the prism?

8(xiii). The apparatus for the production of Talbot's bands may be considered as a transmission echelon grating (of two "steps") and a spectroscope acting together. Show that the echelon is in the single-order position for a wavelength corresponding to a maximum. Calculate the wavelength corresponding to double-order positions (when the plate is of optimum thickness for the production of Talbot's bands). Hence construct a "theory" of the bands. How does this theory explain the fact that bands are not obtained when the plate is inserted in the wrong position?

CHAPTER IX

Measurements with Interferometers

9.1.—Interference methods of measurement provide many examples of experiments in which an accurate result is obtained conveniently and without making excessive demands on the skill of the observer. The accurate result is made possible because the experiment is well designed and the apparatus accurately made. The initial observation is usually a measurement of a displacement in a system of interference fringes. This shows a change in the phase difference between two interfering beams, and indicates a change in optical path difference due either to a mechanical displacement or to a difference of refractive index.

9.2. Classification by Type of Interference.

Interferometers may be divided into the following types:

(a) Instruments in which the wavefront is divided into two or more parts. The division may be made by an opaque screen with a number of apertures (as in Young's experiment, § 5.6) or by means of prisms or mirrors as in Fresnel's experiments (§ 5.9).

(b) Instruments in which the light is divided by means of semi-reflecting surfaces. Part of the light is reflected, and part transmitted. These parts are brought together again by suitable arrangements of mirrors and prisms, and, being coherent, they interfere. The Michelson interferometer is a typical instrument of this type.

Mirrors may be used in either type of instrument as reflectors. The essential feature of the instruments of Type (b) is that at least one mirror is partially reflecting, and that the reflected and the transmitted beams are reunited.

9.3.—An entirely different method of classification is also possible. Instruments may be divided into those which operate by the interference of two beams, and those which employ more than two beams. The Fresnel biprism and the Rayleigh refractometer are examples of instruments of Type (a) which use two beams. The echelon diffraction grating is an instrument of Type (a) employing more than two beams.

The Michelson interferometer is an instrument of Type (b) which uses two beams. The Fabry-Pérot etalon is a multiple-beam device of Type (b).

The fringes produced by instruments of Type (a) are essentially diffraction fringes, and there would be some justification for calling them "diffractometers". The ruled diffraction grating is an instrument of this type. The usual practice is to apply the name "interferometer" to many instruments of Type (a) as well as to instruments of Type (b). This is done because the methods of manufacture and technique of use of many instruments of Type (a) are similar to those of instruments of Type (b). They are therefore called interferometers, but this name is not applied to the ruled diffraction grating which, from the purely technical point of view, may be regarded as a dispersive system alternative to a prism.

9.4. Classification of Uses of Interferometers.

The observations and measurements made with interferometers may be divided into five main classes:

(i) Geometrical measurements.

(ii) Measurements of refractive index.

(iii) Measurement of the ratio between the wavelength emitted by a standard source and a mechanical length.

(iv) Comparison of two wavelengths.

(v) Measurement of distribution of energy as a function of wavelength.

(vi) Investigations of theoretical importance.

The first class includes the testing of optical components such as lenses or prisms, the comparison of mechanical gauges used in machine-shop work, and the measurement of small mechanical displacements. The fourth class includes the observation of the very fine structure in a spectrum line, as well as the comparison of lines of different intensities. The sixth class includes a number of experiments which will be described in later chapters.

9.5. The Testing of Optical Components.

From the point of view of wave theory, the action of an optical component is to alter the direction or shape of wave surfaces. When a parallel beam of light falls on a plane mirror the wave surfaces change in direction but remain plane. When a similar beam falls upon an ideal lens, the plane wave surfaces are changed into spherical wave surfaces whose centres are located at a point in the focal plane. In practice, most optical components do not fulfil their function perfectly. They cause some deformation of the wave surfaces. If a beam of light is reflected by a mirror which is plane except for small local deviations,

§ 9.6 THE TWYMAN-GREEN INTERFEROMETER 335

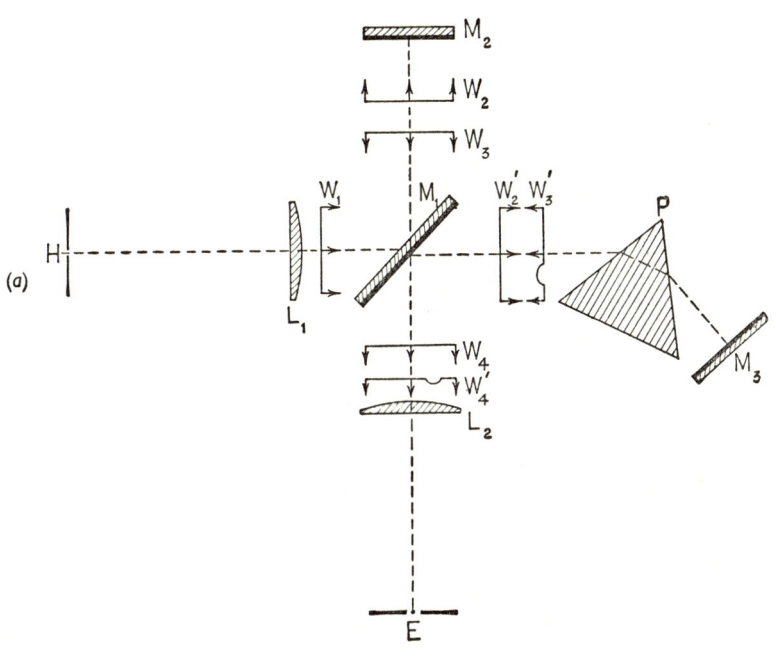

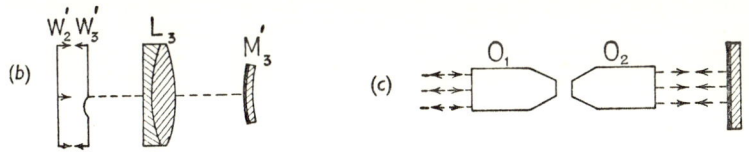

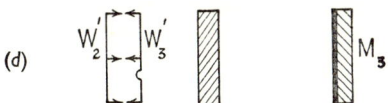

Fig. 9.1.—Twyman-Green interferometer: (a) arrangement for testing a prism, (b) testing a lens, (c) testing a microscope objective, (d) testing a block of glass

these irregularities cause corresponding irregularities in the wave surfaces which represent the reflected waves. A lens may suffer from local irregularities and may also show a somewhat different type of error. The emergent wave surface may be smooth, but may not be of the desired shape. Both these errors may be included in the statement that all paths from the object point to the image point through the lens are not optically equal. It is thus desirable to have an instrument which will test directly the total effect which an optical component, or assembly of components, has upon a wave surface. Such a test is also a test of equality of optical path from object point to image point.

9.6. The Twyman-Green Interferometer.

The instrument shown in fig. 9.1 was designed by Twyman and Green for testing prisms. Light from a monochromatic source is focused by an auxiliary lens upon a small hole in a diaphragm placed at H. The point source so formed is at the focus of the lens L_1. Plane waves emerging from this lens are partly reflected and partly transmitted by the half-silvered mirror M_1. The reflected light is again reflected by the mirror M_2, and is focused by the lens L_2 upon a hole in a diaphragm placed at E. The other part of the light passes through the prism, is reflected by M_3 and, after another passage through the prism, reaches the diaphragm at E. The observer's eye is placed immediately behind the diaphragm. If the prism is perfect, he sees a uniformly illuminated field. The illumination is a maximum if the position of the mirror M_2 is adjusted

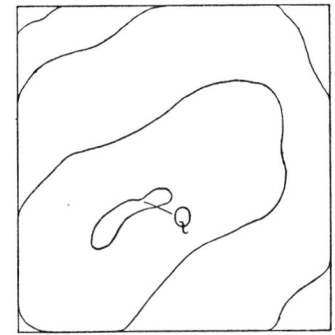

Fig. 9.2.—Contour map formed by fringes of equal thickness

so as to make the difference between the optical paths of the two beams equal to an integral multiple of the wavelength. When the prism is imperfect, the wave surfaces which reach L_2 after reflection at M_3 are not plane. They interfere with the plane wave surfaces from M_2 so as to produce a set of fringes which may be regarded as a contour map of the imperfections in the prism. A typical map is shown in fig. 9.2. Q represents the highest point of a " hill ". The contour lines are usually drawn in wet rouge on the surface of the prism with a paint brush. The excess material may be removed by

§ 9.6   THE TWYMAN-GREEN INTERFEROMETER   337

polishing first at the point Q, and then gradually extending the area of polishing to the other contour lines.

9.7—If it is uncertain whether Q represents the top of a hill or the bottom of a depression, the doubt may be resolved by pressing on the frame of the instrument so as to displace the mirror M_3, and thereby to increase the corresponding path. If the contours expand so as to enclose a larger area, a hill is indicated and *vice versa*. The fringes give the total effect on the wave surface produced by double passage through the prism, and show (in wavelengths) the departure of the wave surface from flatness. These imperfections in the wave surfaces may arise from want of flatness of either or both surfaces of the prism, or from local variations in the refractive index of the material. The instrument does not distinguish between these possibilities. In an optically perfect prism the quantity $(\mu - 1)t$ increases linearly from the apex to the base. Optically perfect prisms are usually obtained by polishing the surfaces so that small differences of thickness compensate for inhomogeneity of the optical material. This process is called *figuring*.

9.8.—It should be noted that variations in the contour lines may be obtained by a tilt of the plane of reference. A small adjustment of either M_2 or M_3 may change the contour map from that shown in fig. 9.3 to that shown in fig. 9.4. The

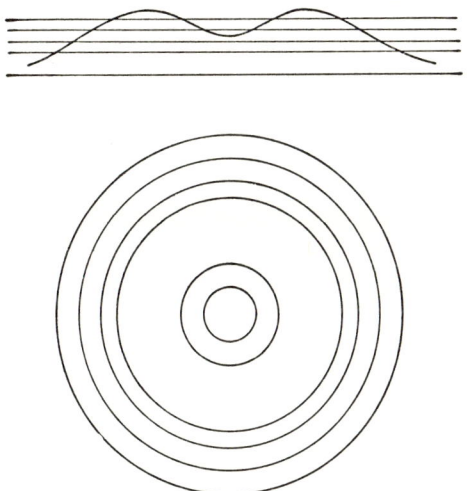

Fig. 9.3.—Contours of local depression (section shown above)

form of the surface is the same in both cases (see sectional diagrams at the tops of the figures) but the plane of section is different. If the operator bases his polishing on either diagram he will obtain a perfect prism, but the angle of the prism obtained by using one diagram will differ slightly from that obtained when the other is used. The skilled operator will adjust the instrument before marking the contours, so as to choose an aspect which requires the minimum polishing to achieve a corrected prism.

9.9.—Although the Twyman-Green interferometer is superficially similar to the Michelson interferometer, its invention marked a radically new departure in interferometry and in optical testing. It differs from the Michelson instrument in the use of the point source which, together with the lens L_1, produces a plane wave surface; it differs

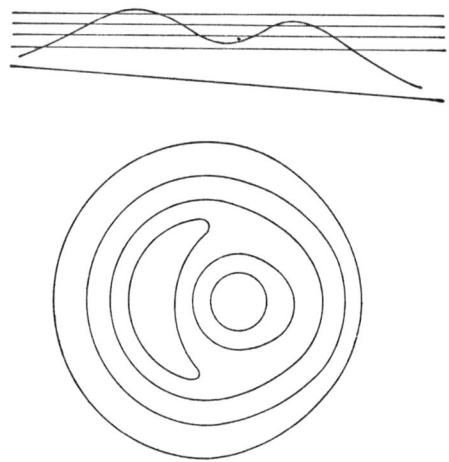

Fig. 9.4.—Change in contours when reference plane is tilted (as shown above)

also in the use of the lens L_2 which arranges that all parts of the emergent wave surfaces enter the observer's eye. It should be noted that the lens L_2 does not act as a telescope and form an image of fringes localized at infinity. The observer's eye is placed *at* its focus, not so as to *view* its focus.

The function of the lens L_2 is to make light from all parts of the field enter the observer's eye. The beams which interfere are nearly parallel, i.e. we are concerned with only narrow pencils of rays. This gives great depth of focus and the fringes are not sharply localized. If the observer puts the marking brush near either surface of a prism and focuses his eye upon it, he will see the fringes in focus, and can mark the part of the surface which must be worked to give correction.

9.10.—The Twyman-Green interferometer may be adapted to test lenses or lens systems (fig. 9.1*b*). If the lens L_3 which is under test changes the incident plane wave into an exactly spherical wave, then a convex mirror M_3' suitably placed will return all the rays along their own paths and the field will be uniformly bright in one adjustment.

The procedure for locating and removing errors is similar to that described for the prism.

There is some difficulty in making spherical mirrors of radius of curvature small enough to test high-power microscope objectives. This difficulty has been overcome by using the surface of a minute drop of mercury as the reflecting surface. When the drop is of the order of a millimetre in diameter, the forces due to surface tension are so much greater than those due to gravity that the form of the drop is effectively spherical. An alternative method is to use an objective O_3 of known high quality, together with the objective O_2 which is under test, so that together they form a telescopic combination.

The interferometer may also be used to test pieces of glass with nearly parallel sides, using the arrangement shown in fig. 9.1d. When a plate shows no fringes the value of $(\mu - 1)t$ is the same at all points, but the surfaces are not necessarily flat.

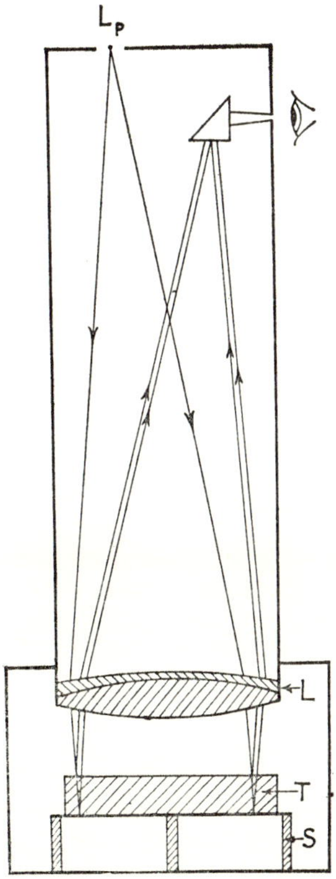

9.11. Fizeau Method.

The apparatus shown in fig. 9.5 may be used for testing the constancy of μt for a piece of glass with nearly parallel sides. A black cloth is placed at the base of the instrument and interference is obtained between beams of light reflected from the top and bottom faces of the test piece T. These beams are of approximately equal amplitude. The function of the lens L is to arrange that a plane wavefront falls nearly normally on the plate. Thus light reaching the observer's eye from any part of the plate has passed through it nearly normally. The fringes seen are fringes of equal optical thickness. They are localized in the plate (§ 5.20), though owing to the smallness of the source they are not very sharply localized. In many ways this arrangement is like a simplified form of the Twyman-Green interferometer. The lens in fig. 9.5 fulfils the functions both of L_1 and of L_2 in fig. 9.1. It does not act as a telescope to focus the fringes. The essentials of this arrangement were originally due to Fizeau, but the form shown is a more recent development.

Fig. 9.5.—Fizeau interferometer

340 MEASUREMENTS WITH INTERFEROMETERS

The homogeneity of an optical material may be tested by cutting a sample and polishing the sides to be plane and parallel. The Twyman-Green interferometer may then be used to determine the variation of $(\mu - 1)t$, and the Fizeau apparatus to determine the variation of μt. When both of these are known the variations of μ and of t may be calculated.

9.12.—An *optical flat* is a piece of material having one surface plane to within one-tenth of a wavelength or better.* A surface may be tested against a glass optical flat by placing the surfaces in contact, and viewing the fringes of equal thickness described in § 5.18. An extended source of light—such as the light of the sky or a diffusing

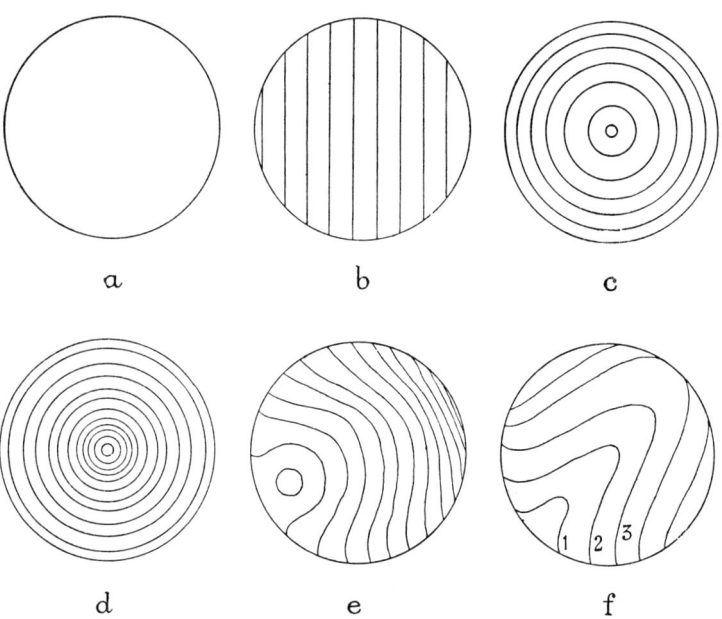

Fig. 9.6.—Fringe systems obtained with Fizeau-type interferometer: (a) plane parallel surfaces, (b) plane surfaces inclined at a small angle, (c) central " hill ", (d) central " depression " at top of " hill ", (e) small " hill " or " depression " at side, (f) " hill " or " valley " running diagonally across plate.

screen illuminated by a mercury arc—may be used. A colour filter is used to select a moderately narrow spectral region. With this arrangement irregularities of about one-twentieth of a wavelength may easily be detected. Some typical appearances are shown in fig. 9.6.

* The highest quality optical flats are plane to about one-hundredth of a wavelength.

9.13.—When it is inconvenient to place the surfaces in contact, a Fizeau type of apparatus may still be used. Since the fringes are seen by nearly parallel light, the surfaces may be widely separated. If the Fizeau arrangement is used with a glass plate as the standard optical flat, extra fringes may be seen owing to reflections between the two surfaces of the plate. These are confusing unless the plate is made wedge-shaped (so that the extra fringes are very close), or of exactly constant optical thickness.

9.14.—It is interesting to consider the production of an optical flat when no standard flat is available for test. When two pieces of glass are ground and polished on one another with a suitable rotary motion, they tend to become spherical. One is convex and the other concave. If the radius of curvature is very large, tests with contour fringes only reveal the accuracy of fit, but do not show that they are not plane. To meet this difficulty three surfaces are worked against each other, in pairs, until the fringes show that each of the three possible pairs fit. Then all three surfaces must be plane.

9.15. Multiple-beam Fringes.

A method of using multiple-beam interference for the examination of surfaces has recently been used by Tolansky.* His apparatus is essentially the same as that shown in fig. 9.5, but he uses a partly reflecting film of silver on both surfaces. The silver is deposited by evaporation in vacuum. Special care is taken to ensure that the light is accurately parallel, and normal to the surfaces. One of the surfaces is a good-quality optical flat, and the other is the natural surface of a crystal, such as quartz or mica. Owing to the multiple reflections between the two surfaces, the bright fringes are sharper than those obtained with the ordinary Fizeau method. "Hills" and "depressions" which are only 30 Å. in height can be detected, and the error in measuring the height is only a few Ångström units in the best cases. The molecule of mica is 20 Å. in thickness, and it is possible to detect (on the surface of mica crystals) regions which are raised above the general surface level by distances varying from 40 Å. to over 20,000 Å. These distances are always multiples of the lattice spacing.

It should be noted that the high linear discrimination is attained only in the vertical direction, and is due to the increase of effective length of path produced by multiple reflection. Some multiple-beam fringes of the type described above are shown in Plate II i, j, k and l. Fringes obtained by the ordinary Fizeau method (§ 9.11) are shown for comparison (Plate II g and h, p. 130).

* Reference 9.11.

9.16. Testing of Mechanical Gauges.

Accurate standards of length are required for high-precision machine-shop work. The standards of length usually consist of cylindrical pieces of steel, whose ends have been polished to be accurately flat and parallel to one another. Two such gauges may be put together by a process known as " wringing ". The surfaces to be " wrung " are carefully cleaned and pressed together with a minute film of paraffin between them. The paraffin is squeezed out by the atmospheric pressure so that the surfaces are forced into good contact. The accuracy of an instrument such as a good screw gauge may be estimated by finding what reading it gives when applied to a test block whose length is known very accurately. The test block itself is liable to wear under constant use, and it is therefore usual to retain certain standards of specially high quality, which are used only to check the ordinary working test block. The following method enables a test block to be rapidly and accurately compared with a standard.

9.17.—The surfaces of the test block are first tested for flatness by the method described in § 9.12. If they are not sufficiently flat, the block has no unique and definite length to be accurately measured.

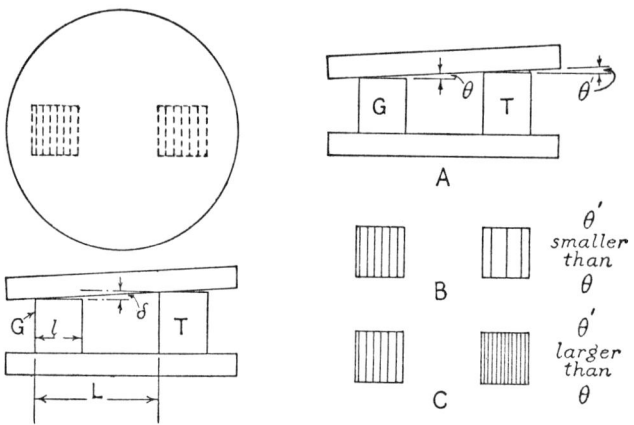

Fig. 9.7.—Testing of end-gauges

If the ends are flat, then one end of the test block and one end of the standard gauge are wrung on to an optically flat steel plate. An optically flat glass plate is placed across the top (fig. 9.7A). This flat will usually rest on one edge of each block, and there will be a wedge of air between the flat and the standard gauge. Interference fringes will be seen, and from their separation the difference of height (δh) between the gauge and the test block may be calculated.* Suppose that the number of fringes per unit length is n, and the distance between the two edges on which the upper plate rests is L, then

$$\delta h = \frac{n\lambda L}{2}. \qquad \ldots \ldots \quad 9(1)$$

It is usual to view the fringes through a filter which passes a narrow region of the spectrum of wavelength 5100Å., or approximately 2×10^{-5} inch. If L is made equal to one inch, then one fringe per inch implies a difference of length of one-hundred-thousandth of an inch. It is not convenient to count fringes whose separation is less than 1/40 inch, and the maximum difference of length which can easily be measured by this method is therefore

$$\delta h = (40L) \times 10^{-5} = 4 \times 10^{-4} L. \quad \ldots \quad 9(2)$$

Thus with optical flats of $2\frac{1}{2}$-inch diameter, a difference as great as one-thousandth of an inch can be measured. Greater differences than this can be conveniently measured by micrometer screw-gauge methods.

EXAMPLES [9(i)–9(v)]

9(i). What will be the appearance of the fringes obtained with the apparatus described in §§ 9.16 and 9.17 if the ends of the test block are flat, but not quite parallel to one another? (b) What changes will occur when the test block is rotated about a vertical axis?

[The fringes will always be straight lines perpendicular to the line of greatest slope. Their separation will change when the block is rotated. See fig. 9.7B and C.]

9(ii). A standard gauge and a test block have each a one-inch square cross-section. The ends of the gauge are plane and parallel, and its length is 2 inches. The ends of the test block are plane, but not quite parallel, and its greatest length is a little less than the length of the gauge. The gauge and the test block are wrung on to an optical flat, so that their centres are 2 inches apart. An optical flat is placed across the top. In one orientation of the test block 20 fringes to the inch are seen in the film above it. When it is rotated through 180 degrees there are 5 fringes per inch. In each position the fringes above the test block are parallel to those above the gauge. What deductions concerning the test block can be derived from these observations?

* Fringes are also seen over the test block, but they do not give the difference of height directly unless the surfaces of the test block are accurately parallel [see Example 9(ii)].

What further information may be obtained by viewing the fringes over the gauge?

> [There are two possible solutions which give the same number of fringes over the test block. In one case the flat rests on the same edge of the test block in both orientations. This situation gives maximum height of test block 1·99990 in., and minimum height 1·99975 in. The other solution gives heights of 1·99980 in. and 1·99970 in. The cases may be distinguished by viewing the fringes over the gauge.]

9(iii). A glass flat is placed on top of a strip of polished steel which can be bent by weights as shown in fig. 9.8a. The fringes obtained are as shown in fig. 9.8b. Give a qualitative discussion of the shape of the surface of the steel, and say generally how the results may be explained. [See answer to 9(iv).]

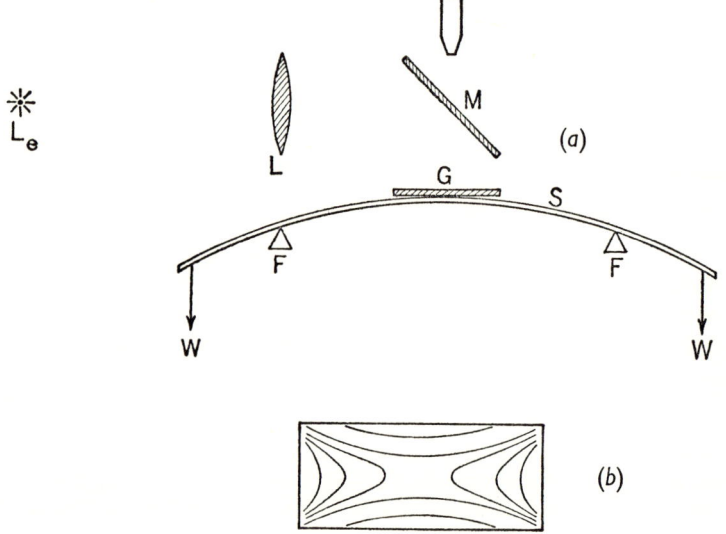

Fig. 9.8.—Cornu's method for the measurement of Young's modulus and Poisson's ratio

9(iv). Show that by means of measurements on the fringes described in Example 9(iii) it is possible to calculate Young's modulus and Poisson's ratio for the steel. Derive the appropriate formulæ.

> [See CHAMPION and DAVY: *Properties of Matter* (Blackie), third edition pp. 78–80.]

9(v). You are given two distance pieces each approximately one centimetre cube. How would you use interference methods to determine the ratio of the volumes? Give some estimate of the percentage accuracy attainable.

> [0·003 per cent accuracy without taking special precautions.]

9.18 Measurement of Mechanical Displacements.

Interference methods have been applied to measure small mechanical displacements in the study of elasticity, and in many other branches of physics. One of the simplest applications of this type is due to Fizeau, who used the apparatus shown in fig. 9.9 to measure the thermal expansion of crystals of which only short specimens were available. Interference fringes are formed in the air-film between the top of the crystal and the plate P. The displacement of the fringes on heating measures the difference between the expansion of the crystal and that of the blocks which define the position of the plate. If the expansion of the material of which the blocks are made is known, the expansion of the crystal may be calculated. If the air-film is wedge-shaped, the change in the difference of length may be obtained by viewing the fringes in a microscope focused on the film, and counting the number which pass the cross-wire. An alternative and in some ways a more convenient method is to make the upper plate slightly spherical, so that Newton's rings are seen. The expansion causes fresh rings to appear or to disappear at the centre and the number of these rings may be counted.

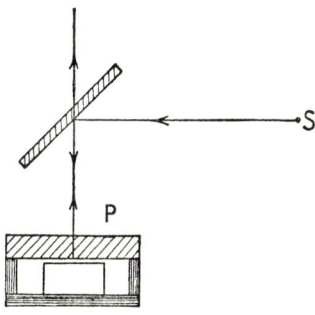

Fig. 9.9.—Fizeau's method for thermal expansion of crystals

The use of interference methods for measuring mechanical displacements is desirable only when sufficient accuracy is not obtainable by more direct means. Interference methods are unlikely to displace the mirror-and-scale method of measuring small angular displacements, because the latter is very convenient, and has sufficient accuracy and sensitivity for most purposes. The use of a high-sensitivity method of measurement in one part of an experiment is not justified unless a corresponding accuracy is obtainable in the other parts of the experiment. When interference methods are used it is necessary to be sure that the advantages of the method are not lost through irregular displacements due to temperature changes, mechanical vibrations, etc. Generally, the simpler interference methods have a rather small range, i.e. they become inapplicable if the path difference exceeds a few dozen wavelengths. For example, the method described in § 9.16 for comparing mechanical gauges fails if the difference between the lengths of the gauges exceeds about 50 wavelengths. The range of interference methods may be extended by the use of compensators (see § 9.23), but this makes the apparatus more elaborate. Thus interference methods should be used only in conjunction with an experimental arrangement whose basic design enables full advantage to be obtained from the accuracy of the interferometer.

9.19. Measurement of Refractive Index and of Small Differences of Index.

Several interference methods have been devised for the measurement of the refractive indices of gases, and for small differences in refractive index of liquids and solids. The most generally convenient and accurate apparatus is the Rayleigh refractometer. Fig. 9.10a is

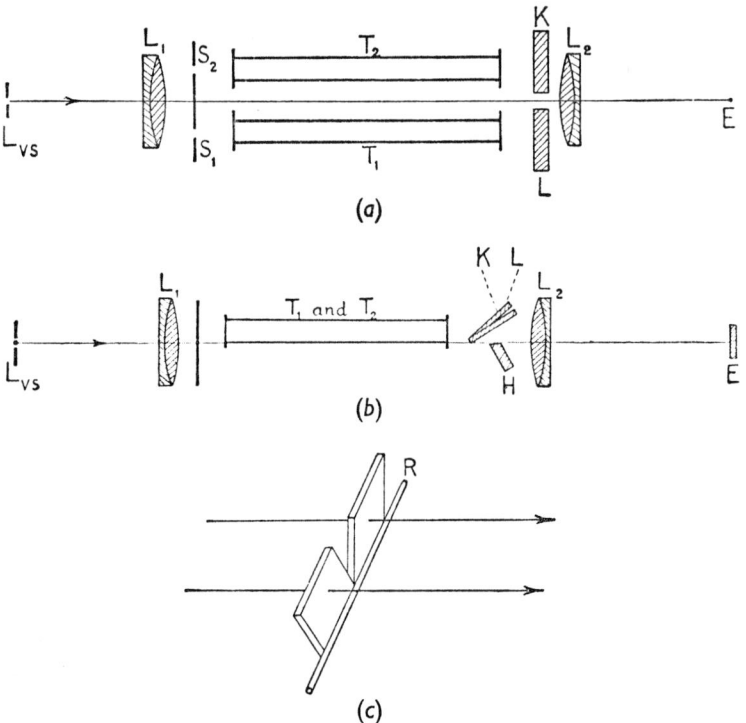

Fig. 9.10.—Rayleigh refractometer: (a) plan, (b) vertical section, (c) compensator

a diagram of the instrument seen from above. Light from a vertical slit source L_{vs} is collimated by the lens L_1 and passes through the tubes T_1 and T_2 and the vertical slits S_1 and S_2. Diffraction fringes are produced in the focal plane of the lens L_2 and are viewed with the aid of the eyepiece E.

Suppose that the length of each tube is t. Then, if there is a small difference ($\Delta\mu$) between the refractive indices of the materials in the

§ 9.19   MEASUREMENT OF REFRACTIVE INDEX   347

tubes, a path difference $\Delta s = t \Delta \mu$ is introduced and the fringes are displaced from the standard position obtained when $\Delta \mu = 0$. The difference of refractive index may be measured either by observing the fringe shift directly or, more conveniently, by a compensation method.

9.20.—The fringes are the diffraction fringes of a grating of two lines. If $2d$ is the width of each slit, and $2e$ is the distance between the centres of the slits, the distribution of illumination in the fringes is obtained by putting $N = 2$, $\theta_1 = 0$ and $\theta_2 = \theta$ in equation 6(17). The relative energy in a direction θ is given by

$$E(\theta) = \left\{ \frac{\sin\left(\frac{2\pi}{\lambda} d \sin \theta\right)}{\frac{2\pi}{\lambda} d \sin \theta} \right\}^2 \left\{ \frac{\sin\left(\frac{4\pi}{\lambda} e \sin \theta\right)}{2 \sin\left(\frac{2\pi}{\lambda} e \sin \theta\right)} \right\}^2, \quad 9(3)$$

which can be put in the form

$$E(\theta) = \left\{ \frac{\sin\left(\frac{2\pi}{\lambda} d \sin \theta\right)}{\frac{2\pi d}{\lambda} \sin \theta} \right\}^2 \cos^2\left(\frac{2\pi}{\lambda} e \sin \theta\right). \quad 9(4)$$

In the instrument made by Hilger and Watts, Ltd., the slits are each 2·5 millimetres wide and the separation is 11 millimetres between centres. Fig. 9.11 shows the variation of illumination in the focal plane of L_2.

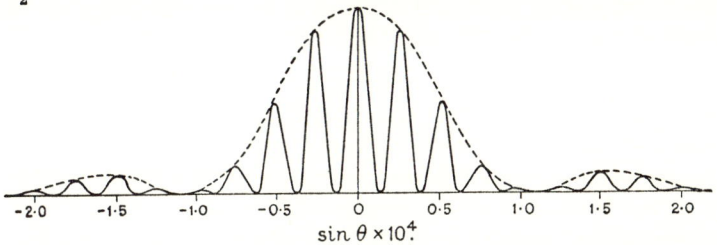

Fig. 9.11

9.21.—The instrument is reliable and convenient in operation only because a number of matters of detail have been carefully considered. The fringes in the focal plane of L_2 are extremely fine (fig. 9.11). They are viewed by means of a cylindrical lens which consists of an accurately made glass rod of diameter about 2 millimetres. This lens gives an effective magnification (in the direction of separation of the fringes) of about 150. The brightness of the field is reduced 150 times. It is still very much brighter than it would be if a spherical lens of the same magnification were used, since the spherical lens would reduce the brightness 22,500 times (i.e. 150^2 times). This is important as the total amount of light passing down the tubes is not very great. In the simple form of the instrument so far described, monochromatic light is used. The refractive index of a gas may be measured by evacuating both tubes, and then counting the number of fringes which pass a fine needle point placed in the focal plane of L_2, when gas is slowly admitted to one tube. This method places a considerable strain on the observer who is very liable to miss one of the fine fringes. Also it is not applicable to a determination of the difference of the refractive indices of liquids.

9.22.—Convenience and accuracy of observation are increased by using as fiducial mark a set of fringes similar to those due to light which passes through T_1 and T_2, instead of a cross-wire. The way in which this is done is shown in fig. 9.10b, which gives a side view of the instrument. Two beams pass below the tubes T_1 and T_2. An independent set of fringes is formed. By tilting the plate H these may be moved vertically so that their upper edge may be brought into coincidence with the lower edge of the fringes due to light which has passed through T_1 and T_2. In this way it is possible to take advantage of the high vernier acuity of the eye. A horizontal displacement between the two fringe systems of only one-fortieth of a fringe width can be detected, although it would not be possible to set a cross-wire on either system to an accuracy better than about one-tenth of a fringe.

9.23.—The accuracy and convenience of the measurement are improved by compensating the optical path difference. The two fringe systems are then used as a null indicator of equality of path. The compensator, in the form originally due to Jamin, is shown in fig. 9.10c. It consists of two glass plates set at an angle to one another, and connected through the rod R, by means of which the system may be rotated as a whole. When the rod is turned the thickness of glass in each beam is altered but, since the glass plates are inclined to one another, the change in path of one beam is slightly greater than that of the other. Thus a considerable rotation of the rod corresponds to a small shift of the fringes.

Rotation of the compensator makes the two systems of fringes slightly inclined to one another. This does not matter in some applications where the fringes are comparatively broad, and are viewed by an ordinary eyepiece. In the modern Rayleigh refractometer, the cylindrical lens has to be set with its axis exactly parallel to the system of fringes. The compensator must be modified so that only a negligible rotation of the fringes is introduced. In the Hilger instrument both plates are fairly thin. One is fixed, and the other rotates with the rod R. A small movement of the single plate introduces a sufficient path difference. A small and accurately reproducible rotation is produced by turning a micrometer screw which presses against a radial arm attached to the rod R.

9.24.—In order to know the refractive index for a definite wavelength it is necessary to use monochromatic light, but the central fringe obtained with monochromatic light is indistinguishable from its neighbours. The systems appear to coincide when the path difference ($t\Delta\mu$) is an integral number of wavelengths. The following method is therefore adopted.

T_1 and T_2 are evacuated (or filled with standard material) and white-light fringes are produced. The compensator is turned until the fringe systems in the upper and lower halves of the field appear to coincide. Monochromatic light is then introduced, and a small alteration is made in the setting so as to bring the two systems into coincidence. The setting of the compensator is read (on the micrometer scale). The material under test is then admitted to one tube, and the adjustment of the compensator is made again, first with white and then with monochromatic light. The final setting of the compensator is read. The difference between the two readings of the compensator gives $t\Delta\mu$ and hence $\Delta\mu$. The compensator is calibrated with monochromatic light, by using it to produce displacements of 1, 2, 3, etc., fringes and noting the corresponding readings on the scale. This calibration must be carried out with a number of different wavelengths suitably spaced through the spectrum.

9.25.—The smallest difference of path which can be detected is about $\tfrac{1}{40}\lambda$ and the largest which can conveniently be measured is about 200λ. The corresponding limits of index are

$$\Delta\mu_{\min} = \tfrac{1}{40}\frac{\lambda}{t} \quad \text{and} \quad \Delta\mu_{\max} = \frac{200\lambda}{t}.$$

With a tube length of 100 centimetres, the instrument will detect a difference of index of about one part in 10^8 and the maximum difference measurable is about one part in 10^4. With a tube length of one centimetre the sensitivity is one part in a million, and the maximum difference measurable is of order one part in 100. The instrument was used by Rayleigh to measure the refractivities of the rare gases helium and argon. The smaller refractivity is $3·5 \times 10^{-5}$ at standard temperature and pressure, and is thus well within the range of the instrument.

Measurements of refractivity can also be used to detect impurities in gases, and the instrument is capable of detecting 0·01 per cent of hydrogen or 0·03 per cent of carbon monoxide in air. A modified portable form of the instrument has been used for detecting "fire-damp" in mines. The refractometer has also been widely used to measure small differences of refractive index of solutions, and hence to indicate differences in composition of solutions of chemical and biochemical interest. The final limiting factor in accuracy and convenience is set by the difficulty of temperature control. With liquids, it is often necessary to wait an hour or more to allow temperature equilibrium to be established. For this reason it is always desirable to choose the shortest tubes which give the necessary sensitivity.

9.26.—An interesting point arises when the dispersion of the material under test is different from that of the compensating plates. Suppose that one of the tubes is evacuated and the other contains material of index μ; suppose also that a difference of thickness t' of material of index μ' is introduced by the compensator. Then the centres of the fringe systems obtained with white light will be undisplaced if the extra paths introduced are traversed in equal times by two groups of waves which emerge from S_1 and S_2 respectively. This will be so if

$$\left(\mu - \lambda\frac{d\mu}{d\lambda} - 1\right)t = \left(\mu' - \lambda\frac{d\mu'}{d\lambda} - 1\right)t'. \quad \ldots \quad 9(5)$$

If
$$\frac{1}{\mu - 1}\frac{d\mu}{d\lambda} - \frac{1}{\mu' - 1}\frac{d\mu'}{d\lambda} = 0, \quad \ldots \quad 9(6)$$

then 9(5) reduces to $(\mu - 1)t = (\mu' - 1)t'$, and the instrument measures $\Delta\mu$ as indicated in the simple theory. However, if $\left|t\frac{d\mu}{d\lambda} - t'\frac{d\mu'}{d\lambda}\right|$ exceeds $\frac{1}{2}$, the test with

white light will not bring the correct pair of fringes into coincidence. Even for smaller dispersions there is an observational difficulty in that the central fringes obtained with white light are blurred to such an extent that the the central fringe cannot be identified with certainty. This difficulty may be overcome by using short tubes to determine a preliminary value of the index. This value is sufficient to show which of the fringes obtained with monochromatic light have to be brought into coincidence when the longer tubes are used.

EXAMPLES [9(vi)–9(xi)]

9(vi). The refractivity of helium is $3·5 \times 10^{-5}$ and that of argon is $2·8 \times 10^{-4}$. Describe how you would use the Rayleigh refractometer to estimate the amount of helium in an argon/helium mixture which may contain from 50 to 100 per cent of argon. Assuming that the gas is to be used at standard temperature and pressure and that the compensator scale covers 200 fringes, calculate an appropriate length of tube. Estimate the accuracy of the determination under optimum conditions. Take $\lambda = 5000$ Å.

[The optimum length of tube is about 80 cm., since a greater length would not permit the whole range of refractivities to be covered. The accuracy of the determination is then such that a difference of 0·006 per cent of argon in the mixture can be detected.]

9(vii). In what way, if any, would your conclusions in relation to the previous problem be modified if the test samples consisted of only one cubic centimetre of gas at S.T.P?

[Since a tube of cross-sectional area much less than 0·2 cm.^{2} is impracticable, the length would have to be reduced to about 5 cm. This would reduce the sensitivity to about 0·1 per cent of argon.]

9(viii). The refractivity of air is $2 \cdot 92 \times 10^{-4}$ and that of helium is $3 \cdot 5 \times 10^{-5}$. It is suspected that a specimen of helium may be contaminated with air. What is the smallest amount of contamination that could be detected by measurement of the refractive index?

[Using tubes 100 cm. long, 0·005 per cent air could be detected.]

9(ix). Discuss how the Rayleigh refractometer might be used to determine whether the refractivity of air is proportional to the density. How great a range of density could conveniently be covered? What lengths of tubes would be desirable?

[A tube one metre long would give 0·1 per cent accuracy for a pressure of about 0·05 atmosphere, and a tube 0·5 cm. long would give 200 fringes displacement with about 70 atmospheres. Hence the range is 0·05 atmosphere to 70 atmospheres.]

9(x). The refractive index of a 4 per cent solution of a certain salt is 1·3388, and of a 6 per cent solution is 1·3418. The refractivity varies linearly between these limits. It is desired to measure the percentage strengths of solutions to within $\pm 0 \cdot 001$ per cent. Explain how the Rayleigh refractometer might be used for this purpose and estimate a suitable length of the tubes.

[Suitable length = 1 or 2 cm.]

9(xi). A Jamin compensator consists of two plates each of thickness t set at an angle of 30 degrees to one another. Obtain an expression for the difference of path introduced when the bisector makes an angle θ with the direction of the two beams.

9.27. Measurement of Wavelength.

The study of the wavelengths of spectrum lines by means of interferometers forms an extension of measurements with grating spectrographs just as the measurement of distance gauges with interferometers increases the accuracy of measurements made with instruments like screw gauges. There is no difficulty in measuring the wavelengths of most spectrum lines to within 0·05 Å. (or one part in 10^5) by means of grating spectrographs. Lines which are too diffuse to be measured within this accuracy on the photograph of a grating spectrum are usually not suitable for study with an interferometer. In a similar way there is no point in trying to measure the length of an end gauge with an interferometer if measurements with a screw gauge show that the ends are seriously non-planar. If large numbers of moderately accurate measurements of wavelength are required, the spectrograph is the appropriate instrument. Interferometers are used:

(a) To determine the ratio between one standard wavelength and the standard metre. This comparison has been made to within one or two parts in 10^7.

(b) To compare wavelengths so as to be able to compile a set of a few thousand secondary wavelength standards. A large number of iron lines have been compared in this way. Spectrographic measurements may thus be referred to secondary standards of wavelength near to the unknown wavelength.

(c) To investigate the fine structure of spectrum lines and to measure differences of wavelength of the order of a few hundredths or thousandths of an Ångström unit.

It is convenient to defer consideration of (a) until the technical methods required for investigation (b) have been described.

9.28. Comparison of Wavelengths by Coincidences.

This method is similar to the well-known method of comparing the periods of two pendulums by observing the interval between times when the phases coincide. Its essentials have already been described (§ 4.11) in connection with the visibility of fringes obtained with a sodium light source and a Michelson interferometer. The Fabry-Pérot interferometer is now usually employed and fringes due to the two wavelengths are observed. The distance between the plates is varied and the separations (e_1, e_2, etc.) when the fringes show maximum clarity are noted. Suppose that λ_1 is to be determined by reference to λ_2 (a known wavelength) and that the fringe of order m for λ_1 coincides with the fringe of order $(m+n)$ for λ_2. The next coincidence will occur after p fringes of λ_1 and $(p+1)$ of λ_2. The observations give only p and not m or n, but the ratio $\lambda_1 : \lambda_2$ may be calculated for

$$\left. \begin{array}{l} 2e_1 = m\lambda_1 = (m+n)\lambda_2, \\ 2e_2 = (m+p)\lambda_1 = (m+n+p+1)\lambda_2, \end{array} \right\} \quad \ldots \quad 9(7)$$

and hence
$$\lambda_1 = \frac{p+1}{p} \lambda_2 \quad \ldots \ldots \quad 9(8)$$

or
$$\lambda_1 - \lambda_2 = \frac{\lambda_2 \lambda_1}{2(e_2 - e_1)}. \quad \ldots \ldots \quad 9(9)$$

Sometimes the number of fringes between coincidences is counted and 9(8) is used. Alternatively 9(9) may be applied. On the right-hand side of the equation approximate values of the wavelengths, derived from spectroscopic measurements, are used. The value of $(e_2 - e_1)$ is obtained from a micrometer screw reading. The right-hand side of 9(9) then gives a more accurate value of $(\lambda_1 - \lambda_2)$ than that originally available. It is usually necessary to observe a number of coincidences. If this is done the method can be made very accurate, but it is rather laborious especially in view of the fact that every pair of wavelengths has to be treated independently.

9.29. Comparison of Wavelengths by Exact Fractions.

This method, which is due to Benoît, depends on the same principle as the method of coincidences, but the principle is applied in a more subtle and elegant way. It is based on the fact that the distance between two coincidences of scales which are divided into different units is the least common multiple of the units of the different scales. Thus if three rulers are divided in units of 2, 3 and 5 inches respectively, and their zeroes aligned, coincidences between the first two occur at every sixth inch, and coincidences between all three occur at every thirtieth inch.

Suppose that we are told that the length of a certain bar is one inch greater than *one* of the lengths at which the three scales coincide, but are not told which one. If a rough measurement of the length of the bar has yielded the value (8 ± 1) feet, we can at once deduce that the length is 91 inches, because no other length would agree with both the data. In the optical problem we determine a given distance by measuring the fraction by which it exceeds an integral number of wavelengths. This measurement is made for three or more different known wavelengths, and we then know that the optical path $(2e)$ is given by

$$2e = (n_1 + f_1)\lambda_1 = (n_2 + f_2)\lambda_2 = (n_3 + f_3)\lambda_3. \quad . \quad 9(10)$$

In this equation n_1, n_2, n_3 are integers whose exact values are unknown. The fractions are known within an error of 2 or 3 per cent of a unit. If e were entirely unknown, knowledge of the fractions in equation 9(10) would only enable us to say that it had one of a certain set of very precisely defined values. Only one of these, however, agrees sufficiently well with a known approximate value of e, and we therefore know that this is the correct one.

9.30.—The method of measuring the fraction with a Fabry-Pérot etalon will now be described. Suppose that the relation between the thickness and λ_1 is given by 9(10). Then bright rings occur for angles of incidence θ_1, θ_2, etc., given by

$$n_1 \lambda_1 = 2e \cos \theta_1 = (n_1 + f_1)\lambda_1 \cos \theta_1,$$
$$(n_1 - 1)\lambda_1 = 2e \cos \theta_2 = (n_1 + f_1)\lambda_1 \cos \theta_2,$$
$$(n_1 - m + 1)\lambda_1 = 2e \cos \theta_m = (n_1 + f_1)\lambda_1 \cos \theta_m. \quad 9(11)$$

If $\mathscr{I}_m$ is the angular *diameter* of the mth ring, we may put

$$\cos \theta_m = 1 - \tfrac{1}{8}\mathscr{I}_m^2,$$

so long as θ_m is small, and we then have

$$1 - \tfrac{1}{8}\mathscr{I}_m^2 = \frac{n_1 - m + 1}{n_1 + f_1} = 1 - \frac{f_1 + m - 1}{n_1 + f_1}, \quad 9(12)$$

or

$$\mathscr{I}_m^2 = \frac{8}{n_1 + f_1}(f_1 + m - 1) = \frac{f_1 + m - 1}{2e} 8\lambda_1. \quad 9(13)$$

A value of f_1 may be obtained by measuring the angular diameters of several rings for values of m from about 3 to about 7, and then plotting $\mathscr{I}_m^2$ against $(m-1)$. The intercept* on the axis gives f_1. If this method is used it is necessary to check by direct calculation that the angles are small enough to enable the approximate value of $\cos \theta$ to be used.

9.31.—The procedure followed when f_1, f_2, f_3 have been measured may be illustrated by means of an example given by Childs.†

The fractions for a certain etalon were measured and found to be

$0.20 \pm .03$ for the neon line $\lambda = 6096.163$ Å.
$0.90 \pm .03$,, ,, ,, ,, $\lambda = 5852.488$ Å.
$0.35 \pm .03$,, ,, helium $\lambda = 5015.675$ Å.

Measurement with a micrometer gave $e = 10.040 \pm 0.005$ mm. This implies that n_1 lies between 32,922 and 32,955. Each of these values is taken in turn and associated with the measured fraction 0.20. The corresponding values of $(n_2 + f_2)$ and $(n_3 + f_3)$ are tabulated:

---
* For higher accuracy the best value of f_1 is computed by the method of least squares.
† Reference 9.3.

§ 9.32 COMPARISON OF WAVELENGTHS

Hypothetical order for $\lambda =$ 6096·163 Å.	Corresponding order calculated for $\lambda =$ 5852·488 Å.	$\lambda =$ 5015·675 Å.
32,922·20	34,292·95	40,014·37
32,923·20	34,293·99	40,015·58
32,924·20	34,295·03	40,016·80
. . . .	. . . .	. . . .
32,943·20	34,314·82	40,039·90
32,944·20	34,315·87	40,041·11
32,945·20	*34,316·91*	*40,042·32*
32,946·20	34,317·95	40,043·54
. . . .	. . . .	. . . .
32,953·20	34,325·24	40,052·04
32,954·20	34,326·28	40,053·26
32,955·20	34,327·32	40,054·47

Within the range covered by the table, the only value of $(n_1 + f_1)$ which makes the three fractions correct is 32,945·20 ± 0·03. The corresponding value of e is 10·04197 ± 0·00001 mm. The nearest value of e which again gives three fractions 0·20, 0·90 and 0·35 within the limits of error, is approximately 10·049 mm. (corresponding to $n_1 = 32,968$). This is excluded by the "rough" measurement with the micrometer. If the initial measurement with the micrometer were less accurate it would be necessary to measure the fractions for 4 or 5 wavelengths.

9.32.—When the thickness of the etalon has been accurately determined in this way, an unknown wavelength (λ_x) can be determined by measuring the fraction (f_x). The order of interference at the centre of the ring system is about thirty to forty thousand, and the preliminary value of λ_x obtained with a grating should be correct to one in 10^5, and should give the integral part of the order without any ambiguity. If a less accurate preliminary value is available, it may be necessary to start by using a shorter etalon (say 2-millimetre separation) and to take the value obtained with this etalon as the preliminary one for use with an etalon of 10-millimetre separation.

9.33.—The method of exact fractions increases the accuracy of the determination of a wavelength from ±0·05 Å. to ±0·005 Å. *If a spectrum line is sharp enough,* a further increase of accuracy (to about ±0·0002 Å.) may be obtained by proceeding to a 100-millimetre etalon. It will be appreciated that this accuracy is obtained only when the plates are very accurately plane and parallel. The wavelengths of a large number of lines may be measured in one experiment by focusing the ring pattern on the slit of a spectrograph with an achromatic lens. If a wide slit is used, the different spectrum lines each show a series of short arcs whose separations give the angular diameters of the rings for the corresponding wavelengths (fig. 9.12). A few known wavelengths are then used to determine the thickness of the etalon and the remainder may then be treated as unknown.*

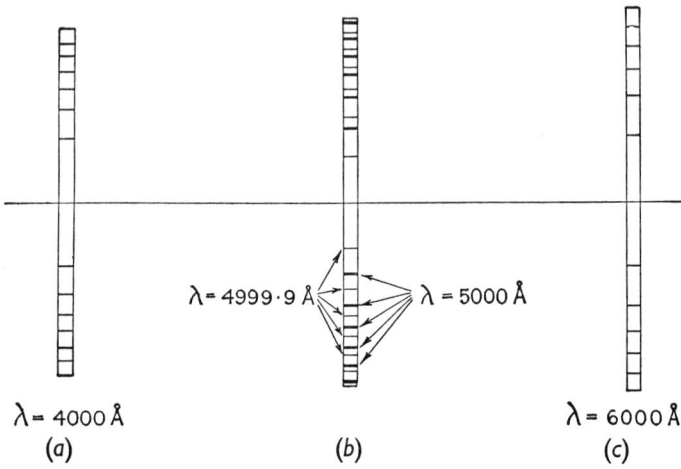

Fig. 9.12.—Diagrammatic representation of pattern obtained in spectrogram for stated wavelengths when the Fabry-Pérot rings are focused on the slit

9.34.—The usual objective of wavelength determinations is to measure the wavelength *in vacuo*, since this value forms a constant of theoretical importance, whereas the wavelength *in air* varies from day to day. If the method described in the last paragraph is used, the *ratio* of the wavelengths obtained is independent of atmospheric conditions, and is equal to the ratio of the wavelengths *in vacuo*, provided that the standards and the unknowns are all located within a fairly short interval of the spectrum. If they are not, a correction has to be made for the dispersion of air under the conditions obtaining during the experiment. It is then also necessary to make a small correction for the variation with wavelength of the phase change after reflection (§ 5.26). An account of the method by which this change is determined is given by Childs (Reference 9.3).

EXAMPLES [9(xii)–9(xv)]

9(xii). An unknown wavelength of less than 6000 Å. is to be compared with a standard wavelength of exactly 6000 Å. Coincidences occur when the separation of the plates of a Fabry-Pérot interferometer are 1·5 mm., 3 mm. and 4·5 mm. Find the unknown wavelength. [5998·8 Å.]

9(xiii). A certain wavelength is known to lie between 5990 Å. and 5992 Å. It gives coincidences with a standard source of 6000 Å. when the separations are

* This procedure is discussed by Meissner (Reference 9.4), whose article includes many interesting photographs of the rings.

§ 9.35   STANDARDS OF LENGTH   357

6 mm. and 6·4 mm., but it is not certain whether these are neighbouring coincidences. Find the unknown wavelength.

[Coincidence period lies between 600 and 750. $2(e_1 - e_2) = 0.8$ mm. $= 1333$ wavelengths. Thus there has been one intermediate coincidence. Exact coincidence period is 667, and $\lambda_2 = \dfrac{667}{668} \times 6000 = 5991$ Å.]

9(xiv). A certain wavelength is known to lie between 5000·0 Å. and 5000·1 Å. Fringes are formed with a Fabry-Pérot etalon of separation exactly 5·0000 mm. The fraction is found to be 0.7 ± 0.05. Find the wavelength to the maximum accuracy which the interferometer measurement justifies.   [5000·07 Å.]

9(xv). Three wavelengths are known to be exactly 4200 Å., 4800 Å. and 5000 Å. A certain etalon is known to have a separation of 10.000 ± 0.001 mm. The fractions are 0·20, 0·06 and 0·46 respectively. The fractions are each measured to an accuracy of ± 0.05. Find the thickness of the etalon.

[9.99961 ± 0.00002 mm.]

("Round" numbers have been inserted in Examples 9(xii)–9(xv) in order to enable the reader to practise the methods without carrying out the large amount of arithmetical work which would be needed if data were taken from real problems.)

9.35. Comparison between Optical and Mechanical Standards of Length.

At present the internationally accepted standard of length is the distance between two fine lines engraved on a platinum bar when the bar is at 0° C. This bar is called "the standard metre" or "the Metre" and is kept in France. The different national standardizing laboratories, such as the National Physical Laboratory in Great Britain and the American Bureau of Standards, hold copies of this standard. These copies have been compared with the standard by the use of high-quality travelling microscopes, and the difference between each copy and the standard is known to about 2.5×10^{-5} centimetre. When accurate interferometric measurements became available, it was suggested that an attempt should be made to determine the relation between the wavelengths corresponding to certain spectral lines and the standard metre. This problem was first attacked in 1892–5 by Michelson* and Benoît, who used a modification of the Michelson interferometer. They found that the ratio between the length of the standard metre and the wavelength of the red cadmium line (in air at 15° C. and 760 mm.) was 1,553,163·5. The result is accurate to about one part in two million. A new determination was made by Benoît,† Fabry and Pérot about fourteen years later, using a set of Fabry-Pérot etalons. The use of a

* Reference 9.5.   † Reference 9.6.

multiple-beam interferometric method, and various other technical improvements, enabled the accuracy to be improved to about one part in five million. The earlier determination is of considerable historical interest, but for all practical purposes it is superseded by the second determination, which we now describe.*

9.36.—*Benoît, Fabry and Pérot* used five Fabry-Pérot etalons of lengths approximately 6·25, 12·5, 25, 50 and 100 centimetres. The separators which determined the distances between the plates were V-shaped bars of Invar. Three types of measurement were involved:

(i) a determination of the length of the shortest etalon in terms of the wavelength of the cadmium red line;

(ii) an intercomparison of the etalons;

(iii) a determination of the difference between the longest etalon and a standard metre (i.e. a copy of "the Metre").

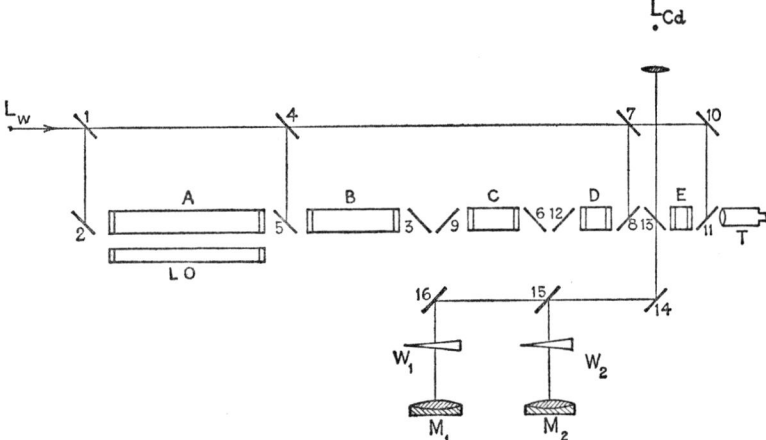

Fig. 9.13.—Apparatus used by Benoît, Fabry and Pérot for the comparison of optical and mechanical standards of length

The experimental procedure was so designed that the final series of experiments could be carried out rapidly and without disturbing the apparatus. In this way, errors due to changes of temperature and of atmospheric pressure were greatly reduced. The arrangement of apparatus is shown in fig. 9.13. L_w is a source of white light, and L_{Cd} is a source of cadmium light. Sixteen mirrors (indicated by numbers)

---

* A complete account of the Michelson-Benoît determination is given in Reference 9.5; see also p. 51 of Reference 9.1. The work of Benoît, Fabry and Pérot is described in Reference 9.6. Later determinations are described in References 9.7, 9.8, and 9.9.

are used to direct the light along desired paths. Arrangements are provided for inserting and removing any of these mirrors without disturbing the rest of the apparatus, or causing temperature changes. W_1 and W_2 are wedges of small angle, T is a telescope, and M_1 and M_2 are low-power microscopes focused upon W_1 and W_2. Mirror 13 is used to direct the cadmium light through the shortest etalon to the observation telescope T; mirrors 14 and 16 to direct it through W_1 to M_1; and mirrors 14 and 15 to direct it through W_2 to M_2.

9.37.—Two preliminary experiments are carried out. In the first, the length of the shortest etalon is measured in terms of the cadmium red line, by the method of exact fractions. The length so obtained may not be the exact length at the time of the final experiment, since there may be changes due to differences of temperature between the days of the preliminary and final experiments. The preliminary measurement does, however, give the length to within one wavelength, and it is necessary to re-measure only the fraction during the final experiment. In the other preliminary experiment the angles of the wedges W_1 and W_2 are determined by measuring the separation of the fringes, using cadmium light. Both of these preliminary measurements may be made with the whole apparatus *in situ*, the other mirrors being removed.

9.38.—In the final experiment, each etalon is compared with its neighbour, by using a suitable arrangement of mirrors. For example, white light may be directed through A, B, and W_1, by inserting mirrors 1, 2 and 3. The Brewster fringes (§§ 5.32 and 5.33) are observed by means of M_1, and measurement of the position of the central fringe then gives the difference between A and 2B. Extension of this procedure gives the difference between A and 16E. Observations on the circular fringes with cadmium light give the number of wavelengths of cadmium light corresponding to the length of E with an error of about 0·01 of a wavelength. The relation between A and the wavelength is then known to an only slightly lower accuracy. The final operation consists in a comparison of the distance between the plates of the etalon A and the distance between two lines engraved on an Invar bar LO. This latter length has previously been compared with the standard metre by the usual method, using travelling microscopes. The two microscopes are each set on one of the marks of the standard, and their readings noted. Without disturbing anything else, the bar LO is substituted for the standard. The algebraic sum of the distances through which the microscopes must be moved to bring them into coincidence with the marks on LO, gives the difference between LO and the standard.

9.39.—A comparison between LO and A which involved setting the travelling microscopes first on two engraved lines on LO and then on the edges of the plates of the etalon, would not be accurate because of the difference in the marks. The travelling microscopes are therefore used to measure the difference between the marks on LO and two fine lines engraved on the edges of the end-plates of A. The edges are ground, polished and silvered in order to give fine marks. The etalon A thus has an " optical length " between its mirror surfaces, and a " mechanical length " between the engraved lines. The difference is determined by an auxiliary experiment in which the plates are mounted with separators which make the distance between the marks nearly one centimetre, and then with a second set of separators which make the distance nearly two centimetres. The optical lengths of these two etalons are measured with cadmium light. Suppose that they are found to be $N_1\lambda$ and $N_2\lambda$, and that the (unknown) sum of the distances from the engraved lines to the surfaces is $X\lambda$. Three marks A, B and C are ruled on a plate so that AB and BC are approximately equal to one centimetre. The small differences

$$(N_1 + X)\lambda - AB = \alpha_1,$$
$$(N_1 + X)\lambda - BC = \alpha_2,$$
and
$$(N_2 + X)\lambda - AC = \alpha_3,$$

are measured with travelling microscopes.

Since AB + BC = AC, we have

$$X\lambda = (N_2 - 2N_1)\lambda + \alpha_1 + \alpha_2 - \alpha_3. \quad \ldots \quad 9(14)$$

9.40.—Thus the final result gives the relation between the standard metre and the wavelength of the cadmium red line emitted by the source L_{Cd}. The error in the interferometric measurements is a few parts in 10^7 for a single measurement but, when the average of repeated measurements is taken, the probable error is reduced to one part in 10^7. The wavelength of cadmium light in *dry* air at standard temperature and pressure is found to be $6\cdot438\,469\,6 \times 10^{-7}$ times the standard metre. The difference between the value found by Benoît, Fabry and Pérot and that obtained by Michelson and Benoît is four parts in 10^7. The earlier determination referred to air containing an undetermined amount of water vapour. There was also a slight uncertainty in the temperature scale. These effects are sufficient to account for the whole of the difference.

9.41. **Recent Work on Standards of Length.**

The relationship between the wavelength of cadmium red light and the Metre was again investigated by Watanabe and Imaizumi in Japan

(1928) and by Sears and Barrell at the National Physical Laboratory (1934). The latter used only three stages of intercomparison. Their subsidiary etalons were one-ninth and one-third of the length of the etalon which was compared with the standard metre. The comparison of etalons whose length ratio is nearly 3:1 was made using the tilt method described in § 5.32, so that the calibrated wedges were not required. The apparatus was more compact, and more accurate temperature control (to within $0.001°$ C.) was possible. The etalons were made of Invar, and quartz plates were "wrung" on to the ends, which were polished so as to be optically flat. The etalons could be evacuated so as to obtain wavelengths *in vacuo*.

During the years 1950–60 a great deal of work has been done on the comparison of optical and mechanical standards of length. The relationship between wavelengths in air and vacuum has been closely studied, leading to a generally accepted formula due to Edlén. The separation of isotopes has provided spectroscopic sources which include lines without hyperfine structure (see § 9.44). Photo-electric devices for detecting the centres of interference fringes with a higher precision than that obtained visually have been developed. The theoretical precision of these devices calculated by the methods discussed in Chapter XX corresponds to an accuracy of 10^{-6} Å., though the accuracy so far obtained is in the region of 10^{-4} Å.

9.42.—The wavelengths of most sources of light are appreciably affected by small changes of pressure and temperature, and by conditions of excitation. For example, the excited atoms in a discharge tube under certain conditions may move predominantly in one direction. The Doppler effect then gives an asymmetrical broadening, i.e. a shift of the mean wavelength. To reduce Doppler effects it is desirable to use an element of high mass number, and the green line of mercury (isotope 198) was extensively studied. Recent work has been concentrated on the 6056 Å. line of krypton (isotope 86). The krypton lamp can be operated at a much lower temperature and is relatively free from other errors.

It is clear that optical standards of length are superior to mechanical standards, though it is likely that in the next few years they will be further improved.

9.43. New Definition of the Metre.

An international commission was appointed in 1953 to study the possibility of defining the Metre in terms of the wavelength of a chosen spectrum line. It is necessary to choose a line which can conveniently be excited in a standard lamp. The line must be free from hyperfine structure (see § 9.44), it must have a reasonably small Doppler width, and its wavelength must not be significantly affected by small variations in conditions of excitation (e.g. by small variations of ambient temperature, of current, or of pressure). On the basis of concordant measurements in five laboratories, the krypton line whose wavelength in air is approximately 6056 Å. was chosen. In 1961 it was decided that "the Metre be defined as exactly 1,650,763·73 wavelengths (in vacuum) of the radiation corresponding to the transition $2p_{10} - 5d_s$ in krypton of mass number 86". The vacuum wavelength of this line becomes, by definition, 6057·80211 Å. and the wavelength in dry air (at 760 mm. and 15° C.) becomes 6056·12525 Å.

A standard lamp developed by Englehard has been studied at the Physikalisch-Technische Bundesanstalt and at the National Physical Laboratory. It is believed that this lamp gives a wavelength within 0·0001 Å. of the ideal wavelength emitted by undisturbed atoms. Most of this difference is due to Doppler shift produced by impact of the exciting electrons and can be eliminated by taking the mean of observations with current in opposite directions. A very small shift which depends on the product of pressure and current was studied and can be eliminated.

9.44. Investigation of Hyperfine Structure.

The use of interferometers has shown that most of the lines which appear to be single when examined in a prism or grating spectrograph, can be resolved into a number of components with separations of a few hundredths or a few thousandths of an Ångström unit. This *hyperfine structure*, as it is called, is of great interest to the theoretical physicist, who can derive important information about atomic nuclei if he is given accurate determinations of the number, intensities and separations of the components. The practical problem involved has two important aspects:

(a) the production of interferometers with sufficient resolving power to separate the components, and

(b) the production of auxiliary apparatus to effect a sufficient separation to prevent confusion owing to overlapping of orders.

There is no serious difficulty in making interferometers of the necessary resolving power. By increasing the separation of the mirrors, the Michelson or the Fabry-Pérot interferometer can be given any desired resolving power. If, however, the resolving power of an interferometer is increased merely by increasing the path difference, there is also a proportionate increase in the overlapping of orders. Thus the

§ 9.45   FINESSE   363

two problems are interconnected. If $\Delta\lambda_A$ is the largest range of wavelength which an interferometer can accept without overlapping of orders, and $\Delta\lambda_R$ is the difference of wavelength between components which are just resolved, we desire $\Delta\lambda_A/\Delta\lambda_R$ to be as large as possible.

$\Delta\lambda_A$ is called the *free spectral range*. If the mth order of interference for λ coincides with the $(m+1)$th order for $\lambda - \Delta\lambda_A$, then

$$m\lambda = (m+1)(\lambda - \Delta\lambda_A), \qquad \ldots \quad 9(15)$$

and if m is large we have

$$\Delta\lambda_A = \frac{\lambda}{m}, \qquad \ldots \ldots \quad 9(16)$$

i.e. the free spectral range is inversely proportional to the order of interference.

9.45. Finesse.

The ratio $\Delta\lambda_A/\Delta\lambda_R$ is effectively equal to the ratio of distance between two orders in the interference pattern, to the width of a single fringe. The latter is measured between the two points for which the energy is half the maximum value. For a Fabry-Pérot etalon, the distribution of energy is given by equation 5(16). When $E/E_{max} = \frac{1}{2}$ we have $L\eta = L\sin^2 \frac{1}{2}\delta_h = 1$, where δ_h is the phase difference when $E/E_{max} = \frac{1}{2}$. Since δ_h is usually small we may put

$$L(\tfrac{1}{2}\delta_h)^2 = 1,$$

so that

$$\delta_h = \pm \frac{2}{L^{\frac{1}{2}}}$$

The separation between two orders corresponds to a phase difference of 2π and the width of a single fringe to $2\delta_h$. The ratio of these two quantities is called the *finesse* (F) and is given in terms of the reflection coefficient (ρ) by

$$F = \frac{\pi}{2} L^{\frac{1}{2}} = \frac{\pi}{4\rho^{\frac{1}{4}}}(1-\rho). \qquad \ldots \quad 9(17)$$

The quantity F is approximately, but not exactly, equal to the equivalent number N of interfering beams discussed in § 8.16. (The latter corresponds to a separation of two fringes which gives a "20 per cent dip" in the combined pattern).

For a ruled diffraction grating the ratio of free spectral range $\Delta\lambda_A$ to limit of wavelength resolution ($\Delta\lambda_R$) is equal to the number of lines in the grating, and for an echelon this ratio is equal to the number of steps.

9.46.—While the resolving power depends on the order of interference (m) multiplied by the number of interfering beams (N), the finesse depends only on the latter number. For a diffraction grating N may be 10^5, for a Fabry-Pérot etalon N may be nearly 100, and for a Michelson interferometer $N = 2$. The Michelson interferometer is, from this point of view, greatly inferior, but we shall see later (§ 9.48) that there are some situations where it has important advantages.

The number of plates in an echelon grating is determined by cost. Echelons up to 36 plates have been made, but partly because of the very much lower cost of the Fabry-Pérot etalon, the echelon has been very little used in recent years.*

9.47. Auxiliary Apparatus.

Sometimes it is possible to separate the lines by the use of colour filters or by interference filters.† Usually it is necessary to use dispersion by a prism or grating. When this is done the light may be passed through the other instrument before or after the interferometer. The arrangement suggested in § 9.33 is often convenient. It is also possible to place the interferometer inside a spectrograph, so that it is in the approximately parallel beam produced by the collimator. This arrangement has often been used with a Fabry-Pérot etalon.

9.48. Interferometry with Fourier Analysis.

Michelson measured the visibility of the fringes obtained with his interferometer as a function of the path difference. He was able, by the use of considerable experimental skill and laborious calculation, to analyse spectra containing small numbers of lines. The development of physical detectors of radiation and of electronic calculating machines has made it possible to record the energy as a function of path difference and to use the record for the analysis of complex spectra. According to equation 4(1) if the energy incident in the wave-number range $\kappa + \frac{1}{2} d\kappa$ to $\kappa - \frac{1}{2} d\kappa$ is $E(\kappa) \, d\kappa$, and if the beam is exactly equally divided at the mirror M_1, the total energy received by the detector (when the path difference is x and the phase difference is κx) is proportional to
$$\int E(\kappa) (1 + \cos \kappa x) \, d\kappa$$
i.e. to
$$\int E(\kappa) \, d\kappa + \int E(\kappa) \cos \kappa x \, d\kappa.$$

If $W(x)$ is the difference between the energy for path difference x and half the energy for path difference 0, then
$$W(x) = C \int E(\kappa) \cos \kappa x \, d\kappa,$$

---

* In 1939 the cost of an echelon of 35 plates was about £1000. The cost of a Fabry-Pérot etalon was then £30, and is now about £75.

† See §§ 5.40 and 12.53.

§ 9.49   FOURIER ANALYSIS   365

where C is a constant which depends on losses of light at reflections, etc. The Fourier transform of $W(x)$ gives $E(\kappa)$, and very complicated spectra may be analysed in this way (see fig. 9.14 which shows results obtained by H. A. Gebbie).

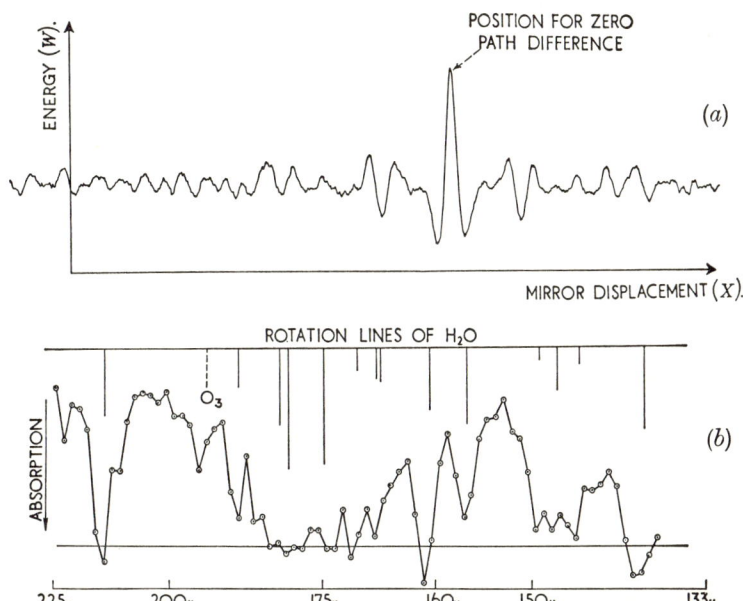

Fig. 9.14.—(a) Variation of energy with path difference, (b) Calculated spectral distribution showing absorption lines due to water vapour.

Crown Copyright Reserved

9.49.—In the visible spectrum where photo-electric detectors may be used, it is usually better to investigate a complicated spectrum either by scanning it with a detector covered by a fine slit, or by using a Fabry-Pérot etalon and a spectrograph together (§ 9.47). In the far infra-red, where the amount of energy is small and no very sensitive detectors are available, the method described in § 9.48 has considerable advantages. It uses the whole energy from a circular region which is of considerably larger area than the slit of a spectrograph. This advantage is, however, lost when the source itself is very small. An error arises from the fact that to obtain the Fourier transform $W(x)$ should be measured from $x = 0$ to ∞, whereas observations extend over only a moderate range of x. The main effect of this limitation is to restrict the range of wave number over which the method can be used.*

* See p. 419 of Reference 12.11 for detailed discussion of this method.

9.50. The Mach-Zehnder Interferometer.

The interferometer designed by Mach and Zehnder* is shown in fig. 9.15. A roughly parallel beam is divided at the half-silvered mirror M_1 and reunited at M_4. This interferometer can be modified in a number of ways for particular applications, and the Michelson interferometer may be regarded as a modification of this design. The wide spacing of the mirrors increases the difficulties of initial adjustment, of mechanical stability, and of temperature control. For some purposes

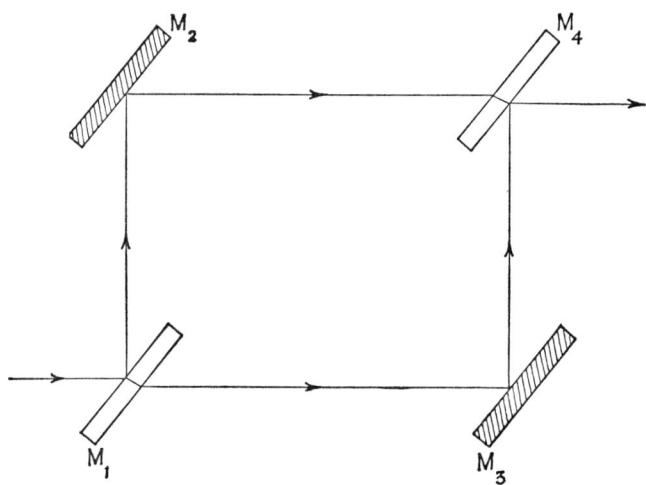

Fig. 9.15.—Mach-Zehnder interferometer

it is essential to have a wide separation of the beams, so that these difficulties must be accepted. The instrument has been used for investigating variations of refractive index (and hence of density) of the air near to an aerofoil in a wind tunnel. The mirrors are arranged so that the region to be studied is between M_2 and M_4, and compensating plates are placed between M_3 and M_4. Interpretation of results is made easier by the fact that the light passes only once along each path. A small adjustment of M_2 and M_3 alters the angle between the rays leaving M_4. Hence the plane in which the fringes are localized can be adjusted so as to lie within the region under test.

* Sometimes called a " round-the-square " interferometer.

9.51. Wave-shearing Interferometers.

In the Twyman-Green interferometer one wavefront (W'_4 in fig. 9.1) which has been transmitted or reflected by the component under test, interferes with a reference wave (W_4) which is made as nearly as possible plane. The relative displacement of the two wavefronts is shown in fig. 9.16a, b, c, i.e. they may be parallel or slightly inclined, and they may be displaced in the direction of propagation. Another kind of displacement is shown in fig. 9.16d, which shows a wave which

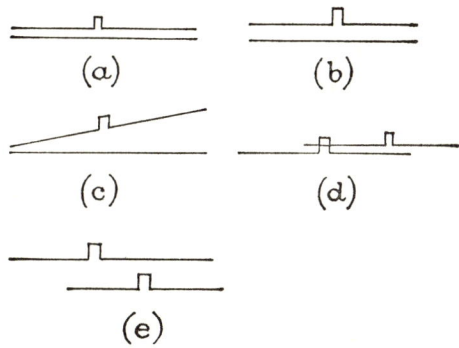

Fig. 9.16.—(a) Deformed wave and reference wave; (b) as (a) but displaced in direction of propagation; (c) as (b) but tilted. (d) Two images of same wavefront with shearing displacement. (e) Combination of shear and displacement shown in (b).

has been divided into two parts (by division of amplitude) which have been displaced relative to one another in a direction perpendicular to the direction of propagation. This is known as wave shearing. The interference pattern due to departures from planarity will be seen as a doubled pattern. One important advantage of wave-shearing interferometers is that it is often possible to secure very good mechanical stability, especially when birefringent crystals are used to produce the displacement.* The method is not very suitable for investigating the contour of a wavefront which shows complicated irregularity, because the two " copies " of the interference overlap one another and interpretation is difficult. It is very suitable for measuring the thickness of a thin film which covers part of a glass plate, and also for certain special applications in the testing of optical systems.† A wave-shearing interferometer has also been used to measure the response function of an optical system.‡

* See § 12.48.   † See Reference 12.8.
‡ See § 7 of Appendix VIII A, § 4 of Appendix VIII C, and Reference 9.12.

It is also possible to produce interference by dividing a beam into two parts and rotating one part relative to the other about an axis parallel to the direction of propagation. The centre of rotation may be either within or without the field of view. Shearing may be regarded as rotation about a point at infinity. In the general case all the different types of displacement may be combined.

9.52. Interferometer Microscope.

The phase-contrast microscope (§ 8.44–48) which is widely used for the examination of transparent objects, does not always give an explicit relation between contrast in the image and phase difference in the object (§ 8.48). Interferometer microscopes are superior in this respect.

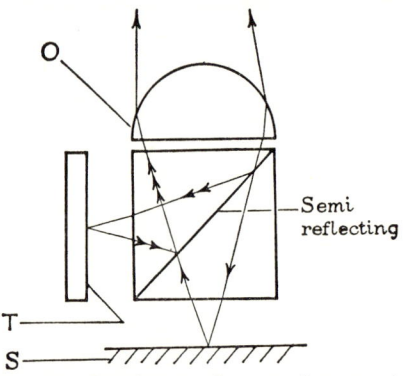

Fig. 9.17.—Interference microscope (low-power)

Microscopes with low- and medium-power objectives for observing two-beam interference have been developed from the Michelson interferometer (fig. 9.17).

A high power and a high aperture are obtained in the instrument designed by Dyson.* Some light from the condenser forms an image of the source in the plane of the object. This light, after traversing the object and being reflected as shown in fig. 9.18, forms the object (and image of the source) near the spherical surface of the glass block B. Light from the condenser, which has been reflected from the spot S and has passed to one side of the object, forms a second image of the source, coincident with the first. Light of both these images passes through a small hole in the silvering of the spherical surface and into the objective of a conventional high-power microscope. If the thickness of the glass plates P_1 and P_2 is correctly adjusted, then the optical paths are equal except for the small differences introduced by the object, and white

* See Reference 9.10.

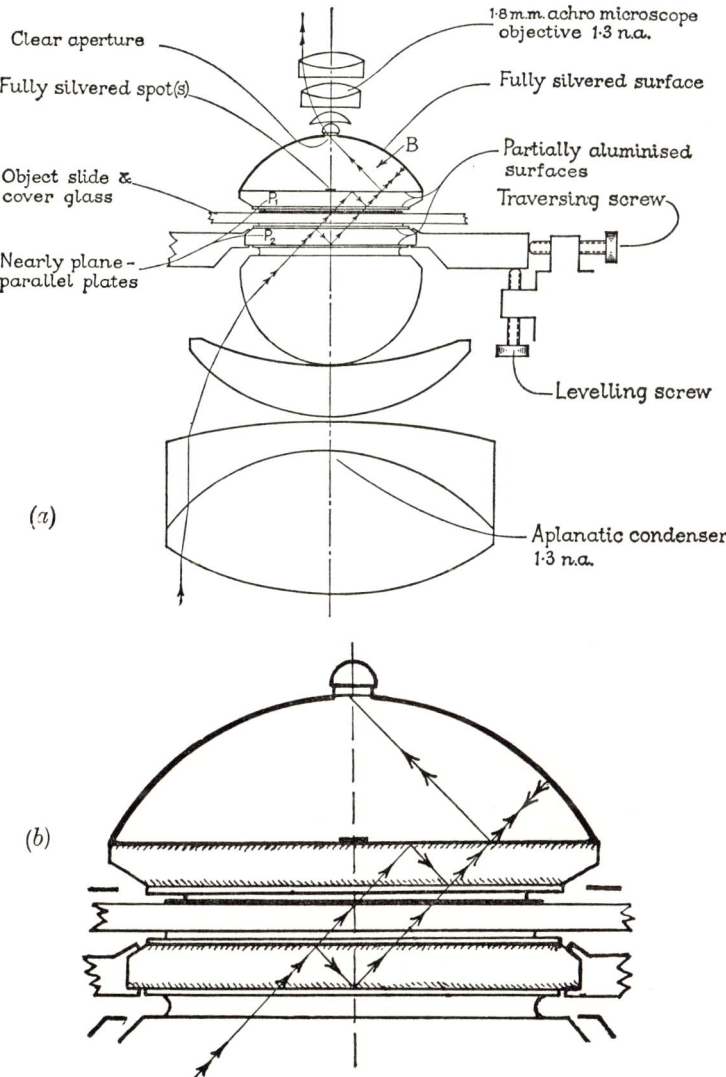

Fig. 9.18a.—Interference microscope (high-power) (b) Enlargement of part

light may be used. In order to be able to make this adjustment both plates are slightly wedge-shaped, and screws are provided for moving the lower one to alter the effective thickness. A similar instrument modified for viewing opaque objects has also been made.*

* Sheared-wave interference has also been used in microscopy (§ 12.51).

REFERENCES

9.1. WILLIAMS: *Applications of Interferometry* (Methuen).
9.2. MICHELSON: *Studies in Optics* (University of Chicago Press).
9.3. CHILDS: *Journal of Scientific Instruments*, 1926, Vol. 3, p. 97 and p. 219.
9.4. MEISSNER: *Journal of the Optical Society of America*, 1941, Vol. 31, p. 405.
9.5. MICHELSON and BENOÎT: *Trav. et Mem. Bur. Int. des Poids et Mesures*, 1895, Vol. 11.
9.6. BENOÎT, FABRY and PÉROT: *ibid*, 1913, Vol. 15.
9.7. WATANABE and IMAIZUMI: *Proc. Imp. Acad. (Tokio)*, 1928, Vol. 4, pp. 3, 51.
9.8. SEARS and BARRELL: *Phil. Trans. Roy. Soc.*, 1932, Vol. 231, p. 75.
9.9. *Ibid.*, 1934, Vol. 233, p. 143.
9.10. DYSON: *Proc. Roy. Soc.*, 1950, Vol. 204, p. 170.
9.11. TOLANSKY: *Proc. Roy. Soc.*, 1945, Vol. 184, p. 41.
9.12. KELSALL: *Proc. Phys. Soc.*, 1959, Vol. 73, p. 465.

CHAPTER X

Detection and Measurement of Radiation

10.1.—The human eye is able to detect and to use electromagnetic radiation in a wavelength range from about 4000 Å. to about 7000 Å. Physical instruments are capable of detecting electromagnetic radiation of a much wider range of wavelength from γ-rays to radio waves (see fig. 1.5) and can also be used to measure radiation in the form of sound or material particles. Certain fundamental concepts (based on the law of conservation of energy and the second law of thermodynamics) apply to all radiation detectors and to all problems of the transport of energy as radiation. In this chapter we shall discuss these general principles in their application to the ultra-violet, visible, and infra-red regions of the electromagnetic spectrum, and to detectors sensitive to this kind of radiation. In the later part of the chapter we shall describe certain properties of the human eye considered as a device for the detection and analysis of light. We shall show how physical measurements can be used to compare the visual efficiencies of different types of lighting and will discuss the specification of colour.

10.2. Selective and Non-selective Detectors.

A beam of radiation constitutes a flux of energy across any surface which intersects the beam. This flux has the dimensions of energy/time, i.e. of power, and may be measured in watts. A *detector* is an instrument which, being placed in a beam of radiation, absorbs the whole or part of the incident energy and gives a meter reading which is called the *signal*. If the signal depends only on the energy flux and not upon the wavelength, then the detector is said to be *non-selective*. For example, suppose that a thin blackened metal strip is placed in the beam (see fig. 10.1). Its temperature will rise until the energy absorbed from the beam is balanced by heat losses due to conduction, convection, or radiation. The increase in temperature may be used to generate an electric current and so give a galvanometer deflection (S) which is the signal. It is not difficult to arrange that this deflection is very nearly proportional to the energy flux (P) in the beam. The detector is then said to be linear, and we may define the *responsivity* (r) by the equation

$$S = rP. \qquad \ldots \ldots \ldots \quad 10(1)$$

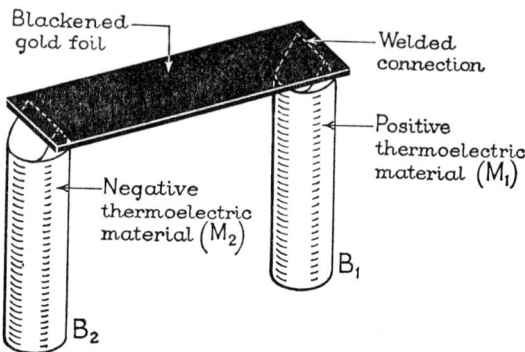

Fig. 10.1.—Schwarz-type thermocouple (schematic diagram more than 10 times actual size)

If the area of the strip is smaller than the area of the beam, then P is the flux incident on the strip. For this reason it is sometimes convenient to express a measurement as flux per unit area (i.e. watts/cm.²), but the symbol P is used above for the total flux and has the dimensions of power.

10.3.—For many detectors the responsivity varies rapidly with wavelength. The responsivity of a photo-cell is zero for wavelengths above a certain threshold wavelength (see § 17.2), rises to a maximum at some shorter wavelength, and then falls off at still shorter wavelengths to less than one per cent of the maximum responsivity (see fig. 10.8). These detectors are said to be *selective*. Suppose that a selective detector has a responsivity r_λ for radiation of wavelength λ. If this detector is placed in a beam of radiation which has a spectral distribution such that $\mathscr{P}_\lambda d\lambda$ represents the flux for a wavelength range $\lambda - \tfrac{1}{2} d\lambda$ to $\lambda + \tfrac{1}{2} d\lambda$, then the overall responsivity r is given by

$$r = \frac{\int \mathscr{P}_\lambda r_\lambda \, d\lambda}{\int \mathscr{P}_\lambda \, d\lambda}, \qquad \ldots \ldots \quad 10(2)$$

i.e. r is the signal per unit energy flux given by this receptor with this kind of radiation. Note that $\mathscr{P}_\lambda$ is flux per unit band width.

Suppose that a surface whose reflection coefficient is ρ_λ for wavelength λ is placed in the beam. Then the overall reflection as evaluated by this detector (i.e. the ratio of the signal produced by the reflected radiation to that produced by the incident radiation) is

$$\rho = \frac{\int \mathscr{P}_\lambda r_\lambda \rho_\lambda \, d\lambda}{\int \mathscr{P}_\lambda r_\lambda \, d\lambda}. \qquad \ldots \ldots \quad 10(3)$$

Similar equations may be written down for a transmission coefficient or the scattering coefficient measured with this detector. Each of the "overall" coefficients depends on (a) the spectral distribution in the beam, (b) the properties of the filter or other material under test, and (c) the properties of the detector.

10.4. Relative Responsivity.

If all the values of r_λ were multiplied by a constant, the value of ρ obtained from equation 10(3) would be unchanged, and similar considerations apply to other properties (e.g. scattering and transmission). It is therefore permissible to use, in these equations, the *relative responsivity* $r_\lambda' = r_\lambda/r_m$, where r_m is the responsivity for some chosen wavelength. It is convenient to choose this wavelength to be one at which the response is a maximum. The responsivity at this wavelength being regarded as the unit, the responsivity at every other wavelength is expressed as a fraction (see fig. 10.8).

10.5. Thermal Detectors.

A thermal detector consists of a *receiver* (which is usually a blackened metal strip which absorbs the radiation) and a device which measures, in arbitrary units, the change of temperature of the receiver. The response of a thermal detector is nearly the same over a wide range of wavelength so that these detectors are effectively non-selective. A radiation thermocouple is shown in fig. 10.1. Radiation absorbed by the blackened gold foil causes thermoelectric electromotive forces at the junctions with two dissimilar materials M_1 and M_2. These are joined to heavier wires of copper at B_1 and B_2. These two junctions form the cold end of the thermocouple, their temperature being only slightly affected by the radiation. The thermal capacity of the strip must be kept low to give a reasonably rapid response (see § 10.9 below). If M_1 and M_2 are short and thick, the temperature rise is reduced by thermal conduction; on the other hand, if they are long and thin, the current is reduced by electrical resistance. A great deal of theoretical and practical research has been devoted to finding suitable materials and optimum dimensions.

In the form shown, due to Schwarz, the blackened strip is 0·3 μ thick. The materials are two different semiconductor mixtures. One is positive with respect to gold and the other negative, so that the thermoelectric electromotive forces are additive. This gives a much larger electromotive force than can be obtained with metal wires, but the semiconductor materials are not very stable, so that care has to be taken not to overheat them when making the junctions. The whole device is enclosed in an evacuated glass envelope with a window of fluorite which is transparent from 0·13 μ to 9 μ.

10.6.—The *bolometer*, originally due to Langley, consists of two blackened metal strips connected in two adjacent arms of a resistance bridge. They are placed close to one another, so that they share small random changes of temperature due to convection, but one strip is exposed to the beam of radiation and the other is not. The change of resistance due to the resulting difference of temperature destroys the balance of the bridge and causes a deflection in the galvanometer. A very sensitive device is obtained by using a metal alloy whose initial temperature is just below the threshold for the superconducting state.*

10.7.—A third type of thermal detector, known as the *Golay cell*, is shown in fig. 10.2. Radiation absorbed in the film A causes a rise in

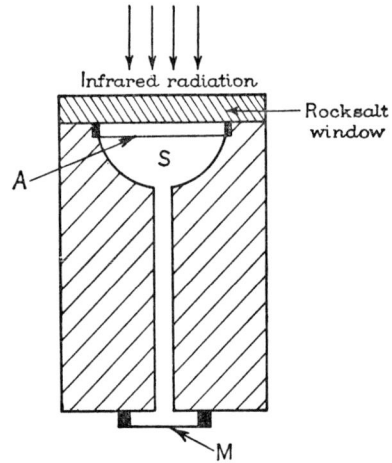

Fig. 10.2.—Golay cell

the temperature in the space S. The resulting increase in gas pressure distorts the membrane M, so that a beam of light reflected from the membrane is defocused. Light then passes an obstacle (on which it was previously focused) and falls on a photo-emissive cell which gives

* See p. 112 of Reference 10.1.

an electrical output. This device is rather fragile but it is simple and has a high responsivity.

10.8. Time-constant of a Thermal Detector.

The small d.c. potential difference generated when a radiation thermocouple or bolometer is placed in a weak beam of radiation cannot be conveniently amplified and is difficult to distinguish from a slow temperature drift, as well as from the random noise effects which will be discussed later (see § 10.13 and Chapter XX). Although certain special devices such as the galvanometer amplifier are available, it is more convenient to interrupt the beam of radiation periodically with a mechanical " chopper ". The resulting variation of the radiation power with time may be analysed into a steady component plus an oscillatory component (similar to that shown in fig. 4.6) whose fundamental frequency is equal to twice the chopping frequency*. An oscillatory variation of temperature produced in the blackened strip on which the radiation falls generates an alternating voltage. This is made the input to an electronic amplifier† which is sharply tuned to the fundamental frequency. A small amount of energy in the higher harmonics does not contribute to the output, and we neglect this energy, i.e. we assume that the chopper produces a sinusoidal variation of incident power.

10.9.—Let $\mathscr{C}_T$ be the thermal capacity of a blackened strip which constitutes the receiver of a thermal detector. Suppose that the temperature of the strip exceeds the temperature T of its surroundings by T_e (where $T_e \ll T$). Then the rate of loss of heat is $\mathscr{G}T_e$, where $\mathscr{G}$ is a constant called the *thermal conductance* between the receiver and its surroundings. The quantity $\mathscr{R} = 1/\mathscr{G}$ is called the *thermal resistance*. In the absence of any external source of heat, the excess temperature will decay according to the equation

$$\mathscr{C}\frac{dT_e}{dt} + \frac{T_e}{\mathscr{R}} = 0. \quad \ldots \ldots \quad 10(4)$$

This equation is similar to the equation for the discharge of an electrical condenser. The solution is

$$T_e = T_e(0)\exp(-t/\tau), \quad \ldots \ldots \quad 10(5)$$

where $T_e(0)$ is the temperature excess at time $t = 0$. The quantity $\tau = \mathscr{C}\mathscr{R}$ is called the *thermal time-constant*.

---

* See p. 116 of Reference 10.1.

† The mirror system of the Golay cell has a resonant frequency which is adjusted to match the chopping frequency.

Suppose that the strip is subjected to a sinusoidally modulated beam of radiation

$$\mathscr{P}(t) = \mathscr{P}_0 \exp(i\Omega t). \quad \ldots \ldots \quad 10(6)$$

Then, we may write instead of 10(4),

$$\mathscr{C}\frac{dT_e}{dt} + \frac{T_e}{\mathscr{R}} = \mathscr{P}_0 \exp(i\Omega t). \quad \ldots \ldots \quad 10(7)$$

The solution contains an exponentially damped term which may be neglected. The sinusoidal term is

$$T_e = \frac{\mathscr{R}\mathscr{P}_0}{(1 + i\Omega\tau)} \exp(i\Omega t), \quad \ldots \quad 10(8a)$$

and the real amplitude is

$$|T_{e0}| = \frac{\mathscr{R}\mathscr{P}_0}{(1 + \tau^2\Omega^2)^{\frac{1}{2}}}. \quad \ldots \ldots \quad 10(8b)$$

For low frequencies of interruption $|T_{e0}|$ is proportional to $\mathscr{R}$ and for high frequencies to $\mathscr{R}/\tau\Omega = 1/\mathscr{C}\Omega$. The time-constants, responsivities, and detectivities of some thermal detectors are given in Table 10.1.

TABLE 10.1

Thermal Detectors: Minimum detectable power

Detector	Area, mm.²	Time-constant, milli-seconds	Minimum detectable power, 10^{-9} W.	Minimum detectable flux, 10^{-8} W./cm.²	Detectivity 10^8 W.$^{-1}$
Bolometer (Ni strip)	6·0	4	3·3	50	3
Bolometer (super-conducting)	1·0	0·5	0·02	2	500
Thermocouple (Schwarz)	1·5	8	2	12	5
Golay cell	10	10	1	10	100

The figures given for minimum detectable power and detectivity refer to a band width of 1 c.p.s. (see § 20.21). When it is possible to use a band width of 0·1 c.p.s. the minimum detectable power is about three times smaller than the value given in column 3.

10.10. Selective Detectors.

In the detectors so far described the initial effect of absorption of radiation is to raise the temperature, i.e. the energy absorbed is dis-

§ 10.11　　　　PHOTO-EMISSIVE CELLS　　　　　　377

tributed among a large number of atoms and molecules. In the selective detectors which we shall now describe, the initial action is to increase the energy of a single electron every time a photon of radiation is absorbed. This causes an electrical (or sometimes a chemical) effect which produces the signal.* This more direct conversion of light energy into electrical or chemical energy has a higher efficiency than conversion which involves the thermal process. The time-constants involved are 10^{-9} second or less. For these and other reasons the detectivity of a good selective detector, in its region of maximum response, is usually much higher than that of any thermal detector. The eye, the photo-emissive cell, and the photographic plate are all selective detectors.

TABLE 10.2

Selective Detectors

Detector	Threshold	Dark current, amps	Minimum power per cycle, W.	Detectivity
Photo-emissive cell				
at 300° K.	$0 \cdot 6\mu$ $= 6{,}000$ Å	10^{-16}	$10^{-15} - 10^{-16}$ at 5000 Å.	$10^{15} - 10^{16}$
at 90° K.	$0 \cdot 6\mu$	10^{-17}	10^{-17}	10^{17}
Photo-conductive cell				
PbS at 300° K.	4μ		2×10^{-12}	5×10^{11}
PbS at 90° K.	5μ		6×10^{-14}	$1 \cdot 6 \times 10^{13}$
PbSe at 20° K.	10μ		2×10^{-11}	5×10^{10}

Notes. (1) The photo-conductive cells do not have a sharp threshold.
(2) The values given are reduced to 1 cm.² area (detectivity $\propto A^{-\frac{1}{2}}$) and at wavelengths for which each cell is near its maximum sensitivity.
(3) For further data see Reference 10.1.

10.11. Photo-emissive Cells.

The simplest form of selective detector is the *vacuum photo-electric cell* (fig. 10.3). Light falls on a suitable metal surface in vacuum and releases electrons. A potential is applied between this surface, which is made the cathode, and an anode. The resulting current is amplified, usually with an electrometer triode in a circuit such as that shown in fig. 10.3. There is no difficulty in obtaining a response to light interrupted at a convenient frequency.

---

* If any of the energy is distributed as heat (e.g. through electronic collisions) this energy does not contribute to the signal.

The minimum flux which can be detected is usually limited by the valve rather than the photo-cell (see § 20.28). It is an advantage to incorporate an amplification device in the same envelope as the photo-cathode (fig. 10.4). In a *photo-multiplier* electrons released from the

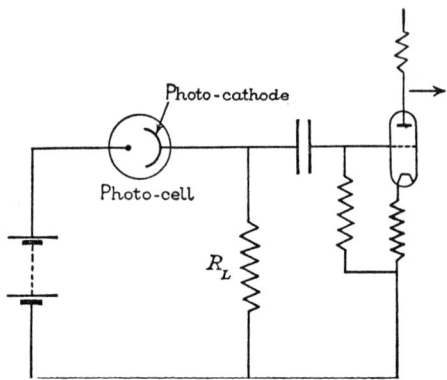

Fig. 10.3.—Photo-cell and associated electrical circuit

photo-cathode are accelerated and are allowed to fall on a suitable metal surface. Secondary electrons, more numerous than the incident electrons, are emitted and the current is amplified. It is usual to adjust the accelerating potential so that an amplification ratio of nearly 5 is obtained, and it is possible to incorporate about 10 stages of amplification to give an overall multiplication of about a million. An external

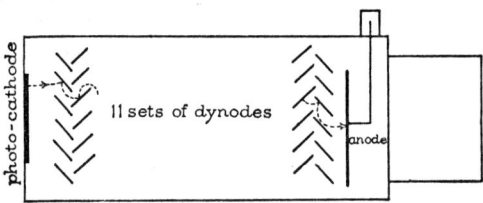

Fig. 10.4.—Photo-multiplier: .... indicate paths of electrons released

amplifier may be added if additional amplification is required. The only important difficulty is the necessity of maintaining the accelerating voltages accurately constant. The relative response curves of some photo-multipliers are shown in fig. 10.8. Photo-electric cells and photo-multipliers are classed together as *photo-emissive* devices.

10.12. Photo-conductive and Photo-voltaic Cells.

The photo-conductive effect consists in a change of resistance, produced by the absorption of radiation, due to the direct transfer of electrons to states in which they are free to move so as to constitute a current. This direct transfer is additional to and much larger than the change in resistance associated with a change in temperature. Many insulators and semiconductors show photo-conductivity when subject to radiation of suitable wavelength, but the effect is fairly small and, for the visible and ultra-violet regions of the spectrum, photo-emissive receptors provide better radiation detectors than any device based on photo-conductivity. In the infra-red region for wavelengths greater than $1 \cdot 3\mu$, no photo-electric cells are available (see Table 17.1). Thin films of certain substances (especially Pb S, Pb Se, and Pb Te) show a large photo-conductive effect in the range 1μ to 8μ. Photo-conductive cells based on these substances are much more sensitive, in this region, than thermocouples and bolometers, except superconducting bolometers. In order to obtain maximum efficiency it is necessary to cool the cells so as to reduce the " dark current " and " noise ". New photo-conductive devices which respond to longer wavelengths are in course of development.*

The device shown in fig. 10.5 is a photo-voltaic cell. The incident radiation passes through a transparent metal film into a semiconducting layer supported on a metal plate. Selenium is often used as the semiconductor. Electrons released by the radiation from the surface of the

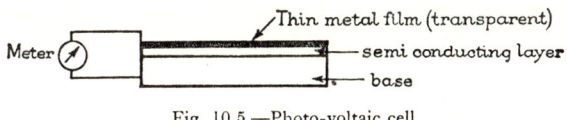

Fig. 10.5.—Photo-voltaic cell

base plate and in the semiconductor pass into the metal film. The contact between this film and the semiconductor is a rectifying contact, i.e. electrons pass out of the semiconductor more easily than they pass into it. A potential is developed between the metal film and the base plate, and a current may be detected in a meter connected as shown in the figure. This type of detector is much less sensitive than photo-emissive detectors, but it is robust and requires no auxiliary apparatus except the meter. The response, when connected in the simple circuit shown, is not linearly proportional to the flux of radiation. This is an

* References 10.1 and 10.9.

advantage when the cell is used in a photographic exposure meter, which is one of the most important applications. Linear response may be obtained, if desired, with suitable auxiliary circuits.

10.13. Minimum Detectable Flux.

The performance of physical measuring instruments—including radiation detectors—is limited by small irregular fluctuations in the output. Some of these fluctuations are due to accidental causes. For example, small varying electrical leaks across the surface of the glass in a photo-multiplier may cause irregular movements of the needle of the output meter. This type of fluctuation may be reduced to negligible proportions by good design of the apparatus and by care in its use. When this has been done, a sufficiently sensitive instrument still shows small irregular fluctuations known as "noise". The existence of this noise and its magnitude in any given arrangement can be predicted from statistical thermodynamics.

The situation is very similar to that discussed in Chapter VIII, where we found that the performance of a good optical instrument (which has been corrected for aberrations) is ultimately limited by diffraction. Just as the effect of diffraction in limiting the useful magnification may be reduced by using a short wavelength as in the electron microscope, so the effect of the fluctuations which we are now discussing may usually be reduced by cooling the detector. The final accuracy may also be increased by averaging observations over a period of time.

When the detail which can be seen in a picture is limited by diffraction, no improvement is obtained by magnification. In a similar way, when the performance of a detector is limited by noise, amplification of signal and noise in the same ratio is not useful. An increase in responsivity is an advantage only if the signal/noise ratio is improved. We therefore distinguish between (a) the responsivity, i.e. the ratio of signal to flux, and (b) the *detectivity*, i.e. the reciprocal, or smallest flux which can be detected under certain standard conditions. The latter quantity is closely related to the error which is involved in the measurement of a flux which is well above the limit of detection.

The analysis of different kinds of noise and the ultimate limits of radiation detectors are discussed in Chapter XX. These problems are of great theoretical interest and are of practical importance for infrared measurements and in some other fields. In this chapter we are mainly concerned with measurements involving beams of radiant energy which are very far above the level at which limits of detection need to be considered. For example at 1 metre from a 100-watt lamp the radiation flux is 10^5 times the weakest flux which can be detected with a Golay cell. Most measurements are made far above threshold.

10.14. The Photographic Plate.

An unexposed plate contains transparent grains of silver bromide. The effect of exposure to light and of the subsequent development is to release finely divided silver so that some of the grains become black. With a moderately " fine grain " emulsion, the individual grains cannot be seen with the naked eye, and parts of the plate which have been exposed to uniform illumination appear to be uniformly black. This blackening may be assessed qualitatively by measuring the ratio of the light transmitted by a blackened region (I) to the light transmitted by an unexposed region (I_0). The quantity

$$D = \log (I_0/I)$$

is called the *density* of the exposed region.

For a given kind of light (e.g. for daylight), the density is a function of the radiation flux P and of the time t of exposure. It was, at one time, thought that the density was determined by the product tP (Reciprocity Law). It is now known that this is not generally true, though for most photographic materials there is a considerable range of conditions where it is approximately true. Suppose that D is determined by the exposure E which, to a first approximation is equal to tP but, in general, is a somewhat more complicated function of t and P.*

It is found that the relation between D and $\log E$ is of the general form shown in fig. 10.6. There is an under-exposure region where light produces only a small effect, a straight-line region, and a region where further exposure produces little or no increase of density. This is known as the over-exposure region. In the straight-line region the photographic plate has some of the properties of a linear detector of radiation. The slope of the curve (usually denoted by γ) is analogous to the responsivity of a thermal detector.

For many purposes the minimum exposure required to obtain an image which can be distinguished from the background is of practical importance. Various methods have been used to define a " speed " which is proportional to the reciprocal of this exposure. This speed

---

* The precise form of the function may be obtained by varying P and then altering t until the original value of D is reproduced.

depends on both the inertia (i), i.e. the intercept of the straight line on the axis, and on γ.

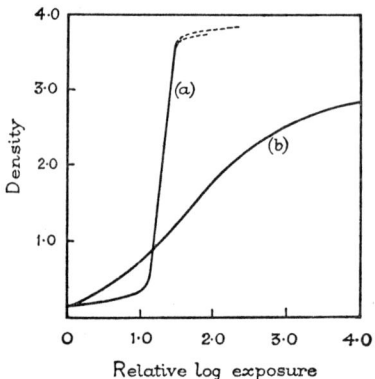

Fig. 10.6.—Photographic plate. Density of exposed and developed plate as a function of exposure for two types of plate.

Relative speeds for different wavelengths are shown in fig. 10.7. Photographic plates can be made sensitive to about 12,000 Å. in the infra-red region and to all wavelengths in the ultra-violet, right down in the X-ray region.

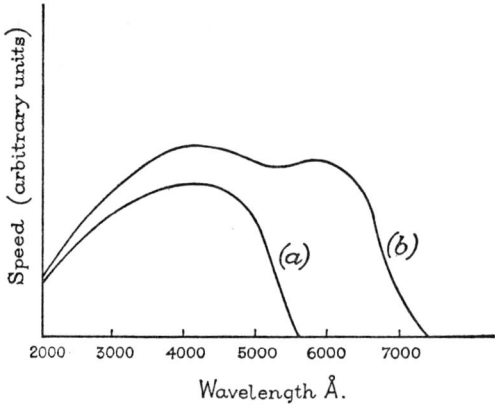

Fig. 10.7.—Sensitivity (γ) of photographic plates as a function of wavelength
(a) isochromatic, (b) panchromatic.

10.15.—The irregular distribution of the grains of a photographic plate produce effects similar to noise in other radiation detectors. Under the action of the developer a few grains become black, even in unexposed regions. The number of grains which become black for a given exposure

10.16. Calibration of a Selective Detector.

A selective detector may be calibrated in the following way. A monochromator is used to produce a beam of radiation whose energy is nearly all in a small wavelength range round some wavelength λ. The selective detector is placed in the beam, and the width of the exit (or some other parameter which controls the flux) is adjusted until the detector gives some chosen reading S_0. The energy flux of the beam is then measured with a non-selective detector. Let $P(\lambda)$ be the total flux for wavelength λ which produces a signal S_0. This procedure is repeated for different wavelengths. If P_m is the lowest energy which produces the standard signal S_0, then the relative response is given by

$$r_\lambda' = \frac{P_m}{P(\lambda)}. \qquad \ldots \ldots \quad 10(9)$$

In this way the responsivity at any wavelength is measured as a fraction of the response at the wavelength λ_m at which the responsivity

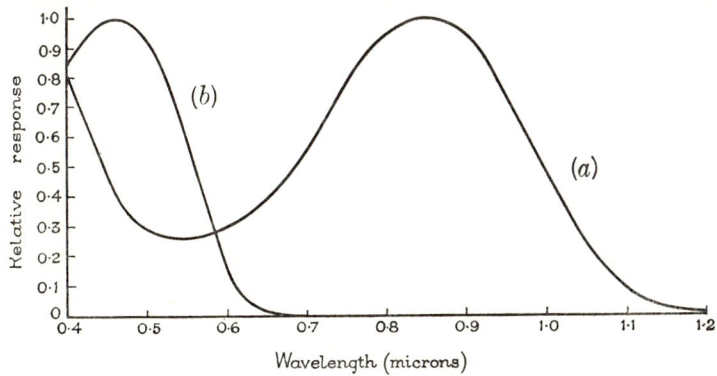

Fig. 10.8.—Relative responsivity of photo-emissive cells: (a) Sb-Cs photo-cathode, (b) Ag-O-Cs photo-cathode

is a maximum. Curves such as those shown in figs. 10.8 and 10.9 are obtained. If the absolute responsivity is required, then the non-selective detector must be calibrated by exposing it to a known fraction of the radiation from a body at known temperature.* If the detector is linear, then the relative response curve is the same† for different values of S_0.

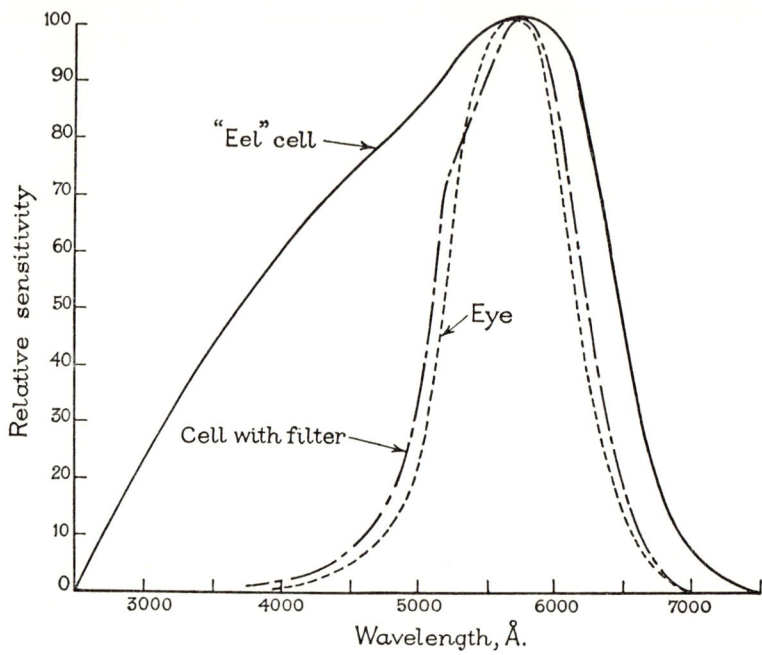

Fig. 10.9.—Relative responsivity of photo-voltaic cell

The procedure described may need modification when the selective detector is much more sensitive than the thermal detector with which it is compared. There are also several other possible procedures for the calibration of the photo-cells and other physical detectors. This one has been described because it is similar to procedures applied to the human eye.

10.17. Physical Photometry.

For many types of physical investigation it is desirable to compare the values (P_1 and P_2) of the radiant flux in two beams of the same spectral distribution. This may be done, with an accuracy of one or

---

* See p. 323 of Reference 10.1.
† If the curve of response against signal has the same shape for different wavelengths, then the relative response curve is also the same for different values of S_0.

two per cent, by measuring each in turn with a calibrated radiation detector, but when only the ratio P_1/P_2 is required, a more accurate value may be obtained by one of the following methods:

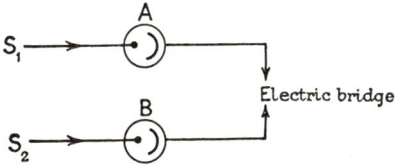

Fig. 10.10.—Physical photometer with two detectors (A and B)

(a) The two beams are allowed to fall on two similar radiation detectors and the outputs, amplified if necessary, are passed into an electronic bridge circuit. Two resistances are adjusted to balance the bridge and their ratio gives P_1/P_2. It is not difficult to make automatic allowance for small differences between the detectors (fig. 10.10).

(b) Each beam is allowed to fall in turn upon the *same* detector, using a rotating mirror or some equivalent device (see fig. 10.11a). The signal then consists of a steady current, plus an alternating component whose amplitude is proportional to $(P_1 - P_2)$. This signal is passed through a sharply tuned a.c. amplifier, so that the steady component is rejected and a rectified output proportional to $(P_1 - P_2)$ is obtained. One beam is then reduced in a known variable ratio until the output is a minimum. The two beams are then judged to be equal and the ratio of reduction gives P_1/P_2.

10.18.—Method (b) is more suitable when the two beams to be compared are very weak. Its accuracy is limited by the fact that the difference signal has to be detected in the presence of three kinds of noise. These are (a) the photon noise due to fluctuations in the steady component of radiation, (b) " electrical noise " in the valves, and (c) " accidental " noise due to the fact that it is very difficult to effect a transfer from one beam to the other without a small overlap or gap.*

The effect of these kinds of noise is reduced by the method shown in fig. 10.11. The device which effects the alternation also controls a beam of light which falls on a second photo-cell. Electrical pulses produced in this way control the rectifier so that it becomes sensitive only at certain points in the cycle of alternation. This has the effect of sharpening the tuning, thereby rejecting some of the photon noise and

---

* A polarization method, available only for the visible and near ultra-violet, is described in § 12.14.

electrical noise. It may also be arranged that the amplifier is insensitive during the times when the transfer from one beam to another is being made so that the " accidental " noise is also rejected.

A second practical difficulty in method (b) is to design a device for *accurately* altering a beam of light in a known ratio. A diaphragm of variable area placed in a parallel beam of light will achieve this effect if the flux per unit area is the same over the whole cross-section. An alternative method is to use a balanced photometric wedge (fig. 10.11b).

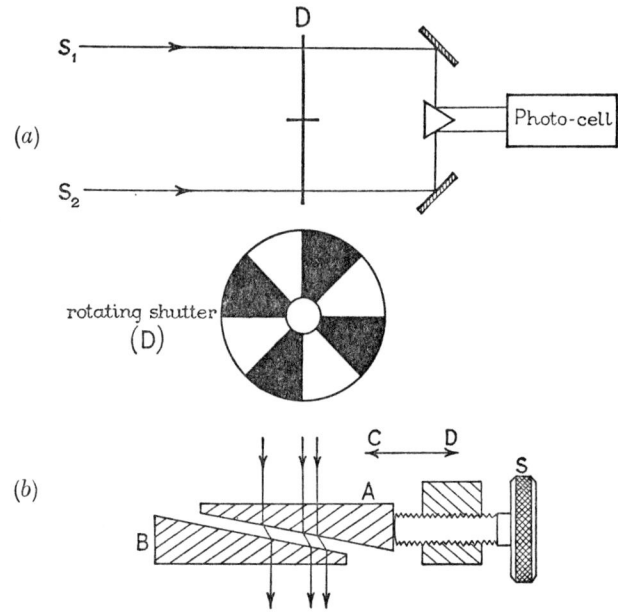

Fig. 10.11.—(a) Light from the sources S_1 and S_2 falls on the photo-cell alternately as the disc D rotates. Contacts on the edges of the disc initiate electrical pulses to control the phase-sensitive circuit amplifier which follows the photo-cell.

(b) The wedge A may be moved by the screws in the direction CD to increase the thickness of the glass in the paths of the beam of light. Note that the thickness is the same at all parts of the beam and there is no deviation of the emergent rays.

A *photometric wedge* may consist of a piece of absorbing glass whose cross-section is a wedge of small angle. This reduces the transmitted light by absorption, and the density (see § 10.14) increases linearly from one edge to the other. It is convenient to use two wedges in opposition, as shown in fig. 10.11b, so as to avoid refraction and to give uniform transmission over an appreciable area. The transmission is then altered by moving the wedges in the direction of the arrow. In colorimetry it is important to use *neutral* wedges, which reduce light of all wavelengths (in the visible spectrum) in the same ratio.

10.19. Spectrophotometers.

The spectral distribution of a beam of radiation may be investigated by allowing it to fall on a monochromator whose output is received by a non-selective detector (fig. 10.12). It is usual to arrange that the

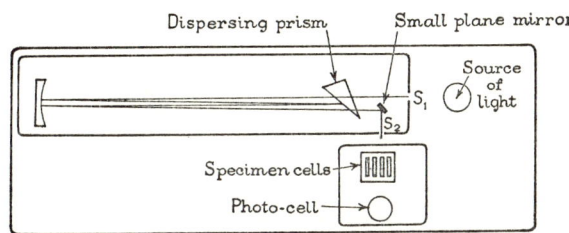

Fig. 10.12.—Spectrophotometer (Hilger UVISPEK)

monochromator is controlled by a motor which also drives the chart of a pen-recorder. A graph showing the radiation flux as a function of wavelength is obtained automatically. This curve must be corrected for variations in the effective transmission of the monochromator and in the response of the detector with wavelength. In the visible and ultra-violet regions of the spectrum, a very sensitive photomultiplier may be used as detector, and the limit of resolution may be determined by the diffraction effects discussed in Chapter VIII. In the infra-red region the limit of resolution is determined by the necessity of using sufficiently wide slits to obtain a detectable signal. Thus the design of detectors of good detectivity is very important in relation to infra-red spectroscopy and spectrophotometry.

10.20. Absorption Spectrophotometry.

The absorption spectrum of a material such as a coloured glass may be investigated using the arrangement shown in fig. 10.12. If P_0 is the flux without the specimen and P is the flux when it is inserted, the transmission factor τ is

$$\tau = \frac{P}{P_0}. \qquad \ldots \ldots \quad 10(10)$$

This factor is important in relation to the properties of a filter, but for obtaining information about the material we require the absorption coefficient (see § 15.5). If ρ is the reflection coefficient and 2α is the absorption coefficient and d is the thickness of the specimen, we have

$$\tau = (1 - \rho)^2 e^{-2\alpha d}, \qquad \ldots \quad 10(11)$$

provided that ρ is small or α is high, so that radiation which is transmitted after being reflected more than once may be neglected. We then have

$$2\alpha = \frac{1}{d} \{ 2 \log (1 - \rho) - \log \tau \}. \qquad \ldots \quad 10(12)$$

If the transmission of light which has suffered two or more reflections cannot be neglected it is necessary to know whether the sides of the specimen are accurately parallel. If the variations of thickness are only a small fraction of a wavelength, the calculation of § 5.26 is applicable and a banded spectrum is obtained. The bands are often observed in infra-red measurements. For the shorter wavelengths of the visible spectrum, it usually happens that, unless special care has been taken in preparing the specimen, variations of thickness are several wavelengths. The reflected beams are then non-coherent with each other and with the main beam, so that intensities must be added. Putting $t = e^{-2\alpha d}$, we then have

$$P = P_0 (1 - \rho)^2 \{ t + \rho^2 t^3 + \rho^4 t^5 + \ldots \}$$

and

$$\tau = \frac{(1 - \rho)^2 t}{1 - \rho^2 t^2}. \qquad \ldots \ldots \ldots \ldots \quad 10(13)$$

The value of t and hence of α may be obtained by solving 10(13) graphically when ρ is known and τ has been measured.

A large proportion of modern instruments are double-beam spectrophotometers. The radiation from a monochromator is divided into two parts which may be compared by using two detectors and a bridge, or by allowing one detector to sample them alternately (see § 10.17). When the two beams have been adjusted to be equal the specimen is inserted in one beam. It is possible to arrange for a servo-mechanism to adjust the position of a calibrated photometric wedge until the beams are equal again. It is usual to arrange for a motor to alter the wavelength setting of the monochromator and turn the drum of a pen-recorder. The position of the pen is related to that of the wedge in such a way that a curve of transmission or of log (transmission) is drawn automatically. Instruments are now available in which the transmission readings are coded and punched on to tape, which passes into a small electronic computer, which calculates the absorption coefficient and either types the values at selected wavelengths or plots a curve. Similar methods are used for measuring the reflection of a surface as a function of wavelength.

The double-beam instrument has the advantage that it does not require a steady source of radiation. It also gives automatic elimination of the strong infra-red absorption due to water vapour and carbon dioxide in the atmosphere. The instruments which plot the transmission or absorption curve directly are usually less accurate than those which are operated manually. The older methods are still the most generally useful, but the automatic machines in some applications

10.21. The Eye as a Detector of Radiation.

When light falls on the eye, retinal receptors are stimulated; electrical pulses pass along the fibres of the optic nerve to the brain, where they are interpreted as visual sensation. The eye is thus able to detect radiation within a certain wavelength range and has some, but not all, of the properties of a physical detector. If two halves of a visual field are illuminated with sources S_1 and S_2 of white light in the simple photometer shown in fig. 10.13, it is possible to move one of

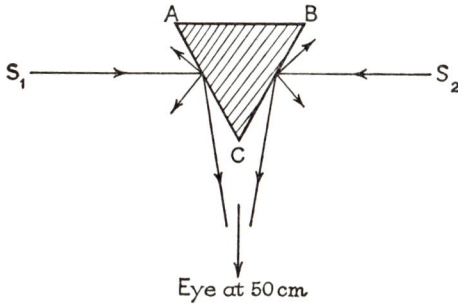

Fig. 10.13.—Visual photometer (schematic diagram)

the sources until the two halves of the field appear equally bright. If the same observer makes repeated trials, or if different observers are used, there will be substantial agreement about the setting which gives equality. The radiation flux measured with a physical detector will then be found to be equal within one or two per cent error. With a physical detector it would be easy to find a setting such that one side gave twice the signal of the other, but if human observers were asked to adjust the sources till one side appeared twice as bright as the other the settings obtained would differ very much from one observer to another, and there would be serious differences between the repeated judgments of any one observer. The human observer is able to judge equality with an accuracy comparable with that of a moderately good physical detector but not to measure ratios.

If one half of the field is illuminated with blue light and the other with yellow, a suitable adjustment will give equal signals with a physical detector, but no adjustment will give identical sensations for the eye, i.e. no increase or decrease of the blue light will make it match the yellow.

10.22. The C.I.E. Photometric Scale.

It has been found possible to measure a relative response curve for the eye using only judgments of equality. This has been done in a number of ways of which the following are the most important:

(a) One half of a photometric field is illuminated with wavelength λ and the other with wavelength $\lambda + \Delta\lambda$, where $\Delta\lambda$ is a fairly small wavelength difference; an observer is able to say when they appear equally bright. There is reasonable agreement between different observers. The energy flux corresponding to equal subjective brightness can be measured with a physical detector, and the inverse ratio gives the relative responsivity of the eye for these two wavelengths. By successive steps it is possible to pass right along the visible spectrum, and the responsivity at any given wavelength can be expressed as a fraction of that at 5500 Å., where the response is maximal.

(b) It is possible, by devices similar to those described in § 10.18 above, to arrange that the eye receives light from two sources alternately. If the frequency of alternation is adjusted to a suitable value (about 10 per second) the difference of hue is no longer noticeable, even though there is a large difference of wavelength. There is, however, a painful flicker which nearly disappears when the position of one source is suitably adjusted. The alternating fields are then said to have equal subjective brightness; the flux of each may be measured, and the relative responsivity calculated. Since it is now possible to use widely differing wavelengths, there is less room for accumulation of errors and more cross-checks become possible.

The Commission Internationale d'Eclairage (C.I.E.) has assembled the results of a number of experiments and has adopted a standard curve for relative response of the average normal human eye. This curve is defined by giving the values of the relative luminous efficiency V_λ (i.e. of the quantity analogous to the relative responsivity of a physical receptor) at suitable wavelength intervals. The curve is shown in fig. 10.14. If these values are accepted it is in principle possible to construct a physical receptor whose measurements of radiation of different wavelengths agree with that of the average human eye. For example, by placing a suitable selection of colour filters in front of a photo-voltaic cell* it is possible to make an instrument whose relative

* See fig. 10.9.

response agrees fairly well with the C.I.E. visibility curve. Spectrophotometric measurements may be used in the following way.

10.23.—Suppose that the spectral distributions of two sources are $\mathscr{P}_1(\lambda)$ and $\mathscr{P}_2(\lambda)$. Then the ratio of the visual effects is

$$\frac{\int \mathscr{P}_1(\lambda) V_\lambda \, d\lambda}{\int \mathscr{P}_2(\lambda) V_\lambda \, d\lambda}. \qquad \ldots \ldots \quad 10(14)$$

If a surface has a reflection factor ρ_λ for wavelength λ, then its overall reflection factor β *as judged by the eye* for light of spectral distribution $\mathscr{P}_\lambda$ is

$$\beta = \frac{\int \mathscr{P}(\lambda) V_\lambda \rho_\lambda \, d\lambda}{\int \mathscr{P}(\lambda) V_\lambda \, d\lambda}. \qquad \ldots \ldots \quad 10(15)$$

The effective reflection factor depends both on the spectral distribution factor $\mathscr{P}_\lambda$ and on the properties of the eye. Note the similarity of equation 10(15) with 10(3). It is possible to deduce the visual reflection factor from a single measurement by a physical detector if the physical detector is adjusted so that its relative response curve agrees with the visibility curve for the eye.

10.24.—The usefulness of the relative luminosity factors (V_λ) defined by the C.I.E. depends on the fact that predictions made from them agree moderately well with practical tests. For example, suppose that a pale green light and a pale yellow light are adjusted so that according to measurements and calculations based on the C.I.E. system they are equal. Then it is found that they give *approximate* equality of comfort in reading small type or performing other visual tasks. Measurements of ease of reading, etc., are not susceptible of high accuracy, but by making a large number of tests of different kinds it is possible to build up a considerable weight of evidence. It is found that the C.I.E. factors represent the properties of the eye fairly well over a useful range of conditions.

10.25. Dark Adaptation.

The photopic curve given in fig. 10.14 is valid from daylight illumination to an illumination a little higher than that of the full moon. At very low levels of illumination (starlight) the visibility factors have changed significantly, the eye becoming relatively more sensitive to blue and less sensitive to red (Purkinje effect). The relative response of the eye changes and the *scotopic visibility* curve (fig. 10.14b) is appropriate under this condition. Under this condition the best vision is obtained by looking a little to one side of the object of interest, whereas at higher brightness direct vision is obviously best. These and other experiments suggest that there are two types of retinal receptors, one of which is responsible for the ability of the eye to discriminate small differences of colour and shape at

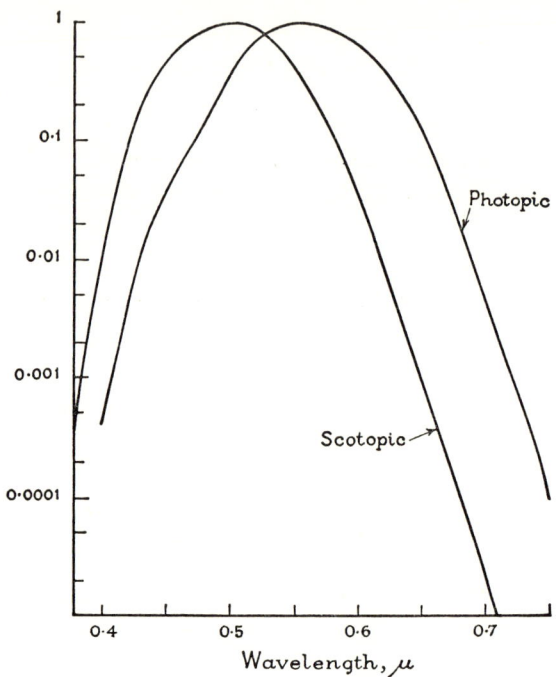

Fig. 10.14.—Visibility factors for the eye
(a) under daylight conditions (photopic),   (b) when dark adapted (scotopic).

high brightness, and the other for the very high sensitivity to extremely weak sources of light. These two are respectively identified with cone-like structures which predominate in the centre of the retina and rod-like structures in the periphery.

On first going into darkness, the sensitivity of the eye is low. After about ten minutes it has increased by a factor of about 10^3. This part of the adaptation is due to an increase in the sensitivity of the cones. After about fifteen minutes, scotopic vision predominates, and after thirty minutes sensitivity has increased by a further factor of about 10^3. The eye can then detect 7×10^{-10} ergs in the form of a short flash of green light falling on the most sensitive part of the retina.

10.26. Photometry—Definitions.

It is convenient to define algebraically four quantities: flux, intensity, illumination, and luminance, which are used in calculations on lighting. These quantities have already been defined verbally in § 2.21 which should be read in conjunction with the following definitions:

(i) *Luminous Flux.* Symbol, F. Unit, the *lumen* (lm.). The luminous flux for a beam of radiation of spectral distribution $\mathscr{P}_\lambda$ is given by

$$F = k \int \mathscr{P}_\lambda V_\lambda \, d\lambda. \quad \ldots \ldots \quad 10(16)$$

The luminous flux is thus proportional to the reading of a physical detector whose relative response curve is the same as the C.I.E. photopic visibility curve. The constant k is discussed in § 10.28.

(ii) *Luminous Intensity.* Symbol, I. Unit, the *candela* (cd.). The luminous intensity of a source in a given direction is the *flux per unit solid angle* within a small solid angle which includes this direction. It is

$$I = \frac{dF}{d\Omega}, \quad \ldots \ldots \quad 10(17a)$$

where Ω is a solid angle.

If a source emits light equally in all directions then

$$4\pi I = F, \quad \ldots \ldots \quad 10(17b)$$

where F is the total flux.

Thus a source which emits 4π lumens has a mean intensity of 1 candela.

(iii) *Illumination.* Symbol, E. Unit, 1 cd./cm.^{2}. The illumination at a given point Q measures the light received per unit area. We have

$$E = \frac{dF}{dS}, \quad \ldots \ldots \quad 10(18)$$

where dS is an element of area surrounding Q.

(iv) *Luminance.* Symbol, L. Unit, 1 cd./cm.^{2}. Luminance is a measure of the light leaving a surface in a given direction. Consider a direction which makes an angle θ with a plane surface, then

$$L = \frac{1}{\cos\theta} \cdot \frac{dI(\theta)}{dS}, \quad \ldots \ldots \quad 10(19)$$

where dS is a small area surrounding a point Q, i.e. the luminance at Q in the direction θ is equal to the intensity in this direction, per unit projected area (see fig. 10.15). If the surface is not plane, it may, for the purpose of this definition, be replaced by an infinitesimal portion of a tangent plane at Q.

Suppose that a person looks at the point Q (fig. 10.15) from a distance R which is large compared with the focal length of the eye. The area of the retinal image

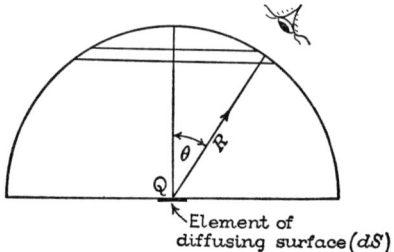

Fig. 10.15

of a small area ΔS is proportional to $\cos \theta \, \Delta S/R^2$. The light received is proportional to $\Delta I(\theta)a/R^2$, where a is the area of the pupil and $\Delta I(\theta)$ is the intensity associated with ΔS. The light per unit area of the retinal image is then proportional to

$$\frac{1}{\cos \theta} \frac{\Delta I(\theta)}{\Delta S},$$

i.e. when ΔS and ΔI are allowed to decrease without limit it is proportional to L.

The *subjective brightness* of a surface (in the neighbourhood of a point Q) is a term used to describe the appearance of a surface to the person viewing it. This " appearance " is related to the state of adaptation of the eye, to the luminance of the surrounding area, etc. In so far as it is related to light received from the neighbourhood of Q, the relevant measure is the luminance. When the state of adaptation and other relevant conditions are the same, two surfaces of equal luminance appear equally bright. The subjective brightness of a surface is unaffected by distance (provided the intervening medium is perfectly clear).

10.27.—A *uniformly diffusing* surface is one for which $I(\theta)$ is proportional to $\cos \theta$, so that L is independent of direction. Such a surface is said to obey *Lambert's cosine law*. It has been shown in § 6.51 that a sufficiently finely ground-glass screen does obey this law.

The flux from a small area dS of a uniformly diffusing surface in a hollow cone between θ and $\theta + d\theta$ (fig. 10.15) is

$$dF = 2\pi L \sin \theta \cos \theta \, d\theta \, dS. \quad \ldots \ldots \quad 10(20)$$

The total flux for angles 0 to θ, obtained by integration, is

$$F_\theta = \pi L \, dS \sin^2 \theta, \quad \ldots \ldots \quad 10(21)$$

and for the whole hemisphere

$$F = \pi L \, dS. \quad \ldots \ldots \quad 10(22)$$

The above definitions of intensity and luminance assume, in accordance with the physical facts, that the flux of a narrow pencil is proportional to the solid angle and that the flux from a small area is proportional to the area. Thus zero angle or zero area imply zero flux; no light or radiant energy is transmitted in a mathematically parallel beam or from a mathematical point source. Table 10.3 shows the relations between (a) various units of illumination and (b) various units of luminance. The names attached to the units are given because they are used in much of the technical literature though some of them are obsolescent. The reader is advised not to use these names in making calculations but to state units in the direct way which makes their meaning immediately obvious (e.g. to speak of $lm./m.^2$ rather than of lux). To convert a quantity expressed in a unit at the side of the table to a unit at the head, *multiply* by the number in the appropriate row and column (e.g. $1\ lm./m.^2 = 10^{-4}\ lm./cm.^2$).

TABLE 10.3

Photometric Units and Conversion Factors

(A) Units of Illumination

Units	$1\ lm./m.^2$	$1\ lm./cm.^2$	$1\ lm./ft.^2$
$1\ lm./m.^2$ (lux)	1·0	10^{-4}	9.3×10^{-2}
$1\ lm./cm.^2$ (phot)	10^4	1·0	9.3×10^2
$1\ lm./ft.^2$ (ft. candle)	10·76	1.076×10^{-3}	1·0

(B) Units of Luminance

Units	$cd./cm.^2$	$cd./ft.^2$	$lm./cm.^2$	$lm./ft.^2$
$cd./cm.^2$ (stilb)	1·0	9.3×10^2	3·142	2.919×10^3
$cd./ft.^2$	1.1×10^{-3}	1·0	3.4×10^{-3}	3·14
$lm./cm.^2$ (lambert)	3.18×10^{-1}	3.42×10^2	1·0	9.29×10^2
$lm./ft.^2$ (ft. lambert)	3.42×10^{-4}	2.92×10^{-1}	1.1×10^{-3}	1·0

10.28. Photometric Units.

The definitions of the four quantities are interrelated, so that if a unit is defined for any one then the units for the others are fixed. The original unit of photometry was a unit of *intensity*, i.e. the intensity of a sperm candle. The present unit is a unit of *luminance*. The *candela* is defined to be such that the luminance of a full radiator or black body (see § 17.27) at the temperature of the melting-point of platinum is 60 candelas per sq. cm.

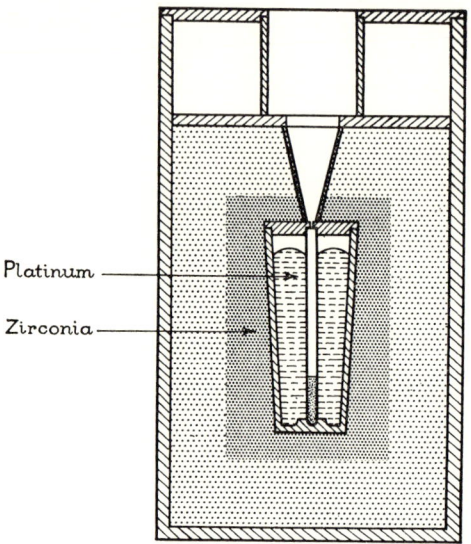

Fig. 10.16.—Standard source related to definition of the candela

The definition having been accepted by the C.I.E. any photometric laboratory can, in principle, prepare a standard source* and use it to

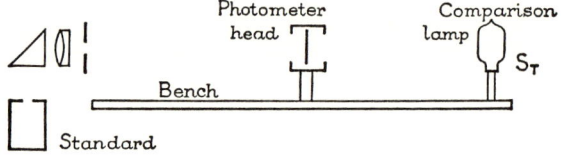

Fig. 10.17.—Comparison of substandard source S_T with the standard

measure the intensities of other sources (by the method shown in fig. 10.17). It is inconvenient to use the standard source for routine measurements, and specially designed electric lamps are used as substandards. The definition of the candela leads through equation 10(17) to the definition of the lumen.

* The practical realization of a satisfactory standard is difficult and requires the resources of a standards laboratory.

If the luminous flux of a beam is measured in lumens by reference to the standard source and the value of $\mathscr{P}_\lambda$ in watts is measured by the methods of spectrophotometry, then the constant k in equation 10(16) is determined experimentally. It is found to be 692 lumens/watt. Since $V_\lambda = 1$ for $\lambda = 5550$ Å., a flux of one watt of radiation of this wavelength constitutes a luminous flux of 692 lumens. It is possible to define the luminous efficiency of a beam of radiation to be

$$K = k \frac{\int \mathscr{P}_\lambda V_\lambda \, d\lambda}{\int \mathscr{P}_\lambda \, d\lambda} \text{ lumens/watt.} \quad \ldots \quad 10(23)$$

The luminous efficiency of a beam of radiation is the light flux per unit of radiant energy. The luminous efficiency (ε) of an electric lamp is the total flux of the emitted light per unit of energy supplied to the lamp. Some of this energy is lost by conduction and convection and by emission of infra-red radiation. Tungsten lamps have efficiencies varying from 12 to 20 lumens/watt, the lamps of lower voltage and higher wattage being more efficient. The efficiencies of fluorescent tubes range from 40 to 60 lm./W. and of sodium lamps from 60 to 90 lm./W.

10.29. Photometric Measurements.

Once the above definitions are accepted, calculations and measurements in photometry involve no further physical principles. They are complicated calculations based on the inverse-square law. In order to

Fig. 10.18.—Photometer sphere. The interior of the sphere and both sides of S are diffuse white.

assess the luminous efficiency of electric lamps it is desirable to be able to measure the total luminous flux. This may be done by measuring the intensity in various directions and then integrating over the solid angle, but a more convenient way is to use the photometer sphere (fig. 10.18).

The photometer sphere is a large sphere whose interior surface is diffuse white. A source S_1 is placed in the sphere at L and the luminance of the hole W is measured in arbitrary units. A substandard source S_T is then substituted for S_1 and the luminance of W is again measured. The ratio of the two luminances is equal to the ratio of S_1 to S_T.

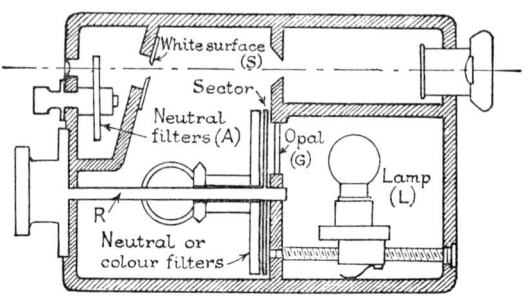

Fig. 10.19—Holophane Illuminometer (Lumeter).

The Holophane Lumeter (fig. 10.19) is one of a number of instruments for measuring luminance. The observer sees the test surface (whose luminance is to be measured) through a hole in the screen S. This screen is illuminated by light from the lamp L which has passed through a window in the opal glass G. The luminance of the screen S is adjusted (until it matches the test surface) by means of a sectoral disc which alters the area of the window at G. The position of the sector is given by a circular scale attached to the rod R. The instrument is calibrated by reference to a white surface placed at a known distance from a standard lamp. The scale of the instrument covers a range of 80:1. Neutral filters placed at A or G may be used to extend the scale upwards or downwards, and colour filters of known transmission (inserted at G) may be used for dealing with coloured sources of light.

The instrument measures *luminance* directly. If the *illumination* of a surface is required, then a standard matt white card (whose diffuse reflection coefficient is about 0·97 and is accurately known) is placed on top of the surface. The flux per unit area emitted by this card (i.e. its luminance) is measured, and dividing by the diffuse reflection coefficient of the card we obtain the flux per unit area incident upon the card, i.e. the illumination of the test surface.

10.30. Lighting Problems.*

The calculation of photometric magnitudes is an essential part of the design of a lighting system, yet it is only a part. The level of illumination required for a

* See Reference 10.7.

given task can be found only by psychophysical tests on considerable numbers of individuals. In road lighting the main objective is to obtain an adequate level of reasonably even illumination on the road without too much glare. The advantages of sodium lamps which are very efficient and can therefore be placed high above the road are considerable. Even here, however, the lighting engineer has to consider the extent to which some people dislike the yellow hue. This consideration of aesthetic preference is more important in a factory than on a road, and still more important in regard to a living room or a cathedral. Contrasts which are too strong are unpleasant, but perfectly uniform shadowless lighting is so dull that it should be used only in certain special situations.

The following values of illumination* are recommended: for reading 15 lm./ft.^{2}, for exceptionally fine work in machine shops 100 lm./ft.^{2}, for operating tables 300 lm./ft.^{2}

10.31. Colour Specification.

An observer with normal colour vision perceives a gradual change of colour from red to blue in a spectrum as the wavelength changes from 7000 Å. to 4000 Å. For monochromatic light there is agreement between the physical scale of wavelength and a subjective scale of colour based on judgments of equality. Two beams of light of the same wavelength are perceived to have the same colour, and two which are perceived to have the same colour are found to have nearly the same wavelength.

This simple correspondence is not valid for mixtures of more than one wavelength. Two beams of light which form a *spectrum match*, i.e. which have the same spectral distribution ($\mathscr{P}_\lambda$) are perceived to have the same colour, but it is also possible to have two beams which give a visual colour match but do not have the same spectral distribution. These are said to constitute a *metameric* match. For example, a mixture in suitable proportions of green and red will match a mixture of yellow with a little blue. Some method of colour specification, other than the spectral distribution, is therefore needed. The object of the investigation which will now be described is to devise a system of colour specification in terms of numbers which are derived from measurements with physical instruments. The numbers specifying two beams (for which the spectral distribution may be different) must be the same if, and only if, an observer with normal colour vision perceives a match.

10.32. Trichromatism.

Fig. 10.20 is a schematic diagram of a colour-matching experiment. The observer views a bipartite field with a dark surround. The left-

* A list of recommended values for many different situations is given in Appendix II of Reference 10.7.

hand side is illuminated by a source S_0 and the right-hand side by a mixture of light from two or more sources S_1, S_2, S_3. . . . The observer

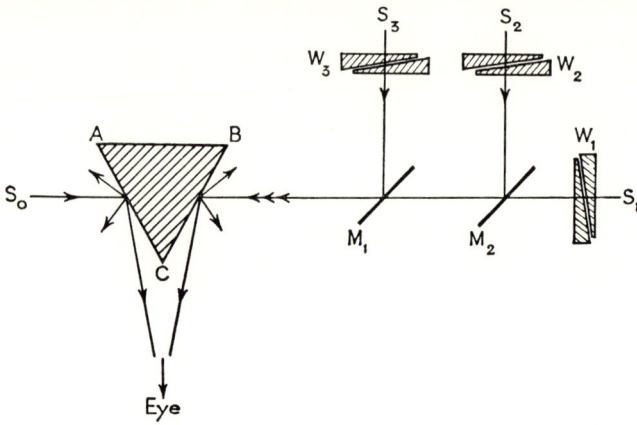

Fig. 10.20.—Schematic colorimeter for three-colour mixture. The sides of prism ABC are matt white. The contributions of the sources S_1, S_2 and S_3 to the illumination of the face BC may be adjusted by means of the neutral photometric wedges W_1, W_2, W_3. M_1 and M_2 are semi-reflecting.

is provided with adjustments by which he can alter the light on the right-hand side until he obtains a match, i.e. until the two sides appear exactly the same.

Let us first suppose that there are two sources illuminating the right-hand side: (i) a source S_E (white light with an equal energy spectrum, $\mathscr{P}_\lambda = $ constant) and (ii) a beam of light S_M from a monochromator (fig. 10.21). The observer is provided with three controls,

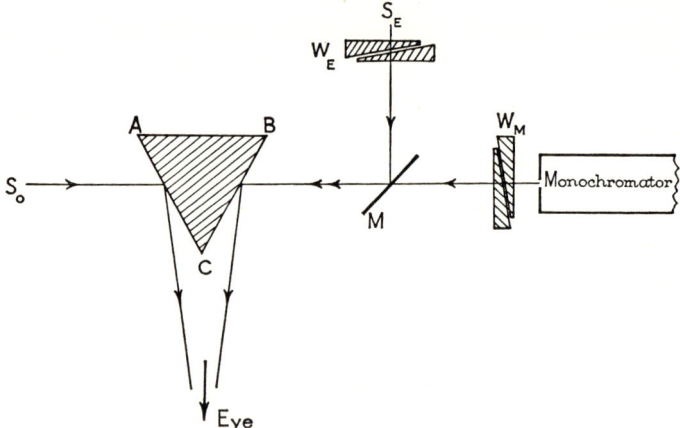

Fig. 10.21.—Schematic colorimeter for mixing a spectrum colour with white

and two of these alter the amounts of light from S_E and from S_M by means of the neutral photometric wedges* W_E and W_M. The third alters the wavelength of the light from the monochromator. It is found that the observer can match a wide range of colours by adjusting the three controls. With purple and certain other colours he cannot obtain a match in this way, but he can then obtain one by adding the light S_M to the left-hand side. Thus we have

$$(S_0) \equiv e(S_E) + m(S_M), \quad \ldots \quad 10(24a)$$

or
$$(S_0) + m'(S_M) \equiv e(S_E), \quad \ldots \quad 10(24b)$$

where the symbol $\equiv$ means " forms a colour match with " and (S_E) and (S_M) stand for unit amounts of light from S_E and S_M. The units for S_E and S_M may be chosen in various ways. If energy units are used, then $10(24a)$ means that

" the light on the L.H.S. from S_0 forms a colour match with e watts/cm.² of light from S_E plus m watts/cm.² from S_M ".

Equation $10(24a)$ includes $10(24b)$ if we allow m to take both positive and negative values.

10.33.—The experimental result that a match can be obtained in the above way enables the colour of the light on the L.H.S. to be specified in terms of physical measurements* made on the R.H.S. The colour may be regarded as having three " components ":

(i) The *luminance*—which is equal to the luminance of e watts/cm.² of S_E plus m watts/cm.² of S_M calculated according to the C.I.E. procedure (§ 10.22).

(ii) The *dominant wavelength* which is the wavelength (λ_M) of the light from the monochromator when a match is obtained.

(iii) The *colorimetric purity* which is the ratio of the luminance of the light from S_M to the total luminance. The two quantities " dominant wavelength " and " purity " taken together constitute the *chromaticity*.

The definitions stated above refer to physical measurements based on judgments of equality of sensation. They are not intended to convey the aesthetic and emotional experience associated with colour. The

* See § 10.18 and fig. 10.11b.

following words describing visual experience are closely associated with the physical measurements,

(a) *Subjective brightness* associated with luminance.
(b) *Hue* associated with dominant wavelength.
(c) *Saturation* associated with colorimetric purity.

Words like " tone ", " weight ", etc., used by artists to convey aesthetic feeling are not related in any precise logical way to each other or to physical measurements. The word " colour " is sometimes used to refer to hue, or to hue and saturation, or with various other meanings.

10.34.—Now consider a slightly different experiment in which S_1, S_2, S_3 (fig. 10.20) are *reference stimuli*, each with a fixed spectral distribution.* The observer can control the energies from each source by means of a photometric wedge. There is a wide choice of reference stimuli, but one should be reddish, another bluish, and the third green. It is found that a match can always be obtained either (a) by adjusting the amounts of the three reference stimuli on the R.H.S. or (b) by adding one reference stimulus to the L.H.S. and then adjusting the amounts of all three. This result may be represented by

$$(S) \equiv r(S_R) + g(S_G) + b(S_B), \qquad \ldots \quad 10(25)$$

where (S_R), (S_G), (S_B) represent energy units for three primaries and r, g, b are numbers. It is understood that one of the three numbers may be negative.

According to the trichromatic theory, first stated by Thomas Young, three numbers are necessary and sufficient to specify colour. This necessity is a logical consequence of the experimental observation that, in general, an observer with normal colour vision requires three controls to make a match. If a colour is specified by reference to three primaries, the actual numbers by which it is specified depend on the choice of primaries, just as the co-ordinate numbers for a point in space depend on the choice of axes. Specification of colour in terms of luminance, dominant wavelength, and spectral purity is analogous to the use of a different kind of co-ordinate system, e.g. polar co-ordinates, to specify a point in space. No change of the method of specification can alter the fact that we are dealing with an experimental situation involving three degrees of freedom.

* The term *primary* was formerly used for a standard reference stimulus.

10.35. Linear Additivity.

It is found in colour-matching experiments that, over a considerable range of conditions, colour properties are approximately additive. If two colour matches are represented by equations such as 10(25), then the equations obtained by addition or subtraction also represent colour matches. As a special case of this additivity, the equation obtained by multiplying both sides of equation 10(25) by a constant factor also represents a colour match. This experimental result is involved in the matching of the colours of surfaces or dyed materials. If two pieces of material have the same colour when viewed by means of standard white light (S_E) at one luminance level, then they also match at higher and lower luminance levels, provided that the spectral distribution of the incident light is not changed. This law is approximately correct from 1000 lm./ft.² to 0·1 lm./ft.² but does not apply at extremely high or very low luminance. It also fails in relation to surfaces which subtend large angles at the observer's eye.

10.36. Chromaticity Diagram.

There are many practical situations when we are interested in the relative proportions of the three reference stimuli and not in the absolute amounts, i.e. we are concerned with chromaticity and not with luminance. Two numbers are then sufficient to specify colour properties. If three reference stimuli are used (as in § 10.34), we may arbitrarily put

$$r + g + b = 1, \qquad \ldots \ldots \quad 10(26)$$

so that if r and g are given, then the value of b is obtained by difference. Chromaticity may then be represented by a two-dimensional diagram.

In discussions of chromaticity it is convenient to use special units for the reference stimuli chosen, so that for white light $r = g = b = \frac{1}{3}$.

The chromaticity diagram shown in fig. 10.22 gives the relative proportion (r) of one primary as abscissa and that of another (g) as ordinates. The additivity law implies that if the chromaticities of two sources of light are represented by points A and D, and their intensities measured in chromaticity units are M_A and M_D, then the colour mixture obtained by adding them has intensity ($M_A + M_D$) and a chromaticity represented by the point C which is the centre of gravity of two masses M_A and M_D placed at A and D.

The pure spectrum colours may be represented by points on a chromaticity diagram, and a line joining these points is called the *pure spectrum locus*. The dominant wavelength of light represented by a point such as D is obtained by drawing a line from the point S (which represents white) through D to the spectrum locus. The spectral purity increases as D approaches the spectrum locus.

It may be seen that the pure spectrum locus is convex and lies outside the corners of the triangle whose corners are (0, 0), (1, 0), and

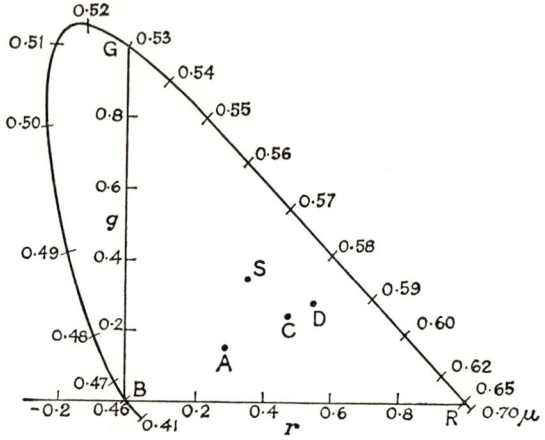

Fig. 10.22.—Chromaticity diagram. The curved line from B to R represents the spectrum locus. Points are marked with corresponding wavelengths

(0, 1). This corresponds with the experimental observation that pure spectrum colours cannot in general be matched by positive mixtures of reference stimuli, even when spectrum colours are chosen as reference stimuli. It is necessary to add a little white, or a little of the third stimulus, to a spectrum colour in order to obtain a match.

10.37. The C.I.E. System of Colour Measurement.

The physical system of measuring luminance requires first the determination of the V_λ function for the average observer, and secondly the establishment of a system of units which enables numerical values of luminance to be calculated when $\mathscr{P}_\lambda$ has been measured. Two steps are also needed before colour coefficients based on measurements of $\mathscr{P}_\lambda$ can be calculated. Firstly it is necessary to determine a series of functions which describe the colour-matching properties of the average observer with normal colour vision. Secondly a set of reference stimuli must be chosen for the numerical specification of colour co-ordinates.

The colour-matching properties of the average observer have been determined by reference to the following three reference stimuli: (R) a deep red (7000 Å.), (G) the mercury green line (5461 Å.), and (B) the mercury blue line (4358 Å.). The relative proportions r, g, and b of these three reference stimuli required to match a unit amount of light of a given wavelength λ may be measured. The results obtained by Wright for 10 observers are shown in fig. 10.23.* Reasonably good

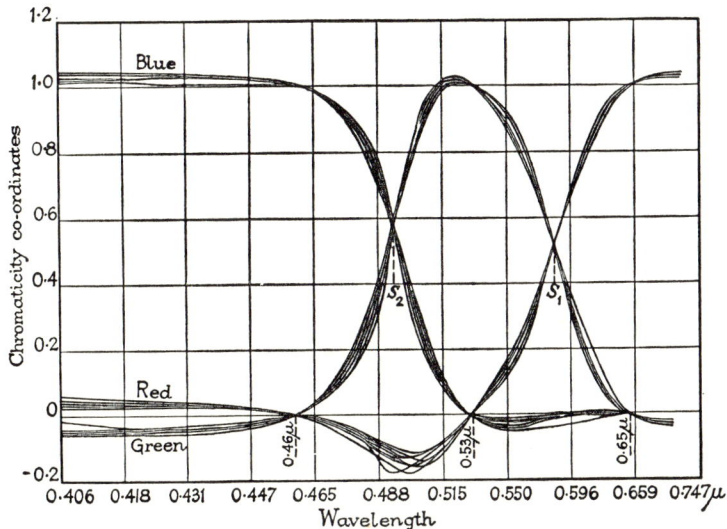

Fig. 10.23.—Chromaticity co-ordinates for 10 observers

agreement is obtained. It will be noticed that (as explained in § 10.36) the amount of one stimulus is usually negative.

The values r, g, b required by the average observer are called *chromaticity co-ordinates*. The results† obtained by Wright and by Guild were combined to provide standard values giving r, g, b as functions of λ, and these functions were adopted by the C.I.E. in 1931.

10.38.—Suppose that, in Euclidean geometry, two systems of axes OU, OV OW and O'U', O'V', O'W' are available. Then co-ordinates measured relative to the first set of axes may be used to calculate the co-ordinates relative to the second set, provided that the relation between the two sets of axes is completely known. With rectilinear axes the transformation equations are linear. The primaries of a colour specification may be regarded as defining a set of axes. It is possible to transfer to a second set of primaries whose colour co-ordinates (when referred to the first set) are known. The additivity law implies that the transformation equations are linear. They are however rather complicated, because in general the second set of axes are not mutually perpendicular when referred to the first set, and also there may be a change of scale (because the units of the

* The results shown refer to reference stimuli 6500 Å., 5300 Å., and 4600 Å.
† See Reference 10.4.

second set of reference stimuli differ from those of the first). For our present purposes it is not necessary to consider the actual equations. It is sufficient that linear transformation is possible.

10.39.—The reference stimuli used in the measurements discussed in § 10.37 were chosen for experimental convenience. The standard reference stimuli used for numerical specification of colours may be chosen for convenience of calculation. They may be any linear functions of stimuli used in experimental work. They need not be experimentally realizable. For example, one " artificial reference stimulus " might consist of a certain amount of red light minus a certain amount of blue light. The luminance of unit quantity of this " stimulus " may be zero. On any chromaticity diagram there is a locus of colours which have zero luminance. This is called the *alychne* (or " no-light line "). The C.I.E. chose, for colour calculations, three artificial " stimuli " X, Y, Z which have the following properties:

(i) X and Z are on the alychne, so that Y alone gives the luminance.

(ii) No part of the spectrum locus is outside the triangle X, Y, Z. Therefore no colour co-ordinates x, y, z are negative.

(iii) The line XY is tangential to the spectrum locus at the red end where the locus is nearly straight. The Z co-ordinate is nearly zero for a considerable range of the spectrum.

The fact that no co-ordinate is ever negative reduces the labour of calculation and the chance of error; the fact that Y alone gives the luminance saves a stage in the calculation. The zero Z co-ordinates also save a little calculation time.

A very extensive and accurate re-measurement of visibility functions and colour-matching functions has recently been carried out by Stiles and Burch.*

10.40. Variations in Colour Vision.†

Visual discrimination of chromaticity is very sensitive, and the small differences between the colour-matching functions among normal observers (fig. 10.23) are of practical importance. A metameric match for one normal observer whose functions deviate from the average in one direction may appear far from a match to another normal observer whose functions deviate in the opposite direction. Two pieces of material dyed with different batches of the same dye will be accepted as a match by all normal observers if (*a*) there is very nearly a spectrum match and (*b*) there is an exact (metameric) match for the average normal observer.‡

About 8 per cent of men and 0·4 per cent of women show deviations from normal colour vision which are very large compared with the differences among normal observers. The main defects are hereditary,

---

* See Reference 10.8. † See Reference 10.5 or 10.3.

‡ It is also *desirable* that the dyes should give a spectrum match because, if they do not, the materials will constitute a match for only one illuminant.

though deficiency of colour discrimination is sometimes associated with illness. Defects of colour discrimination may be classified as follows:

(i) *Monochromatic Vision:* The subject cannot distinguish hue at all—a very rare defect ($\sim$3 in 10^5 males).

(ii) *Dichromatic Vision:* The subject requires only two primaries to match any colour. Dichromats are divided into (*a*) protanopes, (*b*) deuteranopes, and (*c*) tritanopes. Of these (*a*) and (*b*) both fail to distinguish spectrum colours in the red-orange-green region of the spectrum. The protanope has a reduced sensitivity to red light but the V_λ curve for a deuteranope is normal. About 1·3 per cent of males suffer from each of these defects. Tritanopes confuse hues in the blue-green region of the spectrum. They are very rare ($\sim$3 in 10^5 males).

(iii) *Anomalous Trichromatism:* The subject requires three primaries to match any colour but has poor colour discrimination in part of the spectrum. Anomalous trichromats are divided into (*a*) protanomalous (1·0 per cent of males), (*b*) deuteranomalous (4·6 per cent of males), and (*c*) tritanomalous (very rare) according to the type of dichromatic vision to which their defect is related.

Many people who have defective colour vision make correct discrimination by means of auxiliary clues, e.g. they unconsciously memorize the colours of familiar objects, also they know that yellows and greens are usually lighter than reds. These discriminations, very helpful in the situations of everyday life, are unreliable in unfamiliar conditions. Very stringent tests to select people for occupations in which failure of hue discrimination is dangerous are thus necessary.

10.41. Physiological Aspects of Colour Vision.

The C.I.E. system of colour specification and the trichromatic theory upon which it is based constitute an analysis of the information which the brain obtains under the conditions of the standard colour-matching experiments. They show that there are three, and only three, degrees of freedom. In order to understand the processes by which the brain receives this information, it is necessary to study relevant biochemical and biophysical processes, including the chemistry of the retinal pigments and the transmission of electrical impulses along the fibres of the optic nerve.

The simplest method of transmitting information concerning colour to the brain would involve the presence in the retina of three kinds of cones (with different spectral response curves) each directly connected to the cortex. A careful search has failed to reveal this tripartite division of cones though, by studying the light reflected from the retina, Rushton* has shown that at least two pigments are

* See Reference 10.6.

present in the cones. There exists a great deal of complicated information on details of colour discrimination under a wide range of conditions. All of this must be included in any satisfactory physiological theory of colour vision, and no very simple theory so far proposed is adequate.

W. D. Wright* has carried out experiments in which two patches of light (one seen by the left eye and the other by the right) are matched in a modified colorimeter. One eye is then exposed to strong coloured light. It is found that the colour match is greatly altered for a short time, after which there is a gradual recovery to the normal match. There is no doubt that this process of adaptation plays an important part in the appreciation of colour in a picture or in a natural scene, because the eye is continually in motion and the adaptation of any given part of the retina is continually changing. The perceived colour of natural objects is determined by a number of factors in addition to the light actually received from the object. These include the prevailing colours of the scene and of the immediately surrounding objects, and memories of the object seen in other surroundings. Identifications of colour very different from those calculated by applying the C.I.E. data to the light received from the object may sometimes be obtained. These do not invalidate the C.I.E. system or the trichromatic theory which refer to colour matching under experimental conditions designed to eliminate everything except the light received from two patches which are to be matched.

REFERENCES

10.1. SMITH, R. A., JONES, F. E. and CHASMAR, R. P.: *The Detection and Measurement of Infra-red Radiation* (Oxford University Press).

10.2. WALSH, J. W. T.: *Photometry* (Constable), 2nd ed.

10.3. YVES LE GRAND: *Light, Colour and Vision* (translation published by Chapman and Hall).

10.4. WRIGHT, W. D.: *The Measurement of Colour* (Hilger and Watts).

10.5. WRIGHT, W. D.: *Researches on Normal and Defective Colour Vision* (Kimpton).

10.6. RUSHTON, W. A. H.: *Progress in Biophysics and Biophysical Chemistry*, Vol. 9, p. 240, 1959.

10.7. WESTON, H. C.: *Light, Sight and Efficiency* (H. K. Lewis, London).

10.8. STILES, W. and BURCH, J. M.: *Opt. Act.*, Vol. 6, p. 1, 1959.

10.9. BRADDICK, H. J. J.: *Reports on Progress in Physics* (Phys. Soc., London), Vol. XXIII, p. 154, 1960.

* See Reference 10.5.

CHAPTER XI

Velocity of Light and Relativistic Optics

11.1. Historical.

In 1676, the astronomer Römer showed that the velocity of light is finite, although it is very large compared with the velocity of sound. Measurements, accurate to a few per cent, were made by Fizeau, Foucault, and Cornu between 1800 and 1875. It was recognized that the velocity is an important physical constant, but there was then no way of relating the measured value to any physical theory. Maxwell's electromagnetic theory, published in its completed form in 1873, required that the velocity of light (c_L), the velocity of electromagnetic waves (c_W), and the ratio of certain electromagnetic units (c_R) should all be equal. This stimulated experimental work and several determinations of each of these quantities were made in the period 1875–1906. It was found that c_L and c_R were equal within about one part in a thousand. The experimental measurement of c_W was then of lower accuracy (about ± 2 per cent), but within this accuracy c_W was found to be equal to c_L and c_R, so that we may put $c_L = c_R = c_W = c$.

11.2.—Measurement of the velocity of light was associated with attempts to find a variation of the velocity under different physical conditions. The results of these experiments were important in the development of the theory of relativity (1905). In this theory, the constant c is recognized as one of the fundamental physical constants of nature. Work on the accurate measurement of c was continued after 1906. Up to 1940, the most accurate experiments were measurements of the velocity of light (c_L). In 1941 Birge reviewed all existing experiments and estimated c_L at $299{,}776 \pm 4$ km. sec.$^{-1}$. Some observations with radar made during the war suggested that this value was too low, and since 1945 electronic methods of very high precision have been used to measure both c_L and c_W. These two quantities are each found to be equal to $299{,}793 \cdot 0 \pm 0 \cdot 3$ km. sec^{-1}.

We shall next describe methods for measuring c_L and compare the results with measurements of c_W and c_R. We shall then pass to experiments on possible variations of the velocity, and these will form an introduction to those aspects of relativity theory which are concerned with optics.*

11.3. Methods of Measuring the Velocity of Light (c_L)

The direct measurement of a velocity involves the determination of a distance and a transit time. Since the velocity of light is very high, it is necessary to use a large distance and to measure a fairly short time. It is not possible to observe the progress of a continuous beam of light without marking or modulating it in some way. It follows that the velocity measured is the group velocity in the medium. Using electromagnetic waves of radio frequency it is possible to measure the frequency (ν) and the wavelength λ, so that the phase velocity is obtained as the product $\nu\lambda$. This method is not possible with visible light because there is no method of measuring the frequency.

Three methods of modulating the beam have been used: (a) the mechanical shutter, (b) the rotating mirror, and (c) the electronic shutter. In any of these methods the time is derived from a measurement of the frequency of the modulator. The distance is measured by standard surveying or metrological processes. It is also necessary to know the refractive index and dispersion in order to be able to derive c (the velocity in vacuum) from the measured velocity (U) using equation 4(38).

The difference between the *phase* velocity in air and the velocity in vacuum is about 1 part in 3000. The additional group velocity difference (corresponding to the second term on the R.H.S. of 4(38)) is about 1 part in 50,000.

11.4. Indirect Methods.

In principle the velocity of light can be determined by comparing it with the velocity of a moving body. Measurements of the Doppler-Fizeau effect (§ 2.22 and § 11.29), of the aberration of light (§ 11.34), and of the velocity of light in moving media (§ 11.35) thus form indirect determinations of the velocity of light but are usually regarded as establishing certain points of theoretical interest rather than as determinations of the velocity of light. Considered as determinations of the velocity they are much less accurate than direct methods.

* A reader whose main interest is in relativity theory related to optics should omit §§ 11.3 to 11.15.

11.5. Römer's Method.

The planet Jupiter has several satellites whose orbits are so nearly in the plane of the planet's orbit that they pass through the shadow of the planet and suffer eclipse at every revolution. The satellites revolve much more rapidly than our moon, and three of them have periods of $1\frac{3}{4}$, $3\frac{1}{2}$, and 7 days respectively.

Römer observed the eclipses over an extended period and found irregularities ranging up to about 10 minutes. These irregularities were correlated with the variation of the distance between the earth and Jupiter. Assuming that they were due to the varying time taken for light to travel to the earth, Römer obtained a value of 350,000 km. sec^{-1}. The difference of path is about $1 \cdot 5 \times 10^{13}$ centimetres and the time is about 500 seconds.

11.6. Fizeau's Method (mechanical shutter).

Fizeau's apparatus is shown in fig. 11.1. L_{vs} is a vertical-slit source of light and M_1 is an unsilvered piece of plane glass. The light is brought to a focus at F, where it is interrupted by the toothed wheel W, which

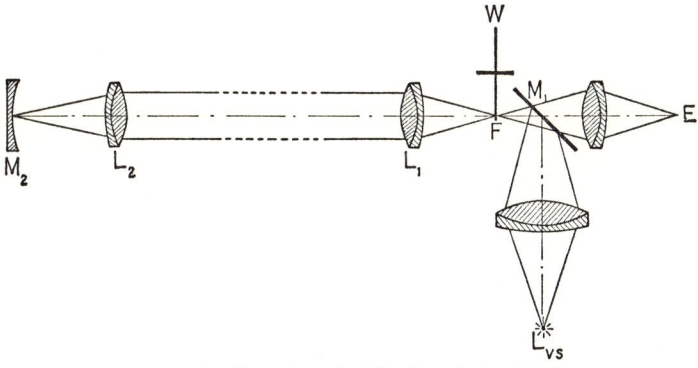

Fig. 11.1.—Fizeau's method for the velocity of light

can be rotated. The point F is in the focal plane of the lens L_1, from which the light goes in an approximately parallel beam to L_2, and to the concave mirror M_2. If the wheel is stationary, some of the returning light passes through M_1, and is seen by the observer through the eyepiece at E. If the speed of the wheel is gradually increased from zero, a stage will be reached when the light which passes through a given space will, on its return, be interrupted by a tooth which has moved into the appropriate position during the time of transit. At a higher speed the returning light will pass through the next space and, at a still higher speed, it will be eclipsed by the next tooth. Fizeau (1849) used a wheel with 720 teeth, and found that the first eclipse occurred when the speed was 12·6 revolutions per second. This gives a transit time of $5·5 \times 10^{-5}$ second. The length of the double path was $1·7266 \times 10^6$ centimetres, and the value obtained for the velocity is 315,000 km. sec^{-1}. Essentially the same method was used by Cornu (1874). The most important error in this method is due to the difficulty of deciding exactly when the image is eclipsed. The variation of light with speed follows a curve very similar to that shown in fig. 11.6a for the variation of signal with distance. It is obviously very difficult to locate exactly the position of a non-zero " flat " minimum.

11.7. Rotating-mirror Method.

This method was first suggested by Wheatstone in 1834 and was first used by Foucault in 1860. It was also used by Newcomb (1882) and by Michelson (1879, 1882, 1927 and 1935).

The apparatus* used in 1927 is shown in fig. 11.2. Light from the slit source L_{vs} was reflected from the octagonal mirror M_1 to the plane mirror M_2, and thence to the mirror M_3, which was slightly separated from M_3'. (M_3 was slightly above

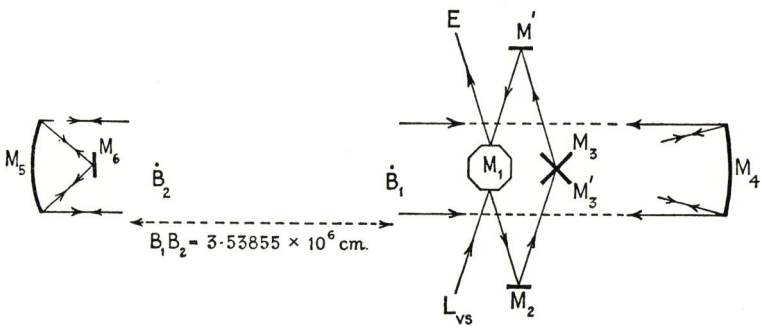

Fig. 11.2.—Michelson's Mount Wilson (1927) experiment

and M_3' was slightly below the plane of the diagram.) From M_3 the light passed to concave mirror M_4, to the concave mirror M_5, and to the plane mirror M_6. It returned, via M_5, M_4, M_3' and M_2', to the octagon, whence it went to the eyepiece E. The right-hand portion of the apparatus was at the Mount Wilson Observatory, and the left-hand portion was about twenty-two miles away on Mount San

* See Reference 11.3.

Antonio. The octagonal mirror made 528 rotations per second, and rotated through approximately one-eighth of a turn during the transit of the light to and fro. If the rotation were exactly one-eighth of a turn, the image would be undisplaced by the rotation. Actually a small deviation has to be measured. The speed of the mirror was controlled by an electrically driven tuning fork. The mean result was 299,798 km. sec.$^{-1}$ It is very difficult to estimate the limits of error and it is no longer of any importance to do this in view of the higher accuracy of experiments since 1945. Errors due to uncertainty in temperature and pressure may be eliminated by placing the whole path in a vacuum. Michelson* planned an experiment of this type which was completed by his collaborators, Pearson and Pease, after his death. They used an evacuated tube 1·6 km. long and, by repeated reflections obtained a total path of 13 km. Although several detailed improvements of technique were incorporated, the random errors were greater than in the Mount Wilson experiment. The result was given as 299,744 ± 11 km. sec.$^{-1}$

11.8. Electro-optical Shutter.

The Kerr cell consists of a glass vessel with flat sides containing two plane electrodes (fig. 11.3). The cell is filled with a liquid whose molecules become polarized by an electric field of about a thousand volts

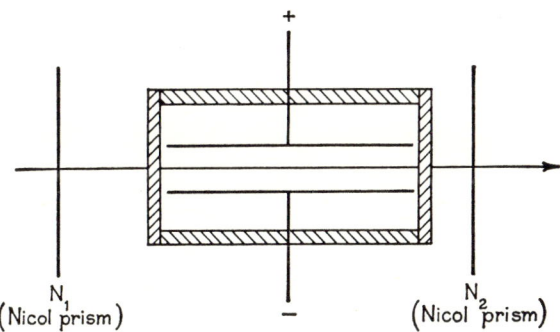

Fig. 11.3.—The Kerr cell

per centimetre, so that their optical properties are changed. The theory of this effect is discussed in § 16.51. For our present purpose it is sufficient to know that, when this cell is placed between two Nicol prisms, the light passing the unit depends on the voltage applied to the electrodes in the manner shown in fig. 11.4. If a steady voltage V_0 is applied to bring the system to the point B, then an additional

* See Reference 11.4.

sinusoidally varying voltage (which does not carry the system beyond the linear range A to C) will produce a sinusoidal variation of light intensity. The whole unit constitutes an electro-optical shutter and

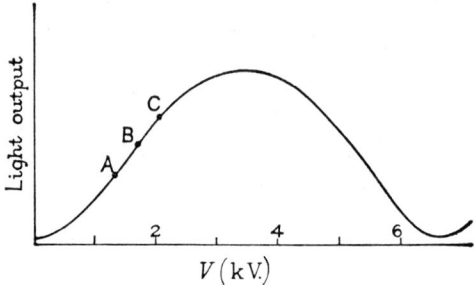

Fig. 11.4.—Transmission of light by the electro-optical shutter

may be used to replace the toothed wheel in Fizeau's experiment, with the advantage that it is possible to interrupt the light more than 10^7 times a second and to know the frequency to better than 1 part in 10^8.

11.9.—The electro-optical shutter was first used for the measurement of the velocity in air by Karolus and Mittaelstaedt (1928) who obtained the value $299,778 \pm 20$ km. sec^{-1}. Anderson (1941), and Hüttel (1940) obtained nearly the same value.* This method was greatly improved

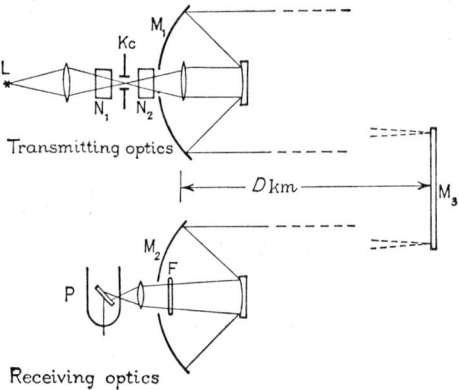

Fig. 11.5.—Bergstrand's apparatus

by Bergstrand (1947–53) who reduced the random errors by a factor of nearly 100.† His apparatus is shown in fig. 11.5. Light from the source

* See References 11.3 to 11.8.   † See References 11.1, 11.2 and 11.9.

§ 11.10   ELECTRO-OPTICAL SHUTTER   415

L passes through the electro-optical shutter, consisting of the Nicol prisms N_1 and N_2 and the Kerr cell K_c, and is transmitted as a parallel beam to the distant mirror M_3 from which it is returned to the photo-multiplier P placed near to the source. A high-frequency radio-oscillator controlled by a quartz crystal is used to produce 2000 volts at 8·33 Mc./s. This voltage is applied to the Kerr cell and a suitable fraction is applied to the photo-multiplier. If both the Kerr cell and the photo-multiplier are suitably biased, the light output varies sinusoidally, and the sensitivity of the photo-multiplier also varies sinusoidally with the same frequency and phase. The phase of the 8·33-Mc./s. variation of light at the photo-multiplier depends on the distance of the mirror M_3. If the path is very small, the photo-multiplier reaches its maximum sensitivity at the moment when the light is a maximum, and then a large current is obtained. As the path is increased from zero the current varies with the distance in the manner shown in fig. 11.6a.

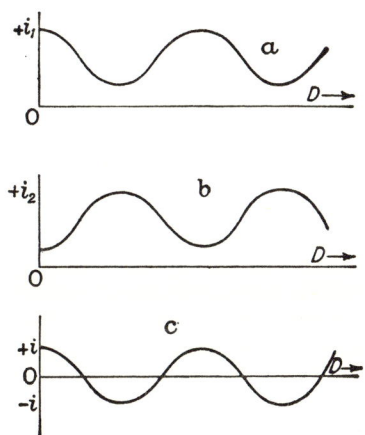

Fig. 11.6.—(a) Variation of current (i_1) with D, (b) Variation of current (i_2) with D, (c) Variation of current $i = (i_1 - i_2)$ with D.

11.10.—It would be possible to obtain a value of the velocity of light by measuring the distance between any two minima of curve 11.6a. If D_N is the distance between minima numbered N_0 and $N_0 + N$ then

$$D_N = \tfrac{1}{4}N \frac{U_a}{p},$$

where p is the frequency of the oscillator = 8·33 Mc./s. and U_a is the group velocity in air. A factor of $\tfrac{1}{2}$ is needed because there are two zero points in each cycle, and a second factor of $\tfrac{1}{2}$ is required to allow for the double path (to and fro) of the light. The distance between successive minima is approximately 9 metres.

11.11.—The accuracy of this method would be seriously limited by the difficulty of locating a flat minimum. By ingenious electronic circuits (which are briefly described in the next paragraph) Bergstrand produced the variation of photo-current with distance which is shown in curve (c), i.e. he arranged that the current i became zero when di/dD was large. The zero points could then be located with high precision. After some preliminary work in 1947, Bergstrand made accurate determinations in 1948, 1949, and 1950. The mean value was $c = 299,793 \cdot 1$ km. sec^{-1}. The results of successive years agreed to $0 \cdot 1$ km. sec^{-1}. Uncertainty in the length of the base line is probably the largest source of residual error and an overall error of $0 \cdot 3$ km. sec.$^{-1}$ is estimated.

11.12.—The variation shown in fig. 11.6c was produced in the following way. Suppose first that a second receiving system exactly identical with the first was supplied with a 8·33 Mc./s. voltage which was 180° out of phase with the voltage applied to the Kerr cell. Then the variation of current with time would be that shown in curve (b). A meter connected so as to register the *difference* of current in the two systems would respond as shown in curve (c). It is difficult to make two pieces of apparatus sufficiently similar and, for this reason, one is used, working alternately as each of the two. The ordinary steady bias on the Kerr cell is replaced by a 50-c./s. " square-wave " form. The high-frequency variations in the light transmitted by the Kerr cell then change their phase 50 times a second. The currents from the two halves of the cycle are fed into a meter whose period is much longer than 0·01 sec. and which reads their difference.

Bergstrand has developed from his experiments a surveying instrument for measuring distances up to several kilometres. This instrument—called a geodimeter—has been used in several countries. Its results are in agreement with the most accurate measurements obtained by other methods. The use of visible light instead of radar pulses is preferred because light is scattered less and is not deviated by weakly ionized air.

11.13. Measurements on Electromagnetic Waves of Radio Frequency.

Values of c have been derived from measurements on electromagnetic waves whose frequencies lie in the range of 100 Mc. sec.$^{-1}$ to nearly 50,000 Mc. sec.$^{-1}$ (the frequency for visible light is nearly 10^9 Mc. sec.$^{-1}$). The following methods have been used:

(i) Measurement of the time of transit using radar methods (Aslakson, Jones). The technique has many features in common with Bergstrand's method for c_L.

§ 11.13 MEASUREMENTS OF WAVES OF RADIO FREQUENCY

(ii) Measurement of the frequency of resonance for a cavity resonator (Essen and Gordon-Smith, Essen, Hansen and Bol). The result does not give c directly but c may be calculated after allowing for certain corrections which Essen determined experimentally.

(iii) Measurement of the wavelength in air corresponding to a given frequency using a microwave interferometer (Froome).

(iv) Combination of observations from the infra-red and microwave regions (see § 11.14 below).

Results of accuracy better than ± 5 km. sec.$^{-1}$ are included in Table 1. It may be seen that there is a very good agreement between the results for different frequencies and that the most accurate results agree with Bergstrand's value within a very small experimental error. As a further check it would be desirable to have a second determination of the velocity of light (c_L) by a high-precision method different from that of Bergstrand.

TABLE 11.1

MEASUREMENTS OF c

Measurements of the Velocity of Light (c_L)

	km. sec.$^{-1}$	
Michelson 1927 (rotating mirror)	299,798	± 4
Mean of all measurements up to 1944	299,773	± 3
Bergstrand 1951	299,793·1	$\pm 0·3$

Measurements of the Velocity of Radio-frequency Waves (c_W)

Essen 1950 (10^4 Mc./s.)	299,792·5	± 1
Hansen and Bol 1950 (3×10^3 Mc./s.)	299,789·3	$\pm 0·4$
Froome 1953 ($2·4 \times 10^4$ Mc./s.)	299,793·0	$\pm 0·3$
Florman 1955 (173 Mc./s.)	299,795	± 3
Aslakson 1952 (300 Mc./s.)	299,794	± 2
Rank, Guenther, Shearer and Wiggins 1953 (infra-red and $4·4 \times 10^4$ Mc./s.)	299,793·2	± 2
Weighted Mean	299,793·0	$\pm 0·3$

Measurement of the Ratio of the Electrical Units (c_R)

Rosa and Dorsey 1906.	299,784	± 30

Note.—Values of the constant c obtained by different methods. Values for velocity in vacuum have been calculated using the appropriate refractive index and group velocity correction. Where there are several experiments by one author, only the latest is included. For c_L and c_W only experiments which show a scatter of less than ± 5 km. sec.$^{-1}$ are included. A complete table is given in Reference 11.1.

11.14. Atomic Standard of Time.

We have seen in § 9.43 that in the near future the wavelength (λ_1) corresponding to a certain spectrum line is likely to be adopted as the standard of length. It has recently been found possible to make a clock whose rate is controlled by the frequency ν_2 corresponding to an atomic transition in caesium vapour; the corresponding wavelength (λ_2) is in the microwave region. The extreme accuracy of this clock makes it probable that, in a few years time, the second will be defined to be such that the frequency associated with a chosen atomic (or molecular) transition is ν_2. Then we should have

$$c = (\lambda_1 \nu_2)\left(\frac{\lambda_2}{\lambda_1}\right), \qquad \ldots \ldots \quad 11(1)$$

where the quantity in the first bracket would be fixed by definition and that in the second would be determined by experiment.

At present, atomic standards of time have not been adopted but the following procedure is used. Certain wavelengths in the infra-red spectrum of HCN are measured accurately in terms of the Metre, using wavelengths in the visible region as intermediate standards. From these results the reciprocal of the wavelength (λ_m) corresponding to a certain absorption in the microwave region can be calculated. The corresponding frequency (ν_m) can be accurately measured by reference to a crystal clock and hence to the astronomical standard second. We then have $c = \nu_m \lambda_m$. The results obtained by this method (see Reference 11.13) are less accurate than the best results obtained by other methods but, since the method is new, it may be capable of further development.

If it ever became possible for the *same* atomic transition to be used for both standards, i.e. if the centimetre were defined so that the wavelength was λ_1 cm. and the second were defined so that the corresponding frequency was sec.$^{-1}$, then we should have $c = \lambda_1 \nu_1$ cm. sec.$^{-1}$ and the velocity of light would be fixed by definition. This definition would refer to light emitted by an atom at rest with respect to the observer and undisturbed by gravitational or electric fields. It would still leave open the question whether such fields or any other physical conditions could affect the velocity.

11.15. Variation of Velocity with Refractive Index.*

Foucault showed that light travels more slowly in water than in air—a result considered as establishing the wave theory against the

---
* See References 11.15 and 11.16.

corpuscular theory. Quantitative measurements have been made by Michelson, Houstoun, and Bergstrand. The results obtained by Houstoun and Bergstrand agree with the values calculated from the group-velocity formula, e.g. for a certain glass with $n = 1\cdot519$, equation 4(38) gives

$$c/U = 1\cdot547$$

and the measured value is $1\cdot550 \pm 0\cdot003$.

11.16. Theory of Relativity.

The word "theory" is used by scientists in two ways. It may mean a co-ordinated description of the results of certain experiments, or it may mean a general method for the description of experiments. The Theory of Relativity is a "theory" in both senses of the word. It started from the results of certain experiments on the velocity of light. In order to obtain a satisfactory description of these experiments, it was necessary to reconsider the basic definitions of words like "length", "mass" and "time". It was then found that certain general difficulties in theoretical physics could be removed if these terms were redefined so as to give them a precise relation to the results of experiments. Concepts invented for a special purpose were seen to be useful in relation to many problems both in optics and in dynamics, and the new definitions became part of the language of theoretical physics. In this chapter we are concerned with deriving some of the main ideas of relativity from optical experiments and with applying these ideas to other optical experiments. The reader should consult textbooks on relativity for a general account of the theory and of its application to dynamical problems.*

11.17. Relative Velocity of Earth and Æther.

Suppose that the velocity of sound is measured by an observer on the ground. In still air, he will obtain a velocity which we may call V, and when there is a wind he measures a velocity $(V + v)$, where v is the component of wind velocity in the direction of propagation. The velocity of waves relative to the observer is simply the vector sum of the wind velocity and the velocity of the waves relative to the air. If the observer had no other method of measuring the wind velocity, he could determine this quantity by measuring the velocity of sound in different directions. He would find that in a certain direction the velocity of sound was a maximum, and that would give the

* References 11.17–11.21.

direction of the wind. The difference between the speed of sound up wind and down-wind would be equal to twice the speed of the wind. It was at one time thought that this method might be used to determine the relative velocity of the earth and the æther. If light is a system of waves in the æther, and the earth is moving through the æther, we have effectively an "æther wind". Experiments on the velocity of light in different directions should determine the direction and speed of the "æther wind" or, as we more usually describe it, the velocity of the earth relative to the æther. This conclusion is valid whether we consider the æther as an elastic solid, or as the seat of the electromagnetic phenomena.

11.18.—The measurement of a possible variation of the velocity with direction is made more difficult because, in terrestrial experiments at least, we cannot measure the time for light to travel along a given path in one direction, but only the transit time to go to a certain point and to return. We shall now show that this implies that, if the velocity (v) of the earth with respect to the æther is a small fraction of the velocity (c) of light with respect to the æther, we can observe only effects of the second order, i.e. differences proportional to v^2/c^2.

Consider first the total transit time to go and to return along a path whose direction is the same as that of the relative velocity of earth and æther. If d is the length of the path, we have

$$T_1 = \frac{d}{c+v} + \frac{d}{c-v} = \frac{2dc}{c^2-v^2}, \quad \ldots \quad 11(2a)$$

and, when v is small compared with c,

$$T_1 = T_0(1 + v^2/c^2), \quad \ldots \ldots \quad 11(2b)$$

where $T_0 = 2d/c$ is the time required for the transit to and fro along a similar path in a stationary æther. For a direction at right angles to the above direction, the velocity of light relative to the earth should be $(c^2 - v^2)^{1/2}$, and the transit time (to and fro) is

$$T_2 = \frac{2d}{(c^2-v^2)^{1/2}}. \quad \ldots \ldots \quad 11(3)$$

When v is small compared with c,

$$T_2 = T_0\left(1 + \tfrac{1}{2}\frac{v^2}{c^2}\right). \quad \ldots \ldots \quad 11(4)$$

§ 11.19   THE MICHELSON-MORLEY EXPERIMENT   421

Further discussion shows that the maximum transit time (to and fro) for different directions is given by 11(2b) and the minimum by 11(4). The maximum difference is thus

$$\Delta T_M = T_1 - T_2 = \tfrac{1}{2} T_0 \frac{v^2}{c^2}. \qquad \ldots \quad 11(5)$$

The most direct way of finding the earth's velocity relative to the æther would consist in measuring the transit time over a certain path, whose length is defined by rigid rods, when the apparatus is placed in different orientations. The direction corresponding to the maximum transit time would be the direction of the relative velocity, and the difference between the transit times for this direction and a perpendicular direction would enable the magnitude to be calculated from equation 11(5). The smallest difference in transit time which could be detected in experiments such as those described in the preceding chapter is about one part in 100,000. This corresponds to a relative velocity of $0\cdot003c$ or 10^8 centimetres per second. The velocity of the earth relative to the sun is about 3×10^6 centimetres per second. An æther-earth relative velocity of this order of magnitude is thus far too small to be detected in a direct experiment. Fortunately indirect methods are much more sensitive.

11.19. The Michelson-Morley Experiment.

About 1887, Michelson and Morley used a modification of the Michelson interferometer (fig. 4.1) to investigate the problem. Suppose that the mirror M_2 (figs. 4.1 and 11.7) is set at a small angle to the reference plane R and is moved until the fringe corresponding to zero order of interference appears in the centre of the field of the telescope. We assume that the plate C exactly compensates for the path in the mirror M_1 (fig. 4.1) and we therefore omit the plate C in fig. 11.7 and regard M_1 as of zero thickness. Then the optical paths from M_1 to M_3, and from M_1 to M_2, are equal; i.e. if d_1 is the geometrical path from M_1 to M_3, and d_2 is the geometrical path from M_1 to M_2, we have

$$n_1 d_1 = n_2 d_2, \qquad \ldots \quad 11(6)$$

or

$$c\left(\frac{d_1}{b_1}\right) = c\left(\frac{d_2}{b_2}\right), \qquad \ldots \quad 11(7)$$

where c is the velocity of light for *a body at rest in the æther in vacuum*, and b_1 and b_2 are the velocities in the regions between $M_1 M_3$ and $M_1 M_2$ respectively. The terms in the brackets in 11(7) are the transit times.

Suppose that the arm M_1M_2 happens to lie in the direction of the earth-æther velocity. Then, for equal paths, the transit time M_1 to M_2 and back is greater than the corresponding transit time from M_1 to M_3 and back. In bringing the fringe of zero order to the centre of the field, we have made the transit times equal by making d_2 slightly less than d_1. If now the apparatus is rotated through a right angle, M_1M_3

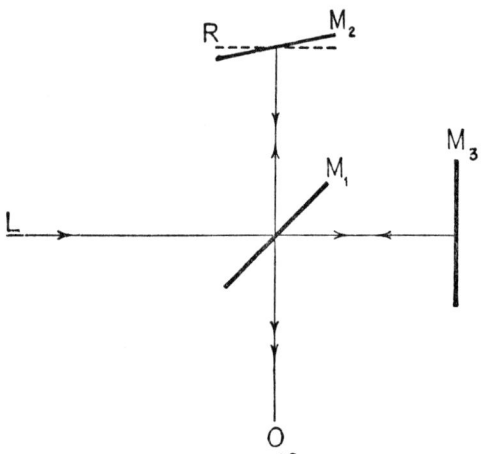

Fig. 11.7.—The Michelson-Morley experiment

will be in the direction of the æther-earth velocity and would have the longer transit time for equal paths. But if the lengths d_1 and d_2 have not altered when the apparatus was rotated, d_1 is the *longer* path, and this further increases the transit time. The difference of transit times is twice that given in equation 11(5), and this difference should produce a fringe movement corresponding to a path difference Δs, given by

$$\Delta s = cT_0 \frac{v^2}{c^2} = 2\frac{v^2}{c^2}d, \quad \ldots \ldots \quad 11(8)$$

where $d = \tfrac{1}{2}(d_1 + d_2)$.

11.20.—At the beginning of the experiment, the direction of the earth-æther velocity is unknown. The fringe of zero order is brought to the centre of the field and the apparatus is slowly rotated, observations of the position of this fringe being made at every sixteenth of a revolution. If the above theory is correct the fringes should move sideways, in a periodic way, the period being half the period of the rotation of the apparatus. When the fringes indicate a maximum transit time for M_1M_2, this arm lies along the direction of the æther-earth velocity. The magnitude of the velocity is determined by observing the amplitude of the fringe movement and applying 11(8). In fact no movement of the fringes could be observed. It was calculated that a movement corresponding to an æther-earth velocity of $3 \times 10^{-5}c$, or about 10^6 centimetres per second, could have been detected. The possibility that at the date of the original experiment the earth happened to be moving with very small velocity relative to the æther was considered. The experiment was therefore repeated at different times of the year. It always gave a null result. The result was later confirmed using more sensitive apparatus capable of detecting a velocity of 10^5 centimetres per second or $3 \times 10^{-6}c$.

11.21.—The apparatus used by Michelson and Morley is shown diagrammatically in fig. 11.8. Each of the arms of the interferometer has been lengthened by allowing reflections from corner to corner.

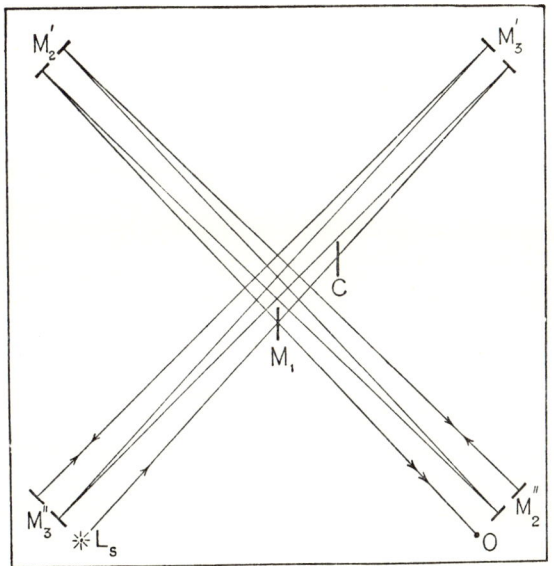

Fig. 11.8.—The Michelson-Morley experiment (multiple reflections)

(Actually there were twice as many reflections as those shown in the diagram.) This method of obtaining a long path is better than a direct increase of the length of the arms, because it is easier to secure temperature control and mechanical rigidity. The effective path was 30 metres and it was estimated that a change in path length of about $\lambda/25$ or $2\cdot 4 \times 10^{-6}$ centimetre could have been detected. Thus the minimum detectable value of v/c, calculated from 11(8), is $2\cdot 8 \times 10^{-5}c$. The experiment was later repeated by Joos, and by Kennedy and Illingworth.* They modified the optical arrangements so that a path difference of about $0\cdot 001\lambda$ could be detected. No movement of the fringes was observed. Miller attempted to make the instrument more sensitive by using very large arms. This led to comparatively large random movements of the fringes owing to temperature variation, etc. He thought that there were small regular movements of the fringes superposed upon these irregular movements, but his "positive" results are generally regarded as within the limits of error.

11.22. The FitzGerald-Lorentz Contraction.

It was suggested by G. F. FitzGerald (1851–1901), and later by H. A. Lorentz, that the null result of the Michelson-Morley experiment might be due to a compensating effect, i.e. a contraction of each arm as the interferometer was turned into the direction of the æther-earth velocity. From equations 11(2a) and 11(3) it may be seen that if the ratio of the length when the arm is orientated in the direction of the æther-earth velocity, to the length when orientated in the perpendicular direction is $(1 - v^2/c^2)^{1/2}$, there will be no difference in transit time, whatever the value of v may be. Lorentz gave reasons, based on the electron theory, for supposing that this contraction might be a universal property of matter. Various attempts were then made to measure v, either by detecting and measuring the FitzGerald-Lorentz contraction, or in other indirect ways. All of these experiments had one feature in common. Their objective was to show that free space is optically or electrically anisotropic. The observers looked for some difference to be produced merely by altering the orientation of their apparatus. All these experiments gave a null result. We shall see that according to relativity theory all these experiments are essentially the same experiment and all must yield a null result. It is not necessary to discuss details, but we may briefly mention the following:

(a) *Rayleigh* (and later *Brace*) sought to detect a photo-elastic effect produced by the FitzGerald-Lorentz contraction.

(b) *Rayleigh* looked for a variation in the optical rotatory power of a quartz crystal when its orientation was altered.

* References 11.23–11.25.

(c) *Nordmeyer* placed two sensitive thermopiles on opposite sides of a small source of light. The currents were balanced and the apparatus rotated. It was expected that when the axis of the apparatus was in the direction of the earth-æther velocity, the optical path to one thermopile would be shorter than the path to the other. The radiation received would be proportional to the inverse square of the optical paths. The balance would therefore be disturbed by rotating the apparatus so that the optical path to the other thermopile became the shorter path.

(d) Many electrical experiments were performed. It was suggested that the resistance of a wire should depend on its orientation because of the contraction. In a similar way the frequency of a quartz crystal vibrator might be expected to depend on its orientation. These electrical experiments were of high sensitivity.

11.23. Special Theory of Relativity.

It is fairly easy to explain the null result of any one of these experiments by the hypothesis of a compensating effect such as the Fitz-Gerald-Lorentz contraction, but it would obviously be unsatisfactory to explain each result by a separate and rather special hypothesis. Certain problems of electrodynamics caused Einstein to re-examine the basic concepts of kinematics and develop a theory in which the measured velocity of light is the same for all observers. Every kinematical problem is stated, directly or indirectly, by reference to a co-ordinate system and to a clock. Suppose that a given dynamical problem is referred to a co-ordinate system x, y, z, t, and the equations of motion are set down. It is possible to express the problem in terms of another co-ordinate system x', y', z', t', if algebraic equations connecting x, y, z, t are available. Such a set of equations is called a transformation group. In the simplest case, if the two co-ordinate systems differ only in that the origin of the dashed system is situated at a distance a from the origin of the undashed system, and along the axis of x, we have

$$x' = x + a; \quad y' = y; \quad z' = z; \quad t' = t.$$

More complicated transformations refer to other geometrical changes (e.g. rotation of axes.)

11.24.—It is possible also to consider systems of axes which are moving with respect to one another. Such systems are considered in

Newtonian mechanics, and it is easy to derive the transformation group:

$$\left.\begin{array}{l} x' = x + vt, \\ y' = y, \\ z' = z, \\ t' = t. \end{array}\right\} \quad \ldots \ldots \quad 11(9)$$

We assume that the axes Ox and Ox' have been chosen to coincide with the direction of the relative velocity. Using this transformation, it can be shown that the laws of mechanics (expressed in Newton's Laws of Motion) are the same in the dashed and in the undashed systems, provided that the systems have no relative acceleration. For a particle moving with constant velocity U along the x-axis in the undashed system, we have

$$\left.\begin{array}{l} U = \dfrac{dx}{dt}, \\ U' = \dfrac{dx'}{dt'} = \dfrac{dx}{dt} + v = U + v, \end{array}\right\} \quad \ldots \quad 11(10)$$

$$\therefore \frac{dU'}{dt'} = \frac{d^2x'}{dt'^2} = \frac{d^2x}{dt^2}. \quad \ldots \ldots \ldots \quad 11(11)$$

The velocities of the particle in the two systems are different, their relation being given by 11(10), but their accelerations are the same and laws like "force = mass × acceleration" are unaffected. Equation 11(10) appears to be in good agreement with experimental results when it is applied to ordinary velocities. For example, the equation can be used to calculate the speed of an aeroplane relative to the ground when its air-speed (i.e. speed relative to the air) and the wind velocity are known. The Michelson-Morley experiment and the associated experiments show that for light

$$c' = c, \quad \ldots \ldots \ldots \quad 11(12)$$

and this indicates that equation 11(10) cannot apply to light.

11.25—Einstein made the following two hypotheses:
(1) *The principle of equivalence*—the laws of physics are independent of the motion of the co-ordinate system to which they are referred. We can never detect absolute motion of bodies through space,

but only the relative motion of one material body with respect to another.

(2) The velocity of light in every co-ordinate system has always the same value (c).

In the *special* theory of relativity (published in 1905), he applied the principle of equivalence to systems in uniform relative motion, but not to systems which are accelerated with respect to one another. In the *general* theory (published in 1915) the principle is applied to all systems. For the present, we consider only the special theory. It is important to note that in respect of systems which have relative motion, but no relative acceleration, the principle of equivalence holds in both Newtonian and in relativistic mechanics. The difference lies in the fact that the relativistic mechanics takes account of the experimental observation that the velocity of light is the same for all systems.

11.26.—Using the two fundamental hypotheses stated above, we may proceed to derive a transformation group which will replace equations 11(9). The derivation is very simple if we accept two assumptions: (*a*) that the equations of transformation are linear and homogeneous, and (*b*) that co-ordinates in directions perpendicular to the direction of the relative velocity are the same in both systems.*

We consider two systems S and S', and choose co-ordinates such that OX and O'X' are both in the direction of the relative velocity. We choose the origins of time and space so that $t' = 0$ when $t = 0$, and at this time O coincides with O'. We imagine a light signal emitted from the origin when $t = 0$. At time t in system S, it will have reached the sphere $x^2 + y^2 + z^2 = c^2 t^2$. The same signal viewed from the system S' will appear at time t' (corresponding to t) to have reached the sphere $x'^2 + y'^2 + z'^2 = c^2 t'^2$. Thus we must have

$$(x^2 + y^2 + z^2 - c^2 t^2) \equiv \gamma(x'^2 + y'^2 + z'^2 - c^2 t'^2), \quad 11(13)$$

where γ is a constant. This equation is derived from the assumption that c is the same for both systems. The principle of equivalence implies that $\gamma = 1$, because, if this were not so, the " light sphere " would not be the same size in both systems. Also we have decided to assume that $y = y'$ and $z = z'$, and hence

$$x^2 - c^2 t^2 \equiv x'^2 - c^2 t'^2. \quad \ldots \quad 11(14)$$

Let the relative velocity be such that O' appears to be moving with

* For a derivation independent of these assumptions see Reference 11.21.

velocity v when viewed from S, and O appears to be moving with velocity $-v$ when viewed from S'. Then $x' = 0$ when $x = vt$, and $x = 0$ when $x' = -vt'$. Hence we must have

$$x' = k(x - vt), \qquad \ldots\ldots \quad 11(15)$$

and
$$x = k'(x' + vt'), \qquad \ldots\ldots \quad 11(16)$$

where k and k' are two constants which must depend on v. Inserting the value of x' given by 11(15) in 11(16), we obtain

$$t' = k\left[t - \frac{x}{v}\left(1 - \frac{1}{kk'}\right)\right]. \qquad \ldots\ldots \quad 11(17)$$

Equations 11(15) and 11(17) give x' and t' in terms of x and t. These values may now be inserted on the right-hand side of 11(14), and the coefficients of x^2, t^2 and xt on the two sides of the identity may be equated. Three equations are obtained, and these may be regarded as simultaneous equations for k and k'. It is found that all three equations are satisfied when $k = k' = (1 - v^2/c^2)^{-1/2}$. The equations of transformation [obtained by inserting the values of k and k' in 11(15), 11(16) and 11(17)] are thus

$$\left.\begin{array}{ll} x' = \dfrac{x - vt}{\sqrt{(1 - v^2/c^2)}}, & x = \dfrac{x' + vt'}{\sqrt{(1 - v^2/c^2)}}, \\[2ex] t' = \dfrac{t - \dfrac{v}{c^2}x}{\sqrt{(1 - v^2/c^2)}}, & t = \dfrac{t' + \dfrac{v}{c^2}x'}{\sqrt{(1 - v^2/c^2)}}, \end{array}\right\} \quad . \quad 11(18)$$

and we have also
$$y = y' \text{ and } z = z'.$$

The equations have the symmetry required by the principle of equivalence, allowing for the fact that the sign of the relative velocity measured in S' is opposite to its sign when measured in S. It may be verified by direct substitution in 11(14) that the velocity of light is the same in both systems.

11.27. Dilation of Time and Contraction of Space.

Let us now consider four consequences which follow from equations 11(18).

(a) *Relativity of Simultaneity.*

From equations 11(18) we see that two events which are simul-

§ 11.27   DILATION OF TIME   429

taneous in the system S, but which occur at different places, are not simultaneous in the system S'. For, if $t_1 = t_2$,

$$t_1' = \frac{1}{\alpha}\left(t_1 - \frac{v}{c^2}x_1\right) \text{ and } t_2' = \frac{1}{\alpha}\left(t_1 - \frac{v}{c^2}x_2\right), \qquad 11(19)$$

where we have written

$$\alpha = (1 - v^2/c^2)^{\frac{1}{2}}. \qquad \ldots \ldots \quad 11(20)$$

Thus t_1' and t_2' are not equal if $x_1 \neq x_2$.

(b) *Dilation of Time.*

In a similar way we see that the interval between two events which occur at times t_1 and t_2, and at the same place (x_1) in system S, is not the same as the interval measured in system S' for

$$\left.\begin{aligned} \Delta t &= t_1 - t_2, \\ \Delta t' &= t_1' - t_2' = \frac{\Delta t}{\alpha}. \end{aligned}\right\} \qquad \ldots \ldots \quad 11(21)$$

Since α is less than unity, $\Delta t'$ is greater than Δt.

(c) *Contraction of Space.*

An observer who is at rest in system S may measure the length of a bar which is also at rest in that system by placing a measuring scale against the bar and reading the co-ordinates of its ends. Let the readings be x_1 and x_2. An observer in S' can also measure the lengths of the same bar by placing a measuring scale (which is at rest in his system) against the bar, but his measuring scale will be moving past the bar. He therefore reads the co-ordinates of the ends *simultaneously*, i.e. at the same time in *his* system. The length he will measure will be

$$x_2' - x_1' = \frac{1}{\alpha}\{(x_2 - x_1) - v(t_2 - t_1)\}, \quad \ldots \quad 11(22)$$

and he will have

$$\left.\begin{aligned} t_2 &= \frac{1}{\alpha}\left(t' + \frac{v}{c^2}x_2'\right), \\ t_1 &= \frac{1}{\alpha}\left(t' + \frac{v}{c^2}x_1'\right), \end{aligned}\right\} \qquad \ldots \ldots \quad 11(23)$$

if he makes the observations at the same time (t') in his system. Substituting in 11(22) from 11(23), we have

$$x_2' - x_1' = \frac{1}{\alpha}\left\{(x_2 - x_1) - \frac{v^2}{\alpha c^2}(x_2' - x_1')\right\},$$

or
$$\left(1 + \frac{v^2}{\alpha^2 c^2}\right)(x_2' - x_1') = \frac{1}{\alpha}(x_2 - x_1),$$

and
$$x_2' - x_1' = \alpha(x_2 - x_1), \qquad \ldots \ldots \quad 11(24)$$

Since
$$1 + \frac{v^2}{\alpha^2 c^2} = 1 + \frac{v^2}{c^2 - v^2} = \frac{1}{\alpha^2}.$$

Thus the length measured in system S' is less than that measured in system S in the ratio $\alpha : 1$.

(d) Addition of Velocities.

Suppose that a particle is moving in the common direction of the x and x' axes and that its velocity as measured by an observer in the system S is U, and as measured by an observer in the system S' is U'. Then

$$U = \frac{dx}{dt} \quad \text{and} \quad U' = \frac{dx'}{dt'}.$$

$$U = \frac{d(x' + vt')}{d\left(t' + \frac{v}{c^2}x'\right)}$$

$$= \frac{\frac{d}{dt'}(x' + vt')}{\frac{d}{dt'}\left(t' + \frac{v}{c^2}x'\right)} = \frac{\frac{dx'}{dt'} + v}{1 + \frac{v}{c^2} \cdot \frac{dx'}{dt'}}.$$

Hence
$$U = \frac{U' + v}{1 + \frac{vU'}{c^2}}. \qquad \ldots \ldots \quad 11(25)$$

This law of addition of velocities applies only when the two velocities are in the same direction. It is the relativistic equation corresponding to the Newtonian relation given by equation 11(10). It is in agreement with the hypothesis of the constant velocity of light because, if $U' = c$, we have

$$U = \frac{c + v}{1 + vc/c^2} = c. \quad \ldots \ldots \quad 11(26)$$

Thus the addition of any velocity (positive or negative) to the velocity of light leaves this particular velocity unchanged.

11.28.—The conclusions of the last paragraph, that space and time measurements depend on the velocity of the observer, appear to be contrary to our " intuitive " ideas of space and time. These concepts are derived from experience, in which the observer is either at rest with respect to the objects observed, or moving with a velocity which is a small fraction of the velocity of light. The dilation of intervals and contraction of lengths are then much too small to be observed.* It is then natural to think that lengths and intervals are the same for all observers and hence to think of them as fixed objects having an existence independent of any observer. They are so conceived in Newtonian mechanics and this idea leads to equation 11(10) for the law of addition of velocities. In this law, all velocities differ according to the motion of the observer. Einstein starts from the assumption that in physics we deal only with *measured* length and *measured* time. These quantities are significant only when we have clearly defined the process of measurement.

Suppose that in the system of S, light signals are emitted at times t_1 and t_2. An observer in system S' can note the difference between the times at which they are received. He does not regard this as the correct interval between the events, because he knows that the source has moved between the emission of the two flashes. He has to make an allowance for the difference in time of transit. According to Newtonian mechanics, this allowance must be made so that the interval measured in system S' is the same as that measured in system S. This method of making the allowance cannot be reconciled with the constant velocity of light. According to relativity theory, the allowance must be adjusted so that the velocity of light is the same for both observers. The intervals are then unequal. We cannot have both the equality of intervals and the constant velocity of light. The Michelson-Morley experiment, and other experiments which we shall describe later, furnish very strong evidence in favour of accepting the constant velocity of light. We shall see that there is also direct evidence for the

---

* For an observer moving at 60 m.p.h. past the scene which he observes, α differs from unity by about one part in 10^{14}.

inequality of intervals and for the velocity addition theorem [equation 11(25)]. If we accept the inequality of intervals (and the corresponding inequality of lengths), it follows that a statement concerning a length or a time is incomplete unless the frame of reference is stated. If the given data in a problem do not all refer to the same frame, they must be converted to the same frame by means of equations 11(18)—or some equivalent process must be carried out.

11.29. Experiments in which Source and Observer are in Relative Motion.

We shall now develop equations giving the frequency and apparent direction of light emitted by a source which is moving with respect to the observer. The medium between source and observer has unit

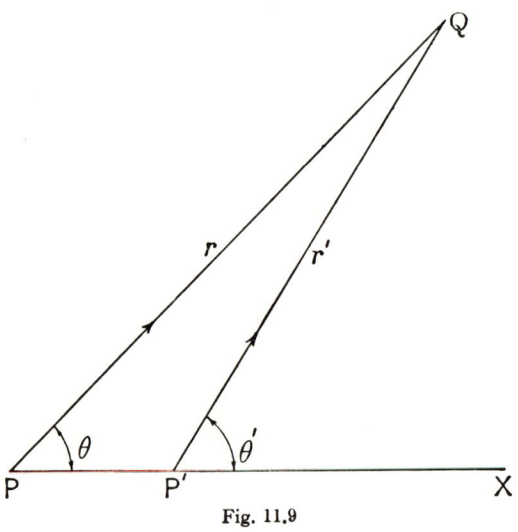

Fig. 11.9

refractive index. The observer is at rest at Q in system S, and the source is at rest in S' (fig. 11.9). Let the waves emitted from P' be represented by

$$\xi' = \frac{A'}{r'} \exp i\{(\omega' t' - \kappa' r') + \epsilon'\}. \qquad 11(27)$$

Let the ray from P' to the observer at Q make an angle θ' (measured in system S') with the x' axis. Then $r' = x' \cos \theta' + y' \sin \theta'$, and we have

$$\xi' = \frac{A'}{r'} \exp i\{\omega't' - \kappa'x' \cos \theta' - \kappa'y' \sin \theta' + \epsilon'\}. \quad 11(28)$$

To the observer in system S, the same beam is represented by

$$\xi = \frac{A}{r} \exp i\{\omega t - \kappa x \cos \theta - \kappa y \sin \theta + \epsilon\}. \quad 11(29)$$

But the expression derived by applying the transformation equations 11(18) to equation 11(28) must also represent the beam observed in the S system, and must therefore agree with 11(29) at all places and times, i.e.

$$\omega t - \kappa x \cos \theta - \kappa y \sin \theta + \epsilon$$
$$\equiv \frac{\omega'}{\alpha}\left(t - \frac{vx}{c^2}\right) - \frac{\kappa'}{\alpha}(x - vt)\cos\theta' - \kappa'y\sin\theta' + \epsilon'. \quad 11(30)$$

Equating the coefficients of x and t, and remembering that $\omega/\kappa = \omega'/\kappa' = c$, we have

$$\omega = \frac{1}{\alpha}(\omega' + \kappa'v \cos \theta'),$$

or
$$\omega = \frac{\omega'}{\alpha}\left(1 + \frac{v}{c}\cos\theta'\right); \quad \ldots \quad 11(31)$$

and
$$\kappa \cos \theta = \frac{1}{\alpha}\left(\kappa' \cos \theta' + \frac{v\omega'}{c^2}\right),$$

$$\kappa \cos \theta = \frac{\omega'}{\alpha}\left(\frac{\cos \theta'}{c} + \frac{v}{c^2}\right),$$

$$\cos \theta = \frac{\omega'}{\omega\alpha}\left(\cos \theta' + \frac{v}{c}\right),$$

$$\cos \theta = \frac{\cos \theta' + \frac{v}{c}}{1 + \frac{v}{c}\cos \theta'}. \quad \ldots \ldots \quad 11(32a)$$

The frequency of the light observed in the system S is given by 11(31), and in this system the position of the source is at P (fig. 11.9), the angle θ being given by 11(32a). It is found that both equations 11(31) and 11(32a) are verified by experiment (§§ 11.30, 11.31 and 11.34).

EXAMPLES [11(i)–11(v)]

11(i). Show that the transit time (to and fro) for a path which makes an angle θ to the direction of the relative velocity is given by

$$T_\theta = \frac{2d}{c^2 - v^2} \{c^2 - v^2(1 - \cos^2\theta)\}^{\frac{1}{2}}.$$

Hence show that T_1 and T_2 [equations 11(2b) and 11(4)] are maximum and minimum velocities respectively.

11(ii). Show that equation 11(32a) may be written

$$\sin\theta = \frac{\alpha \sin\theta'}{1 + \frac{v}{c}\cos\theta'}. \qquad \ldots \ldots \quad 11(32b)$$

[From 11(32a) we have $(1 + \cos\theta) = (1 + \cos\theta')\left(1 + \frac{v}{c}\right)\bigg/\left(1 + \frac{v}{c}\cos\theta'\right)$ and a similar expression for $(1 - \cos\theta)$. We obtain 11(32b) by putting $\sin^2\theta = (1 + \cos\theta)(1 - \cos\theta)$.]

11(iii). Show that 11(32b) implies that

$$\sin\theta' = \frac{\alpha \sin\theta}{1 - \frac{v}{c}\cos\theta}, \qquad \ldots \ldots \quad 11(32c)$$

and obtain an expression for $\cos\theta'$.

[Equation 11(32c) and a corresponding expression for $\cos\theta'$ are obtained by applying the principle of equivalence to 11(32b) and 11(32a). They may be verified algebraically.]

11(iv). Show that 11(32a) is consistent with the requirement that the coefficients of y in 11(30) must be equal.

$\left[\text{Remember that } \frac{\omega}{\kappa} = \frac{\omega'}{\kappa'} = c.\right]$

11(v). Light (emitted from a source in S') is limited by stops which obstruct all the light except that within a small cone of solid angle $d\Omega'$ (measured in S'). Show that the solid angle measured by an observer in a system S (which is approaching the source with velocity v) is given by

$$\frac{d\Omega}{d\Omega'} = \frac{1 - v/c}{1 + v/c}. \qquad \ldots \ldots \quad 11(33)$$

[Differentiating 11(32b) we obtain

$$\cos\theta\, d\theta = \left[\frac{\alpha\cos\theta'}{1+\frac{v}{c}\cos\theta'} + \frac{v}{c}\frac{\alpha\sin^2\theta'}{(1+\frac{v}{c}\cos\theta')^2}\right]d\theta'.$$

When $\theta = \theta' = 0$, we have $\quad d\theta = \dfrac{\alpha}{1+v/c}\,d\theta'$,

and 11(33) follows since $\quad \dfrac{d\Omega}{d\Omega'} = \left(\dfrac{d\theta}{d\theta'}\right)^2.\ ]$

11.30. Radial Doppler Effect.

Equation 11(32) shows that when $\theta' = 0$ we have also $\theta = 0$. In this condition source and observer are approaching directly along the line of sight when v is positive. The relation between the frequencies is then

$$\alpha\omega = \omega'(1+v/c), \quad \ldots \quad 11(34a)$$

or $\quad\quad\quad\quad \lambda(1+v/c) = \alpha\lambda'. \quad \ldots \quad 11(34b)$

This differs from the non-relativistic expression 2(58) only in respect of the factor α. Experiments of the type described in § 2.24 are not sufficiently accurate to decide between the two formulæ. The difficulty is not in the optical part of the experiment. In the early experiments on the Doppler effect, the atoms were not all moving in precisely the same direction, so that θ' [in equation 11(31)] was not known exactly, and v was known only with moderate accuracy. This makes it impossible to calculate the term in the bracket to an accuracy of better than about one part in a thousand. Also the lines are broadened owing to the variation of the component of the velocity in the line of sight.

11.31. Dilation of Time.

If a beam of atoms is observed in a line which, *according to the observer*, is at right angles to the direction of the relative velocity, then $\cos\theta = 0$, and from 11(32a) we see that $\cos\theta' = -v/c$. Inserting this value in 11(31), we have

$$\omega = \omega'\frac{(1-v^2/c^2)}{(1-v^2/c^2)^{1/2}} = \omega'\alpha. \quad \ldots \quad 11(35a)$$

Hence $\quad\quad \lambda = \dfrac{\lambda'}{\alpha} = \dfrac{\lambda'}{(1-v^2/c^2)^{1/2}}, \quad \ldots \quad 11(35b)$

where λ is the wavelength observed in system S, and λ' is the wavelength which would be observed by an observer at rest with respect to the source. This change is called the *transverse Doppler effect*.

The transverse Doppler effect has not been observed for light,* but Ives and Stilwell† and also Otting‡ have checked equation 11(34b) in the following way. Suppose that two sources have equal and opposite speeds towards and away from the observer. The equation 11(34b) applies to the source which is approaching, and for the receding source we have

$$\lambda\left(1 - \frac{v}{c}\right) = \alpha\lambda'', \qquad \ldots \ldots \quad 11(35c)$$

so that
$$\lambda = \alpha\lambda_m, \qquad \ldots \ldots \quad 11(35d)$$

or
$$\Delta\lambda = \lambda_m - \lambda = \tfrac{1}{2}\frac{v^2}{c^2}\lambda, \qquad \ldots \ldots \quad 11(35e)$$

where $2\lambda_m = \lambda' + \lambda''$.

Ives and Stilwell produced a collimated beam of fast-moving hydrogen atoms and molecules. They arranged a spectrograph to receive light from the beam seen nearly end on and also in a mirror. The difference between the mean of the displaced lines and the undisplaced (due to light from atoms not in the beam) was measured. Lines of atomic and molecular hydrogen were used. Velocities ranging from about $4 \times 10^{-3}c$ to $7 \times 10^{-3}c$ were used. The variation of λ with v was that given by equation 11(34b). The experiment forms a satisfactory and very direct verification of the dilation of time. There is no corresponding direct verification of the contraction of space. This part of the theory is verified indirectly by the experiments described in § 11.35.

EXAMPLES 11(vi) and 11(vii)

11(vi). Calculate the difference between the Doppler shift obtained from 2(57) and that obtained from 11(34b) for particles whose velocities of approach are (a) $0.1c$, (b) $0.01c$, and (c) $0.003c$. Take the wavelength of the light to be 6000 Å.

[(a) 27 Å., (b) 0.30 Å., (c) 0.027 Å.]

* Recently the transverse Doppler effect has been observed for γ-rays using the Mossbauer effect.
† Reference 11.31. ‡ Reference 11.32.

§ 11.33 REFLECTION OF LIGHT BY A MOVING MIRROR

11(vii). A certain source emits light of wavelength 6000 Å., measured by an observer for whom the source is stationary. Find the displacements (a) for an observer who observes a transverse motion of the source, and (b) for an observer who observes a recession at 89° 55′ to the line of sight. In each case the velocity is 0·0031c.

[(a) 6000·03 Å. from equation 11(35b); (b) 6000·06 Å. To derive the second result use the formula $\omega' = \dfrac{\omega}{\alpha}\left(1 - \dfrac{v}{c}\cos\theta\right)$ obtained by applying the principle of equivalence to 11(31). Insert the value $v = -0·0031c$, since the source is receding.]

11.32.—It is sometimes thought that the contraction of space implied in equation 11(24) is the contraction suggested by FitzGerald, and that this contraction is verified by the Michelson-Morley experiment. This idea is not consistent with the relativity theory because FitzGerald's hypothesis was put forward as an *alternative* to the hypothesis of a constant velocity of light. The parts of the apparatus in the Michelson-Morley experiment are not in motion relative to each other, or to the observer. Only one frame of reference is involved, and therefore there is no contraction of space or dilation of time to be considered. It has also been suggested that, because transits to and fro are involved, the Michelson-Morley experiment does not prove anything about the velocity of light *in one direction*. Essentially the experiment shows that if $c(\theta)$ is the velocity in a direction which makes an angle θ with an axis fixed with respect to the earth, then

$$\frac{1}{c(\theta)} + \frac{1}{c(\theta + \pi)} = \text{a constant independent of } \theta.$$

The repetition of the experiment at a different time of year shows that a similar relation holds when the earth has a different velocity relative to the sun, though the constants are not necessarily equal. Eddington has analysed the significance of this relation.* He concludes that a logical argument based on the Michelson-Morley experiment and on other generally accepted results shows that the velocity of light is the same in all directions and for all observers. It is not, however, strictly correct to say that the Michelson-Morley experiment *by itself* proves this proposition.

11.33. Reflection of Light by a Moving Mirror.

We wish to calculate the law of reflection of light at a plane mirror which is moving (relative to the observer and the source) in the direction of its own normal (fig. 11.10). Let S be the system in which the mirror is stationary, and S′ the system of the

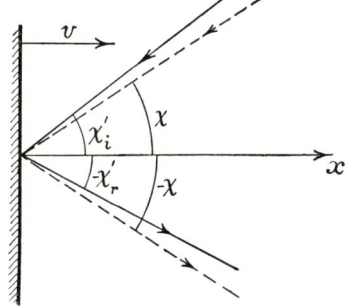

Fig. 11.10.—Reflection at moving mirror

* Reference 11.19.

observer. Let χ be the angle of incidence measured in S. Then the angle of reflection, measured in S, will be $-\chi$, since the ordinary law of reflection is valid in S. Let the angles of incidence and reflection in S' be χ_i' and $-\chi_r'$. Then we may apply 11(32b) first to obtain the relation between χ and χ_i', and again for the relation between χ and χ_r'. In the second application we must change the sign of v, because the incident beam travels towards, and the reflected beam away from, the mirror. Thus we have

$$\sin \chi = \frac{\alpha \sin \chi_i'}{1 + \frac{v}{c} \cos \chi_i'} \quad \text{and} \quad \sin(-\chi) = -\frac{\alpha \sin \chi_r'}{1 - \frac{v}{c} \cos \chi_r'}.$$

Thus the law of reflection is

$$\frac{\sin \chi_i'}{1 + \frac{v}{c} \cos \chi_i'} = -\frac{\sin \chi_r'}{1 - \frac{v}{c} \cos \chi_r'}. \qquad \ldots \quad 11(36)$$

EXAMPLES [11(viii)–11(x)]

11(viii). Show that if ω_i' and ω_r' are the circular frequencies of the incident and reflected radiation respectively, then

$$\omega_i'\left(1 + \frac{v}{c} \cos \chi_i'\right) = \omega_r'\left(1 - \frac{v}{c} \cos \chi_r'\right). \qquad \ldots \quad 11(37)$$

[In S, the frequency of the incident and reflected radiation is the same. Let this frequency be ω, and use 11(31) to determine the relations between ω and ω_i', and between ω and ω_r'.]

11(ix). A point source of light is placed at the focus of a lens whose focal length is f, and a plane mirror is set normal to the axis of the lens so as to give an image which coincides with the object when the mirror is stationary. Show that the displacement of the image when the mirror moves with speed v in a direction perpendicular to its normal is approximately $2vf/c$.
[Apply equation 11(32).]

11(x). Show that, in the experiment described in the preceding example, there is a change of wavelength proportional to v^2/c^2.
  [Let ω be the circular frequency for an observer whose frame S is fixed relative to the mirror, and let ω_i' be the frequency measured in S'. Then 11(31) gives $\omega_i' = \omega\alpha$. For the return beam we have, approximately, $\cos \theta' = 2v/c$, and 11(31) then gives $\omega_r'(1 + 2v^2/c^2) = \omega\alpha = \omega_i$. The wavelength of the return beam is thus increased by $\Delta\lambda = 2\lambda v^2/c^2$.]

11.34. Aberration Experiments.

Returning to equation 11(32a) and to fig. 11.9, we see that an observer in the S system has to look in a direction θ in order to view an object which in the S' system is situated in the direction θ'. Considering the simplest case when $\theta' = \frac{1}{2}\pi$, we see that the difference ($\Delta\theta$) between θ and θ' is then given by

$$\sin(\Delta\theta) = \sin(\tfrac{1}{2}\pi - \theta) = \cos\theta = v/c. \quad \ldots \quad 11(38)$$

The angle $\Delta\theta$ is known as the angle of aberration. Aberration was first observed by Bradley, who found an apparent difference between the angular positions of stars at different time of the year. The effect was additional to the well-known parallax effect, and was ascribed to the reversal of the earth's velocity in its orbit. Bradley used his observations to determine the velocity of light. At present it is perhaps more useful to regard the velocity of light as known, and to use the aberration effect to determine the orbital velocity of the earth.

Airy and Hoek observed the angle of aberration both (a) with an ordinary telescope and (b) with a telescope filled with water. It was expected that there would be a difference in the angle and that the difference would determine the velocity of the earth relative to the æther. No difference was observed. A rather complicated explanation of this result based on the Fresnel convection coefficient (§ 11.35) was given later. Relativity theory gives a much simpler explanation.

Suppose that, when the tube is filled with air, the observer in system S turns his telescope so that he sees a star in the centre of the field of view. *In his system*, the light from the star falling on his telescope is represented by a system of nearly plane waves whose wave normals are in the direction of the axis of his instrument. Filling the telescope tube with water makes no difference to this angular relation, and the star is seen in the same direction. The situation would, of course, be quite different if a material medium filled the whole region between source and observer.

11.35. Experiments with a Moving Medium.

In 1818 Fresnel suggested that it should be possible to determine the velocity of light in a moving medium by measuring the optical thickness of a moving plate. This experiment was carried out by Fizeau. His arrangement was, in effect, a modified form of the Rayleigh refractometer (fig. 11.11). Interference is observed at O between light which has passed from M_2 to M by the lower path, returning by the upper path, and light which has passed from M_2 to M by the upper path returning by the lower path. The displacement of fringes due to reversing the direction of liquid flow is measured. This displacement is proportional to the velocity of the liquid. The change of velocity of light could be calculated from the change of optical path, using 11(6), and it was found that the effective velocity of light in the moving medium was

$$b' = b + v\left(1 - \frac{1}{n^2}\right). \qquad \ldots \quad 11(39)$$

It had been expected that the velocity would be $(b + v)$ according to the Newtonian velocity addition equation 11(10). Fizeau's result was, at first, explained by saying that the æther was convected with a moving medium, but acquired only a fraction of the velocity of the medium.

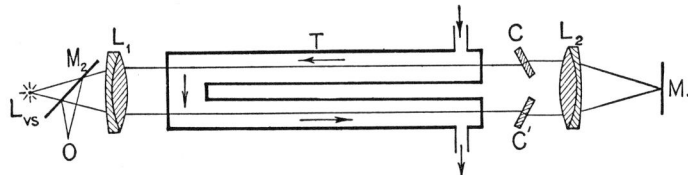

Fig. 11.11.—Transmission of light in a moving medium

The factor $(1 - 1/n^2)$ was called the *Fresnel convection coefficient*. This somewhat peculiar assumption was not derived from any satisfactory theory. In relativity the result does not require any special assumption. Applying the velocity addition equation 11(25), and writing b and b' in place of U' and U, we have

$$b' = \frac{b + v}{1 + vb/c^2} = \frac{b + v}{1 + v/nc}. \qquad \ldots \quad 11(40)$$

When v is small compared with c, this may be written

$$b' \doteqdot (b + v)\left(1 - \frac{v}{nc}\right)$$
$$\doteqdot b + v\left(1 - \frac{1}{n^2}\right),$$

in agreement with equation 11(39).

This experiment is of importance as a direct verification of the velocity addition theorem. It also shows that it is not possible to explain the null result of the Michelson-Morley experiment by saying that the æther is completely convected with the apparatus. The medium being air, the convection coefficient would be nearly zero, whereas a convection coefficient of unity would be needed to explain the null result. Fizeau's experiment was repeated by Michelson and Morley, and by Zeeman. Part of the object of these later experiments was to investigate a small correction due to the dispersion of the medium. The fundamental result [stated in equation 11(39)] was confirmed.

11.36. Relation between Mass and Energy.

We have seen that length and time are relative quantities, i.e. their values differ according to the movement of the frame of reference in which they are measured. It is reasonable to suppose that most derived quantities, such as momentum, energy, force, etc., will also be relative quantities, and that only certain rather special functions of length and time will be invariant (i.e. the same for all observers). It is shown in textbooks on relativity* that the general methods of dealing with dynamical problems, which were invented by Hamilton on the basis of Newton's laws, may be retained if we regard the mass of a body as a function of its velocity. On this basis we have

$$m = m_0/\alpha, \qquad \ldots \ldots \quad 11(41)$$

where m_0 is the mass of the body in a frame in which it is at rest. m_0 is called the *rest mass* or the *proper mass*. m is called the *relativistic mass* or simply "the mass". The momentum (P) and energy (E) of a body are then defined to be

$$P = mv = \frac{m_0 v}{(1 - v^2/c^2)^{1/2}}, \qquad \ldots \quad 11(42)$$

$$E = mc^2 = \frac{m_0 c^2}{(1 - v^2/c^2)^{1/2}}. \qquad \ldots \quad 11(43)$$

When v is small compared with c, the energy is given by

$$E = m_0 c^2 + \tfrac{1}{2} m_0 v^2 = E_0 + \tfrac{1}{2} m_0 v^2. \qquad \ldots \quad 11(44)$$

The energy thus consists of a constant part corresponding to the rest mass of the body, and a part corresponding to the kinetic energy.

An electrical charge e, distributed uniformly over a sphere of radius r_0, would have a potential energy e^2/r_0. Putting this energy equal to mc^2 we obtain

$$r_0 = \frac{e^2}{mc^2}. \qquad \ldots \ldots \ldots \quad 11(45)$$

The quantity r_0, so defined, is often called the "radius of the electron", even though the detailed picture of an electron as a charge distributed over a sphere is not generally accepted.

11.37. Mass, Momentum and Energy of the Photon.

From equations 11(42) and 11(43) we may derive the relation

$$E^2 = m_0^2 c^4 + c^2 P^2. \qquad \ldots \ldots \quad 11(46)$$

* Reference 11.19 or 11.21.

There is for light, however, direct experimental evidence (§ 17.21) that
$$E = cP. \qquad \ldots \ldots \quad 11(47)$$
This relation is consistent with 11(46) if, and only if, the rest mass associated with light is zero. That some such assumption must be made concerning light may be seen by considering 11(42) or 11(43) alone. From these equations we see that a **material particle** would have to acquire an infinite momentum and an infinite energy in order to move with the velocity of light. We can, however, imagine a particle whose rest mass is extremely small, and whose velocity is extremely near to c. A suitable relation between the velocity and the rest mass will give a finite momentum and energy. The photon may be regarded as the limiting case when rest mass has tended to zero and velocity to c. In this sense, a photon may be said to have zero rest mass. The relativistic mass m is given by
$$m = \frac{E}{c^2} = \frac{h\nu}{c^2}, \qquad \ldots \ldots \quad 11(48)$$
where h is Planck's constant (§ 17.1).

The mass associated with a quantum of visible light is of order 10^{-33} gramme. Thus an atom whose mass is of order 10^{-24} to 10^{-23} gramme loses only a very small fraction of its energy when a quantum of visible light is emitted. The mass of the energy received per year by the earth from the sun is of the order 6×10^{10} grammes, and the total amount emitted from the sun per year is 1.4×10^{20} grammes.

11.38.—If mass is associated with radiant energy, interaction of a beam of radiation with a gravitational field may be expected. Two such interactions have been found:

(a) A beam of light in a direction at right angles to a gravitational field is deflected. According to the general theory of relativity the deflection is approximately twice that calculated on Newtonian theory for particles moving with velocity c. Even in the intense gravitational field of the sun, the deflection is very small, the calculated value (on relativity theory) being 1·75 seconds of arc. This curvature has been measured by photographing the star field surrounding the sun during an eclipse. This photograph is compared with one taken six months earlier at night. The outer stars form a frame of reference, since light from them has not passed near the sun and has not been deflected. The positions of stars whose light has passed near the sun may be measured on both plates using the outer stars as reference points. It is found that the images of these stars in the photograph taken during the eclipse are displaced towards the sun. The deflection calculated from measurements at Sobral and Principe* in 1919 gave deflections of $1·98 \pm 0·12$ and $1·61 \pm 0·3$ seconds. Later measurements† gave $1·72 \pm 0·1$ and $1·82 \pm 0·15$ seconds. The four measurements taken together form a fairly good verification of the theory.

(b) A beam of radiation in the direction of the gravitational field should gain potential energy and there should be a corresponding effect. If the mass of a photon at the earth's surface is $h\nu/c^2$, the energy at height H should be $h\nu(1 - gH/c^2)$. This loss of energy does not produce a change of velocity but of frequency‡ so that

$$m' = h\nu' = h\nu\left(1 - \frac{gH}{c^2}\right). \quad \ldots \quad 11(49)$$

The change of ν (or of λ) for $H = 1000$ metres is only one part in 10^{13} and changes in optical wavelengths of this order cannot be detected. For light leaving the intense gravitational field of the sun the change should be 2 in 10^6. Differences of this magnitude can easily be detected in terrestrial measurements (see § 9.40) but observations of wavelengths in the solar spectrum are affected by local variations of velocity (giving a Doppler effect) and of magnetic and electric fields (Zeeman and Stark effects) so that the gravitational effect cannot be established with certainty. Recent measurements on γ-ray spectra appear to have established the existence of the very small wavelength change which is expected for $H = 30$ metres.

11.39. Interference in a Rotating System.

Rotation is often thought to constitute a serious difficulty in relativity theory. An observer in an enclosure can detect the rotation of his system by observing the centrifugal force, or by observations on a system like a Foucault pendulum. It is suggested that he thereby detects absolute motion. According to general relativity theory he detects, not absolute motion, but motion relative to the main gravitational lines of force produced by all the masses of the universe. If all exterior masses were removed, rotational effects such as centrifugal force should disappear. In relativity theory rotational forces are represented by suitable terms in the expressions which define the curvature of space-time, and hence the gravitational fields of force. In most practical conditions, the predictions of relativistic theory in

---

* Reference 11.19.   † References 11.27 and 11.28.
‡ As found in the Compton effect (§ 17.23).

regard to rotation agree with those of non-relativistic mechanics, apart from minor corrections which are too small to be detected. We shall now describe two experiments on the interference of light. One, due to Sagnac, may be regarded as analogous to a mechanical experiment on a spinning top. The other, due to Michelson, is analogous to the Foucault pendulum experiment since it depends upon the rotation of the earth.

11.40.—The apparatus used by Sagnac is shown in fig. 11.12. The interfering beams traverse the square in two opposite directions, and the fringes produced at Q are recorded photographically. The whole apparatus including the source and camera is rotated about once a

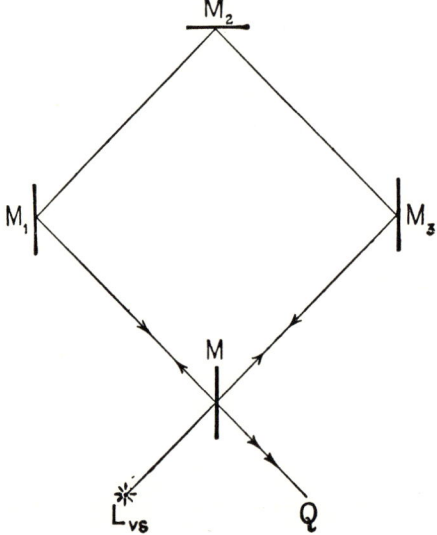

Fig. 11.12.—Sagnac's experiment

second. The fringes are found to be displaced from the positions occupied when the apparatus is at rest. According to non-relativistic theory, if the component of the velocity of one of the mirrors in the direction of the propagation of light is v, the velocity of light in one direction is $(c + v)$ and in the other is $(c - v)$. If the length of path for each beam is S when the mirrors are stationary, there is a difference in transit time of

$$\frac{S}{c-v} - \frac{S}{c+v}$$

when the system is rotating.

When v is small compared with c, the corresponding path difference is

$$\Delta S = \frac{2v}{c} S. \qquad \ldots \ldots \quad 11(50)$$

The observed displacement of fringes is in agreement with this expression.

EXAMPLE 11(xi)

11(xi). Show that for a rectangular circuit the effective path difference is approximately

$$\Delta S = \frac{4A}{c} \Omega, \qquad \ldots \ldots \ldots \quad 11(51)$$

where A is the area of the circuit and Ω is the angular velocity.

11.41.—Michelson used the rotation of the earth and increased the area of the circuit to compensate for the slow angular velocity. Since he was unable to vary the rate of rotation, he used two circuits, one of large area (2000 ft. × 1100 ft.) and the other of small area. One set of fringes was formed by the interference of two beams of light which had traversed the main circuit in opposite directions. These were compared with a set which had similarly traversed the smaller circuit and a shift of 0·230 fringe was observed, the calculated value being 0·236. This result was obtained only when effects due to variations of pressure and temperature had been reduced by enclosing both circuits in pipes which were evacuated.

11.42.—It is sometimes stated that the rotation experiments are " equally well " explained on (a) non-relativistic theory, (b) special relativity theory, (c) general relativity theory. This is not correct. The " explanation " on non-relativistic theory given in § 11.40 assumes that the æther is entrained with the rotating apparatus. This, however, is quite inconsistent with the non-relativistic account of the " æther-drag " phenomenon (§ 11.35). Special relativity is not applicable to any system involving rotation, and therefore does not give any explanation. Langevin* has shown that general relativity does give a satisfactory account of the phenomenon. This is the only theory to account for these results without creating inconsistencies elsewhere.

11.43. The Nebular Red-shift.

The spectrum of light from a nebula shows absorption lines similar to the Fraunhofer lines in the solar spectrum, but with a displacement toward the red end of the spectrum. It is found that this displacement varies regularly with the brightness of the nebula, i.e. the fainter nebulæ give the greatest displacements. It is generally accepted that the fainter nebulæ are fainter mainly because they are more distant, and, using other astronomical data, an expression has been derived

* Reference 11.26.

giving the relation between brightness of the nebula and distance. If this relation is accepted, the increase of wavelength ($\Delta\lambda$) at a distance of d parsecs* is given by

$$\Delta\lambda/\lambda = 1{\cdot}7 \times 10^{-9} d. \qquad \ldots \quad 11(52)$$

This relation was discovered by E. G. Hubble, after whom it is named "Hubble's law". It is fairly accurately verified for distances up to the order of 10^6 parsecs, i.e. to the limit of the observations.

It is nearly certain that this phenomenon has an important bearing on the theory of light as well as on cosmological theory. Various interpretations have been proposed. The most generally accepted is that of the "expanding universe". According to this theory, the red-shift is a radial Doppler effect. A uniform expansion of the whole universe would require that an observer at any point would observe a general recession of the nebulæ, the rate of recession being proportional to the distance from himself. If the red shift is due to a Doppler effect, we may put $\Delta\lambda/\lambda = v/c$ and equation 11(52) gives approximately

$$v = 50d, \qquad \ldots \ldots \quad 11(53)$$

where v centimetres per second is the velocity of recession for a nebula whose distance is d parsecs. The most distant nebulæ are estimated to be more than 10^6 parsecs away and to be receding with a velocity of more than 10^8 centimetres per second.

11.44. Cherenkov Radiation.

A conical shock wave stretching back from a projectile moving through a gas with a speed higher than the speed of sound has often been photographed. An analogous effect is obtained when an electron enters a medium with a speed (v) greater than the phase velocity (b) of light in the medium. This radiation was first reported by P. A. Cherenkov in 1934.

Suppose that an electron moves from A to B (fig. 11.13) in unit time and that a wavelet starts from each point on the track at the instant when the electron passes. Then Huygens' construction may be used to find the direction of the surfaces of constant phase exactly as it was used in § 3.13 to find the wave surfaces of the refracted and reflected beams. This direction must be such that the wavefronts form a cone of semi-vertical angle θ given by the relation

$$\sin\theta = \frac{b}{v} \quad \text{or} \quad \cot\theta = \left(\frac{v^2}{b^2} - 1\right)^{\frac{1}{2}}. \quad \ldots \quad 11(54)$$

* 1 parsec = 3×10^{18} centimetres.

§ 11.44   CHERENKOV RADIATION   447

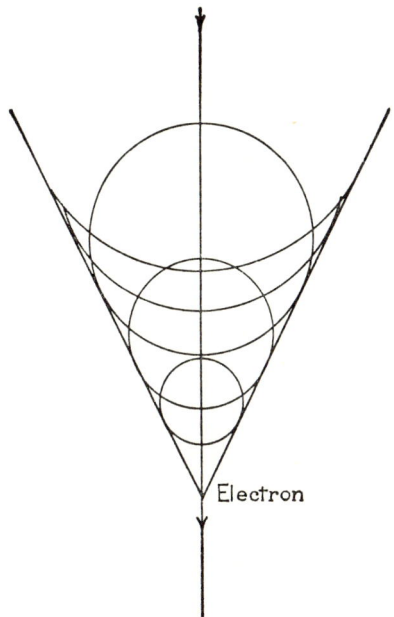

Fig. 11.13

In a dispersive medium the surfaces of constant phase are unchanged, but the main energy is concentrated in a thin conical shell whose vertex is at the moving charge and whose semi-vertical angle is given by*

$$\cot \theta' = \left(\frac{v^2}{b^2} - 1\right)^{\frac{1}{2}} + \frac{\omega v^2}{bc} \frac{dn}{d\omega} \left(\frac{v^2}{b^2} - 1\right)^{-\frac{1}{2}}$$

$$= \left(\frac{v^2}{b^2} - 1\right)^{-\frac{1}{2}} \left[\frac{v^2}{b}\left(\frac{1}{b} + \frac{\omega}{c}\frac{dn}{d\omega}\right) - 1\right], \quad \ldots \quad 11(55)$$

where ω is the circular frequency.

Using equation 4(40) this may be written

$$\cot \theta' = \left(\frac{v^2}{b^2} - 1\right)^{-\frac{1}{2}} \left(\frac{v^2}{bU} - 1\right). \quad \ldots \quad 11(56)$$

Thus the group velocity (U) enters into the expression for the angle of the cone, but further investigation shows that energy is propagated in directions per-

* See Reference 11.34.

pendicular to those given by 11(54). Thus the cone defined by 11(56) may be thought of as " side-slipping " as it advances.

The Cherenkov radiation of a high-energy electron is sufficiently intense to be registered by a photo-multiplier, and the effect is used for the detection of high-energy electrons. γ-rays may also be detected if they are sufficiently energetic to release fast electrons.*

* See References 11.35 and 11.36.

REFERENCES

Measurement of the constant c
General References:

11.1. BERGSTRAND: *Handbuch der Physik*, 1956, Vol. 24, p. 1.
11.2. ESSEN: *Nature*, 1950, Vol. 165, p. 582.
Methods for measuring c_L
11.3. MICHELSON: *Astrophysical Journal*, 1927, Vol. 65, p. 1.
11.4. MICHELSON, PEARSON and PEASE: *ibid.*, 1936, Vol. 82, p. 26.
11.5. KAROLUS and MITTAELSTAEDT: *Phys. Zeits.*, 1928, Vol. 29, p. 698.
11.6. MITTAELSTAEDT: *Annalen d. Physik*, 1929, Vol. 2, p. 285.
11.7. HÜTTEL: *ibid.*, 1940, Vol. 37, p. 365.
11.8. ANDERSON: *J.O.S.A.*, 1941, Vol. 31, p. 187.
11.9. BERGSTRAND: *Archiv. Fysik*, 1951, Vol. 3, p. 479. *Nature*, 1950, Vol. 165, p. 405.
Methods for measuring c_W
11.10. ESSEN: *Proc. Roy. Soc.* A, 1950, Vol. 204, p. 260.
11.11. FROOME: *ibid.*, 1954, Vol. 223, p. 195.
11.12. ASLAKSON: *Nature*, 1951, Vol. 168, p. 505.
Combination of Infra-red and Radio-frequency
11.13. RANK, GUENTHER, SHEARER and WIGGINS: *J.O.S.A.*, 1957, Vol. 47, p. 148.
Ratio of the Electrical Units (c_R)
11.14. ROSA and DORSEY: *Bull. Bur. Stand.*, 1907, Vol. 3, p. 433.
Velocity in Matter
11.15. BERGSTRAND: *Ark. Fysik*, 1954, Vol. 8, p. 457.
11.16. HOUSTOUN: *Proc. Roy. Soc. Edinburgh* A, 1944, Vol. 62, p. 58.

Relativistc Optics
11.17. EINSTEIN: *Relativity* (Methuen).
11.18. JOOS: *Theoretical Physics* (Blackie).
11.19. EDDINGTON: *Mathematical Theory of Relativity* (Cambridge University Press).
11.20. TOLMAN: *Relativity, Thermodynamics and Cosmology* (Oxford University Press).
11.21. MCCRAE: *Relativity Physics* (Methuen).
11.22. MICHELSON and MORLEY: *Phil. Mag.*, 1887, Vol. 24, p. 449.
11.23. KENNEDY: *Nat. Acad. Sci. Proc.*, 1926, Vol. 12, p. 621.
11.24. ILLINGWORTH: *Phys. Rev.*, 1927, Vol. 30, p. 692.
11.25. JOOS: *Annalen d. Physik*, 1930, Vol. 7, p. 385.

11.26. LANGEVIN: *Comptes Rendus Acad. Sc.*, 1921, Vol. 173, p. 831.
11.27. *Lick Observatory Bull.*, 1923, Vol. 11, p. 141, and 1928, Vol. 13, p. 130.
11.28. ST. JOHN: *Astrophysical Journal*, 1925, Vol. 67, p. 195.
11.29. ADAMS: *Proc. Nat. Acad. of Science (U.S.A.)*, 1925, Vol. 11, p. 382.
11.30. HUBBLE: *The Observational Approach to Cosmology* (Oxford University Press).
11.31. IVES and STILWELL: *J.O.S.A.*, 1941, Vol. 31, p. 369.
11.32. OTTING: *Phys. Zeits.*, 1939, Vol. 40, p. 681.
11.33. McVITTIE: *Cosmological Theory* (Methuen).
11.34. MOTZ and SCHIFF: *Am. Journ. of Phys.*, 1953, Vol. 21, p. 258.
11.35. WINCKLER and ANDERSON: *Rev. Sci. Inst.*, 1952, Vol. 23, p. 765.
11.36. *General Bibliography on Cherenkov Radiation* (published by Atomic Energy Research Establishment, Harwell).

CHAPTER XII
Polarized Light

12.1. Scalar and Vector Wave-theories.

In the experiments described in Chapters II–IX, all planes which include the wave normal are equivalent. If, for example, the wavefront is a horizontal plane, anything that can be said concerning a vertical north-south plane is equally true of a vertical east-west plane. The phenomena of interference and diffraction which we have described lead naturally to a wave theory, but the quantity whose periodic fluctuations constitute the waves need not necessarily be a vector quantity. If these were the only experiments on light we should naturally tend to use a scalar wave theory because of its greater simplicity.

We now come to consider experiments in which the results depend on the relative orientation of different parts of the apparatus with respect to planes through the wave normal. These results cannot be described in terms of a scalar wave-theory, but are adequately described by a theory in which light is represented by the periodic fluctuations of a quantity which has direction as well as magnitude. The disturbance at any moment is then represented by a vector, which specifies the direction of the disturbance as well as its magnitude.* In an isotropic medium the vector is always in the wavefront, and the ray is normal to the wavefront. The result of the experiments which will now be described lead to the assumption that there are two types of light, called *polarized light* and *unpolarized light*. We find that we have to represent the former by a vector whose magnitude and orientation vary in a related way as the phase of the light alters. When the orientation remains constant and only the amplitude varies, the light is said to be *plane-polarized*. When the amplitude remains constant, but the orientation of the vector varies regularly so that the end of the representative vector moves uniformly round a circle, the light is said to be *circularly polarized light*. There is another type of

---

* It should be understood that this representation is entirely different from the previous " vector representation " in which the direction of the vector represented the phase.

polarized light in which both amplitude and orientation vary in such a way that the end of the representative vector moves smoothly round an ellipse. This kind is called *elliptically polarized light*.

A beam of unpolarized light may be regarded as the resultant of two beams, polarized in two different planes and having no permanent phase relation (§§ 12.17 and 12.31). The variation of the direction of the vector which represents this resultant is not related, in any regular way, to the variation of its magnitude. Most of the polarization phenomena are subject to dispersion (i.e. they vary with the wavelength of the light), and some of the effects due to dispersion are considered in §§ 12.38–12.44. In the earlier part of this chapter it is assumed that the light is monochromatic.

12.2. The Experiment of Malus.

Ordinary light may be plane-polarized by reflection at the unsilvered surface of a transparent medium such as glass. This phenomenon was discovered by Malus, who allowed light to be successively reflected at two such surfaces. If the relation of the two surfaces is that shown in fig. 12.1, the light is strongly reflected.

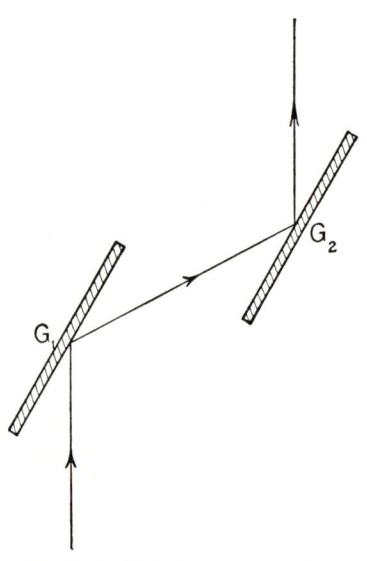

Fig. 12.1.—Malus' experiment. Successive reflections at two unsilvered mirrors (G_1 and G_2).

If the second piece of glass G_2 is turned so as to reflect the beam out of the plane of the paper, then the amount of reflected light is greatly reduced. Thus the first reflection alters the light so that it is capable of being strongly reflected in the plane of the paper, but is not capable of being strongly reflected (by an unsilvered mirror) in a perpendicular plane. These results may be described by saying that the first mirror polarizes the light, and the second reveals that it is polarized. An arrangement which produces a beam of plane-polarized light from a beam of unpolarized light is called a *polarizer*. An arrangement which detects plane-polarized light is called an *analyser*. Any piece of apparatus which is capable of acting as a polarizer is capable of acting as an analyser and vice versa.

§ 12.3   DEFINITION OF THE PLANE OF POLARIZATION   453

In the experiment of Malus the first unsilvered mirror is regarded as a polarizer, and the second as an analyser, but the experiment might equally well be performed with the light travelling in the reverse direction. When a polarizer and an analyser are oriented so as to pass the maximum amount of light, they are said to be *parallel*. When the relative orientation is such that the light emerging from the system is a minimum, they are said to be *crossed*. Two unsilvered mirrors are parallel when the reflections are in the same plane, and are crossed when the reflections are in perpendicular planes.

12.3. Definition of the Plane of Polarization.

The description of a parallel beam of unpolarized light is complete when the direction of propagation, the amplitude, and the frequency have been stated. To complete the description of a beam of plane-polarized light, it is necessary to give an additional datum which specifies an azimuth. It is usual to state the plane in which the beam is most strongly reflected at an unsilvered glass surface, and this plane is called the *plane of polarization*. It should be emphasized that this choice is purely a matter of convention. There is no logical reason why the plane of minimum reflection should not be called the plane of polarization, and some writers have adopted this convention. The important thing is that our definition of plane of polarization must be such that, given a beam of plane-polarized light, we can determine the plane of polarization by a simple physical test. The most simple method is to measure amounts of light reflected in different planes. At a certain stage in the elastic-solid theory of light, it was important to know whether the direction of vibration, which was usually called the direction of the "light vector", was in, or perpendicular to, the plane of polarization. For the discussions of this chapter, this question is of no significance and, for convenience, we assume that the light vector is *normal* to the plane of polarization. In Chapter XIII we shall show that, in the electromagnetic theory, a beam of plane-polarized light in an isotropic medium is represented by a magnetic vector in the plane of polarization, and an electric vector in a perpendicular plane. That is to say, we shall describe further experiments which show that the single " light vector ", which is sufficient for the description of the experiments discussed in this chapter, must be identified with the electric vector of Maxwell's theory.

12.4. Brewster's Law.

In § 12.2 we did not discuss the ratio of the maximum amount of light transmitted when the polarizer and analyser are parallel, to the minimum obtained when they are crossed. The variation of this quantity with the angle of incidence (θ) was investigated by Brewster, who showed that this ratio is very large for an angle θ_p given by

$$\tan \theta_p = \mu. \qquad \ldots \ldots \quad 12(1)$$

This relation is known as *Brewster's law*, and the angle which satisfies it is known as the *polarizing angle*. A beam of light which gives zero transmission for one orientation of an analyser is said to be completely plane-polarized.

If a beam which is completely plane-polarized is added to a beam which is unpolarized, the result is said to be partially polarized. When a beam of partially polarized light is passed through an analyser, there is a maximum for one orientation and a minimum for another, but the minimum is not zero. By this test * the light reflected from an unsilvered mirror is very nearly completely polarized when $\theta = \theta_p$, and is partially polarized for any other value of θ except $\theta = 0$. It was at one time thought that the light reflected at the polarizing angle was completely plane-polarized, but detailed experiments which will be discussed later (§ 14.17) show that this is not so.

12.5. Polarization by Transmission.

If the light passing through a plate of glass falls upon an analyser, it is found to be partially polarized (unless $\theta = 0$). For one transmission, the degree of polarization is small. The ratio of the maximum reflection coefficient given by one orientation of the plate to the minimum (obtained with a perpendicular orientation) is largest when the light is incident at the polarizing angle, but this maximum ratio is only about 1·1 : 1. When a beam of light is incident at the polarizing angle upon a pile of parallel plates (fig. 12.2), the degree of polarization of the transmitted light increases with the number of plates. A pile of twenty-five plates gives strong polarization. If the transmitted light is reflected at the front surface of an unsilvered mirror (used as an analyser), the maximum reflection is obtained when the analyser is turned to reflect the beam out of the plane of the paper (fig. 12.2),

---

* We assume for the moment that auxiliary tests such as those described in § 12.28 have shown that elliptical polarization is not present.

i.e. when its orientation is at right angles to that which would give maximum reflection for a beam which has been reflected from an unsilvered surface. For this reason we say that the transmitted light is polarized in a plane perpendicular to the plane in which the reflected light is polarized.

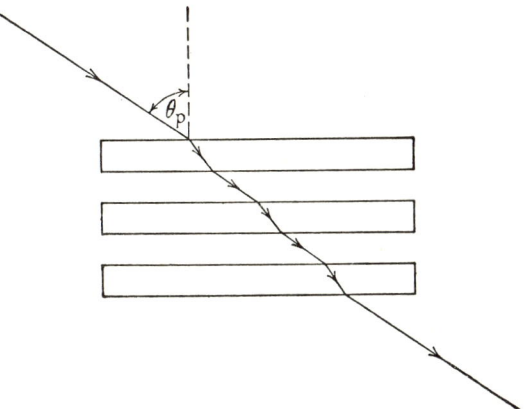

Fig. 12.2.—Polarization by transmission through a pile of plates

12.6. Double Refraction.

Crystals of the cubic system are optically isotropic. Each cubic crystal has a single refractive index, and crystalline media of this type behave like non-crystalline materials such as glass. Other crystals are optically anisotropic. The phenomena observed when a beam of unpolarized light enters a crystal of this latter kind depend on the relation between the direction of the beam and the axes of crystal symmetry. When the beam is plane-polarized, the effects also depend upon the relation between the plane of polarization and the crystal axes. In general, when a beam of light enters an anisotropic medium, it is divided into two parts which are refracted in different directions. This phenomenon is called *double refraction* or *birefringence*. From the theory which will be developed later it is possible to derive general laws of double refraction. These laws cannot be stated completely in any brief and simple way and, for our present purpose, it is sufficient to consider certain special cases.*

* In the course of the discussion in this chapter and in Chapter XVI, we shall state some of the symmetry properties of certain crystals. The reader who wishes to relate these statements to the general systematic classification of crystals is advised to consult References 12.1 and 12.2.

12.7.—Calcium carbonate crystallizes in rhombohedra to form a mineral which is called *calcite* or *Iceland spar*. The shape of the crystal is shown in fig. 12.3, in which ABCDA'B'C'D' represent the corners of the crystal. Two of the corners A and A' each contain three obtuse angles. The direction of a line making equal angles with each of the three edges meeting at A is called the *principal axis* of the crystal. In a perfectly formed crystal, the six faces are similar, and the line AA' is then in the direction of the axis.* The plane ACA'C' is called a *principal plane*. The principal axis and the principal plane are

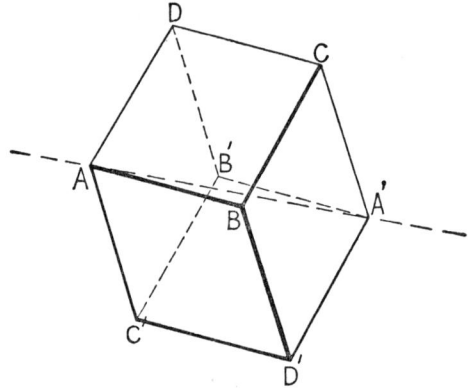

Fig. 12.3.—Regular crystal of calcite

defined by directions. Any line parallel to AA' may be called a principal axis, and any plane parallel to ACA'C' may be called a principal plane. It is possible to draw a line and a plane, in the directions of the principal axis and principal plane respectively, through any point in the crystal. These definitions of the principal axis and the principal plane refer to the symmetry of the crystal form, and not to the optical properties. We shall see later that there are, in general, two directions in a crystal which are of special importance in relation to the optical properties. These are called *optic axes*. The optic axes do not always coincide with any of the axes of crystal symmetry, though there is usually a fairly simple geometrical relation between the directions of the optic axes and the axes of crystal symmetry. In calcite, the two optic axes coincide, and the crystal is said to be *uniaxial*. The single optic axis also coincides with the principal axis of crystal sym-

---

* It should, however, be understood that the axis is defined by the angles which it makes with the appropriate faces. This definition applies to crystals which have not grown with perfect regularity, or to a broken piece of a crystal.

metry which has been defined above. These relations correspond with the fact that the laws of double refraction in calcite are not as complicated as the general laws applying to some other types of crystal.

12.8.—The following experiments may be carried out with two calcite plates which have been optically worked so that two plane faces of each plate are parallel, and so that the angle between the optic axis and the normal to the polished surfaces is the same for each plate. The exact value of this angle is not important provided that it is not too near zero or $\frac{1}{2}\pi$, i.e. the optic axis must not be in, or perpendicular to, the polished surface. For simplicity of description we shall discuss the case for which the normal to the surfaces is in a principal plane, and the optic axis is at about 45° to the surface (fig. 12.4a, p. 459).

A narrow beam of unpolarized light incident normally on one of the plates, is found to divide into two beams. One, called the *ordinary ray*, goes straight through; the other, called the *extraordinary ray*, is deflected on entering the crystal and emerges parallel to its original direction.* The extraordinary ray always lies in the principal plane which passes through the point at which the light enters the crystal. If the crystal is rotated about the normal to the polished surfaces, the extraordinary ray rotates with it. The separation of the two emergent beams is proportional to the thickness of the plate.

If the emergent beams are allowed to fall upon a second plate, whose optic axis is parallel to that of the first plate, two beams emerge from this second plate (fig. 12.4b). They are in the same plane as those emerging from the first plate, but have a greater separation. The same final result would be obtained by passing the light through one plate whose thickness is equal to the *sum* of the thicknesses of the plates. If now the second plate is rotated through an angle π, the deflections in the two plates are of opposite sign and the combination behaves like a single plate of thickness equal to the difference of the thicknesses of the two plates (fig. 12.4c). If the second plate is rotated through $\frac{1}{2}\pi$, there are still only two beams, but the beam which passed straight through the first plate is deflected in the second, and the beam which was deflected in the first plate is undeflected in the second. Thus the ordinary ray for the first plate behaves as an extraordinary ray in the second plate and vice versa (fig. 12.4d).

If the second plate is given an intermediate orientation with respect to the first, then there are four emergent beams (fig. 12.4e). Let

* The effect is best seen in calcite which is not of the highest optical quality, since this scatters a small amount of light, and so reveals the paths of the rays inside the crystal.

us call the ordinary beam which emerges from the first plate O_1, and the extraordinary beam E_1. Then the four images due to the beams emerging from the second plate may be called O_1O_2, O_1E_2, E_1O_2 and E_1E_2. O_1O_2 has always the same brightness as E_1E_2, and O_1E_2 has always the same brightness as E_1O_2.

If the second plate is rotated from the position in which its axis is parallel to that of the first, the following changes occur. First of all O_1E_2 and E_1O_2 are of zero brightness, and there are only two beams emerging from the second plate. As the plate is rotated O_1E_2 and E_1O_2 increase in brightness, and O_1O_2 and E_1E_2 decrease. When the plate has been rotated through an angle of $\frac{1}{4}\pi$, the four images are of equal brightness. When it has rotated through $\frac{1}{2}\pi$, O_1O_2 and E_1E_2 are of zero brightness, and there are again only two beams. As the second plate is rotated through another right angle, the same changes occur in the reverse order. When the total rotation is π, there are again only two images, and these are of equal brightness. The deflections of the images are now in the same line, but in reverse directions (fig. 12.4c). If the plates are of equal thickness, the images are superposed.

12.9.—These observations on double refraction, taken by themselves, give evidence of the polarization of light since the refraction in the second plate of either of the two beams which emerge from the first plate depends on the orientation of the beam with respect to the crystal axes. All the phenomena are consistent with the supposition that the ordinary and extraordinary ray are polarized in two mutually perpendicular planes. This evidence for the existence of the polarization of light is quite independent of the experiments of Malus. It did, in fact, lead Huygens to the basic idea of transverse waves more than 150 years before Malus' experiment was performed.

The experiments on polarization by reflection and by transmission have been described separately in order to show that each set, taken by itself, leads to the concept of polarized light. When this point is accepted, it is convenient to discuss them together. When the two beams emerging from a single calcite plate are examined by reflection at an unsilvered surface, it is found that the ordinary beam is polarized in the principal plane, and the extraordinary beam in a perpendicular plane. Further tests show that when a beam which has been polarized by reflection is incident normally upon a calcite plate, its behaviour depends on the relation between the plane of polarization and the principal plane of the crystal. When the plane of polarization is

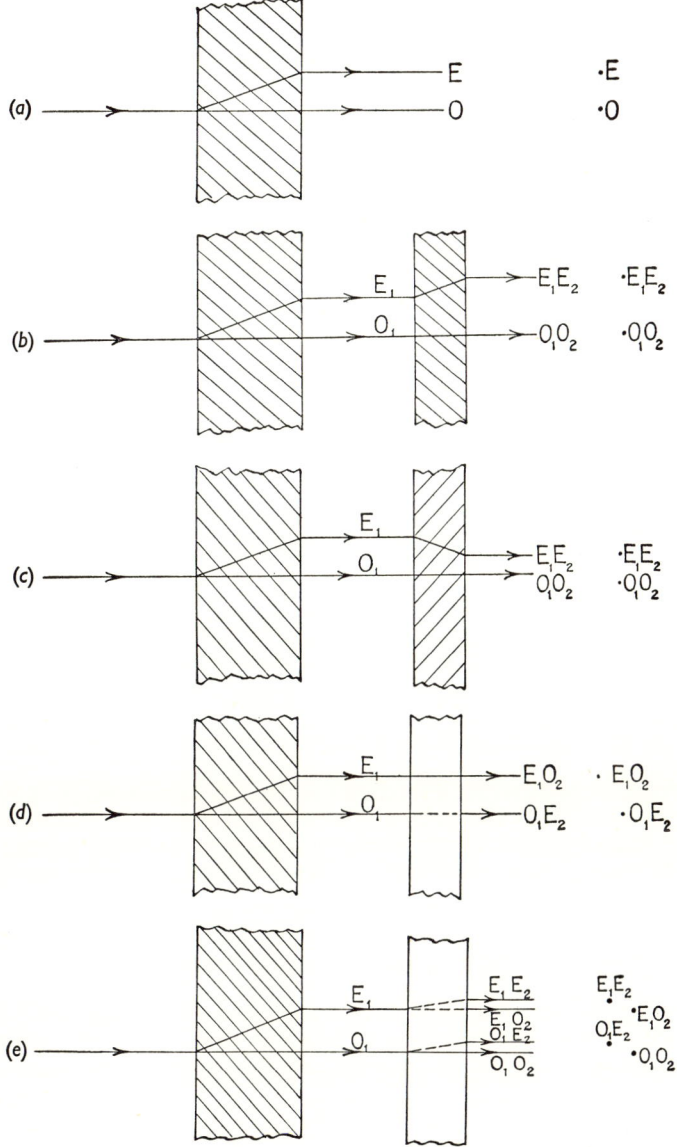

Fig. 12.4
(a) Refraction of light by a calcite plate.
(b) Refraction by two plates with the same orientation.
(c) Refraction by two plates, one rotated through π about the direction of the incident ray.
(d) Refraction by two plates, one rotated through $\frac{1}{2}\pi$.
(e) Refraction through two plates, one rotated through $\frac{1}{4}\pi$.

(The dots on the right-hand side show the relative positions of the spots of light received on a screen perpendicular to the direction of incidence. Dotted lines indicate rays passing out of the plane of the paper.)

parallel to the principal plane of the crystal, then there is only one image formed by an ordinary emergent beam, i.e. the light goes straight through. When the plane of polarization and the principal plane of the crystal are mutually perpendicular, there is only an extraordinary beam, which suffers a displacement in passing through the crystalline plate. For intermediate orientations there are two beams.

12.10. Malus' Law.

It is found that if ψ is the angle between the plane of polarization and the principal plane, the relative brightnesses of the images corresponding to the ordinary and the extraordinary beam are proportional to $\cos^2 \psi$ and $\sin^2 \psi$ respectively. Neglecting small losses due to reflection and scattering, the sum of the brightnesses is always equal to the brightness of the image obtained with the crystal removed. It is also found that when the angle between the principal axes of two calcite crystals is equal to ψ', the brightnesses of the $O_1 O_2$ and $E_1 E_2$ images are proportional to $\cos^2 \psi'$, and those of the $O_1 E_2$ and $E_1 O_2$ images are proportional to $\sin^2 \psi'$. Finally, it is found that when a beam of light is twice reflected (at the polarizing angle), the brightness of the image produced by the twice-reflected beam is proportional to $\cos^2 \psi''$, where ψ'' is the angle between the two planes of reflection. This last relation is known as *Malus' law*.

All these observations are consistent with the representation of plane-polarized light by a light vector which can be resolved into components like any other vector. It is supposed that when light is incident upon a glass surface at the polarizing angle, only the component polarized in the place of incidence is reflected. If the incident light is already polarized in this plane, it is all reflected. If it is polarized in a plane which makes an angle ψ'' with the plane of incidence, then the amplitude of the reflected wave is proportional to $\cos \psi''$, and the relative energy is proportional to $\cos^2 \psi''$. In a similar way, when light is incident in the appropriate way upon a calcite crystal, the component polarized parallel to the principal plane forms the ordinary beam, and the component polarized in the perpendicular plane forms the extraordinary beam. Detailed consideration shows that this hypothesis is consistent with all the observations on the variations in the brightness of the images. The fact that the results of calculations based on the resolution and composition of vectors are in agreement with experiment justifies the use of a vector wave representation.

12.11. Methods of producing Plane-polarized Light.

As we have seen in §12.2, plane-polarized light may be produced by reflection at the Brewsterian angle, or by transmission through a pile of plates. The former method involves great loss of light, since only a few per cent of the incident beam is reflected. The latter method does not give complete polarization and, to obtain a high degree of polarization, it is necessary to use an inconveniently large number of plates. For this reason many methods of producing plane-polarized light by means of double refraction have been devised. The simplest method is to use a thick piece of calcite, and to insert stops so as to

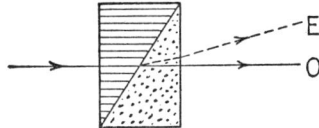

Fig. 12.5.—Rochon prism (dots indicate optic axis perpendicular to the plane of the paper).

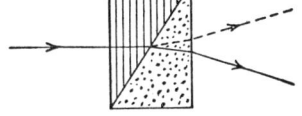

Fig. 12.6.—Wollaston prism (dots indicate optic axis perpendicular to the plane of the paper).

remove either the extraordinary or the ordinary beam. Since the separation is not very great, it is necessary to use a narrow beam. The prisms of Rochon (fig. 12.5) and of Wollaston (fig. 12.6) produce two beams of light, polarized in mutually perpendicular planes and travelling in different directions. The orientations of the optic axes are shown in the figures. It will be noticed that the Wollaston prism produces the wider separation, but the Rochon prism leaves one ray undeviated. This is an advantage in certain applications. These prisms are usually made either with quartz or with calcite. The former is more easily worked to high optical quality, but the latter provides the larger separation.

12.12. Nicol, Foucault, and Glan-Thompson Prisms.

The difference in the angles of refraction for the ordinary and extraordinary rays suggests the possibility of separating them by

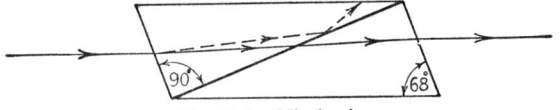

Fig. 12.7.—Nicol prism

arranging that one is totally reflected, and the other transmitted at a thin film separating two pieces of calcite. This possibility was first realized by Nicol, who cut a calcite crystal in a way shown in fig. 12.7, and cemented the two pieces together with Canada balsam. The extraordinary ray is transmitted, and the plane of polarization of the transmitted light is perpendicular to the plane of the diagram.

Calcite prisms of large size are expensive and, in order to obtain a bright source of polarized light, it is desirable to concentrate the light on the Nicol. The angular divergence of the cone which can be used is limited by the difference

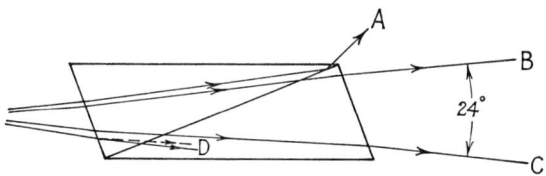

Fig. 12.8.—Angular field of Nicol prism; rays B and C limit the useful field. Outside this range either both components of ray A are totally reflected, or both components of ray D are transmitted at the interface.

between the critical angle for the ordinary and extraordinary rays. By drawing extreme rays, as shown in fig. 12.8, it is found that the maximum permissible divergence of the transmitted beam is 24°. The Nicol prism has the disadvantage that the emergent light is slightly elliptically polarized owing to a secondary effect due to the inclined end faces.

The Glan-Thompson prism (fig. 12.9) is designed to give a wider field and more perfect plane-polarization. The exact angle at which the crystal is cut varies according to the purpose for which it is designed. The prism shown in the diagram may be regarded as typical. The design of this type of prism is discussed in detail in Reference 12.3. It is not necessary that Canada balsam should be used as the separating layer, though it is most generally useful for the polarization of visible light. A prism of the Nicol type with air as the separation film was devised by Foucault for the polarization of ultra-violet radiation. Such a prism is transparent to 2300 Å.

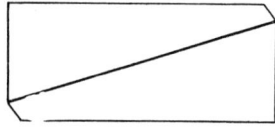

Fig. 12.9.—Glan-Thompson prism

12.13. Polarization by Absorption.

It has long been known that when unpolarized light is passed through tourmaline, the emergent light is partially plane-polarized. The crystal is doubly refracting, and the ordinary beam is much more strongly absorbed than the extraordinary beam. The natural crystal is strongly coloured and, for most wavelengths, absorbs a considerable part of the extraordinary, as well as of the ordinary beam. It is not suitable as a polarizer and its properties are chiefly of theoretical interest. A series of artificial materials, which polarize by absorption, have been developed by the Polaroid Corporation, U.S.A., following

§ 12.14   USES OF POLARIZING DEVICES   463

an invention by E. H. Land. The Polaroid type H film contains iodine which has been imbibed in an initially transparent plastic sheet of polyvinyl alcohol. The polarizing unit is an iodine polyvinyl alcohol complex which has been oriented by stretching the film.* This material transmits nearly 80 per cent of light polarized in one plane and less than 1 per cent of light polarized in the perpendicular plane. For wavelength 5500 Å., two pieces transmit up to 40 per cent of incident unpolarized light when parallel, and less than 0·01 per cent when crossed. At the extreme blue end of the spectrum the polarizing action is not quite so good and nearly 0·1 per cent of the incident light is transmitted. The residual light seen when a powerful source is viewed through two crossed pieces of Polaroid film is therefore blue. For an earlier type of film (known as type J) the residual light was mainly red. Large sheets of the material (up to 20 in. × 50 in.) are obtainable. Polaroid film offers the most convenient and inexpensive method of obtaining a strong source of light which is nearly completely plane-polarized. Prisms of the Glan-Thompson type are superior for use in instruments when it is important to have a very high degree of polarization for all wavelengths transmitted.

12.14. Uses of Polarizing Devices.

Polarizing devices are used in a variety of ways in scientific instruments, and in industry. In some experiments it is desirable to be able to reduce the effective intensity of a source of light in an accurately known ratio. This may be done by inserting a polarizer and an analyser between the source and the point of observation. The light

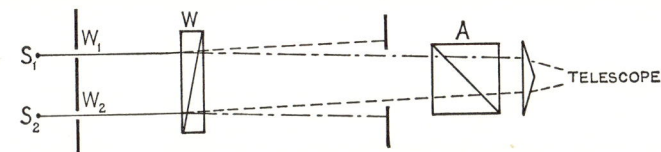

Fig. 12.10.—Polarization photometer

transmitted is proportional to $\cos^2 \theta$, where θ is the angle through which the analyser has been rotated from the parallel setting. This method is accurate and sensitive when the ratio of reduction is not less than 1 : 10 [Example 12(ii)].

A photometer based on this principle is shown in fig. 12.10. Light from the two sources S_1 and S_2 is polarized in two mutually perpen-

* The author is indebted to the Polaroid Corporation for supplying this technical information.

dicular planes by the Wollaston prism W, and the field is viewed through the analyser A which is rotated until the two halves appear equally bright. The ratio of illumination falling on the windows W_1 and W_2 is equal to $\tan^2 \theta$. If the ratio of the intensity of the weaker source to that of the stronger source is less than about $1:5$, a filter of known transmission is placed in front of one window.

Polarizing devices are used in industry to detect strains in glassware. The glass is placed between a polarizer and an analyser which are crossed, so that the field is dark except in the strained regions which possess double refraction. Polaroid spectacles are worn to reduce glare due to sunlight reflected by the sea. In a similar way Polaroid screens are sometimes inserted in front of reading lamps to reduce reflection from glossy paper. In both of these applications the polarizing device is only partially effective because only part of the light is reflected at the polarizing angle. It has been proposed that all motor-headlights be covered with Polaroid film oriented at 45° to the vertical and that each driver be provided with film oriented at the same angle as that over his own headlights (and therefore at right angles to the film over the headlights of a car travelling in the opposite direction). He thus sees the headlights of an oncoming car only as glare-free blue discs. The advantages of this scheme are obvious. The disadvantages include a serious loss of light which it is proposed to make good by using 125-watt headlights. The overall merits of the device, and the prospects of its being generally adopted, depend on considerations which are not purely a matter of optics and which lie outside the scope of this book.

12.15. Interaction of Beams of Plane-polarized Light.

The conditions under which two beams of polarized light may produce interference fringes were investigated by Fresnel and Arago, whose results may be summarized as follows:

(1) Two beams of light plane-polarized in mutually perpendicular planes do not produce interference fringes under any condition.

(2) Two beams of light plane-polarized in the same plane interfere under the same conditions as two similar beams of unpolarized light, *provided that they are originally derived from the same beam of plane-polarized light, or the same component of a beam of unpolarized light.*

(3) Two beams of plane-polarized light derived *from perpendicular components of unpolarized light,* and afterwards rotated into the same plane, do not produce interference fringes under any condition.

12.16.—The generalizations stated in the preceding paragraph were derived from a rather lengthy and complicated set of experiments. The essential points are shown by the following experiments.

An apparatus similar to that used by Young in the original discovery of interference is used, and a polarizing device is placed in front of each of the slits (fig. 12.11). A pile of mica plates was actually used, but for a modern demonstration a piece of Polaroid film would be more convenient. The following results were obtained:

(i) If the polarizer P_C is omitted, and P_A and P_B are set parallel to one another, interference fringes are obtained. If they are set to polarize the two beams in mutually perpendicular planes, no interference fringes are obtained.

(ii) With the three polarizers in position, and with P_A and P_B set to polarize in parallel planes, the orientation of P_C affects the total illumination on the screen S, but not the distribution. So long as there is any illumination, fringes are obtained. In this case the interfering beams are both derived from the same polarized beam, and they are polarized in the same plane. Their plane of polarization is not the same as that for the beam from which they are derived, except when P_A, P_B and P_C are all parallel.

(iii) A doubly refracting plate of calcite is placed behind each slit. The two plates are of equal thickness. Their principal planes are at right angles to one another, so that the ordinary ray

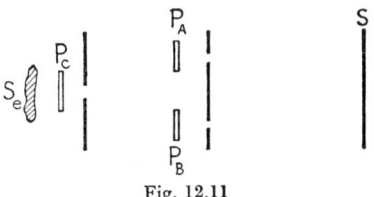

Fig. 12.11

passed by one plate is polarized in the same plane as the extraordinary ray passed by the other. Two sets of fringes are obtained. These are displaced to the right and left of the system obtained when the plates are removed. Further investigation shows that one set is due to the interference of the ordinary beam transmitted by the upper plate, and the extraordinary beam transmitted by the lower plate. The other set is due to the other pair of beams. The sign of the displacements indicates that, for calcite, the ordinary beam is retarded with respect to the extraordinary beam, i.e. the optical thickness of the crystal (and therefore the refractive index) is greater for the ordinary than for the extraordinary ray.

(iv) Two polarizers and a doubly refracting crystal C are placed behind the slits, as shown in fig. 12.12. The two polarizers are set with their planes perpendicular to each other and at an angle of $\frac{1}{4}\pi$ to the principal plane of the crystal. No fringes are observed. In this condition an extraordinary and an ordinary beam pass each slit. The four beams are of equal amplitude and, as in experiment (iii), there are two pairs polarized in the same plane. If, however, we consider either of these pairs, we see that its members have been derived from perpendicular components of the unpolarized source. No interference is obtained, indicating that

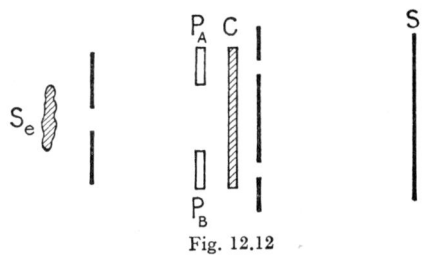

Fig. 12.12

these components are non-coherent. Similar results may be produced by inserting polarizing devices in appropriate parts of the other pieces of apparatus which are commonly used to produce interference fringes with unpolarized light. It should, however, be remembered that the polarizing devices may cause phase retardations. If these are too large, no interference will take place even if the conditions (1) and (2) stated in § 12.15 are fulfilled. Also the polarization may alter the relative amplitudes of reflected beams and thereby affect the distribution of illumination in the interference fringes. It is even possible that one of two interfering beams may be eliminated and, if this happens, the fringes disappear.

12.17.—The vector representation of polarized light is in accord with the observation that two beams polarized in mutually perpendicular planes cannot produce interference fringes. Two vectors situated in perpendicular planes cannot annul one another, because each has no component in the plane containing the other. The vector representation would also lead us to expect that if a long train of waves polarized in a given plane is resolved into two (e.g. by the use of a Rochon prism), the beams should have a permanent phase relation. They are not able to interfere because they are situated in mutually perpendicular planes, but a component of each, polarized in an intermediate plane, may be selected. These two components interfere, provided that they are brought together without the introduction of an unduly large path difference. Since beams derived from mutually perpendicular components of unpolarized light do not interfere, it follows that, if unpolarized light is to be represented by a single transverse vector, it must be assumed that the plane of the representative vector changes in an irregular way.*

12.18. Circularly Polarized Light and Elliptically Polarized Light.

Although two disturbances in mutually perpendicular planes cannot give interference fringes, even when there is a permanent phase relation, the interaction of such vibrations does produce a type of light which has special properties of its own. Consider two disturbances, one in the xz plane and the other in the yz plane and both travelling in the direction OZ. They may be represented by

$$\xi_x = a \cos(\omega t - \kappa z) = a \cos \phi, \quad \ldots \quad 12(2a)$$

and

$$\xi_y = b \cos(\omega t - \kappa z + \epsilon) = b \cos(\phi + \epsilon). \quad . \quad 12(2b)$$

These vibrations have the same frequency and velocity of propagation, but their amplitudes differ, and they have a permanent phase difference ϵ. Let us first consider the special case when $\epsilon = 0$. The resultant vibration is then represented by a vector of length $(a^2 + b^2)^{1/2}$. It lies in a plane which includes OZ and makes an angle $\chi = \tan^{-1} b/a$ with the x axis. Thus the resultant of these two disturbances is, in this special case, a linear disturbance represented by a vector in a plane intermediate between the planes of the vectors which represent the component disturbances.

* See § 12.31 for a further discussion of this point.

§ 12.18   ELLIPTICALLY POLARIZED LIGHT   467

Now consider a second special case when $\epsilon = -\tfrac{1}{2}\pi$. Then we may write
$$\xi_y = b \sin(\omega t - \kappa z) = b \sin \phi. \qquad \ldots \quad 12(3)$$
At any instant, the resultant is represented by a vector. If we plot ξ_x and ξ_y along two axes as shown in fig. 12.13, we see that, as ϕ varies, the magnitude and direction of the resultant alter. We have:

(i) when $\phi = 0$, $\quad \xi_x = a$ and $\xi_y = 0$;
(ii) when $\phi = \tfrac{1}{4}\pi$, $\quad \xi_x = a/\sqrt{2}$ and $\xi_y = b/\sqrt{2}$;
(iii) when $\phi = \tfrac{1}{2}\pi$, $\quad \xi_x = 0$ and $\xi_y = b$.

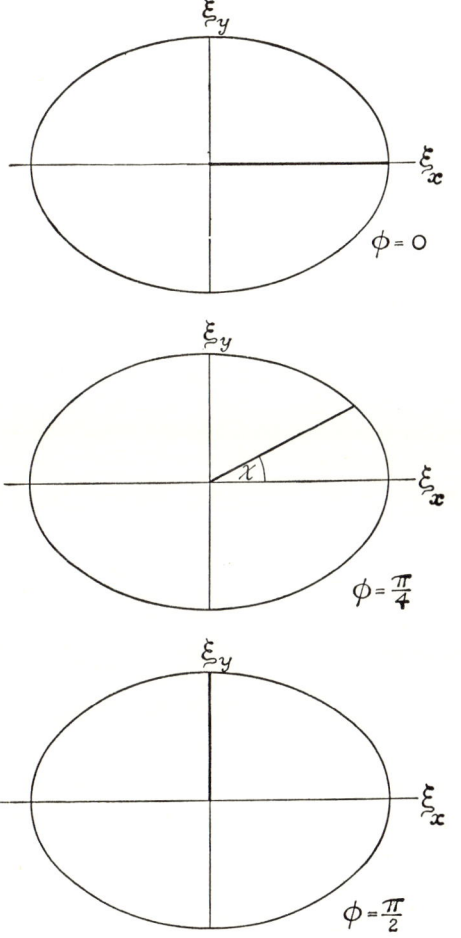

Fig. 12.13.—Vector representation of elliptically polarized light

The figure shows the resultant for these values of ϕ. It indicates that both the magnitude and orientation of the resultant vary with ϕ in a periodic way. The resultant rotates once when ϕ changes by 2π and, as it rotates, there is a gradual fluctuation in its magnitude. The changes may be expressed analytically by noting that the x and y co-ordinates of the end of the resultant are equal to ξ_x and ξ_y. Combining 12(2a) and 12(3), we see that these co-ordinates satisfy the relations

$$\frac{\xi_x^2}{a^2} + \frac{\xi_y^2}{b^2} = 1, \qquad \ldots \ldots \quad 12(4)$$

and
$$\tan \chi = \frac{\xi_y}{\xi_x} = \frac{b}{a} \tan \phi. \qquad \ldots \ldots \quad 12(5)$$

Equation 12(4) implies that the end of the resultant always lies on an ellipse. This type of light is called *elliptically polarized light*. When $a = b$, the ellipse becomes a circle, and the light is called *circularly polarized light*.

In understanding the properties of elliptically and circularly polarized light it is important to remember that ϕ may alter through a variation of t or of z. At any one place the resultant rotates and, in general, changes in magnitude with a time-period $2\pi/\omega$. The change in the magnitude of the resultant is not usually simple harmonic, but follows the variation of the radius vector of the ellipse. At any one time the direction of the resultant varies from point to point along the direction of propagation. It has a space-periodicity $\lambda = 2\pi/\kappa$. When z increases by λ, the vector makes a complete rotation, and the amplitude follows the variation of the radius vector of the ellipse given by 12(4). When the light is circularly polarized, the magnitude of the representative vector remains constant as the wave advances. The component (in any direction perpendicular to the direction of propagation) varies sinusoidally.

12.19.—So far we have considered only two special cases:

(i) $\epsilon = 0$

and (ii) $\epsilon = -\tfrac{1}{2}\pi$.

Before considering the general case, we may consider the cases

(iii) $\epsilon = \pi$

and (iv) $\epsilon = \tfrac{1}{2}\pi$.

§ 12.19 ELLIPTICALLY POLARIZED LIGHT 469

It is easily verified that when $\epsilon = \pi$, the resultant is a linear vibration in a plane whose angle with the xz plane is given by $\tan \chi = -b/a$. If $\epsilon = \tfrac{1}{2}\pi$, we have

$$\xi_y = -b \sin(\omega t - \kappa z), \quad \ldots \quad 12(6)$$

instead of 12(3). When 12(6) is combined with 12(2a), we again obtain equation 12(4), but equation 12(5) is replaced by

$$\tan \chi = \frac{\xi_y}{\xi_x} = -\frac{b}{a} \tan \phi. \quad \ldots \quad 12(7)$$

Thus the end of the vector, which represents the resultant, rotates round the ellipse when ϕ increases, but in a clockwise direction. This type of elliptically polarized light is known as right-handed, or positive elliptically polarized light—the type discussed in § 12.18 being called left-handed or negative. In right-handed elliptically or circularly polarized light, the representative vector at any given point rotates clockwise when viewed by an observer who receives the beam of light.

We shall now show that when ϵ has some value other than one of those considered so far, the resultant is still elliptically polarized light, but the axes of the representative ellipse are not coincident with OX and OY. We need to eliminate ϕ from equations 12(2) so as to obtain a relation between ξ_x and ξ_y which is independent of ϕ. We have, from 12(2a),

$$\frac{\xi_x}{a} = \cos \phi, \quad \ldots \quad 12(8)$$

and from 12(2b), $\quad \dfrac{\xi_y}{b} = \cos \phi \cos \epsilon - \sin \phi \sin \epsilon.$

Squaring, $\quad \dfrac{\xi_y^2}{b^2} - 2 \dfrac{\xi_y}{b} \cos \phi \cos \epsilon + \cos^2 \phi \cos^2 \epsilon = \sin^2 \phi \sin^2 \epsilon,$

and, substituting from 12(8), we obtain

$$\frac{\xi_y^2}{b^2} - 2 \frac{\xi_x \xi_y}{ab} \cos \epsilon + \frac{\xi_x^2}{a^2} \cos^2 \epsilon = \left(1 - \frac{\xi_x^2}{a^2}\right) \sin^2 \epsilon,$$

or $\quad \dfrac{\xi_x^2}{a^2} + \dfrac{\xi_y^2}{b^2} - 2 \dfrac{\xi_x \xi_y}{ab} \cos \epsilon - \sin^2 \epsilon = 0. \quad \ldots \quad 12(9)$

This is the equation of an ellipse for which one axis makes an angle ψ with the x axis, where ψ is given by

$$\tan 2\psi = \frac{2ab \cos \epsilon}{a^2 - b^2}. \quad \ldots \quad 12(10)$$

EXAMPLES [12(i)–12(vi)]

12(i). Suppose that the effective intensity of a source of light is reduced by the use of a polarizer and analyser whose relative orientation is θ. Show that the percentage error in the intensity due to an error $\Delta\theta$ in the setting is $-(200\tan\theta)\Delta\theta$.

12(ii). Using the data of the preceding example, show that if the scale of the analyser can be read to $0\cdot1°$, an accuracy of 1 per cent is obtainable for a setting which reduces the intensity in a ratio of approximately 1 : 10.

12(iii). Find the ratio of the relative energies of the beams O_1O_2 and O_1E_2 (see § 12.8) when the relative orientation of the two crystals is θ. [$\cot^2\theta$.]

12(iv). Show that if two coherent beams of circularly polarized light of equal amplitude (one left-handed and the other right-handed) are superposed, the resultant is plane-polarized. What determines the plane of polarization?

[The plane of polarization of the resultant contains the direction for which the components of the constituents are in phase.]

12(v). Show that the resultant of two coherent beams of elliptically polarized light is in general another beam of elliptically polarized light.

12(vi). Write down the conditions that the resultant of the preceding example shall be (a) plane-polarized, (b) circularly polarized.

[(a) The resultant components for any two directions of vibration must have the same phase.

(b) Taking any pair of axes at right angles, the resultant components must be of equal amplitude, with phases differing by $\frac{1}{2}\pi$.]

12.20. Huygens' Wave Surface in Crystals.

The phenomena of double refraction indicate that the velocity of propagation of a beam of light in a crystal depends on the relation between the direction of propagation and the crystal axes. Also for a given direction of propagation the velocity depends on the relation between the plane of polarization and the crystal axes. When double refraction was discovered by Bartolinus, Huygens saw that in order to apply his method of constructing rays (§ 3.8) to crystals, it was necessary to invent a special form of wave surface for crystals. Since there are two rays, it is necessary that the wave surface shall consist of two sheets. The observation that one ray always obeys both laws of refraction was taken to indicate that one sheet is a sphere. Huygens assumed, as the simplest available hypothesis, that the other sheet is an ellipsoid of revolution. He assumed that the spheroid touches the sphere either internally, as shown in fig. 12.14a, or externally, as shown in fig. 12.14b. In either case, the whole wave surface is formed by revolving the curves about the line which joins the points of contact. In the direction of this line there is only one speed of propagation, and this direction is called the *optic axis*. Huygens thought that

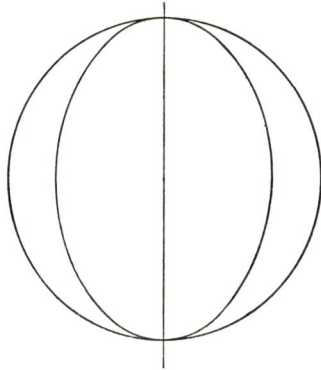

Fig. 12.14a.—Section of wave surface of positive uniaxial crystal

all crystals were uniaxial, and that this type of wave surface was universally applicable. Later, more extensive observations showed that the general form of the wave surface is more elaborate (fig. 16.6). It is still a surface of two sheets, but neither sheet is spherical, and the

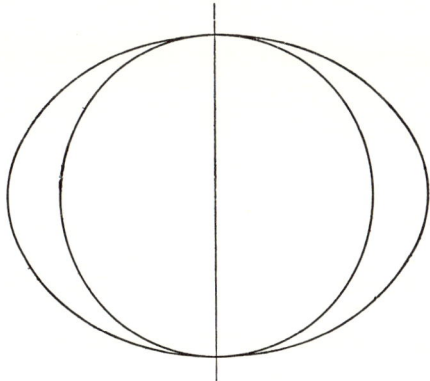

Fig. 12.14b.—Section of wave surface of negative uniaxial crystal

two sheets interpenetrate in a more complicated way. The most general type of crystal has two optic axes (i.e. two directions for which there is only one speed of propagation). The uniaxial crystal may be regarded as a special case in which the two axes coincide.

12.21. Verification of Huygens' Wave-surface for Uniaxial Crystals.

The form of the wave surface has been examined experimentally by Stokes, Glazebrook, and others, using modern instruments to measure the angles of refraction for different directions of incidence. The results show that for uniaxial crystals the part of the wave surface corresponding to the extraordinary ray is accurately an ellipsoid of revolution.

Earlier experiments mainly due to Malus are interesting. The following is a brief summary of these experiments.

(i) *To show that one sheet of the surface is spherical*, a composite prism is built up consisting of slices cut in different directions from a piece of calcite (fig. 12.15). There is one ordinary spectrum, the same for all slices, and a series of extraordinary spectra, most of which are deviated out of the plane of incidence. Measurements on the ordinary spectrum determine the value of the refractive index (μ_o) for any chosen wavelength.

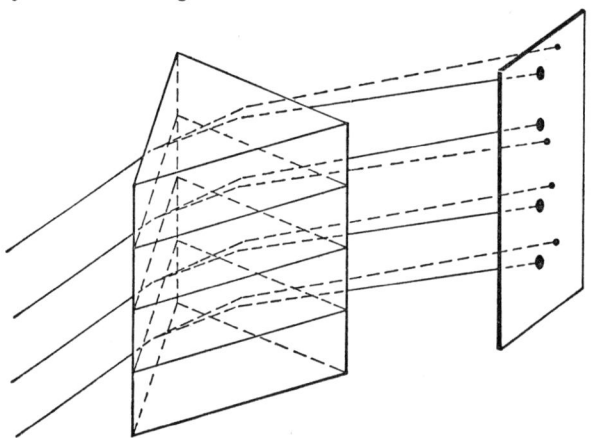

Fig. 12.15.—Refraction by composite calcite prism

(ii) *To show that one section of the other sheet is circular*, a crystal of calcite is cut so as to give a prism with its refracting edge parallel to the optic axis. Two spectra are obtained. They are both in the plane of incidence. One is polarized in the principal plane of the crystal, and the other in a perpendicular plane. For a given wavelength the index for the ordinary ray is found to be μ_o (as before), and a different index (μ_e) is found for the extraordinary ray. In this experiment the extraordinary ray obeys both the laws of refraction, and differs from the ordinary ray only in having a different index. This requires that the whole wave surface must be a surface of revolution. Fig. 12.16a shows Huygens' construction of the two refracted wavefronts.

Since both rays obey the sine law, measurements of the two critical angles for total reflection give μ_o and μ_e directly. These measurements may be made

§ 12.21 WAVE SURFACE FOR UNIAXIAL CRYSTALS   473

using a refractometer of the Abbe or Pulfrich type, with a polarizer attached. In this way, using monochromatic light, the indices may be conveniently measured with an accuracy of about 1 in 10^5 (i.e. to the fourth decimal place).

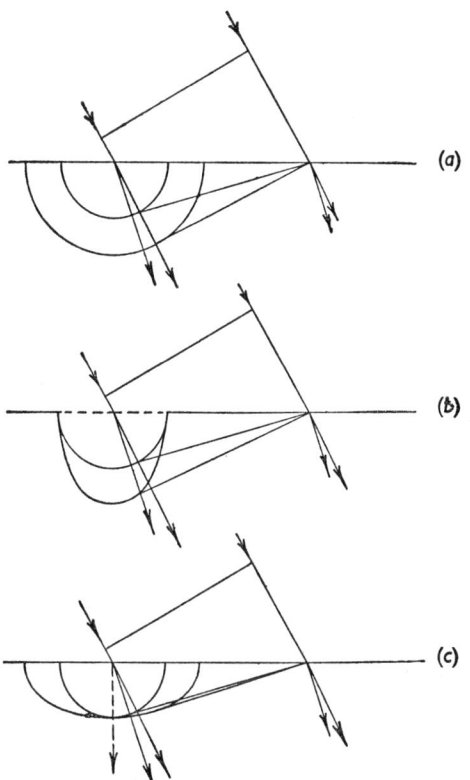

Fig. 12.16.—Huygens' construction

(a) Optic axis parallel to surface and perpendicular to plane of incidence.
(b) Optic axis parallel to surface and to plane of incidence.
(c) Optic axis normal to surface.

(The ellipticity of the second sheet of the wave surface has been exaggerated in order to show the construction more clearly. In calcite, the ratio of the axes of the ellipse is approximately 1·1 : 1.)

(iii) *To investigate the refraction when the optic axis is parallel to the face of the crystal and to the plane of incidence.* The apparatus is shown in fig. 12.17a. Two scales AB and AC are engraved on a piece of polished steel which forms a table on which the crystal is placed. The scales are observed through the telescope T, whose inclination to the vertical may be read on the scale P. The table is adjusted so that the faces of the crystal are horizontal. The crystal is turned so that the principal plane is perpendicular to AC. The line AC is then displaced in a direction perpendicular to itself. Suppose that the ordinary image of a point D on AC coincides with the extraordinary image of a point E on AB. Then, if e is the thickness of the crystal,

$$DE = e(\tan r_e - \tan r_o),$$

where r_e is the angle of refraction for the extraordinary ray, and r_o is the angle of refraction for the ordinary ray. r_o may be derived by measuring the angle of incidence on the scale P, and using the relation $\sin i = \mu_o \sin r_o$. DE may be measured and used to give r_e, when r_o and e are known. It is found that, for dif-

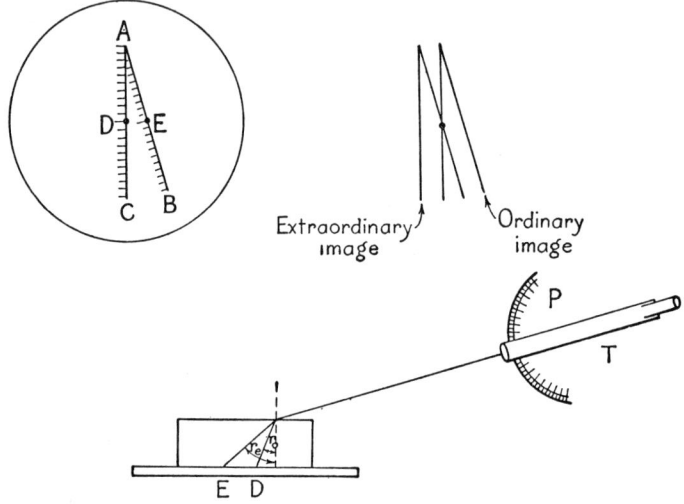

Fig. 12.17a.—Apparatus for the investigation of the shape of the wave surface

ferent values of the angle i, the ratio $\tan r_e/\tan r_o$ is constant and is equal to μ_e/μ_o. Huygens' construction for this case is shown in fig. 12.16b. From the coordinate geometry of the figure it may be shown that the above relation between r_e and r_o is consistent with the assumption that the section of the two sheets of the wave surface is made up of a circle and an ellipse, which touch at two points in the way shown [see answer to Example 12(viii), p. 479].

12.22. Transmission of Polarized Light in a Thin Anisotropic Plate.

Suppose that a parallel beam of plane-polarized light is incident normally upon a thin anisotropic plate, and the relation between the plane of polarization and the crystal axis is varied by rotating the crystal about a line normal to its surface. It is found, in general, that there are two orientations in which the emergent light is plane-polarized. If the crystal does not possess the property of optical rotation (which will be considered in § 12.35), the plane of polarization of the emergent beam is the same as that of the incident beam. Two lines may be drawn on the plate (or on its mount) showing the directions in which the plane of polarization cuts the plate when the orientation is such that the emergent light is plane-polarized. The directions of these lines are called the two *privileged directions* for the given anisotropic plate. It is found that they are always perpendicular to one another.

We have seen in § 12.20 that relations of this type hold for uniaxial crystals like calcite. Further experiments show that similar results are obtained, in general, for a slice cut from any crystal in any orientation. The reason why there are two, and only two, privileged directions is that the wave surface is a surface of two sheets. In simple uniaxial crystals there is one direction (the optic axis) in which a plane-polarized beam is transmitted as a plane-polarized beam, no matter how the plane of polarization is orientated. In this direction there is only one velocity of wave propagation. A slice cut normal to the optic axis has no specially privileged directions. More complicated effects are obtained with " optically active " crystals (§ 12.37).

12.23.—The optical thickness of an anisotropic plate may be measured with an interferometer, using light plane-polarized in different planes. A simple result is obtained only when the plane of polarization is parallel to one of the privileged directions. It is found that the optical thickness for light polarized parallel to one privileged direction is greater than the optical thickness for light polarized parallel to the other privileged direction. This implies a difference in wave velocity, as we should expect from the form of Huygens' wave surface. The privileged direction corresponding to the larger velocity (and the lower refractive index) is called the *fast direction*. The other is called the *slow direction*. Let us now consider a beam of plane-polarized light, the direction of whose plane of polarization does not coincide with either of the privileged directions. We have seen above (§ 12.6) that when this is so there are two emergent beams which are parallel to one another, but displaced in a direction perpendicular to the direction of propagation. We now suppose that the anisotropic plate is so thin that the displacement sideways may be ignored. We should then expect that elliptically or circularly polarized light would be produced by the superposition of the two emergent beams which have travelled through the plate at different speeds, and have thus acquired a phase difference. We shall show, in the next paragraph, that this is so.

12.24.—Let us choose the fast and slow directions respectively as the OX and OY directions of a system of co-ordinate axes. Then OZ is the direction of propagation. The surface on which the light is

incident may be taken as the XOY plane. The incident beam may then be represented by
$$\xi_0 = a \cos \omega t. \qquad \ldots \ldots \quad 12(11)$$
If the plane of polarization makes an angle ψ with OX, the components ξ_x and ξ_y (polarized parallel to OY and OX respectively) may be represented by*
$$\xi_{x0} = a \sin \psi \cos \omega t \qquad \ldots \ldots \quad 12(12)$$
and
$$\xi_{y0} = a \cos \psi \cos \omega t. \qquad \ldots \ldots \quad 12(13)$$

After the light has passed through a thickness z of the plate, the components are
$$\xi_x = a \sin \psi \cos \omega(t - z/b_1) \qquad \ldots \quad 12(14)$$
and
$$\xi_y = a \cos \psi \cos \omega(t - z/b_2), \qquad \ldots \quad 12(15)$$
where b_1 and b_2 are the fast and slow velocities of propagation.

In writing equations 12(14) and 12(15) we assume that propagation is normal to the plate. This is not strictly correct. In general, neither beam travels normally to the slice, and the two directions are not identical.† We should insert $b_1 \cos \alpha_1$ for b_1, and $b_2 \cos \alpha_2$ for b_2, where α_1 and α_2 are the deviations of the two beams from the normal. Thus b_1 and b_2 are not two velocities in the same direction. In practice the values of α_1 and α_2 are fairly small and, for our present purpose, it is a sufficient approximation to assume that b_1 and b_2 are the velocities in the direction normal to the slice.

If the thickness of the crystal is e, the two components will emerge with a phase difference (ϵ_p) given by
$$\epsilon_p = \omega e \left(\frac{1}{b_2} - \frac{1}{b_1} \right) = \frac{\omega e}{c} (\mu_2 - \mu_1)$$
$$= \frac{2\pi e}{\lambda} (\mu_2 - \mu_1). \quad \ldots \quad 12(16)$$

In this expression λ is the wavelength in air. The emergent beams are represented by
$$\xi_x = A \cos (\omega t - \kappa z - \delta) \qquad \ldots \ldots \quad 12(17)$$
and
$$\xi_y = B \cos (\omega t - \kappa z - \delta - \epsilon_p), \quad \ldots \quad 12(18)$$
where
$$A = a \sin \psi, \quad B = a \cos \psi, \qquad \ldots \ldots \quad 12(19)$$
and
$$\delta = \frac{\omega}{b_1} e. \qquad \ldots \ldots \ldots \quad 12(20)$$

---

* Remember that the plane of the vector represented by ξ_0 is at right angles to the plane of polarization.

† In *uniaxial* crystals, the ordinary beam is normal to the slice.

§ 12.25 QUARTER-WAVE PLATE

We may alter the origin of time so as to eliminate δ, and 12(17) and 12(18) are then replaced by

$$\xi_x = A \cos(\omega t - \kappa z), \quad \ldots \ldots \quad 12(21a)$$
$$\xi_y = B \cos(\omega t - \kappa z - \epsilon_p). \quad \ldots \quad 12(21b)$$

The form of these equations is the same as that of equations 12(2a) and 12(2b). It indicates that, in general, the emergent light is elliptically polarized. Under special conditions the ellipse may reduce to a circle or a straight line.

12.25. Quarter-wave Plate.

An anisotropic plate for which the difference of optical thickness is a quarter of a wavelength is called a quarter-wave plate. A plate of this thickness introduces a phase difference of $\frac{1}{2}\pi$. A plate which gives a phase difference of π between the two components is called a half-wave plate, and a similar notation is applied to plates of other thicknesses. When plane-polarized light is incident upon an anisotropic plate the state of polarization in the emergent light depends upon (a) the difference of optical thickness, and (b) the relation between the plane of polarization of the light and the privileged directions of the plate. The calculations for any given condition may be made using equations 12(16), 12(19), 12(21a) and 12(21b). The following cases are of special importance:

(i) When plane-polarized light is incident upon a whole-wave plate, the emergent light is plane-polarized in the same plane as the incident light.

(ii) When plane-polarized light is incident upon a half-wave plate, the emergent light is plane-polarized. If the plane of polarization of the incident light makes an angle ψ with one of the privileged directions, then the plane of polarization of the emergent beam makes an angle $-\psi$ with the same direction, i.e. the plane has effectively been rotated through an angle 2ψ (fig. 12.17b, p. 478).

(iii) When plane-polarized light is incident upon a quarter-wave plate, the emergent light is in general elliptically polarized. The axes of the ellipse are parallel to the privileged directions in the plate, and the ratio of the axes is given by 12(19). When the plane of polarization of the incident beam bisects the angle between the privileged directions, the light emerging from a quarter-wave plate is circularly polarized.

All the above properties depend on the *difference* of the optical thicknesses of the plate. It is of interest to consider the state of the vibration inside the crystal. From equations 12(14) and 12(15) we see that if we choose a definite value of z (i.e. if we consider a particular place in the crystal), the disturbance at that point is similar to the disturbance produced by a definite type of polarized light in an isotropic medium, i.e. the disturbance is the resultant of two vectors with

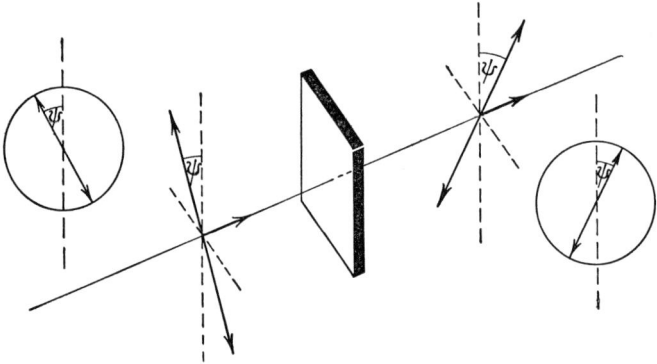

Fig. 12.17b.—" Rotation " of the plane of polarization by a half-wave plate

a constant phase difference. Thus at one point the disturbance may be that of elliptically polarized light, and at another it may correspond to plane-polarized light. The *progression* of a disturbance in an anisotropic medium is not similar to that of any kind of light in an isotropic medium. In the anisotropic medium the phase difference between the components, and hence the state of the polarization, changes as the wave advances.

12.26. Two or more Plates in Series.

From the above discussion we should expect that the effects of transmission through two similarly oriented plates would be additive. This is found to be so. For example, if two quarter-wave plates are superimposed so that the " fast " directions coincide, the effect is exactly the same as that of a half-wave plate. If the two quarter-wave plates are superimposed so that the fast direction of one coincides with the slow direction of the other, then the total optical path is the same for both components. The plates have no effect on the state of polarization of the incident light. Generally the effects of thin plates which are superimposed so that the privileged directions coincide are algebraically additive. When the privileged directions do not coincide, the effect of each plate must be calculated successively. The resultant state of polarization produced by the first plate is calculated in the way described above. It is then regarded as a beam incident on the second plate and is resolved in two new directions (i.e. the privileged directions of the second plate).

EXAMPLES [12(vii)–12(xiv)]

12(vii). A narrow beam of light enters a crystal of monammonium phosphate at grazing incidence in a direction at right angles to the optic axis, which is parallel to the surface of the crystal. The separation of the ordinary and extraordinary beams at the opposite, parallel face of the crystal is 2·5 mm. If $\mu_o = 1\cdot525$ and $\mu_e = 1\cdot479$, calculate the thickness of the crystal. [5·1 cm.]

12(viii). Show that when an ellipse and circle touch as shown in fig. 12.14b, a line joining the points of contact of the tangent to the ellipse and the circle from a point on the common axis is perpendicular to this axis. Hence show that $\tan r_e/\tan r_o = \mu_e/\mu_o$.

12(ix). A uniaxial crystal is cut so that the optic axis is perpendicular to the refracting surface (fig. 12.16c). Show that the refracted rays and the optic axis are in the same plane, and that
$$\tan r_e = \frac{\mu_o \sin i}{\mu_e \sqrt{(\mu_e^2 - \sin^2 i)}}.$$
How would you test this relation experimentally?

12(x). Show that circularly polarized light may be produced with a three-quarter-wave plate, and also with certain plates of greater thickness.

12(xi). How may a quarter-wave plate be made to produce (a) right-handed and (b) left-handed circularly polarized light?

[Suppose the slow direction of the quarter-wave plate to be in the direction OX, and the fast direction along OY, the direction of propagation of the light being the positive direction of OZ. Then, if plane-polarized light, whose vibration direction is at $+\pi/4$ to the OX direction, is incident on the plate, the transmitted light is right-handed circularly polarized.]

12(xii). Design an arrangement to produce a vertical beam of elliptically polarized green light. The axes of the ellipse are to be in the ratio 3 : 1, and the direction of the larger axis to be north-south.

[A mercury lamp with green filter directs a beam vertically through a polarizing prism set to transmit light polarized in a plane making an angle $\cot^{-1} 3$ with the N-S direction. The light is then passed through a quarter-wave plate whose fast and slow directions are N-S and E-W respectively.]

12(xiii). How may an anisotropic plate be made to change a right-handed elliptically polarized beam of light into a left-handed beam?

[Use a half-wave plate suitably oriented. In the special case of circularly polarized light the orientation does not matter.]

12(xiv). Two plates of thicknesses e_1 and e_2 are put together so that the fast direction of one coincides with the slow direction of the other. They are of different materials. The refractive indices are μ_1 and μ_1' for the fast and slow directions respectively in plate 1, and μ_2 and μ_2' for plate 2. Given that the first plate is a whole-wave plate, that the combination acts as a quarter-wave plate, and that $e_1 = 2e_2$, derive a relation between the refractive indices.

$$[5(\mu_1 - \mu_1') \text{ or } 3(\mu_1 - \mu_1') = 2(\mu_2 - \mu_2').]$$

12.27. Analysis of Polarized Light.

The additive property may be used in the detection and analysis of circularly and elliptically polarized light. Consider, for example, a method for distinguishing between ordinary light and circularly polarized light. If a Nicol prism is placed in the beam and rotated, both these kinds of light behave in the same way. The amount of light transmitted is the same for all orientations of the analyser. If the beam is first passed through a quarter-wave plate and then through an analyser, the situation is quite different. The quarter-wave plate will change the circularly polarized light into plane-polarized light, which is extinguished at a suitable setting of the analyser. If, however, ordinary light is transmitted through a quarter-wave plate and an analyser, the amount of light transmitted is the same for all orientations. Similar methods may be used to distinguish between elliptically and plane-polarized light.

12.28.—In Chapter IV it was shown that a beam of light which has one definite wavelength must be represented by an infinite wave-train. An extension of the discussion shows that *a beam which has one definite wavelength must be completely polarized*. If the disturbance is not represented by a vector in one plane, it must be represented as the resultant of two vectors in two perpendicular planes. The variation of each of these vectors must be represented by an expression of simple harmonic form. The two expressions must be valid from $-\infty$ to $+\infty$. There must therefore be a permanent phase-relation between them, and the resultant is plane-polarized if the phase difference is a multiple of π. Otherwise the resultant is elliptically or circularly polarized.

Let us imagine that we have a source of light with very small damping which emits wave trains of different polarizations, so that one train lasts for a period of order 100 seconds (i.e. much longer than the trains given by laboratory sources). Suppose that the resultant of a number of these wave trains is analysed by an apparatus which displays the polarization ellipse on the screen of a cathode-ray tube. A "snapshot" of the screen will, in general, show an ellipse. An observer who watches the screen will see the parameters of the ellipse slowly change as some wave trains die out, and new ones begin. These variations will be completely irregular in the sense that no observation of the process will lead to any rational prediction of the detailed course of future alterations.

Now suppose that the wave trains become shorter and shorter. The observer will notice the irregular variations becoming more rapid and, when the average length of a wave train is of the order 10^{-2} second, or shorter,* he can observe only a general illumination covering a circular area whose boundary is the envelope of all the ellipses previously observed. The observer will see a steady pattern on the screen if, and only if, the wave trains emitted by the atoms are all polarized in the same way. When this condition is satisfied we have coherence between the components polarized in perpendicular planes, even though the wave trains are not infinitely long.

12.29.—The fact that beams of unpolarized light can produce interference fringes is in agreement with the above analysis. If unpolarized light is resolved into two components, each will form its set of interference fringes separately. When the path lies entirely in isotropic media, the two sets of fringes will coincide. The *average* illumination at any point is equally divided between the components. If the path lies partly in a doubly refracting medium, then the two fringe systems may no longer be superimposed and may confuse one another.

12.30. The Stokes Parameters.

Suppose that a beam of elliptically polarized light is such that it may be regarded as the resultant of two coherent plane-polarized vibrations with amplitudes a along OX and b along OY and a constant phase difference ϵ. The following quantities are known as the Stokes parameters:

$$\left. \begin{array}{ll} S_0 = \overline{a^2} + \overline{b^2} & S_1 = \overline{a^2} - \overline{b^2} \\ S_2 = 2\,\overline{ab \cos \epsilon} & S_3 = 2\,\overline{ab \sin \epsilon} \end{array} \right\} \quad . \quad . \quad 12(22)$$

If the light is strictly monochromatic, a, b and ϵ are constant (so that the mean values $\bar{a}$, etc., are equal to the constant values), but if the light is polarized, but not monochromatic, a and b may vary together, ϵ remaining constant (see § 12.31) so that the two components are mutually coherent (see §§ 5.1–5.8 and Appendix V A). In either case we have, *for polarized light*,

$$S_0^2 = S_1^2 + S_2^2 + S_3^2. \quad . \quad . \quad . \quad 12(23)$$

S_0 is equal to the relative energy of the beam.

12.31. The Poincaré Sphere—Representation of Polarized Light.

Let ψ be the angle between one axis of the ellipse and OX and $\tan \chi = \pm b/a$, $(-\pi/4 < \chi < \pi/4)$, the positive sign being associated with left-handed and the negative with right-handed elliptically polarized light. Combining 12(10) with 12(22) we obtain:

---

* The wave trains which represent light are much shorter (of order 10^{-7} second or less).

482   POLARIZED LIGHT

$$S_1 = S_0 \cos 2\chi \cos 2\psi, \qquad \ldots \ldots 12(24a)$$
$$S_2 = S_0 \cos 2\chi \sin 2\psi, \qquad \ldots \ldots 12(24b)$$
$$S_3 = S_0 \sin 2\chi. \qquad \ldots \ldots \ldots 12(24c)$$

This implies that S_1, S_2, S_3 are the Cartesian co-ordinates of a point P on a sphere of radius S_0, the spherical co-ordinates of P being 2χ and 2ψ (see fig. 12.18a). For circularly polarized light $\bar{a} = \bar{b}$ and $\epsilon = \pm \pi/2$, so that right-handed circularly polarized light is represented by the north pole and left-handed by the south. Plane-polarized light ($\delta = 0$) is represented by points on the equator ($S_3 = 0$). The sphere (which is known as the *Poincaré sphere*) is useful for certain kinds of calculations on polarized light.*

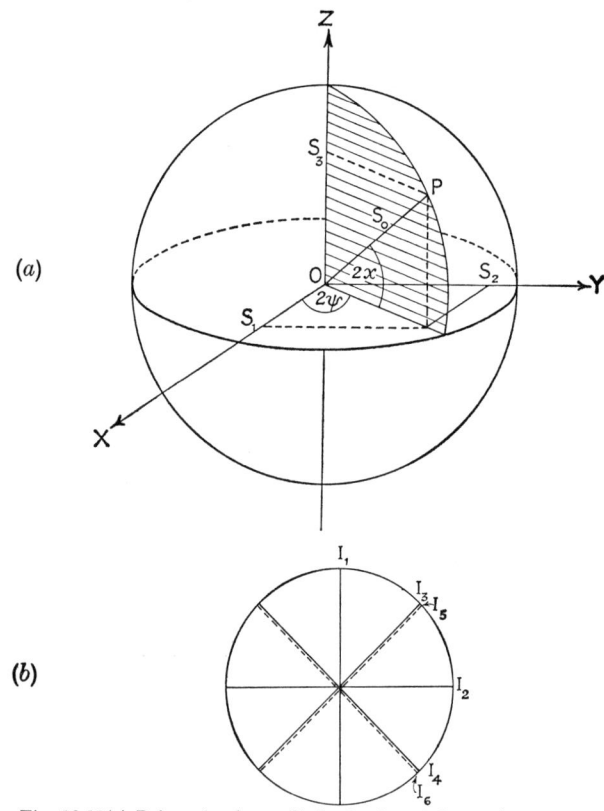

Fig. 12.18(a) Poincaré sphere, (b) I_1, I_2, I_3 and I_4 are the amounts of light transmitted when a Nicol prism is oriented as shown. I_5 and I_6 are obtained when the Nicol follows a quarter-wave plate which produces a phase difference of $\pi/2$ between horizontal and vertical directions.

* See Reference 12.10 and pp. 30 and 550 of Reference 5.8.

12.32. Representation of Unpolarized Light.

12.32.—In representing unpolarized light we have to take into account three experimental results:

(i) The illumination produced by resolution in any plane (e.g. with a Nicol) is independent of the orientation of the plane of resolution.

(ii) This property is unaffected by previous relative retardation of any rectangular components into which the light may have been resolved (i.e. if the beam is passed first through a thin crystalline plate and then through a Nicol, the amount of light transmitted is independent of the orientation either of the plate or of the Nicol).

(iii) Interference fringes can be produced with unpolarized light.

Applying equations 12(22) we see that these experimental results imply that for unpolarized light $S_1 = S_2 = S_3 = 0$. For a mixture of polarized and unpolarized light

$$S_0^2 > S_1^2 + S_2^2 + S_3^2. \qquad \ldots \quad 12(25a)$$

Such a mixture may always be split into two parts, one of energy $S_0 - S_0'$ which is unpolarized and one of energy S_0' (where $(S_0')^2 = S_1^2 + S_2^2 + S_3^2$) which is polarized. The latter part may be analysed to give the axes of the ellipse (and their orientation) by using equation 12(10). The Stokes parameters may be determined by measuring the light transmitted by a Nicol prism in the six conditions indicated in fig. 12.18b. Then

$$S_0 = I_1 + I_2; \quad S_1 = I_1 - I_2; \quad S_2 = I_3 - I_4, \quad S_3 = I_5 - I_6. \qquad 12(25b)$$

In practice the accurate quantitative analysis of polarized light is carried out by methods which involve judgments of equality in bipartite fields (see § 12.46).

EXAMPLES [12(xv) and 12(xvi)]

12(xv). How may a Nicol prism and a quarter-wave plate be used to distinguish between right- and left-handed circularly polarized light?
[See answer to Ex. 12(xi), p. 479.]

12(xvi). How may the procedure of § 12.27 be used to derive the proportion of unpolarized light in a mixture of right-handed circularly polarized light and unpolarized light.
[Insert a quarter-wave plate, and compare the maximum and minimum amounts of light transmitted by a rotating analyser.]

12.33. The Babinet Compensator.

The method of § 12.27 may be developed into a general analysis of polarized light. More sensitive tests, some based upon colour effects which will be described later, have been devised for the detection of a small proportion of polarized light in a mixture. Special pieces of apparatus have also been invented for more accurate and convenient measurements on elliptically polarized light. The most generally useful of these is the *Babinet compensator*.* This consists of two quartz wedges cut in different directions and oriented as shown in fig. 12.19a. The arrangement is similar to the Rochon prism but in the compensator the angles of the wedges are so fine that there is no effective separation of the rays. The lower wedge can be moved relative to the frame (in which the upper is held) by means of a micrometer screw, so as to alter the total thickness. The difference of optical path in the compensator varies linearly from one side to the other. The central difference of path can be altered by a known amount by turning the screw. The compensator is used in conjunction with a Nicol prism or a piece of Polaroid film as an analyser. It is viewed through a low-power microscope.

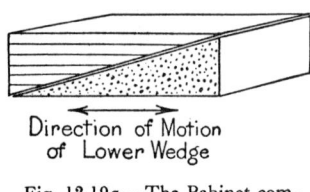

Fig. 12.19a.—The Babinet compensator

12.34.—The compensator is first calibrated using plane-polarized light produced by a polarizing prism. The analyser and polarizer are crossed, and the compensator is placed between them, oriented so that the plane of the analyser bisects the angle between the privileged directions for the wedges (see fig. 12.19b). A series of dark bands is seen in the field of the microscope. These correspond to points at which the phase difference introduced by the two wedges is equal to a multiple of 2π. For these points the emergent light is plane-polarized in the plane of the incident light, and is extinguished by the analyser. For points half-way between these points, the light is plane-polarized in a plane perpendicular to that of the incident light. For points intermediate between the positions where the emergent light is plane-polarized, it is elliptically polarized. If the analyser is rotated, the fringes at first become less clear, and then they become clear again, but the bright and dark bands are found to have changed places. The movement of the screw needed to bring successive fringes under the crosswire of the microscope (and hence to alter the phase difference at the centre by 2π) is measured. Let this distance be d. Now

---

* For a general description of other types of compensator, often of greater sensitivity but of more limited application, see Reference 12.6.

suppose that, still using plane-polarized light, the instrument is first adjusted so that a dark band is seen in the centre, and then the micrometer screw is turned through a distance $\frac{1}{4}d$. The phase difference produced at the centre is then equal to $(2n\pi \pm \frac{1}{2}\pi)$. For our purposes this is equivalent to a phase difference of $\frac{1}{2}\pi$. The polarizer is removed and the unknown beam of elliptically polarized light is admitted. The compensator and analyser are rotated independently

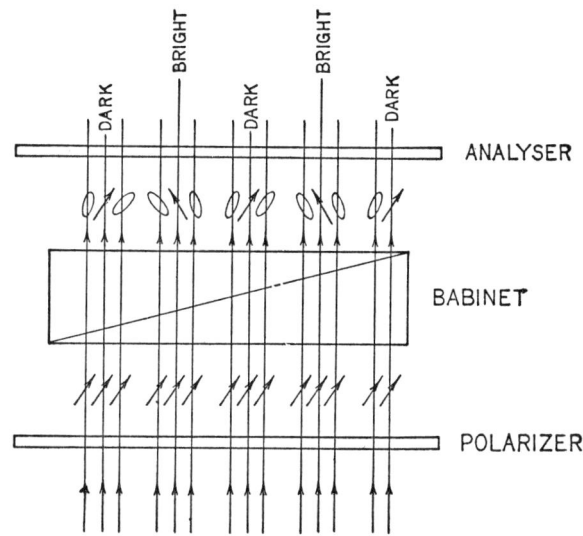

Fig. 12.19b.—The formation of dark bands with the Babinet compensator between crossed Nicols

until the centre of a dark band again appears under the central crosswire. The emergent light at the centre of the analyser must now be plane-polarized. Since the compensator introduces a phase difference of $\frac{1}{2}\pi$ at this point, the axes of the ellipse must be parallel to the privileged directions of the compensator. This determines the directions of the axes of the ellipse.

To determine the ratio of the axes, the analyser is rotated until the bands are as clear as possible, with the centre band dark. The analyser is now oriented perpendicular to the direction of the resultant of the two components of the elliptic vibration whose phase difference has been compensated. The tangent of the angle which the analyser now makes with the principal directions of the compensator is therefore equal to the ratio of the axes of the ellipse.

12.35. Rotatory Polarization.

When a beam of plane-polarized light passes through certain substances, the light remains plane-polarized but the plane of polarization is gradually rotated. This property is possessed by quartz and some other crystalline substances, and also by some liquids and vapours. The liquids include certain oils, such as turpentine, and solutions of certain substances, especially the sugars. These substances are said to be *optically active*. For solutions, the rotation is proportional to the concentration, as well as to the length of path. It is thus proportional to the number of molecules in the line of sight. This property is called *natural rotation* and must be distinguished from *magnetic rotation* (§ 16.50).

Natural rotation may be in either sense. A right-handed rotation (also called a positive rotation) is clockwise to an observer looking in the direction in which the light is travelling. Substances which give a right-handed rotation are called *dextro-rotatory*, those which give a left-handed rotation are *laevo-rotatory*. The *specific rotation* of a solution is equal to the rotation produced by a column 10 centimetres long, divided by the concentration of the active substance. The concentration is expressed in grammes of active substance per cubic centimetre of the solution.

The *molecular rotation* is the specific rotation multiplied by the molecular weight.

The following figures show the order of magnitude of the effects:

Rotation of a 10-cm. column of a solution of cane sugar (0·1 gm. per cc. of solution) = 6·67°.

Rotation of a 10-cm. column of essence of turpentine = −29·6°.

Rotation of a piece of quartz 1 mm. thick = ±21·7°.

12.36.—In the vector representation, a beam of plane-polarized light may be regarded as the resultant of two equal beams of circularly polarized light, one right-handed and the other left-handed. Let the right-handed beam have components

$$\xi_{xr} = -a \cos \omega(t - z/b) = -a \cos \phi \quad . \quad . \quad 12(26)$$

and
$$\xi_{yr} = a \sin \omega(t - z/b) = a \sin \phi. \quad . \quad . \quad 12(27)$$

§ 12.36   ROTATORY POLARIZATION

Let the left-handed beam have components

$$\xi_{xl} = a \cos \omega(t - z/b) = a \cos \phi \quad \ldots \quad 12(28)$$

and
$$\xi_{yl} = a \sin \omega(t - z/b) = a \sin \phi. \quad \ldots \quad 12(29)$$

Then the resultant is plane-polarized. The plane of polarization is the xz plane, the representative vector

$$\xi = 2a \sin \omega(t - z/b) = 2a \sin \phi \quad \ldots \quad 12(30)$$

being in the yz plane.

The phenomenon of optical rotation may be included in the vector representation by assuming that, in optically active media, circularly polarized light is transmitted unchanged, but the velocity of left-handed circularly polarized light is not the same as that of right-handed circularly polarized light. After the light has travelled through a distance e of the optically active medium, the two components have a phase difference (ϵ_e) given by

$$\epsilon_e = \omega e \left(\frac{1}{b_r} - \frac{1}{b_l} \right) = \frac{2\pi e}{\lambda} (\mu_r - \mu_l), \quad \ldots \quad 12(31)$$

where b_l and b_r are the speeds for the left-handed and right-handed components respectively; μ_l and μ_r are the corresponding indices and λ is the wavelength in air. The light after emerging, at $z = 0$, from the optically active material is represented by

$$\left. \begin{array}{l} \xi_{xr}' = -a \cos \phi', \\ \xi_{yr}' = a \sin \phi', \\ \xi_{xl}' = a \cos (\phi' + \epsilon_e), \\ \xi_{yl}' = a \sin (\phi' + \epsilon_e), \end{array} \right\} \quad \ldots \quad 12(32)$$

where
$$\phi' = \omega \left(t - \frac{e}{b_r} - \frac{z}{c} \right), \quad \ldots \quad 12(33)$$

and the resultant has plane-polarized components in the xz and yz planes given by

$$\left. \begin{array}{l} \xi_x = -a \cos \phi' + a \cos (\phi' + \epsilon_e) = 2a \sin \tfrac{1}{2}\epsilon_e \sin (\phi' + \tfrac{1}{2}\epsilon_e), \\ \xi_y = a \sin \phi' + a \sin (\phi' + \epsilon_e) = 2a \cos \tfrac{1}{2}\epsilon_e \sin (\phi' + \tfrac{1}{2}\epsilon_e). \end{array} \right\} \quad 12(34)$$

These two components are in phase, and the resultant is a vibration in a plane making an angle ψ with the yz plane, where

$$\tan \psi = \frac{\xi_x}{\xi_y} = \tan \tfrac{1}{2}\epsilon_e. \quad \ldots \quad 12(35)$$

Thus the plane of polarization has been rotated through an angle

$$\psi = \tfrac{1}{2}\epsilon_c = \frac{\pi e}{\lambda}(\mu_r - \mu_l). \quad \ldots \quad 12(36)$$

This angle is proportional to e, and to the difference of the refractive indices for the two circularly polarized components.

Fresnel demonstrated the above difference of refraction directly. He used right-handed and left-handed quartz prisms as shown in fig. 12.20. Owing to the difference of refractive index the light is split into two beams, one right-handed circularly polarized, and the other left-handed. This phenomenon is called *allogyric birefringence*. If the incident light is unpolarized, the two beams have no permanent phase-relation, and can never be brought to interference. If the incident light is plane-polarized, the two emergent beams are coherent. If, by the use of suitable quarter-wave plates, they are both transformed into plane-polarized light (with the same plane of polarization) they may be made to interfere.

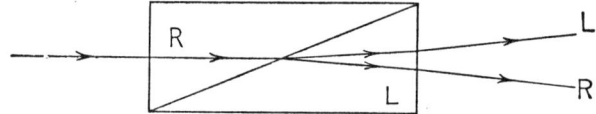

Fig. 12.20.—Fresnel's demonstration of allogyric birefringence

12.37.—Solutions of sugars and similar liquids are optically active, but isotropic. There is only allogyric birefringence and no birefringence of the ordinary kind obtained with calcite. In substances like quartz, optical activity is associated with ordinary birefringence. We have seen that a plate of inactive crystal transmits unchanged light travelling normal to the slice and polarized in one of two planes. Plane-polarized light with any orientation of the polarization is transmitted along the axis. In an active (but isotropic) substance like a sugar solution, circularly polarized light is transmitted unchanged. In quartz, circularly polarized light is transmitted unchanged when the wave normal is in the direction of the optic axis. For a direction inclined to the optic axis, only elliptically polarized light is transmitted unchanged, and for a given direction only two particular kinds of elliptically polarized light. The two ellipses are similar to one another in the orientation of the axes, and in the ratio of the minor to the major axis, but have opposite senses of rotation. The ellipses become circles for one particular direction of the wave normal (i.e. the optic axis), and shrink into lines for one other direction. In this direction (56° 10′ to the optic axis) plane-polarized light is transmitted unchanged. In quartz, the whole phenomenon is symmetrical about the single optic axis. Much more complicated effects are obtained when a biaxial crystal is also optically active.*

* Reference 12.2.

12.38. Dispersion of Birefringence and Optical Rotation.

All methods of producing and analysing polarized light are to some extent affected by dispersion, though in some experiments the effect is much more important than in others. The polarization of light by reflection is affected since the Brewsterian angle is a function of the index of the reflecting medium. It is not, however, a rapidly varying function of the index, and the light incident at angles near the Brewsterian angle has a very high degree of polarization (§ 14.9). Consequently, if a parallel beam of white light is incident upon a sheet of glass at the correct Brewsterian angle for a wavelength near the middle of the spectrum, the whole reflected beam is very nearly completely polarized. If it is examined with an analyser, only slight colour effects can be observed. The effects of dispersion are shown much more strongly in connection with the transmission of polarized light through thin anisotropic plates.

12.39.—Suppose that a parallel beam of white light passes through a polarizer, a plate of quartz cut perpendicular to the optic axis, and an analyser (fig. 12.21). Owing to the effects of dispersion, the rotation decreases as the wavelength increases. For certain wavelengths the rotation will be such that the light emerging from the crystal is not transmitted by the analyser. For intermediate wavelengths, some

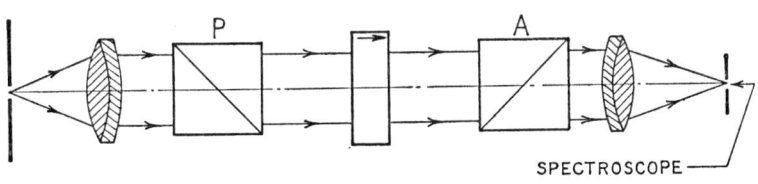

Fig. 12.21.—Apparatus for the investigation of the dispersion of optical rotation

light will be transmitted. If the light from the analyser is examined in a spectroscope, a channelled spectrum is seen. The total rotation will vary rapidly with wavelength when the plate is thick, giving a large number of close bands. When the plate is thin, there will be a small number of broad bands. The light transmitted by a fairly thin plate has a colour which depends upon its thickness, and upon the relative orientation of the analyser and polarizer. Suppose, for example, that the analyser and polarizer are crossed, and the thickness of the plate is such that a rotation of $5\pi/2$ is obtained for wavelength 5500 Å., and rotations of 2π and 3π for wavelengths 6900 Å. and

4600 Å. Then the transmitted light is green in hue.* If the analyser is rotated to the parallel position, a purple hue is obtained. When the plate is extremely thin, the total rotation is small, and its variation with wavelength is negligible. The transmitted light is then nearly white. Neither are colours obtained when the plate is very thick, because the spectrum then contains a large number of equally spaced bands, and the same fraction of each region of the spectrum is transmitted.

12.40.—The rotation (ψ) would be independent of wavelength if ϵ_c were independent of wavelength. From 12(36), we see that this would require the difference of refractive indices ($\mu_r - \mu_l$) to be proportional to the wavelength. This condition is not usually fulfilled.

Let α be the angle through which it would be necessary to rotate the polarizer *in the direction of the rotation of the optically active substance*, in order to make it parallel to the analyser. Then the amount of light transmitted is a maximum at a wavelength for which

$$\psi(\lambda) = n\pi + \alpha, \quad \ldots \ldots \quad 12(37)$$

and a minimum when

$$\psi(\lambda) = \tfrac{1}{2}(2n+1)\pi + \alpha. \quad \ldots \ldots \quad 12(38)$$

EXAMPLES [12(xvii)–12(xxi)]

12(xvii). A Babinet compensator is adjusted and used according to the method suggested in § 12.34. What would you expect to observe if the " unknown " beam happened to be circularly polarized?

[In the initial setting the cross wire would be at the centre either of a bright fringe or of a dark fringe. (For the reason why there are two possibilities, see examples 12(xv) and 12(xi)). Rotation of analyser and compensator, as one unit, does not affect the fringes. Rotation of analyser alone causes the fringes to change in visibility. For four orientations they disappear and, when they reappear, the dark fringe has been replaced by a bright fringe. The clearest fringes are obtained when the analyser is at $\pi/4$ to the privileged directions of the compensator.]

12(xviii). Using a plate of quartz 4·374 cm. thick, placed between crossed Nicols, dark bands were observed at wavelengths 5990, 5510, 5130, 4820, 4560, 4340 Å. Assuming that the rotation for the sodium D line ($\lambda = 5893$ Å.) is 21·34

---

* Every beam of light can be regarded as the sum or difference of a certain amount of white light, plus light of a given wavelength. This wavelength defines the hue. White light, plus light of a certain hue, is complementary to white light, minus light of the same hue. For a detailed account of colour nomenclature see Reference 12.7.

§ 12.41   COLOURS OF THIN PLATES   491

degrees per millimetre, and using the above results, plot a curve showing the variation of rotation with wavelength. Show that the rotation per millimetre (ρ) is given by

$$\rho = -2 \cdot 10 + \frac{8 \cdot 14}{\lambda^2},$$

where ρ is in degrees and λ is in microns.

12(xix). Using the formula of Example 12(xviii), find the thickness of the thinnest quartz plate which would give a maximum of transmission at 5460 Å. (i) when the polarizer and analyser are crossed, and (ii) when they are at 45°.
[(i) 3·57 mm. (ii) 1·78 mm.]

12(xx). Design an arrangement to have zero transmission for 6870 Å., and maximum transmission for 6563 Å. Calculate the thickness of a suitable plate of quartz.   [5·45 cm.]

12(xxi). If a plane of polarization can be located with an accuracy of ±10 minutes of arc, what are the corresponding limits of error in the difference between μ_r and μ_l when this difference is measured with a plate 1 cm. thick, and using light of wavelength 5000 Å?   [±4·6 × 10⁻⁸.]

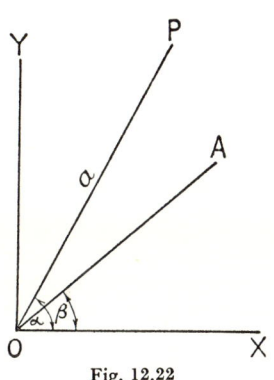

Fig. 12.22

12.41.—When a plate of anisotropic material is placed in a parallel beam of light between a polarizer and an analyser (using the apparatus shown in fig. 12.21), colour effects are obtained if the plate is thin. If white light, which has passed through a thick plate, is passed into a spectroscope, the spectrum is channelled. The amount of light of a given wavelength which is transmitted may be calculated in the following way.

Let OX and OY be the two privileged directions for the anisotropic plate, and let OP and OA represent the settings of the polarizer and the analyser (fig. 12.22). The light incident upon the plate has components

$$a \cos \alpha \cos \phi \quad \text{along OX,}$$
and
$$a \sin \alpha \cos \phi \quad \text{along OY.}$$
    . . . . 12(39)

The light emerging from the plate is represented by

$$a \cos \alpha \cos \phi' \quad \text{along OX,}$$
and
$$a \sin \alpha \cos (\phi' + \epsilon_p) \quad \text{along OY,}$$
    . . . 12(40)

where ϕ and ϕ' are epoch angles, and ϵ_p is given by 12(16). The light transmitted by the analyser is represented by

$$a \cos \alpha \cos \beta \cos \phi',$$
and
$$a \sin \alpha \sin \beta \cos (\phi' + \epsilon_p). \qquad \ldots \quad 12(41)$$

We may regard the light which has passed the analyser as two beams polarized in the same plane and originally derived from the same beam of plane-polarized light. They are thus in a condition to interfere. The resultant illumination is equal to the sum of the squares of the coefficients of $\cos \phi'$ and $\sin \phi'$ (see § 3.4), i.e.

$$E = (a \cos \alpha \cos \beta + a \sin \alpha \sin \beta \cos \epsilon_p)^2$$
$$+ (a \sin \alpha \sin \beta \sin \epsilon_p)^2. \quad 12(42)$$

It is convenient to write 12(42) in a form in which a part involving ϵ_p is separated from a part not involving ϵ_p. This leads to

$$E = a^2 \cos^2 (\alpha - \beta) - a^2 \sin 2\alpha \sin 2\beta \sin^2 \tfrac{1}{2}\epsilon_p. \quad 12(43)$$

The first term depends only on the relative orientation of the analyser and polarizer. It is a maximum when they are parallel, and zero when they are crossed. It is known as the " white " term, since it is independent of wavelength. The second (or " colour " term) depends on ϵ_p (and hence on λ), and also on α and β. It is zero whenever either the polarizer or the analyser is parallel to one of the privileged directions. Rotation of *either* analyser *or* polarizer through a right angle (keeping the rest of the system fixed) alters the sign of this term.

12.42.—The first term on the right-hand side of equation 12(43) represents the light which would be transmitted by the analyser and polarizer if the crystal plate were removed. This light would be white and the effect of the crystal plate is to add (or, in certain relative orientations of analyser and polarizer, to subtract) a certain amount of coloured light. Addition gives one hue and subtraction gives the complementary hue.* For a plate of given material and thickness there are thus two characteristic hues. These characteristic hues are obtained only when the parallel beam is incident normally. A small tilt of the plate alters the hue of the transmitted light. A strong saturated colour is obtained when $\alpha = +\pi/4$ and $\beta = -\pi/4$. This makes the first term on the right-hand side of equation 12(43) equal to zero and gives the second term its maximum value. If the analyser and polarizer are rotated from this setting (as one unit), the colour remains saturated but the amount of light transmitted is reduced. If the polarizer is fixed ($\alpha = \pi/4$) and the analyser is rotated, the colour becomes more and more desaturated until the colour term becomes zero at $\beta = -\pi/2$ or $\beta = 0$. Further

* See footnote to § 12.39.

rotation of the analyser gives the complementary hue. The colour effects are conveniently observed with a thin plate of mica or with some kinds of transparent plastics (obtainable from general laboratory suppliers). The "chameleon" shown in Plate IV (p. 628) is made of mica of two different thicknesses. Each part gives one hue in Plate IV*e* and, by rotation of the analyser, the complementary hue in IV*f*. The channelled spectrum obtained with a thicker plate may conveniently be observed with a piece of selenite one millimetre thick.

12.43.—Owing to dispersion, a given quarter-wave plate of anisotropic material can produce a phase difference of a quarter-period for only one wavelength. In the absence of any special requirement, it is usual to make the plate exactly right for a wavelength in the yellow region of the spectrum. If a parallel beam of white light, plane-polarized in a plane which bisects the privileged directions, is incident upon such a plate, the yellow part of the emergent light is circularly polarized, and the other wavelengths are elliptically polarized. In a similar way, if plane-polarized light is incident upon a plate which is a half-wave plate for yellow light, the emergent light is not completely plane-polarized. A Nicol prism set to extinguish the yellow light will allow small amounts of neighbouring wavelengths, and larger amounts of more distant wavelengths, to pass. The emergent light contains a preponderance of blue and red, and has an easily recognized hue called the *tint of passage*.

12.44. The Biquartz.

Similar effects may occur owing to the dispersion of optical rotation. This property has been used to provide a sensitive method of locating the plane of polarization of a beam of light. Two pieces of quartz, each producing a rotation of $\frac{1}{2}\pi$ (but in opposite senses) for yellow light, are put together (fig. 12.23). This arrangement is called a *biquartz*. If plane-polarized white light is passed through a biquartz, the yellow part is rotated through a right angle in each half of the field, and is extinguished by a Nicol set parallel to the original plane of polarization. Light of other wavelengths is transmitted in similar proportions in the two halves of the field. They both show the same hue, i.e. the tint of passage. If, however, the Nicol is rotated through a small angle, one half of the field becomes more blue and the other more red. The eye is very sensitive

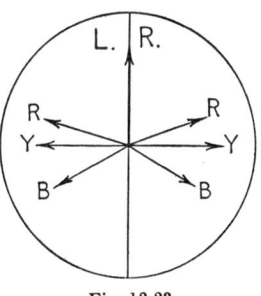

Fig. 12.23

to small differences of hue between two large uniform regions placed side by side, and the Nicol can be set with high precision. An alternative way of making the setting is to pass the light into a spectroscope, so that it produces two spectra, one above the other. There is a dark band in each spectrum. When the Nicol is in the correct setting, the bands coincide. When it is rotated slightly, one band moves to longer and the other to shorter wavelengths. The changes of hue produced by rotating the Nicol may be used to detect the presence of a small fraction of polarized light in a beam of white light.

12.45. Saccharimetry.

Accurate estimation of the strengths of sugar solutions can be made by measuring the specific rotation (§ 12.35). Many instruments, called *saccharimeters*, have been devised for this purpose. The simplest type of saccharimeter consists of a polarizer, a cell for containing the optically active solution, and an analyser, together with the lenses necessary to allow a parallel beam of light to pass through the solution and enter the observer's eye.

The cell is first filled with water and the analyser is turned until no light passes. The cell is then filled with the solution under test, and the analyser is rotated until the field is again dark. The angle (α) through which the analyser has been turned is read on a circular scale. Since, under practical conditions, the angle of rotation (ψ) is never greater than π, it follows that either $\psi = \alpha$ or $\psi = \pi - \alpha$. To distinguish between these possibilities, the solution is diluted to half-strength, and the new value of α is measured.

12.46.—With the above arrangement the curve of illumination against angular setting passes through a flat minimum (i.e. it touches the axis) and location of the angle for zero illumination is inaccurate.* Methods which involve judgment of equality between two halves of a bipartite field are considerably better. Owing to the dispersion of rotatory polarization monochromatic light (sodium yellow) is usually employed for accurate polarimetry, and the biquartz cannot then be used; but the following device gives a bipartite field. The analyser consists of a Glan-Thompson prism from which a small wedge has been removed (fig. 12.24). The remaining pieces are reunited to form a *Cornu-Jellett prism*. The principal planes of the two parts of this analyser make a small angle 2δ (called the *half-shadow angle*) with each other. The setting is made on the external bisector of this angle,

* Compare §§ 11.6 and 11.11.

so that an error of δ on one side of the desired position makes the left-hand part of the field dark, and an error of δ on the other side makes the right-hand part dark. Thus a very great change in relative illumination is produced by a small variation of angle and the setting can be made accurately.

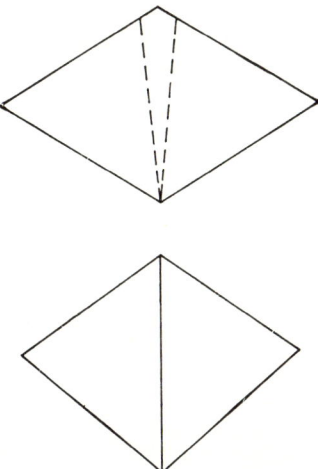

Fig. 12.24.—The Cornu-Jellett prism

12.47.—If the plane of polarization of the light incident on the analyser makes an angle ψ with the external bisector of the half-shadow angle, the amounts of light transmitted in the two parts of the field are proportional to $\sin^2(\delta + \psi)$ and $\sin^2(\delta - \psi)$. If $\delta \ll 1$ and $\psi \ll \delta$, the mean is proportional to δ^2 and the difference to $4\psi\delta$, so that the ratio α of the difference to the mean is $4\psi/\delta$. The curve of α against ψ cuts the axis at an angle proportional to $1/\delta$. Decreasing δ increases the slope but decreases the total illumination—so that there is an optimum value for δ. This value depends on the intensity of the source.

The half-shadow device (of which there are several types) may be used either as analyser or as polarizer. The accuracy of setting in a good visual instrument is a few seconds of arc, and a similar accuracy is obtained by photo-electric photometry.

EXAMPLES [12(xxii)–12(xxv)]

12(xxii). Show that when analyser and polarizer are crossed, the second term in 12(43) is always positive. Hence only one hue can be obtained.

12(xxiii). With a specimen of selenite 0·913 mm. thick, and with analyser and polarizer crossed, dark bands were obtained at 6543, 6167, 5830, 5540, 5266

5030, 4810, 4590, 4405 Å. Assuming that the difference of refractive indices for the fast and slow directions is independent of wavelength over the range covered, calculate this difference of indices.

[If successive bands occur at wavelengths $\lambda_0, \lambda_1, \ldots \lambda_k$, we may write $(n + k)\lambda_k = e(\alpha - \gamma)$, where e is the thickness, and α and γ the refractive indices of the crystal. From the slope of the straight line obtained on plotting $1/\lambda_k$ against k, the value of $(\alpha - \gamma)$ may be found. (0·012.)]

12(xxiv). Discuss the production of interference fringes with circularly polarized light. Derive conditions corresponding to those for plane-polarized light (§ 12.15).

[(i) Two beams of circularly polarized light of opposite sense do not produce interference fringes under any condition.

(ii) Two beams polarized in the same sense produce interference fringes under the same conditions as two beams of unpolarized light, provided that they are originally derived from the same beam of polarized light. The beam from which they are derived may be either plane or circularly polarized.

(iii) Two beams of light, circularly polarized in the same sense, derived from perpendicular plane-polarized components of unpolarized light, do not interfere. Two beams derived from right-handed and left-handed circularly polarized components of unpolarized light also do not interfere.]

12(xxv). What are the corresponding conditions for elliptically polarized light?

[Some interference is obtained if the conditions for circularly polarized light are fulfilled. Fringes with completely dark minima are obtained only when, in addition, the ellipses are similar and similarly oriented.]

12.48. The Savart Plate.

When a parallel beam of light is incident normally on a birefringent plate (as shown in fig. 12.4) the emerging wave-surface corresponding to the extraordinary ray has been sheared* with respect to that corresponding to the ordinary ray, and a phase difference has been introduced. It is sometimes desirable to eliminate the phase difference while retaining the shearing effect. The Savart plate (fig. 12.25a) consists of two pieces of calcite, or other birefringent material, which are accurately equal in thickness and whose optic axes are oriented as shown in the figure (OP and O'P'). It is essential that the angle between the optic axis and the normal to the surface shall be the same for the two pieces, and desirable that it shall be near to 45°.

Suppose that light polarized parallel to OA is incident normally on a Savart plate from below (fig. 12.25b). An ordinary ray, polarized along OX (i.e. in the same plane as the optic axis) and an extraordinary ray, polarized along OY, will emerge from the lower half with a phase

---

* See § 9.51.

§ 12.48   THE SAVART PLATE   497

difference and also a relative shear in the direction OX (see fig. 12.25b). The ordinary ray in the lower half becomes the extraordinary in the upper half and vice versa. Since the angle between the normal to the

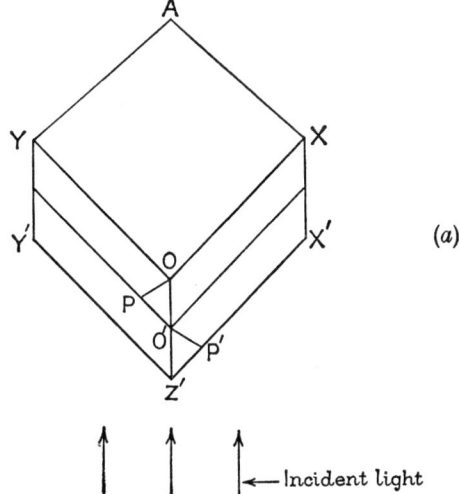

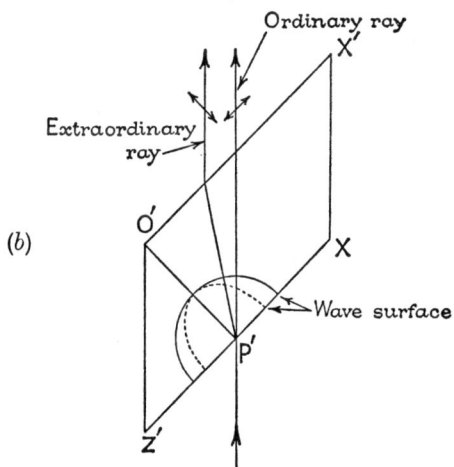

Fig. 12.25 The Savart plate

crystal slice and the optic axis is the same in the two parts, the total phase difference is zero. The shear in the top half is in the OY direction, and there is thus a resultant shear in the direction bisecting OX and OY. The two emergent waves are polarized parallel to OX and OY but they are coherent, having been derived from plane-polarized light; an analyser parallel (or perpendicular) to OA will select equal components which will give sheared-wave interference if there are irregularities in the incident wave surfaces.

12.49.—If a ray in the plane OZ'A, slightly inclined to OZ', is incident, symmetry in regard to the optic axes is maintained, and there is no phase difference between the emerging beams. If however a ray inclined in the perpendicular plane (YY'XX') is incident, it is nearer the optic axis than a normal ray in one part and further from it in the other, and a phase difference is introduced. It may be shown that, for small inclinations, this phase difference is proportional to the inclination. If convergent plane-polarized light is incident, fringes parallel to the OA direction are obtained. The Savart plate, together with an analyser, may thus be used to detect a small proportion of plane-polarized light in the presence of a strong beam of unpolarized light. The Savart plate and the analyser are rotated together and the fringes are most clearly seen when the plane of polarization is parallel to OA.

12.50. Interferometric Devices using Birefringence.

In recent years (1948–60) a considerable number of interferometers, interference microscopes, and interference filters using birefringent materials have been developed. The paths of the beams of light which interfere are usually close together and may lie almost completely within a small volume of a solid. Adequate temperature control and good mechanical stability are easily obtained. Path differences in the birefringent material are proportional to $(\mu_1 - \mu_2)t$ and $(\mu_1 - \mu_2)$ is of order 10^{-2} to 10^{-3} so that the accuracy required in making optical components is less than that required when path differences depend on $(\mu - 1)t$. In order to obtain coherence it is necessary to select one component of unpolarized light, and one-half of the light is lost in the polarizer but losses in the remainder of the system are usually small. The overall loss of light is considerably less than when a beam is divided and reunited at semi-reflecting surfaces (as in the Michelson interferometer) or passed through narrow slits (as in the Rayleigh refractometer). The only general disadvantage of instruments depending on birefringence is that each one is rather narrowly specialized for a particular application, but this follows a general trend in the design of modern instruments.

12.51. Interference Microscope.

Fig. 12.26 shows an interference microscope designed by Lebedev. The beam of light from the condenser, polarized so that its plane bisects the privileged directions of the birefringent plate P_1, is restricted to a narrow pencil. It is split by P_1 into two beams, one of which passes through the specimen while the other passes to one side of it. The planes of polarization are rotated through 90° by a suitably oriented

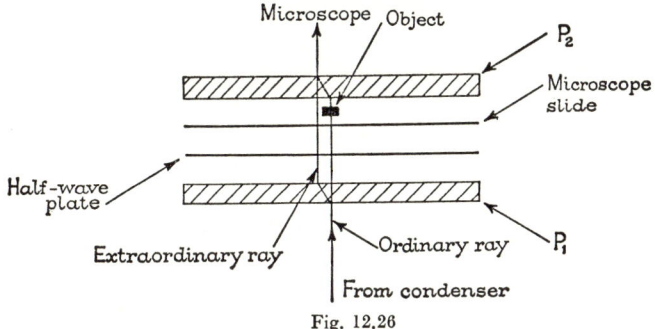

Fig. 12.26

half-wave plate (see § 12.25) before the beams enter the second plate P_2 which is similar to P_1 and similarly oriented. Both the wave shear and the difference of path produced in P_1 are removed by P_2 leaving only the path differences produced by the specimen. These are revealed by interference between components selected by an analyser (oriented either parallel or perpendicular to the polarizer) in the eyepiece of the microscope. The thickness of the plates P_1 and P_2 needed to produce a sufficient separation of beams, prevents the use of a high-power objective, and the restriction of the beam from the condenser limits the aperture.

12.52. Wave-shearing Interference Microscope.

In many interference microscopes, the interferometric element is in front of the objective or incorporated in it.* There is, however, an important advantage in placing the interferometer element after the objective, because the divergence of the rays is then reduced. Françon† has developed a wave-shearing interferometer microscope by putting a small Savart plate in the eyepiece. This instrument may be used to observe phase-contrast objects and is free from the edge-effects described in § 8.48. With white light it is possible to arrange that differences of phase in the object are represented by differences of colour (hue) in the image. In one form of this design a coloured strip corresponding to a known (and variable) phase difference occupies part of the field. The phase difference in this part is altered until its colour matches that

* See § 9.52. † See Reference 12.8.

found in an area where phase difference is to be measured. The unknown and known phase differences then being equal, the former is obtained from the latter. Van Heel has applied this method to the measurement of thin films *in vacuo.**

12.53 Birefringent Filters.

The light transmitted when a birefringent plate is placed between a polarizer and an analyser may be examined spectroscopically using an arrangement similar to that shown in fig. 12.21. A channelled spectrum (§ 5.29 and Plate IIf, p. 130) is obtained. The distribution of energy in this spectrum may be derived from equation 12(43). When $\cos(\alpha - \beta) = 0$ the minima are zero, and they are also zero when $\alpha = \beta = \pi/4$. Equation 12(43) may then be written

$$E = a^2(1 - \sin^2 \tfrac{1}{2}\epsilon_p) = a^2 \cos^2 \tfrac{1}{2}\epsilon_p. \quad . \quad . \quad 12(44)$$

The maxima occur at wavelengths for which $\epsilon_p = 2n\pi$ (where n is an integer). Substituting for ϵ_p from equation 12(16) and putting μ_d for $\mu_2 - \mu_1$, we see that the wavelength (λ_n) of the nth maximum is given by

$$\frac{\mu_d}{\lambda_n} = \frac{n}{e}. \quad . \quad . \quad . \quad . \quad . \quad 12(45)$$

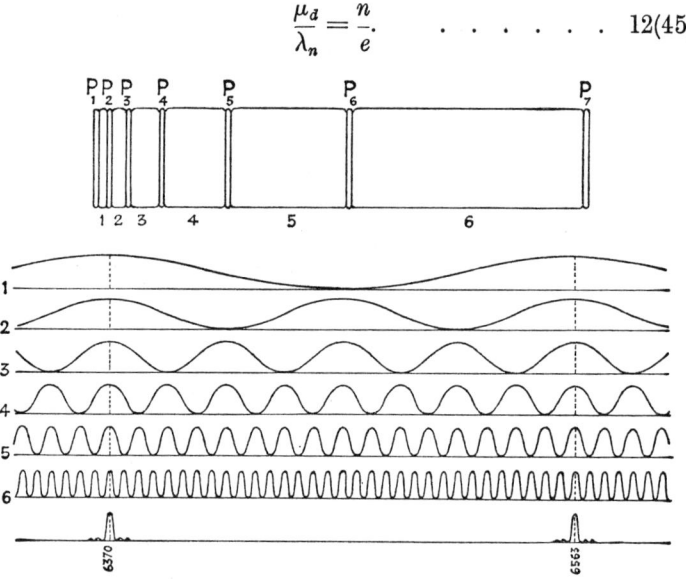

Fig. 12.27.—Lyot filter. (*a*) Arrangement of plates and polarizers. (*b*) Light transmitted through individual plates acting alone and (at bottom) through the whole filter.

* See p. 408 of Reference 12.11.

§ 12.54   BIREFRINGENT FILTERS   501

The wavelengths of the minima are obtained by putting $(n + \tfrac{1}{2})$ for n in equation 12(45). If we neglect the variation of μ_d with wavelength (see example 12(xxiii)), we obtain for the separation of successive maxima

$$\frac{1}{\lambda_n} - \frac{1}{\lambda_{n-1}} = \frac{1}{e\mu_d}, \qquad \ldots \quad 12(46)$$

so that the difference of wavelength constant is inversely proportional to $\mu_d\, e$. When the thickness is doubled, the separation of maxima is halved (fig. 12.27b). Thus an arrangement of N plates whose thicknesses are $e, 2e, 4e, \ldots, 2^{N-1}e$, separated by polarizers as shown in fig. 12.27a, will transmit certain narrow regions of the spectrum and give nearly zero transmission elsewhere. One of the transmitted regions may be selected by using a glass or gelatine filter.

12.54.—This birefringent filter was designed by B. Lyot* who used six quartz plates of thicknesses ranging from about 1·2 mm. to 71 mm. The polarizers are prisms of Iceland spar matched with glass so that the extraordinary ray is undeviated. By cementing the components (or immersing them in a suitable liquid) internal reflections are almost eliminated, giving a maximum transmission of 40 per cent. The half-width of the transmitted regions is about 3 Å. Using this filter to isolate certain spectral lines Lyot was able to obtain photographs of the solar corona when the sun was not eclipsed.

The separation of the maxima transmitted by the Lyot assembly is determined by the thickness of the thinnest plate, and the sharpness of the line by that of the thickest. There is thus a ratio of approximately 2^N between the separation and the width of the band passed. This width may be calculated in the following way. The light which emerges from P_2 may be regarded as consisting of two components. These have relative phases 0 and ϵ_1. In the second plate each of these is split into two parts whose relative retardations are 0 and $2\epsilon_1$, so that the light passing P_3 may be regarded as having four components whose phases are $0, \epsilon_1, 2\epsilon_1$ and $3\epsilon_1$. By an extension of this argument, the light passing P_{N+1} consists of 2^N components with successive phase differences ϵ_1. The formula for the resultant is the same as that for a grating of 2^N elements with a phase difference ϵ_1 between light from successive elements. It is

$$\frac{E}{E_0} = \frac{\sin^2 2^N \epsilon_1}{2^{2N} \sin^2 \epsilon_1}. \qquad \ldots \quad 12(47)$$

* See Reference 12.9.

The difference of wavelength $\Delta\lambda$ between a maximum and the next minimum is the same as the resolution limit for the grating if the variation of μ_d with λ is neglected. It is then given by

$$\frac{\lambda}{\Delta\lambda} = \frac{2^N \epsilon_1}{2\pi} = \frac{\mu_d e_n}{\lambda}, \qquad \ldots \ldots \quad 12(48)$$

where $e_n = 2^N e$ is the thickness of the thickest plate. For the filter used by Lyot equation 12(48) gives $\Delta\lambda = 6$ Å. at 6000 Å., i.e. a half-width (see § 4.13) of 3 Å.

REFERENCES

12.1. BRAGG, W. L.: *The Crystalline State* (Bell).

12.2. WOOSTER: *Crystal Physics* (Cambridge University Press).

12.3. THOMPSON, SILVANUS P.: *Trans. Optical Convention*, 1905.

12.4. RAYLEIGH: *Scientific Papers*, Vol. III, pp. 140–147.

12.5. HURWITZ: *Journal of the Optical Society of America*, 1945, Vol. 35, p. 525.

12.6. JERRARD: *ibid.*, 1948, Vol. 38, p. 35.

12.7. WRIGHT: *The Measurement of Colour* (Hilger and Watts).

12.8. FRANÇON: *Opt. Act.*, 1954, Vol. 1, p. 50.

12.9. LYOT: *Ann. d'Astrophys.*, 1944, Vol. 7, p. 1.

12.10. JERRARD: *J.O.S.A.*, 1954, Vol. 44, p. 634.

12.11. STRONG: *Concepts of Classical Optics* (Freeman, S. Francisco).

LIST OF SYMBOLS

The *paragraph numbers* indicate the places where symbols are introduced or defined. Use of various symbols as auxiliary constants (e.g. α in § 18.16) is not included in the list.

A, a Real amplitude or Fourier coefficient, 2.4, 2.6, 4.17.
A_{mn}, B_{mn}, etc.   Einstein coefficients, 17.37.
    B Fourier coefficient, 2.6.
    b Phase velocity in a material medium, 2.9, 2.11, 4.30.
    c Velocity of light in vacuum, Chap. XI.
    D Detectivity, 20.21.
  $D(s)$ Optical transfer factor, 8.34.
    E Relative energy, 2.18, 5.2.
    e (i) Charge of the electron.
    e (ii) Thickness of a film, 5.13.
    F Power of a lens system, 7.13.
    f f-value, 15.22.
    g Ray velocity, 16.9.
    H (i) Information content, 20.4.
$H, \mathscr{H}$ Energy (Hamiltonian function), 2.7, 18.25.
    h Planck's constant, 17.1.
    I Intensity of light source, 10.26.
    k Boltzmann's constant, 17.30.
    L Luminance, 10.26.
    m (i) Order of spectrum, 6.13.
    m (ii) Spatial frequency (displacement), 8.36.
    m (iii) Mass; relativistic mass, 11.36.
    m_0 Rest mass, 11.36.
    M_T Transverse magnification, 7.7.
    M_α Angular magnification, 7.7.
    n Index of refraction to vacuum, 3.11.
    n   Complex index, 15.5.
    $\mathscr{N}$ Number of dipoles per unit volume, 15.21.
    N Number of molecules per unit volume, 15.22.
    P (i) Complex amplitude, 2.26.
    P (ii) Radiation flux, 10.2.
    P (iii) Relativistic momentum, 11.37.
    p (i) Momentum.
    p (ii) Order of interference, 4.9.
    $\mathscr{P}_\lambda$ Flux per unit wavelength interval, 10.3.
    q Co-ordinate, 2.3, 18.4.

LIST OF SYMBOLS

r Responsivity, 10.2.
s Spatial frequency (energy), 8.34.
T (i) Period, 2.4.
T (ii) Absolute temperature, 17.27.
U Group velocity, 4.29.
U_{mn} Interaction energy, 19.3.
V Potential energy, 2.4.
V_λ Photopic visibility factor, 10.23–5.
v Velocity of a material body, 2.22.
W (i) Aberration function, 8.26.
W (ii) Total energy (especially of e.m. field), 13.13.
U, W Special functions, 6.19–20.

LIST OF SYMBOLS

GREEK LETTERS

- α (i) Relativity constant $= (1 - v^2/c^2)^{1/2}$, 11.27.
- α (ii) Angle between **E** and **D** in crystal, 16.7.
- α (iii) Constant of Gaussian curve, 4.21.
- α (iv) $2\alpha =$ Absorption coefficient, 15.5.
- γ Damping constant, 4.25, 15.20.
- γ_{12} Phase coherence factor, Appendix VA.
- δ Phase difference, 2.4.
- ϵ Dielectric constant, 13.7. 16.2.
- Θ Principal angle of incidence, 15.10.
- θ (1) Angle of reflection in a thin film, 5.13.
- θ_1 Angle of incidence in medium (1), 3.13. 14.5.
- θ_1' Angle of reflection in medium (1), 3.13. 14.5.
- θ_2 Angle of refraction in medium (2), 3.13, 14.5.
- κ Wavelength constant, 2.11.
- $\varkappa$ Extinction coefficient, 15.5.
- $\varkappa_s$ Wave vector, 18.25.
- λ Wavelength in the medium,* 2.11.
- μ Refractive index to air, 3.11.
- ν Frequency, 2.11.
- ξ Disturbance or fluctuation, 2.9.
- ρ (i) Auto-correlation function, Appendix IVB, 17
- ρ (ii) Reflection coefficient, 5.26.
- ρ (iii) Energy density in e.m. field, 17.19.
- $\boldsymbol{\rho}$ (i) Current density, 13.5.
- $\boldsymbol{\rho}$ (ii) Unit vector in ray direction, 16.5.
- σ (i) Spread function, Appendix VIIIA, 2.
- σ (ii) Electrical conductivity, 13.5.
- σ (iii) Stefan's constant, 17.27.
- τ (i)   Time-constant of thermal detector, 10.9.
- τ (ii) Life of an excited state, 17.38.
- ϕ (i)   Phase, 2.4, 4.30.
- Φ, ϕ (ii) Scalar potential, Appendix XIIIA.
- Φ, ϕ (iii) Wave functions for e.m. field, 18.27, Appendix XIXA, 9.
- χ Scalar potential, Appendix XIIIA.
- ψ (i) Azimuth, 12.10, 15.11.
- ψ (ii) Wave function without time, 18.11.
- Ψ (i) Principal azimuth, 15.11.
- Ψ (ii) Wave function with time, 18.18.
- ω Circular (or angular) frequency, 2.4.
- Ω Angular momentum, 17.24.
- Ω Modulation frequency, 10.9.

* In Chap. VIII, λ is used for wavelength in air and λ' for wavelength in medium.

INDEX TO VOLUMES I AND II

VOLUME I : Chapters I–XII   VOLUME II : Chapters XIII–XX
References are to paragraphs.—References in heavy type either give the definition of a quantity or are more important than other references under the same heading.

Abbe, theory of the microscope, 8.19–22
aberration, 8.24–26
— astigmatic, 8.29
— astronomical, 11.29; 11.34
— chromatic, 3.19; 8.32
— comatic, 8.28
— function, 8.26
— spherical, 8.27
absorbing media, Chap. XV.
absorption and dispersion, 15.24–41; Appendix XIXA
— and emission processes, Chap. XIX; Appendix XIXA
— and f-value, 15.27–29; 17.41
— and life of an excited atom, 17.41
— and scattering, 15.4; **15.42**; Appendix XIXA
— and transition probabilities, 18.22; Appendix XIXA
— at limit of a spectral series, 17.12
— coefficient, 15.5
— electromagnetic theory, 15.5 ff
— in gases, 15.24–5
— in liquids and solids, 15.31
— in metals, 15.33–41
— lines, 15.27
— of resonance radiation, 19.13
— photo-electric, 17.12–3
— quantum theory, Appendix XIXA
— spectra, 4.5
achromatic fringes, 5.34–40
— lines, 16.37; 16.39
— systems, 7.24
activity, optical, 12.35–40; 16.43; 16.49
— — induced by magnetic field, 16.50
aelotropic, 3.12n
aether, 11.17
Airy, G. B., on aberration of light, 11.34
— on achromatic fringes, 5.39
— on diffraction at a circular aperture, **6.41**; 8.3; 8.5

Airy, G . B., on Talbot's bands, Appendix VIIID
allogyric birefringence, 12.36
alychne, 10.39
amplitude, real, 2.4; complex, 2.26; 3.6
analyser, 12.2
analysis of radiation, 20.33
angular momentum, 17.24–6; 19.4; 19.23
— relations between **D, E, H**, etc., 16.7–8
anisotropic media, Chap XVI
— plate, 12.22–26
anisotropy, 3.12; electrical 16.2–4
— natural optical, 16.5–42; 16.44; 16.58; relation to crystal structure, 16.45–8; dispersion, 12.38; 16.46
— optical, induced by electric field, 16.51–4; Appendix XVIA; by magnetic field, 16.55; by mechanical strain, 16.56–7; by movement of liquid, 16.58
— relation to molecular structure, 16.47; 16.60
anomalous dispersion, **3.18**; **15.27**; 15.29; 17.41
antinode, 3.21
anti-reflecting films, 5.22
aperture, see *diffraction*
— numerical, 8.21
Arago, 12.15
astigmatism, 8.29
atomic energy states, see *states*
— oscillators, 4.6; 18.16; **18.21–4**; 19.1; 19.7
auto-correlation function, Appendix IVA 17
axes of single ray velocity, 16.15
— optic (single wave - velocity), **16.6**; 16.17
— — relation to crystal structure, 16.45–6

INDEX

Babinet, theorem, 6.46; compensator, 12.33
balance, principle of detailed, 17.35
Balmer series, 17.4
band spectrum, 4.3
banded (or channelled) spectrum, 5.30; 12.39; 12.41-2
bands, Talbot's, Appendix VIIID.
Bartolinus, 1.13
beats, 4.29
bending of light rays in gravitational field, 11.38
Benoît, 5.33; 9.29; 9.35-40
Bergstrand, measurement of c, 11.9, 11.13
biaxial crystals, 16.22-30; 16.38-9
Billet split lens, 5.9
biprism, Fresnel's, **5.9**; 5.38
biquartz, 12.44
birefringence, 1.13; **12.8-9**; 12.20-1; 16.20-30
black-body radiation, see *temperature radiation*
" blaze " grating, 6.25-6
" blooming ", 5.22
Bohr, N., 17.6; 17.43; 18.1; 19.8; 19.33; Appendix XIXA
bolometer, 10.6
Boltzmann (Maxwell-Boltzmann statistics), 17.34; 18.38
— constant, 17.30; 17.33
— law, 17.30; 17.35
— theory of temperature radiation, 17.28
Born, M., 3.2; calculation of birefringence, 16.48
Bothe and Geiger, 17.23
boundary conditions, 6.31; 14.1; 18.13
Brackett, 6.25; Brackett series, 17.4
Bradley, 11.34
Bragg, W. L., theory of birefringence, 16.48
breadth of spectral lines, see *width*
Brewster, D., fringes of superposition, **5.32**; 9.38
— law of the polarizing angle, **12.4**; 14.8; 14.17
— photo-elastic effect, 16.56
brightness, 2.21
— subjective, 10.33
brushes, 16.31; 16.37
Buisson, 5.32

Cabannes, 15.46
camera, 7.37
cardinal points, 7.9

Carvallo's paradox, 4.34
Cassegrain mounting, **7.34**
catadioptric system, 7.9
Cauchy, dispersion formula, 3.18
channelled spectra, 5.30; 12.39; 12.41-2
Cherenkov radiation, 11.44
chromatic aberration, 7.23; 8.32
chromaticity, 10.33
C.I.E. photometric scale, 10.22
— colour measurement, 10.37
circularly polarized light, 12.1; **12.18**; 14.15; 16.41-2; 17.24; 19.24-6
Coblentz, 17.27
coding, 20.47
coefficient, see *absorption, Einstein, extinction, reflection*.
coherence, **5.3-8**; Appendix VA; 6.12; 8.35-43
— and Rayleigh scattering, 15.44
— and resonance radiation, 19.13
— and stimulated emission, Appendix XIXC
— degree of, 5.8; Appendix VA
— of polarized light, 12.15; 12.28 ff.
— partial, 5.3; 5.8; Appendix VA
— phase coherence factor, Appendix VA
coherent amplification of light, Appendix XIXA
— beams, 5.3
— illumination, 8.36
collisions, effect on width of spectral lines, 4.25
— excitation and ionization by, 17.11
— of second type, 17.15
colour related to wavelength, 1.13; 10.13
— specification, 10.31
— vision, 10.31-41
colours, complementary hue, **12.39**n 12.42
— of thin films in white light, **5.12**; 5.22; 5.24
— of thin plates in polarized light, 12.38; 12.41; 16.31-43
coma, 8.28
compensator, Babinet, 12.33
— Jamin, 9.23
— Michelson, 4.8
complementary hues, **12.39**n; 12.42
— screens, 6.46
complex amplitude, 2.26; 3.6
Compton effect, 17.23; 18.4; Appendix XVIIA; XIXA, 14
concave grating, Appendix VIB
conical refraction, 16.24-30

508   INDEX

conservation of energy in absorption and emission of light, 1.9; 2.18; 17.6; 18.7; Appendix XIXA, 6, 11
contact, optical, 6.29
continuity, equation of, 13.14
continuous spectrum, 4.2; 17.13
contour fringes, theory, 5.18; applications, 9.6–17
Cornu spiral, Appendix VID
— measurement of the velocity of light 11.6
Cornu-Jellet prism, 12.46
corona, or halo, formed by diffraction, 6.47–8
corpuscular theory, 1.10; 3.31–4
correlation, Appendix IVA, 17–18
— auto and cross, Appendix IVB
— interferometer, Appendix VA
— of phase (see *coherence*)
— see also *Michelson stellar interferometer*
Cotton-Mouton effect, 16.55
Coudé focus, 7.34
counter, photon, 17.18
critical angle, 14.15
— potentials, 17.11
crystals, biaxial, 16.22–30; 16.38–40; 16.45–8
— colours of thin crystal plates, 12.38; 12.41; 16.31–43
— double refraction, 1.13; **12.8–9**; 12.20–1; 16.20–30
— optical activity, 12.35–40; 16.43; 16.49
— structure related to optical anisotropy, 16.45
— uniaxial, **12.20–1**; 16.19; 16.36–7
curvature of field, 8.29

damped harmonic wave, Appendix IVB, 13
damping, natural, 4.25
dark adaptation, 10.25
Davisson and Germer, 18.2
De Broglie, L., 18.1; 18.18
degree of coherence, 5.8
density, optical, 3.11
detailed balance, principle of, 17.35–7
detectivity, 10.31; 20.25–7
detectors, 10.2 ff
— photo-conductive, 10.12
— photo-emissive, 10.11; 20.27
— photo-voltaic, 10.12
— thermal, 10.5 ff.; 20.25
dielectric, propagation of e.m. waves in, **13.8–10**; 15.18–32

dielectric constant, 13.6; in relation to refractive index, 13.9; ϵ-quadric, 16.4
diffraction, 1.12; 6.1; Chap. VI; Kirchhoff's formula, Appendix VIA; St. Venant's hypothesis, 6.33
— by irregular screens, 6.51
— by narrow slit, 6.56
— by sound waves, 6.50
— Fraunhofer, Chap. VI
— — by a circular aperture, 6.9; 6.41; circular obstacle, 6.10; 6.47
— — by a number of similar apertures, 6.42
— — by a rectangular aperture, 6.39
— — by a slit aperture, 6.3; 6.36; 6.56
— — by grating, 6.12
— — in optical instruments, Chap. VIII
— — in relation to Babinet's theorem, 6.46
— — in relation to rectilinear propagation, 6.57
— — in relation to the Uncertainty Principle, 18.5
— — with a very narrow slit source, 6.56
— Fresnel, 6.3; 6.52; Appendix VID
— — by circular aperture, 6.9; circular obstacle, 6.10
— — in relation to rectilinear propagation, 6.57
— — slit aperture, 6.3; Appendix VID
— — straight-edge, Appendix VID
— — zone plate, Appendix VIC
— gratings, 6.12–6.30
— — amplitude, 6.27
— — blaze, 6.23–5
— — concave, Appendix VIB
— — crossed, 6.16
— — echelette, 6.25
— — echelle, 6.28
— — echelon, 6.28
— — method of manufacture, 6.26
— — phase, 6.27
— — plane, 6.12
— — resolving power, 8.10
— — three-dimensional, 6.18
— — two-dimensional, 6.16–17
— of electrons, 18.2
dioptre, 7.13
dipoles, induced by electric field, 13.6
— in quantum mechanics, 18.21; 19.3; 19.6–12; 19.23
— radiation from, Appendix XIIIB
— see also *oscillators*

INDEX

Dirac, 19.1; 19.3; 19.9; 19.16; 19.33; Appendix XIXA
dispersion, 3.17
— anomalous, 3.18; **15.27**
— electro-magnetic theory, 15.18–47
— in dielectrics, 15.18
— in electrically excited gases, 19.11
— in metals, 15.33
— of birefringence, **12.38**; 12.43; 16.1; **16.46**
— of optical rotation, 12.38–9
— quantum theory, 19.11; Appendix XIXA
— relation to scattering, 15.42–7
— relations, Appendix XIXC
displacement current, 13.7
— interference methods of observing small displacements, 9.18
— of spectrum lines, see *Doppler effect.*
— — — due to gravitational field, 11.38
distance, optical, 3.30
distortion, 8.31
Ditchburn, 20.48
dominant wavelength, 10.33
Doppler-Fizeau effect, radial, **2.22–5**; 11.4; 11.29; 11.30; 17.23; 17.29; 17.42; effect on width of spectral lines, 4.25; 15.29
— — transverse, 11.31
double refraction, 1.13; **12.8–9**; 12.20–1; **16.20–30**
Dove prism, 7.35
Drude, 3.24; 15.12
Dyson, 9.52

Eagle mounting, Appendix VIB, 6
echelette, 6.25
echelle, 6.28
echelon, 6.28–9; 9.44
Eddington, 11.17
Edser-Butler method, 5.31
Einstein, coefficients, **17.37**–8; 18.24; 19.1–3; Appendix XIXA
— photochemical law, 17.16
— photon theory, 1.16; **17.17**; 18.29; 18.40; 19.33
— relativity theory, 1.17; **11.23** ff.
elastic-solid theory, 1.14; 14.7
electric field vector, 13.4
electrical units, ratio of, 11.13
electromagnetic field, quantum theory, 18.25
— — representation by potentials, Appendix XIIIA; 18.25–6

electromagnetic spectrum, 1.15
— theory of light, 1.14; Chaps. XIII–XV
— waves, 13.10
electrons, diffraction of, 8.23; **18.2**
electro-optical effect, 16.51–4
elliptically polarized light, 12.18–9
emission of light, Einstein coefficients, 17.37
— — — quantum theory, Appendix XIXA
— spectra, 4.1
— theory of light, 1.6
empty magnification, 8.8
energy, conservation, 1.9; **2.18**; 17.6; **18.7**; Appendix XIXA, 6, 11
— density (ρ), 17.27
— flux or rate of flow, 2.19; 2.21; **13.14**
— of a photon, 1.16; **11.37**; 17.1; 17.17
— of interaction (radiation and matter), **19.1–3**; 19.8; 19.22
— of the electromagnetic field, 13.13; 18.25–6
— relation to mass, 11.36
— — to Uncertainty Principle, 18.7
— relative, 2.18; 2.21
epoch angle (ϕ), 2.4
ϵ-quadric, or index ellipsoid, 16.4
eriometer, 6.48
Essen, 11.13
etalon, Fabry and Pérot, **5.28**; 9.2; 9.28–33; 9.44 f.
Ewald, 16.48
exact fractions, 9.29–33
excited states of atoms, **17.8**; 17.38–40
extinction coefficient, 15.5
eye, 7.30; 20.48
— as a detector of radiation, 10.21–26
— limit of resolution, 8.7
— normal and abnormal colour vision, 10.31–41
eyepieces, 7.32

Fabry and Pérot, 5.32; 5.33; etalon, **5.28**; 9.2; 9.28–33; 9.44–6; interferometer, **5.28**; 9.44; relation of wavelength to metre, 9.35–43
Faraday, 13.1; effect, 16.50
fast and slow directions for crystal slice, 12.23
Fellgett, Appendix VIIIA
Fermat's principle, 6.58 ff.; 8.3; 16.5; 18.9
Fermi, 19.18
fibre optics, Appendix VIIIA

fidelity, 20.47
field curvature, 8.29
— lens, 7.29
— stop, 7.28
figuring, 9.7
film, interference in thin, $4.8n$; **5.12** ff.
— non-reflecting (or anti-reflecting), 5.22–3; 5.25
— reflecting film of high efficiency, 5.24
filters, birefringent, 12.53
— interference, 5.40
finesse, coefficient, 9.45
FitzGerald-Lorentz contraction, 11.22
Fizeau, **2.22–5**; testing of surfaces, **9.11–3**; 9.15; measure of thermal expansion, 9.18; velocity of light, 11.1; 11.4; 11.6; (in moving medium, 11.35)
Fizeau-Doppler effect, see *Doppler*
flat, optical, 9.12–14
fluctuations, 20.8; 20.23
fluorescence, 17.14–5
flux, 2.21; 10.2–3; 10.26; Chap. XX
flying-spot microscope, 20.46
focal points, 7.10
forbidden lines, 19.5–6
— transitions, 18.24; 19.4–5
form factor, 6.19; 6.43
Foucault, 11.39; polarizing prism, 12.12; velocity of light, 11.1; 11.7; 11.15
— knife-edge test, Appendix XIIIc, 2
Fourier, 4.15–23; 4.34; 6.34; 8.33 ff.; Appendix VIIIA; 9.48; 20.12
— integrals, Appendix IVB; 4.19
— series, 4.17–23; Appendix IVB
— transform, Appendix IVB; 20.12
Fox Talbot's bands, Appendix VIIID
fractions, exact, 9.31–3
Françon, 12.52
Fraunhofer diffraction, Chap. VI (see *diffraction*); 6.3; 6.11; 8.3; 8.4; 8.19
— lines, **4.5**; 11.43
frequency, 2.4; circular, 2.4; angular, 2.4
Fresnel, 3.9
— biprism, **5.9**; 5.38; 9.3
— convection coefficient, 11.20
— diffraction, Chap. VI (see *diffraction*), 3.9; 6.3–10; 6.52; Appendices VIc and VID
— equation, 16.6
— integrals, 7.15
— interference of polarized light, 12.15
— mirrors, **5.9**; 9.2
— reflection formulæ, 14.7

Fresnel rhomb, 14.15
— zones, Appendix VIc; **16.5**; zone plate, Appendix VIc
fringes, interference, see *interference fringes* and *diffraction*
f-sum rule, 18.22
f-value, **15.22**; 15.27–9; 17.40–3; 18.22; 19.12; 19.33

Gabor, 6.53
Gaussian wave group, 4.21; Appendix IVB, 14
Gerlach and Stern experiment, **17.26**; 19.16
Gibbs, 17.30
Glan-Thompson prism, 12.12
Glazebrook, 12.21
Golay cell, 10.7
Gouy's experiment, 6.61; 9.4
grating, diffraction, see *diffraction grating*
gravitational field, displacement of spectral lines, 11.38
Grimaldi, 1.12; 5.7
group velocity, **4.29–31**; 11.3
— wave, **4.9**; 4.32; 5.39; 8.13–15
— — dispersion, Appendix IVB, 15
— — relation to Uncertainty Principle, 18.30

Hagen (and Rubens), 15.12
Haidinger fringes, 5.17; conical refraction, 16.27
half-period zones, 6.7–10; Appendix VIc
half-wave plate, 12.25
half-width of spectrum line, **4.13**; 4.25; 17.42; half-value width, $4.13n$
halos formed by diffraction, 6.47–8
Hamilton equations, 2.7; 11.36; 17.30; 18.25; 19.33
— principle of least action, 18.10
— theory of conical refraction, 16.24
Hanbury Brown, Appendix VA
harmonic motion, Chap. II
— oscillator, see *oscillator*
Havelock's law, 16.51
Heisenberg's Uncertainty Principle, **18.4–8**; 19.33
Hertz, 13.1; 19.3; 19.7
high-efficiency reflecting films, 5.24
history of theory of light, Chap. I (for summary see fig. 1.6), 19.33–4
hologram, 6.53
Hooke, 5.19

INDEX

Hopkins, H. H., on aberrations, 8.26
— on coherence, Appendix V$_A$
— on transfer function, Appendix VIII$_A$
Hubble's law of the red-shift, 11.43
hue, **10.33**; 12.39; 12.42
Huygens, early ideas on wave theory, 1.13
— wave surface for crystals, 12.20–1; 16.19–30
Huygens' construction, 3.8; 6.5; principle, 3.8; 6.5; 19.23
— — applied to lens, 3.16; mirror, 3.14
— — applied to reflection and refraction, 3.11; 3.13
hyperfine structure, 9.44

Iceland spar (calcite), 12.7
illumination of surface, 2.21
inclination factor, 3.9; 6.6; 6.32
incoherent radiation, see *coherence*
indeterminism, **18.8**; 18.29–31
index of refraction, see *refractive index*
induction, electric, 13.6
information theory, 20.3
— transmission, 20.39
infra-red radiation, fig. 1.5; **4.4**; 15.16–7; 15.31
— detectors, 10.2; **10.5–8**; 10.12; 20.25
insulating medium, waves in, **13.8–10**; 15.18–32
intensity of source, 2.21
— of spectral lines, see *f-value*
interaction, energy, 19.1–3; 19.8; 19.22; Appendix XIX$_A$, 5, 10–12
— of independent sources of light, 5.2
— of polarized light, 12.15
— of radiation and matter, Chaps. XVII, XVIII
— process in quantum mechanics, Chap. XIX
interference, 1.12; theory, Chap. V; applications, Chap. IX
— conditions for, 5.6; 12.15
— in a rotating system, 11.39
— of finite wave-trains, 4.33
— of polarized light, 12.15
— order, 4.9
interference fringes, 5.5; applications, Chap. IX
— — achromatic, 5.34–40
— — Brewster, 5.32
— — conditions for observation, 5.6
— — contour, 5.18; 9.6–18
— — Fabry and Pérot, 5.26; **5.28**; 8.16
— — filters, 5.40

interference fringes for thin films, 4.8n; **5.12** ff.
— — for two sources side by side, 5.7
— — Haidinger, 5.17
— — localization, 5.20
— — multiple-beam (Fabry-Pérot), see above
— — — (Tolansky), 9.15
— — Newton's rings, 1.12; **5.19**; 5.40; 9.18
— — of constant inclination, 5.17
— — of constant optical thickness, 5.18
— — of constant path-difference, 5.16
— — of superposition, **5.32**; 9.38
interferometer, auxiliary apparatus for use with interferometers, 9.47
— classification of interferometers, 9.2–4
— Fabry-Pérot, **5.28**; 9.31; 9.50
— Fizeau, **9.11**; 9.18
— Hanbury Brown and Twiss, Appendix V$_A$
— intensity correlation, Appendix V$_A$, 7
— Mach-Zehnder, 9.50
— Michelson, **4.8**; Appendix IV$_A$; 5.18; 9.2; 9.3; 9.9; 9.28; 9.35; 9.44
— Michelson stellar, Appendix V$_A$
— microscope, 9.52
— overlapping of orders, 9.44
— resolving power, 8.16; 9.44
— Twyman-Green, 9.6–10
— wave-shearing, 9.51
interferometry with Fourier analysis, 9.48
— limitations, 20.36–7
intermediate states, 19.9; Appendix XIX$_A$, 15
inverse photo-electric effect, 17.18
— square law, 2.20
ionization potential related to series limit, 17.11–3
isochromatic lines, 16.35; surfaces, 16.34
iso-clinic lines, 16.57
isoplanatism, Appendix VIII$_A$, 3
isotropic, 3.12
Ives' stationary light waves, 3.22

Jamin compensator, 9.23
Jeans, 17.30; 18.25
Jellet prism, 12.46
Joule, 13.14; 15.35

Kerr cell (or shutter), 16.53; applied to measure velocity of light, 11.18;

INDEX

Kerr cell applied to measure life of excited state, 17.39
— electro-optical effect, 16.51; Appendix XVIA
Kirchhoff formula, 6.1; Appendix VIA; 13.11
— law of reflection and emissivity, 15.16
Kramers dispersion formula, 19.11
Kramers-Kronig relation, Appendix XIXB

Lambert, law of absorption, 15.5
— law of diffuse reflection, 10.27
laser, Appendix XIXc
Laue, 6.18
least action, Hamilton's principle, 18.10
— time, Fermat's principle, 6.58 ff.; 16.5; 18.9
length, interference test of end standards, **9.16–7**; 9.41–3
— optical and mechanical standards 9.41–3
lens, 7.2
— field, 7.29
— Huygens' construction, 3.16
— power, 7.18
— systems, 7.2
— telephoto, 7.37
— zoom, 7.37
life of an excited state, 17.38–40
limit of resolution, see *resolving power*
line spectra, 4.6–7
Linfoot, Appendix VIIIA
Lipson, H., 6.54
liquid crystals, 16.58
Lloyd's experiment on conical refraction, 16.24–7
— mirror, **5.9**; 5.34; 5.38
localization of fringes, 5.20
Lorentz, H. A., 10.12; 19.14
— correction to dispersion theory, 15.20
— relativistic contraction, 11.22
Lorenz, L., correction to dispersion theory, 15.20
lumen, 10.26; 10.28
luminance, 2.21, 10.26
Lyot filter, 12.53

Mach-Zehnder interferometer, 9.50
magnetic moment of atom, 19.16
magneto-optics, 16.50; 16.55
magnification relation, 7.7
— useful and empty, 8.8; optimum, 8.23
magnifiers, 7.31–2

Malus' experiment, 1.13; 12.2
— law, 12.10
Mascart, 5.17
maser, optical (laser), Appendix XIX
mass and energy, 11.36
mass of a photon, **11.37**; 17.17; 18.41; 19.33
matrix elements, 18.20–4; 19.3
Maupertuis, 18.10
Maxwell conditions, 7.8
— electromagnetic theory, 1.14; Chaps. XIII–XVI; 18.27
— equations, 13.2; **13.7**
— theory of the velocity of light, 1.14; 10.1; 13.9
Maxwell-Boltzmann statistics, 17.34; 18.38
metals, optical properties, 15.1–17; 15.33–41
— propagation of a refracted wave in a metal, Appendix XVA
metameric match, 10.31
metre, definition in terms of wavelength, 9.43
— relation between wavelength and metre, 9.35–43; **9.43**
Michelson, 9.48
— echelon and echelette gratings, 6.25; **6.28–30**; 9.44
— experiment on the earth's rotation, 11.39; 11.41
— interferometer, **4.8**; 5.18; 9.2; 9.3; 9.9; 9.28; 9.44; 19.30
— — adjustment, Appendix IVA
— relation between metre and wavelength, 9.35; 9.40
— stellar interferometer, Appendix VA
— velocity of light, 11.1; 11.7; 11.15
— visibility of fringes, 4.10–4; 4.23–5
Michelson-Morley experiment, 11.19; 11.32
Michelson-Williams reflecting echelon, **6.28–9**; 9.46
microscope, 7.33
— Abbe theory, 8.19
— coherent illumination, 8.35
— electron, 8.23
— eyepieces, 7.32
— flying-spot, 20.46
— interferometer, 9.52
— non-coherent illumination, 8.35
— objective, testing, 9.10; spectra formed in focal plane, 8.19
— optical, formation of image, by 8.19

microscope optimum magnification, 8.23
— phase contrast, 8.44–8
— resolving power, 8.17; 8.18; 8.21
Millikan, 17.2
mirror, Huygens' construction for a spherical mirror, 3.14–5
— Lloyd's, **5.9**; 5.34; 5.38
mirrors, Fresnel's **5.9**; 9.2
moiré fringes, 6.17
momentum of atom, 19.16
— of light, angular, **17.24–6**; 19.23–4
— — linear, **11.34**; 13.15; 17.12; 17.17; 18.29
monochromator, 4.7; 7.36
Moseley, 17.5
multi-channel devices, 20.34
multiple-beam interference, 5.26; 9.15 ff.; 20.37
multipole radiation, **19.7**; 19.23; Appendix XIIIB, 12

nebular red-shift, 11.43
Newton, discovery of spectrum colours, 3.17
— opposition to wave theory, 1.11
Newton's equation, 7.12
Newton's rings, 1.12; **5.19**; 9.18
Nicol prism, 12.12
nodal points, 7.13
nodes, 3.20; 14.12
noise, 10.13; **20.7** ff.
— spectrum, 20.17
non-coherent illumination, 5.3; 8.42; Appendix VIIIA
non-reflecting films, 5.22–3; 5.25
numerical aperture, 8.21

obliquity function (or inclination factor), 3.9; 6.6; 6.32
oculars, 7.31–2
optic axes of crystal, 16.6; 16.17; 16.45–6
optical activity, natural, **12.35–40**; 16.43; 16.49; magnetic, 16.50
— components, testing, 9.5
— constants of absorbing media, 15.5; of anisotropic media, 16.44
— density of a medium, 3.11
— flat, 9.12–4
— lever, 20.38
— path and path difference, 3.30
— standards of length, 9.35–43
— transfer factor, 8.34
— — function, **8.33** ff.
optimum magnification, 8.23

order of interference, 4.9; of spectrum, 6.13
— — overlapping of orders, **6.13**; 9.44–7
oscillator (simple harmonic), elementary theory, Chap. II; 4.6
— — — quantum theory, 18.16; 18.21–4; 19.1; 19.7
— — — in dispersion theory, 15.20 ff.
— — — in theory of radiation, Appendix XIIIB; 18.25–9; 19.1–3; Appendix XIXA
oscillators, atomic, 4.6
— electric, dipole or Hertzian, Appendix XIIIB (see also above).
— magnetic dipole, multipole, quadripole, etc., 19.7

paraxial rays, 7.3
Parseval's theorem, Appendix IVB, 16
partial coherence, 5.8; Appendix VA
Paschen-Bach effect, 19.14
passage, tint, 12.43
path, optical, 3.30
Pauli, 18.35
Pellin-Broca prism, 7.35
pentagonal prism, 7.35
period, 2.4
Pérot, see *Fabry*
perturbation theory, 19.3; Appendix XIXA, 2
Petzval curvature, 8.30
phase change on reflection, 3.28
— contrast microscope, 8.44–9
— — test, Appendix VIIIc, 3
— or phase angle, 2.4; 2.12
— reversal, 3.28
— velocity, 2.9; 2.16; 11.3
photo-elasticity, 16.56
photo-electric cell, 10.11
— — effect, 17.2–3; 17.13
— — inverse, 17.18
photographic plates, 10.14; 20.44
photometer, 10.17
— sphere, 10.29
photometric measurements, 10.29
— summation, 5.1
— units, 10.27; 10.28
photometry, 2.21
photo-multiplier, 10.11
photon, angular momentum, 17.25; 19.23–4
— concept due to Einstein, 1.16; **17.17**
— counter, 17.18
— energy of, **11.37**; 17.17; 18.27

photon, linear momentum, **11.37**; 17.17; Appendix XVIIA; 18.1; 18.29; 18.40; 19.23; 19.31
— mass of, **11.37**; 17.17; 18.41; 19.33
— noise, 20.30
— statistics of indistinguishable photons, 17.34; 18.33–8
— theory of light pressure, 17.21
— — of photochemical action, 17.16
— — of photo-electricity, 17.3
photons distinguished from corpuscles, 17.17; 18.30; 18.40–2; 19.33
— related to Uncertainty Principle, 18.30
photopic, 10.25
photo-voltaic cell, 10.12
physiological optics, 1.6–8; 10.31–41; 20.48
Planck's constant, 1.16; 17.33
— law of temperature radiation, 17.32–7; 18.28; 18.38–9
— quantum theory, 1.16; 17.1; 18.27; 18.40; 19.33
plane-polarized light, see *polarized light*.
plate, transmission of polarized light in a thin, **12.38**; 12.41; 16.31–43
Poincaré sphere, 12.31
polar molecules, 13.6
polarization of a dielectric, 13.6
— of light, 12.1; by doubly refracting materials, 1.13; **12.6**
— — by absorption, 12.13; by reflection, 1.13; **12.2**; 14.8–10; by transmission, 12.5
— — by Nicol prism, etc. (see *Nicol*, etc.); 12.11; 12.12
— — degree of, 12.9
— — rotation of plane, **12.35–40**; 14.10; 16.43; 16.49; 16.50; (see also *optical activity*)
— of resonance radiation, 19.18–9
polarized light, analysis, 12.27–8
— — circular, 12.1; **12.18**; 14.15
— — coherence relations, 12.15
— — elliptical, 12.1; **12.18**
— — interference, 12.15
— — place, 12.1; (definition of plane of polarization, 12.3)
— — plane (relation of plane to electric vector), 14.8–14
— — propagation in birefringent media, 1.15; 12.22–6; Chap. XVI
— — propagation in optically active media, 16.43
— — ways of producing, see *polarization*
polarizer, 12.2

polarizing devices, uses, 14.14
Polaroid film, 12.13
Porro prism, 7.35
potentials, scalar and vector, Appendix XIIIA
power of an optical system, 7.6; 7.12
— spectrum, 6.49; Appendix IVB, 16
Poynting's theorem, 13.14
— vector, **13.14**; 14.16; 16.5
pressure, broadening of spectral lines, **4.25**; 15.29
— of light, 17.19–22
principal angle of incidence, 15.10
— axes of crystal symmetry, 12.7
— azimuth, 15.11
— dielectric constants, 16.4
— maxima for diffraction, 6.28
— phase velocities, 16.4; 16.6
— planes in crystal, 12.7
— points, 7.10
— refractive indices, 16.4
— stresses (photo-elasticity), 16.57
prisms, 7.35
— Fresnel's biprism, 5.9; Foucault, 12.12; Glan-Thompson, 12.12; Nicol, 12.12; Rochon, 12.11; Wollaston, 12.11
— resolving power, 8.9
privileged directions of thin crystal slice, 12.22
profile, **2.9**; 4.15; Appendix IVB
projection system, 7.39
propagation constant, 2.11
— equation of, 2.9
— in a dispersive medium, 4.28; Appendix IVB
— in an absorbing medium (metals, etc.), Chap. XV
— in an anisotropic medium, Chap. XVI
— in an isotropic medium, Chap. II.
— of waves in one dimension, 2.9; in three dimensions, 2.13
pulsance, $2.4n$
pulse, 4.6
pupil, entrance, 7.27
— exit, 7.27
purity of a spectrum, 8.13
Purkinje effect, 10.25

quadripole radiation, 19.7; 19.23
quantization of the electromagnetic field, 18.25
quantum, 1.16; 17.1
— state, 18.32
— statistics, 18.33–9

INDEX

quantum theory, atomic oscillators, 18.21-2
— — historical development, 1.16; 19.33
— — of dispersion, 19.11; Appendix XIXA
— — of light pressure, 17.21
— — of polarized light, 19.23
— — of radiation, Chap. XVIII
quarter-wave plate, 12.25
quartz, absorption, 15.3; optical activity, 12.35-8; reststrahlen, 15.32

radar waves (or radio waves), velocity of, 11.13
radiation, absorption, Chap. XV; by dipole, Appendix XIIIB; by multipole, Appendix XIIIB, 12; definition of intensity of source, 2.21; density, 17.27; emission, 1.16; quantum theory, Chaps. XVII-XIX; pressure, 17.19-22
— resonance, 15.7; 15.29; **17.14**; 19.13; 19.18-20
— temperature (or black-body), 17.27-34
radiometer effect, 17.19
Raman, 15.46
— effect, 15.48; **19.8-11**; 19.21-2; Appendix XIXA, 14
ray, definition of, 1.11; in an anisotropic medium, 16.5; 16.10; relation to wave theory, 6.62
— surface, 16.14
— velocity, 16.9
Rayleigh, 3rd Baron (J. W. Strutt), 4.12; 5.2; 11.22; 11.35; 13.11; 19.3
Rayleigh criterion, 8.4; 8.18
— on aberration of lenses, 8.12
— on achromatic fringes, 5.39
— on action of a prism, 8.14
— on diffraction gratings, 6.23
— on group velocity, 8.14
— on nature of white light, **4.34**; 8.14
— on reflection coefficients, 14.17
— on resolving power, 8.2
— on temperature radiation, **17.30**; 18.25; 19.33
— on theory of the scattering of light, 15.46
— refractometer, 9.3; **9.19-26**
— scattering, 15.46; 19.8-11; 19.13; 19.21; Appendix XIXA, 14
Rayleigh, 4th Baron (R. J. Strutt), on resonance radiation, 17.14; experiments on scattering of light, 15.46
rectilinear propagation, 1.11; 6.57

red-shift in spectra of nebulæ, **11.43**; 19.34
reference plane, 4.8
reflecting power, 15.7
reflection and refraction at surface of an absorbing medium, **15.6-17**; Appendix XVA; of a transparent medium, 3.11; Chap. XIV
— — — corpuscular theory, 3.31-4
— — — electromagnetic theory, Chaps. XIV, XV
— — — Huygens' wave theory, 3.13, 6.14
— — — laws, 3.11-2; 6.14; **14.2**
reflection by a moving mirror, 11.18
— coefficient, 3.26; 14.8
— polarization, **12.4**; 14.8; 14.17
— total, 14.15-6
— see also *films* (non-reflecting and high efficiency) and *reststrahlen*
refraction of rays in a gravitational field, 11.38
refractive index, real, 3.11; complex, 15.5; see also *dispersion* and *refractometer*
refractivity, 3.18
— molecular, 15.26
refractometer, Rayleigh, 9.3; **9.19**
relative energy, 2.18; 2.21
relativity, Chap. XI
— of simultaneity, 11.27
— special theory, 11.23
— velocity addition theorem, 11.27
resolving power (or limit of resolution), definition, **8.3** ff.
— — eye, 8.7
— — Fabry and Pérot etalon, 8.16
— — grating, 8.10
— — interferometers, 9.44-8
— — microscope, 8.17 ff.
— — prism, 8.9
— — Rayleigh criterion, 8.4
— — telescope, 8.5
resonance radiation, 15.7; 15.29; **17.14**; 19.13; 19.18-20
response function, 8.33; Appendices VIIIA, C
responsivity, **10.2**; 10.4
reststrahlen, 15.32
retina, 1.8
rhomb, Fresnel's, 14.15
Ritz, 17.5
Rochon prism, 12.11
Römer, 1.13; 10.1; **10.5**
rotation of plane of polarization, natural, **12.35-40**; 16.43; 16.49; magnetic, 16.50

rotatory power, 12.35–7; dispersion 12.38–40
Rowland circle, Appendix VIB, 3
Rubens, 15.12; 15.16; 15.32
Rutherford, 17.6
Rydberg, 17.5

saccharimetry, 12.45–7
Sagnac, 11.25–6
Saha, 17.9
St. Venant's hypothesis, 6.33
sampling points, 20.13
— theorem, 20.12–16
saturation, 10.33
Savart plate, **12.48–9**; 12.52
scattering, by atoms and molecules, 15.42–8
— by bound electrons, Appendix XIIIB, 11.
— by free electrons, Appendix XIIIB, 10; Appendix XIXA, 20
— coherent and non-coherent, 19.13
— experiments, 15.46
— Raman, 15.48; **19.8–11**; 19.21–2; Appendix XIXA, 14
— Rayleigh, **15.46**; 19.8–11; 19.13; 19.21; Appendix XIXA, 1, 14–9
— relation to dispersion theory, 15.45–7
— Tyndall, 15.48
schlieren method, 8.49
Schmidt camera, Appendix VIIIB, 4
scotopic, 10.25
secondary spectrum, 7.23
selection rules, 19.4
Sellmeier, 15.24
Selwyn, Appendix VIIIA, 1
sensitized fluorescence, 17.15
series limit, 17.12
— Lyman, Balmer, etc., 17.4
sign convention, 7.4
signal/noise ratio, 10.12; 10.13; 10.18; 20.19
signal power, 20.10
simple harmonic motion, 2.3 ff.
— — addition, 3.3 ff.
— — oscillator, see *oscillator*
sinusoidal distribution, 3.31
sky, blue colour, 15.46
Smekal, 19.21
Sommerfeld, 6.31
space, relativistic contraction, 11.12
spatial frequency, 2.11; 3.31
spectra, 4.1
— absorption, 4.5; 17.8

spectra, band, 4.3
— banded or channelled, 5.30; 12.39; 12.41–2
— continuous, 4.2; 4.6–7
— emission, 4.2; 17.8
— excitation, 17.10
— formed in focal plane of microscope objective, 8.19
— infra-red and ultra-violet, 4.4
— line, 4.2; 17.4–6
— series, 17.4
spectrograph, 4.1
spectrophotometry, 10.19; 10.20; 20.31
spectroscope, 4.1; **8.9**; 8.10
spectrum, discovery, 3.17; purity, 8.13
spiral, Cornu's, Appendix VID
spread function, Appendix VIIIA, 2
standard source, 10.28
standards of length, 9.35–43
standing waves, see *stationary waves*
Stark effect, 19.17
states, metastable, 19.5; quantum, 18.32; stationary (see below), superposition, 19.25–8; symmetrical and anti-symmetrical, 18.35
stationary states, **17.7**; 17.38; 18.13; 18.17–9
— waves, 3.20; 14.12; 18.13; Appendix XIIIA, 3
statistics, quantum, 18.33–9
Stefan, 17.27
Stokes, 12.21; 17.41; 19.22
— lines and anti-Stokes lines, 19.22
— parameters, 12.30
stops, 7.36
— aperture, 7.27
— field, 7.28
structure factor, 6.43
Strutt, J. W., see *Rayleigh* (3rd Baron).
Strutt, R. J., see *Rayleigh* (4th Baron).
sun, spectrum, 4.5
superposition, fringes, 5.32
— states, 19.25–8; waves, 3.1; 13.11; **18.34**; 19.25–8
wave functions, 18.34; 19.25–8
surface, isochromatic, 16.34
— normal, 16.17
— ray, 16.14
— testing of optical, 9.6; 9.11
— wave, **2.13**; 3.8–13; 16.14

tactile theory, 1.6
Talbot (Fox Talbot), Talbot's bands, Appendix VIIID

INDEX

Taylor, G. I., 19.30
telephoto lens, 7.37
telescope, limit of resolution, 8.5
— limit of useful magnification, 8.8
telescopic systems, 7.9; **7.20**
television system, 8.43
temperature radiation, 17.27–34
terms, spectroscopic, 17.5
testing optical components, 9.5; Appendix VIIIc
— angles of cube, octagon, etc., 9.19
— end gauges, 9.16–8
— lenses, 9.10
— microscope objective, 9.10
— optical flats, 9.11–3
— — systems, Appendix VIIIb
— plane surfaces, 9.11–3
— prism, 9.6–9
theory, nature of scientific, 1.1–4; 11.16
thermocouple, 10.2
thin films, non-reflecting, 5.22
— — high-efficiency reflecting, 5.24
Thompson (Glan-Thompson prism), 12.12
Thomson, G. P., 18.2
Thomson, J. J., 15.48
time, dilation, 11.27
— Fermat's principle of least time, 6.58; 8.3; 16.5; 18.9
— periodic, 2.4
tint of passage, 12.43
Tolansky, 9.15
total reflection, 14.15–6
transfer function, 8.33; Appendices VIIIa, c
transition probabilities, **17.37–43**; 18.21–4; 19.1; 19.4; Appendix XIXa
— — for multipole radiation, 19.7
— — for Raman effect, 19.21
— — permitted and forbidden, 18.24; 19.4
— wavelength, 15.37
transitions between states, 17.6; 17.8
transmission, see *propagation*
transport of energy and momentum, **2.18**; 13.14–5; 16.9; 17.21
trichromatism, 10.32
Twyman-Green interferometer, **9.6–10**; 9.11
Tyndal scattering, 15.48

ultra-violet radiation, 4.4
umbra and penumbra, 1.11
uncertainty principle, 18.4–8; 18.31; Appendix XIXa

uniaxial crystals, 12.20–1; 16.19; 16.36–7
useful and empty magnification, 8.8; 8.23

Van Citteret, Appendix VIIIa
Van Heel, 12.52
vector, light, 1.13; 12.3; 14.8; 14.13
— model of an atom, 19.16
— potential, Appendix XIIIa, 1
— representation of S.H.M., 2.8; 3.5; 3.7
velocity, ray velocity, 16.9; principal velocities, 16.6
— of light, 1.13; 2.16; 3.17; Chap. XI
— — Fresnel convection coefficient, 11.35
— — group, 4.29; 11.3; 18.41
— — in moving media, 11.35
— — independent of movement of observer, 11.19; **11.25**; 11.27–8
— — phase (or wave), 2.16; 11.3
— — relation to dielectric constant 13.9
— — relation to ratio of electrical units, 11.13
— — variation with refractive index, 3.17; 11.15
Verdet's constant, 16.50
visibility factor, 2.21; 10.25
— of interference fringes, **4.10–4**; 4.23–5; 5.14
vision 20.48; see *eye*
— colour, 10.31–41

wave and particle conflict, 1.10; 3.31; 18.3; **19.29–34**
— band, Appendix IVb, 12
— equation, 2.15; 18.13–20
— function, 18.13
— group, **4.16**; 4.32; 6.34; 6.64; 18.41
— — Gaussian, **4.21**; Appendix IVb, 14–5
— — propagation in a dispersive medium, **4.28**; Appendix IVb, 15
— guides, 3.31
— in relation to ray optics, 6.58–65
— mechanics, 18.9
— packet, see *wave group*
— profile, 2.9; 4.15
— shearing, 9.51; 12.52
— spherical, 2.20; 19.23
— surface, 2.13; Huygens' construction for, isotropic media, 3.8–13; in anisotropic media, 16.14

wave surface in a biaxial crystal, 16.14–8; 16.22–30
— — in a uniaxial crystal, 12.20–1; 16.19
— train, Chap. IV; 18.7; definition, 4.15; Appendix IVB, 4–14
wavelength, 1.13; **2.11**; comparison, 9.28; 9.29; measurement, 9.36
—constant, 2.11
waves of irregular profile, 4.15
— on a rod, 2.17
— properties of electromagnetic, 13.10
— representation by complex quantities, 2.26; 3.6
— — by vectors, 2.8; 3.5
— sine or simple harmonic, Chap. II; damped harmonic, Appendix IVB, 13; evanescent, 6.55; longitudinal, 1.13; **2.17**; plane, 2.10; 2.14; progressive, 2.9; spherical, 2.20; stationary, **3.20**; Appendix XIIIA, 3; 14.12; 18.13
wedge, interference, **5.18**
white light, 4.33–4
width, half-width of spectrum line, **4.13**; 4.25; 17.42; Appendix XIXA, 8
— half-value, 4.13n
Wien, experiment on Doppler effect, 2.24
— laws of temperature radiation, 17.27–9; 17.33
— measurement of life of an excited state, 17.39; 17.41

Wiener, 3.22–3; 14.12
Williams, W. E., reflecting echelon, 6.29; 9.44
window, entrance, 7.28
— exit, 7.28
Wolf, E., Appendix VA, 6
Wollaston prism, 12.11
Wood, R. W., on gratings, 6.25
— on resonance radiation, 17.14
Wooster, 16.47

X-rays, 17.5; Appendix XVIIA

Young T., boundary wave theory of diffraction, 6.1; eriometer, 6.48; interference experiment, **5.6**; 5.38; 9.2; colour vision, 10.34

Zeeman, 11.35
— effect, 19.7; **19.14–6**; 19.17; 19.18
Zehnder, 9.50
Zernike, 5.8; 8.44
— limitations of interferometry, 20.36
— phase-contrast microscopy, 8.44 ff.
— phase-contrast test, Appendix VIIIc, 3
zone, Fresnel, **6.7** ff.; 16.5; zone plate, Appendix VIc
zoom lens, 7.38